INTRODUCTION TO ATOMIC PHYSICS

HARALD A. ENGE   Massachusetts Institute of Technology
M. RUSSELL WEHR   Drexel (Emeritus)
JAMES A. RICHARDS   State University of New York, Delhi

ADDISON-WESLEY PUBLISHING COMPANY
Reading, Massachusetts · Menlo Park, California · London · Sydney · Manila

WORLD STUDENT SERIES EDITION

FIRST PRINTING 1973

A complete and unabridged reprint of the original American textbook, this World Student Series edition may be sold only in those countries to which it is consigned by Addison-Wesley or its authorized trade distributors. It may not be re-exported from the country to which it has been consigned, and it may not be sold in the United States of America or its possessions.

Preface

This book is part of a series of four separate texts covering the most important areas of modern physics. The other three volumes are: H. A. Enge, *Introduction to Nuclear Physics*, Addison-Wesley, 1966, D. H. Perkins, *Introduction to High-Energy Physics*, Addison-Wesley (in press), and a text, *Introduction to Solid-State Physics*, to be published later.

The present text covers basically the area of atomic physics with wave mechanics, but it also has chapters on solid-state physics and nuclear physics. The book is suitable for a one-semester or two-trimester course in modern physics. The complete series of four books or any combination starting with the present volume can be used for a series of courses in modern physics.

The material covered in this book is arranged roughly in chronological order, not because the historical sense is so important, but because it has proved to be pedagogically advantageous. However, subjects, such as x-rays and nuclear physics, which developed parallel to the basic understanding of the atom and were parts of it, are treated in late chapters.

Chapters 1 through 5 and Chapter 10 are revised and "upgraded" chapters from Wehr and Richards' *Physics of the Atom*. Most of the rest of the material has been written by H. A. Enge, and both the "upgrading" and the new chapters are based on a course taught for a number of years at the Massachusetts Institute of Technology. This one-semester course covered atomic physics with quantum mechanics and was followed by a second-semester course in nuclear physics.

It is unavoidable in any modern physics text that a significant step-up in the level of difficulty occurs at the point where wave mechanics is introduced. The theory of wave mechanics is considerably more abstract than anything the average student has encountered at this point in his study of science. There is no way to soften the blow, although the science libraries are full of attempts. It is my experience that attempts to make wave mechanics look plausible by half-hearted "derivations" are misleading and leave the students frustrated because they are (of course) missing something in the derivations. I have therefore introduced wave mechanics as a series of postulates and justify the theory by the agreement between predicted and measured behaviors of atomic systems.

Prerequisites for a full understanding of the material covered here are courses in mechanics, electricity and magnetism, and differential equations. A few simple matrix multiplications are used, and a short appendix on matrix mechanics is included for those students who have not covered this subject.

It is a pleasure to acknowledge the cooperation, help, and advice of M. R. Wehr and J. A. Richards, Jr., particularly with respect to the upgrading of the material from their earlier book. This is also the place to acknowledge the fact that the atomic physics course referred to above was first developed at M. I. T. by W. W. Buechner, from whom I took it over. The organization of the material in this book is basically as it was presented by Buechner. Many details of presentation and many problems have also been retained. My sincere thanks go to Mrs. Mary E. White who typed the manuscript, corrected the English, and otherwise helped in many ways.

December 1971   H.A.E.

Contents

Chapter 7   Wave Mechanics of the Hydrogen Atom

Chapter 8   Some Methods in Wave Mechanics

Chapter 9   Many-Electron Atoms

Chapter 10   X-Rays and Crystallography

CHAPTER 1

The Atomic View of Matter

1-1 INTRODUCTION

Atomic Physics is a relatively young science, having been developed mostly in this century. However, the idea that matter is built up of atoms (particles) is a very old one. The Greek philospher Democritus (c. 460–370 B.C.), for example, theorized that not only matter but also the human soul consists of particles. Democritus had one very essential characteristic needed by every student of science, the inquisitive mind. He lacked the scientific method (Galileo Galilei, 1564–1642) and, of course, the technology needed to get any further.

Because atomic physics deals with objects (atoms) and events that are not *directly* observable with man's senses, its development often leads along paths which run counter to common sense. As we consider things and events that are orders of magnitude removed from everyday experience, the difficulty of understanding their nature increases. Our common sense enables us to understand the relationship between a brick and a house. Conceiving of the earth as round may involve a little uncommon sense, but for most people it presents no great difficulty. However, the relationship between water and a water molecule is more difficult. While we can see the earth, whether flat or round, we cannot see a water molecule even with the best of instruments. All of our information about single water molecules is of an indirect kind, yet it is a very unsophisticated chemist for whom the concept of a single water molecule is not a part of his common sense. As a man's knowledge expands, more and more facts assume the aspect of "common sense." Certain velocity relationships are common sense. To an observer in a moving car, the velocity of another moving car appears different than to an observer standing beside the highway. In fact, a very young child once observed when the car in which he was traveling was passed by another, "We are backing up from the car ahead." However, the statement made by Albert Einstein that the velocity of light is the same for all observers regardless of their own velocities is initially very uncommon sense.

In Appendix 3 we attempt to show that his statement is reasonable and can appropriately be incorporated into our common sense. The conflict between the earth's actual roundness and its apparent flatness is resolved conceptually, i.e., by imaginative understanding, with the realization that the earth is a very big sphere. Somewhat similarly, the apparent conflict between our statements about relative velocities is resolved conceptually with the realization that the velocity of light is a very large velocity. Democritus, who could propose an atomic theory in about 400 B.C., would have the courage and imagination to face the ideas that lie before us.

It is the business of philosophers to discuss the nature of reality. It is the business of physicists (once called natural philosophers) to discuss the nature of physical reality. Philosophy, therefore, includes all of physics and a lot more besides. It is natural, then, that physics should have a continuing influence on philosophy. As physical discovery is quickly put into engineering practice and made to bear on man's physical environment, so it also affects the formulation of philosophical theory and bears directly on man's outlook and interpretation of life.

The old or classical physics of Newton was extraordinarily successful in dealing with events observed in his day. Using methods he developed, it is simple to equate the earth's gravitational force on the moon to the centripetal force and obtain verifiable relationships about the behavior of the moon. The same methods can be extended to orbits which cannot be regarded as circular. In fact, three observations of a new comet enable astronomers to foretell with great accuracy the entire future behavior of the comet. Given a certain amount of specific data known as initial or boundary conditions, classical Newtonian mechanics enables us to determine future events in a large number of situations. It is easy to move a step further and argue that what Newton has demonstrated to be true often, is true always, and that given sufficient initial data and boundary conditions, laws may be found which show every future event to be determined. The motion of a falling leaf or the fluctuations in the price of peaches may be very complex phenomena. It may require tremendous amounts of data and the application of very complicated laws which we do not yet understand to be able to make predictions in these cases. The important philosophical consequence of classical mechanics was not that every problem had been solved, but that a point of view had been established. It was felt that each new discovery would fall into the Newtonian mechanistic framework. Philosophical questions like the following became more pressing. Do we humans make decisions which alter the course of our lives or are we, like the bodies of the solar system, acting according to a set of inflexible laws and in accordance with a set of boundary conditions? Are we free or is our apparent ability to make decisions an illusion? Is everything we do beyond our responsibility, having been determined at the time of creation? Although mechanistic philosophy is rather repulsive when applied to ourselves, we nevertheless lean heavily upon it in interpreting things that go on about us. Indeed, the whole argument over whether human behavior is influenced more by heredity or environment is based on the assumption that human behavior is determined by some combination of the two.

To the extent that this mechanistic philosophy is based on classical physics, it is due for revision. Upon examination of events that are either very large or very small, we find that classical physics begins to fail. When a new theory or a modified theory has had to be applied in order to describe experimental observations, it has often resulted that the new theory is very different from classical physics. The method of attack, the mathematical techniques, and the form of the solution are often quite different. At one point we shall show that the observations of natural phenomena are inherently *uncertain*. It becomes evident, then, that if some circumstance had led to the development of atomic physics before classical physics, the influence of atomic physics on philosophy would have been against mechanism rather than for it.

Atomic physics has given us electronics and all that that word implies, including radio, radar, television, computers, etc. Atomic physics has given us nuclear energy. The new physics is as successful with submicroscopic events as classical physics was with large-scale events. But it may be that the most important benefits that can result from the study of atomic physics are philosophical rather than technical.

1–2 CHEMICAL EVIDENCE FOR THE ATOMIC VIEW OF MATTER

The speculations of Democritus and of the Epicurean school, whose philosophy was based on atomism, were not the generally accepted views of matter during the Middle Ages and the Renaissance. The prevailing concepts were those of Aristotle and the Stoic philosophers, who held that space, matter, and so on were continuous, and that all matter was one primordial stuff which was the habitat of four elementary principles—hotness, coldness, dryness, and wetness. Different materials differed in the degree of content of these principles. The hope of changing the amount of these principles in the various kinds of matter was the basis of alchemy. Not until the development of quantitative chemistry in the last half of the eighteenth century did the experimental evidence needed for evaluating the conflicting speculations about the constitution of matter begin to appear.

Antoine Lavoisier of France was outstanding among the early chemists. He evolved the present concept of a chemical element as "the last point which analysis is capable of reaching"; and he concluded from his observations on combustion that matter was conserved in chemical reactions.

In 1799 the French chemist J. L. Proust stated the law of definite or constant proportions, which summed up the results of his studies of the substances formed when pairs of elements are combined. The law is: *in every sample of any compound substance, formed or decomposed, the proportions by weight of the constituent elements are always the same.* This statement actually defines chemical compounds, because it differentiates them from solutions, alloys, and other materials which do not have definite composition.

The principal credit for founding the modern atomic theory of matter goes to John Dalton, a teacher in Manchester, England. His concern with atoms seems to have originated with his speculations about the solubilities of gases in water and with his interest in meteorology, which led him to try to explain the fact that the atmosphere is a homogeneous mixture of gases. Eventually, he believed that an element is composed of atoms that are both *physically* and *chemically* identical, and that the atoms of different elements differ from one another. In a paper he read at a meeting of the Manchester Literary and Philosophical Society in 1803, Dalton gave the first indication of the quantitative aspect of his atomic theory. He said, "An enquiry into the relative weights of the ultimate particles of bodies is a subject, as far as I know, entirely new: I have lately been prosecuting this enquiry with remarkable success." This was followed by his work on the composition of such gases as methane (CH_4), ethylene (C_2H_4), carbon monoxide (CO), carbon dioxide (CO_2), and others which led him to propose the law of multiple proportions in 1804. This law states: *if substance A combines with substance B in two or more ways, forming substances C and D, then if mass A is held constant, the masses of B in the various products will be related in proportions which are the ratios of small integers.* The only plausible interpretation of this law is that when elementary substances combine, they do so as discrete entities or atoms. Dalton emphasized the importance of relative masses of atoms to serve as a guide in obtaining the composition of other substances, and stressed that a chemical symbol means not only the element but also a fixed mass of that element. The introduction of the concept of atomic masses* was Dalton's greatest contribution to the theory of chemistry, because it gave a precise quantitative basis to the older vague idea of atoms. This concept directed the attention of quantitative chemistry to the determination of the relative masses of atoms.

An important law pertaining to volumes of gases was announced by Gay-Lussac in 1808. He said that *if gas A combines with gas B to form gas C, all at the same temperature and pressure, then the ratios of the volumes of A, B, and C will all be ratios of simple integers.* Two examples of this law are (a) the combining of two volumes of hydrogen and one volume of oxygen to form two volumes of water vapor, and (b) the union of one volume of nitrogen and three volumes of hydrogen to produce two volumes of ammonia. The following are symbolic forms of these reactions:

---

*   It has been customary, particularly among chemists, to talk about atomic *weights.* This may be because chemists can determine relative atomic masses by weighing macroscopic samples of matter. To a physicist, the *mass* of an atom is much more meaningful than the weight. In these days of space travel, weightlessness is commonplace, but a substance never loses its mass.

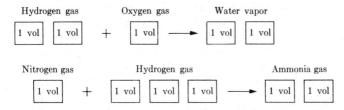

It is obvious that Gay-Lussac's law, like the law of multiple proportions, implies that the substances which participate in these reactions participate in discrete or corpuscular amounts. The ratio between the number of shoes worn to the number of people wearing them is almost an exact integer, namely two, showing that both people and shoes are discrete entities. The ratio of the number of tomatoes used per serving of tomato soup is quite a different kind of situation, and if the ratio is integral it is only by coincidence.

Gay-Lussac's law supported the work of Dalton, but it also raised difficult questions about the composition of an element in the gaseous state. In the case of the first reaction given, does each atom in the given oxygen gas divide to spread through the two volumes of water vapor? If so, the indivisibility of atoms must be abandoned. Or does each entity in the oxygen gas consist of a multiplicity of atoms? If so, how many atoms are grouped together? Similar questions can be raised about each of the gases in the two reactions given. It is evident that the numerical values of the relative masses of the atoms determined from these reactions will depend upon the answers to these questions.

In 1811, Avogadro, an Italian physicist, proposed the existence of different orders of small particles for the purpose of correlating the works of Dalton and Gay-Lussac. He postulated the existence of "elementary molecules" (atoms) as the smallest particles that can combine to form compounds, and the existence of "constituent molecules" (molecules of an element) and "integral molecules" (molecules of a compound) as the smallest particles of a body that can exist in the free state. He went on to state (without proof) a very important generalization, known as Avogadro's law, that *at the same temperature and pressure equal volumes of all gases contain the same number of molecules.* From this law and his concepts of atoms and molecules, Avogadro showed that the ammonia-producing reaction required that nitrogen gas consist of diatomic molecules and that oxygen must also be diatomic to account for the water-vapor reaction. He further concluded that water must consist of a union of two atoms of hydrogen and one atom of oxygen.

Unfortunately, the ideas advocated by Avogadro received little notice even when revived by Ampere in 1814. The notion that hydrogen and other gases were composed of diatomic molecules was ridiculed by Dalton and others, who would not conceive of a combination of atoms of the same kind. They asked, "If two hydrogen atoms in a container filled with this gas can cling together, why do not all cling together and condense to a liquid?" This is indeed a very good question. Science was not able to give a satisfactory answer until over a century later. (See the discussion of the covalent bond in Section 11-2.)

In the next two sections in this chapter we will describe some of the methods which were and still are used to determine the relative masses of atoms. The results obtained by the analytical chemists using these several methods during the first half of the nineteenth century were often contradictory. They frequently obtained different values for the atomic mass of the same element. By the 1850's inconsistencies were so numerous that many felt that the atomic theory of matter would have to be discarded. However, the contradictions were resolved in 1858 by the Italian chemist Cannizzaro, who had an intimate knowledge of the then known methods for determining atomic masses and a broad grasp of the whole field of chemistry. He showed that Avogadro really had provided a rational basis for finding atomic masses, and that the inconsistent results obtained by various experimenters resulted from a lack of clear distinction between atomic masses, equivalent masses, and molecular masses. The views of Cannizzaro received the approval of the scientific world when they were adopted by the international conference on atomic masses which met in Karlsruhe, Germany, in 1869. This, then, is the year in which the fundamental ideas of modern chemistry were widely accepted.

1-3 MOLECULAR MASSES

After Cannizzaro had clarified and established some of the basic definitions in chemistry, Avogadro's law opened the door to one of the methods for determining molecular masses. No one had any idea of what the mass of a single molecule was, but once there was a way of isolating equal numbers of different kinds of molecules, the relative masses could be determined. The hydrogen molecule was found to be the lightest molecule, and the hydrogen atom proved to be the lightest atom. In 1815 Proust had proposed that the relative atomic mass of hydrogen be arbitrarily taken as one. On this basis most other light atoms and molecules had relative masses which were nearly integers. But, for reasons to be discussed later, it turned out that the atomic masses of many of the heavier atoms were not very nearly integers. Hydrogen appeared to be a poor basis for the system, and more nearly integral atomic masses for all atoms could be obtained by making a heavier atom the basis of the system.

For many years physicists and chemists used two different systems, both based on the mass of oxygen. On the physics scale, the mass of the isotope (Section 2-7) of oxygen having 8 protons and 8 neutrons in the nucleus was set at 16. On the chemistry scale the natural mixture of oxygen isotopes was given an average mass value of 16. In 1961 the two scales were replaced by a common atomic-mass scale, in which the mass of the carbon isotope ^{12}C (6 protons and

6 neutrons) is set to 12. On this scale, the atomic mass of hydrogen is not exactly unity, although it is nearly so.

These relative molecular and atomic masses are all dimensionless ratios. If about four parts by weight of hydrogen were combined with 32 parts by weight of oxygen, about 36 parts by weight of water vapor can be formed, according to the familiar equation, $2H_2 + O_2 = 2H_2O$.

Chemists as well as physicists measure amounts of material in grams or in moles. A *mole* is defined as the amount of a given substance containing the same number of molecules as the number of atoms in 12 grams of ^{12}C. One mole of ^{12}C is 12 grams, one mole of carbon in its natural mixture of isotopes is 12.01115 grams, one mole of H_2O is 18.0153 grams, etc. The number of atoms in 12 grams of ^{12}C (number of molecules in a mole) is called Avogadro's number or the *Avogadro constant*, N_A, and it is of basic importance in physics and physical chemistry. (Note that the mole and the Avogadro constant have been defined in terms of 12 grams of ^{12}C. This is the modern practice. However, these definitions do not always conform to the MKSA system of units.* Therefore, we will on occasion use the kilomole, kmole, which is 1000 moles. Obviously a kilomole of carbon 12 has a mass of 12 kilograms.)

The value of the Avogadro constant was of relatively minor importance to chemistry in the early nineteenth century and its magnitude was not even estimated until Loschmidt did so in 1865. We will discuss Perrin's method of determining it later in this chapter. Here is an interesting case where knowing the existence of a number was more important than knowing its magnitude as, for example, in determining the relative masses of the atoms involved in the ammonia-producing hydrogen-nitrogen reaction previously described. The value of the Avogadro constant is by modern measurements

$$N_A = (6.02217 \pm 0.00004) \times 10^{23}$$

particles per mole. Only after the magnitude of the Avogadro constant was known could the absolute mass of an atomic particle be computed. Since N_A ^{12}C atoms of 12 u (mass units) is 12 grams, the mass (in grams) of one unit is clearly

$$1 \text{ u} = 1/N_A = (1.66054 \pm 0.00001) \times 10^{-24} \text{ g}.$$

It follows from Avogadro's law that the volume of a mole of a gas is the same for all gases. The normal volume of a perfect gas or the standard molar

---

* For students not familiar with the MKSA system, a brief review is given in Appendix 1.

volume of an ideal gas, V_0, is the volume occupied by a mole of the gas at a pressure of 1 standard atmosphere and a temperature of 0°C. The value of V_0 is

$$(2.24136 \pm 0.00030)^* \times 10^{-2} \text{ m}^3 \text{ per mole.}$$

1–4 ATOMIC MASSES

Avogadro's law provided a systematic method for determining molecular masses, but a large amount of quantitative data on the formation of various compounds were required before the atomic masses of the known elements could be determined. The situation is somewhat like the following: Suppose that man A pays man B \$1.00 in coin, using no coin smaller than quarters, and that we wish to determine how this is done. He may do this in any one of four ways:

a) one \$1.00 coin,

b) two 50¢ coins,

c) one 50¢ and two 25¢ coins,

d) four 25¢ coins.

If man B now pays man C 25¢, possibilities (a) and (b) are eliminated, but there is still a doubt as to how the original transaction was made. By careful observation of further transactions of those who spend the original \$1.00, it could be determined just what coins A must have had originally.

An aid to the solution of this puzzle was the empirical discovery by Dulong and Petit, in 1819, that for most elements in the solid state the specific heat per mole at constant volume is about 6 cal·mole^{-1}·°K^{-1}. The law of Dulong and Petit permits a rough independent determination of atomic masses by dividing this constant by the specific heat measured in calories per gram. We shall discuss the theoretical basis of this law in Section 3–15.

The masses of atoms are now measured on the ^{12}C scale in mass spectrometers with an almost fantastic precision. (Uncertainties of about one part per million are not uncommon.) See Section 2–8.

---

*   If it seems strange that this and some other constants are given with the uncertainty expressed to more than one significant figure, refer to the article, "Probable Values of the General Physical Constants," by R. T. Birge, [*Phys. Rev. Suppl.* **1** (1929), p. 6]. We note here only that the concepts of probable errors and significant figures do not correspond completely. If the probable error can be determined to less than 10 percent of itself, then more than one significant figure is required to express it.

Principal articles containing the values of various constants are: "Values for the Physical Constants Recommended by NAS-NRC," *Nat. Bur. Std. (U.S.) Tech. News Bull.* **47** (1963), p. 175; "World Sets Atomic Definition of Time," *Nat. Bur. Std. (U.S.) Tech. News Bull.* **48** (1964), p. 209; Mechtly, E. A., *The International System of Units*, NASA SP-7012. Washington, D.C.: U.S. Government Printing Office (1964); Cohen, E. R. and J. W. M. Du Mond, "Our Knowledge of the Fundamental Constants of Physics and Chemistry in 1965," *Rev. Mod. Phys.* **37** (1965), p. 537.

1-5 PERIODIC TABLE

Probably the most significant discovery in all chemistry, aside from the atomic nature of matter, was the periodic properties of the elements, now depicted in the familiar periodic table of the elements (*Appendix 2*). The chemical properties of this table are probably familiar to most readers of this book; the physical properties will be discussed later. The table was proposed independently by Meyer and by Mendeléev in 1869. Its usefulness lay both in its regularities and in its irregularities. One interesting irregularity in the original table was that in order to have the elements fall in positions consistent with their chemical properties, it was necessary to leave numerous spaces unoccupied. Mendeléev suggested that these spaces would be filled with as yet undiscovered elements. Using his table, he was able to describe in considerable detail the properties these elements could be expected to have when they were discovered. It was nearly one hundred years before all the predictions that Mendeléev made were fulfilled.

Reflect, for a moment, on the vast simplification that the chemical discoveries here outlined provide. Looking about us, we see innumerable kinds of materials. The atomic view indicates that these materials are of discrete kinds whose number, however large, is not uncountable. The discovery of elements is a further simplification in that the many materials we encounter are shown to be composed of only about one hundred chemically distinguishable materials, many of which are rare. It turns out that even these elements are not a heterogeneous group but are subject to further classification into a periodic table. The problems of chemistry are many; however, it is easy to see that things are much simpler than might at first appear.

1-6 PHYSICAL EVIDENCE FOR THE ATOMIC VIEW OF MATTER

In our discussion thus far, all atomic properties have been inferred from studies of gross matter. In 1827 the English botanist Robert Brown observed that microscopic pollen grains suspended in water appear to dance about in random fashion. At first the phenomenon was ascribed to the motions of living matter. In time, however, it was found that any kind of fine particles suspended in a liquid performed such a perpetual dance. Eventually it was realized that the molecules of a liquid are in constant motion and that the suspended particles recoiled (Brownian movement), when hit by the molecules of the liquid. However, long before the equations for Brownian movement were derived early in the twentieth century, the particles of matter were thought of as moving about in a random manner and undergoing frequent collisions. Such processes are decidedly in the domain of physics. How can the principles of mechanics be applied to molecular collisions?

The simplest state of matter to consider was a gas. The ideal gas law, for n moles of a gas is $pV = nRT$, where R is the universal gas constant per mole and p, V, and T are the pressure, volume, and temperature, respectively. This law was a well-established *empirical* relationship, and its derivation was one of the objectives of physics. The application of classical physics to the mechanics of gases is called the *kinetic theory of gases*. Although Daniel Bernoulli had some success in developing this theory as early as 1738, the principal contributions that led to its establishment were made between 1850 and 1900 by Clausius, Maxwell, Boltzmann, and Gibbs.

1–7 KINETIC THEORY OF GASES; MOLAR HEAT CAPACITY

Early in our study of physics, we investigated the mechanics of bodies that can be regarded as particles. The study of extended bodies was treated by introducing certain averages, and the translational problem of extended bodies was solved by introducing the concept of a *center of mass* that moves as though it were a particle. The study of rotational properties of extended bodies was similarly facilitated by the introduction of another average property of the body, its *moment of inertia*. In the kinetic theory of gases, we assume that pressure, volume, temperature, etc., are *averages* of properties of all the molecules of a gas. Kinetic theory is a large and elegant subject. We can convey its spirit by deriving the ideal gas law and a few other relationships.

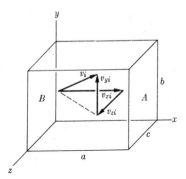

Fig. 1–1 Container with gas of N particles.

Consider a rectangular container, the edges of which are parallel to the x-, y-, and z-axes and have dimensions a, b, and c, as shown in Fig. 1–1. There are N identical particles, each of mass m, in the box moving in random directions with a wide range of speeds. These identical particles may be, but are not necessarily, atoms or molecules.

We assume that the particles are very small so collisions between them are rare compared to collisions with the plane walls of the container. Neglecting minor forces such as gravity and intermolecular forces, we shall consider that the only forces acting on the particle are those resulting from collisions with the walls. We number the particles $1, 2, \ldots, i, \ldots, N$. Figure 1–1 shows the ith particle, whose velocity is v_i. This velocity may be broken into the rectangular components v_{xi}, v_{yi}, and v_{zi}, as shown. We assume collisions to be perfectly elastic such that when a particle strikes a wall the velocity component related to the axis that is perpendicular to that wall is reversed in direction but unchanged in magnitude. The other two velocity components remain unchanged. Thus if the particle strikes side A, the x-component of its momentum is changed from $+mv_{xi}$ to $-mv_{xi}$. The net change in the x-component of its momentum is

$$(-mv_{xi}) - (+mv_{xi}) = -2mv_{xi}.$$

Since collision with the wall causes the particle to change its momentum, the wall experiences an impulsive force. This impulsive force is unknown because we cannot estimate the time of contact in a meaningful way. Fortunately, it is not the impulsive force but the average force from repeated hits that we seek. Since collisions with the top, bottom, far, and near sides have no effect on v_{xi}, and since collisions with ends A and B merely reverse the direction of v_{xi}, we see that the time interval between successive hits on side A is the total x-distance, $2a$, divided by the x-component of the velocity or $2a/v_{xi}$. By applying Newton's second law, we find the average force F_i of the wall on the ith particle to be

$$F_i = \frac{\Delta(mv)}{\Delta t} = \frac{-2mv_{xi}}{2a/v_{xi}} = -\frac{mv_{xi}^2}{a}. \tag{1–1}$$

This force is equal in magnitude and opposite in direction to the force of the particle on the wall and thus the particle produces an average pressure on side A given by

$$p_i = \frac{-F_i}{\text{area}} = \frac{-F_i}{bc} = \frac{mv_{xi}^2}{abc} = \frac{mv_{xi}^2}{V}, \tag{1–2}$$

where V is the volume of the container.

The pressure we have computed is due to but one, the ith, particle. The pressure from each particle is computed the same way. Adding the pressures from the N identical particles, we have

$$p = \sum_{i=1}^{N} p_i = \frac{m}{V} \sum_{i=1}^{N} v_{xi}^2. \tag{1–3}$$

To evaluate the sum on the right-hand side of the equation we note (see Fig. 1–1) that

$$v_i^2 = v_{xi}^2 + v_{yi}^2 + v_{zi}^2. \tag{1–4}$$

Since this equation holds for each of the particles, we can add the corresponding equations and obtain

$$\sum_{i=1}^{N} v_i^2 = \sum_{i=1}^{N} v_{xi}^2 + \sum_{i=1}^{N} v_{yi}^2 + \sum_{i=1}^{N} v_{zi}^2. \tag{1–5}$$

We now define the *mean square velocity*, $\overline{v^2}$, to be the average of the sum of the squares of the velocities; therefore

$$\overline{v^2} = \left(\sum_{i=1}^{N} v_i^2 \right) \Big/ N. \tag{1–6}$$

Applying this definition to all terms in Eq. (1–5), we find that it becomes

$$\overline{v^2} = \overline{v_x^2} + \overline{v_y^2} + \overline{v_z^2}, \tag{1–7}$$

and, substituting terms from Eq. (1–6) into Eq. (1–3), we get

$$p = \frac{m}{V} N \overline{v_x^2}. \tag{1–8}$$

Since we assume these velocities to be completely random in direction and magnitude, the three mean square velocity components must be equal or $\overline{v_x^2} = \overline{v_y^2} = \overline{v_z^2}$. This assumption enables us to deduce from Eq. (1–7) that

$$\overline{v^2} = 3\overline{v_x^2} = 3\overline{v_y^2} = 3\overline{v_z^2}. \tag{1–9}$$

The square root of the quantity $\overline{v^2}$ is called the *root-mean-square speed, or velocity*, v_{rms}. Substituting $\overline{v_x^2}$ from Eq. (1–9) into Eq. (1–8), we get

$$p = \frac{Nm}{V} \frac{\overline{v^2}}{3}$$

or

$$pV = \tfrac{1}{3} Nm\overline{v^2}. \tag{1–10}$$

When the particles in the container are the molecules of a gas, then the number of moles n of the gas in the container equals the total number of molecules N in it divided by the number of molecules in a mole N_A, the Avogadro constant. Therefore we have $n = N/N_A$ or $N = nN_A$. Since the product of the mass of a molecule and the Avogadro constant is the molecular mass M, we can express the total mass of the gas in the box as $Nm = nN_A m = nM$. When this result is substituted in Eq. (1–10) it becomes

$$pV = \tfrac{1}{3} nM\overline{v^2}. \tag{1–11}$$

This is not the result we sought, $pV = nRT$, so we have as yet no justification for the many assumptions we have made. The result is interesting, however, because it contains the pV term, and the term $\tfrac{1}{3} nM\overline{v^2}$ has a familiar look. If we write

$$\tfrac{1}{3} nM\overline{v^2} = \tfrac{2}{3}(\tfrac{1}{2} nM\overline{v^2}), \tag{1–12}$$

the quantity in parentheses is clearly the total *translational* kinetic energy of the molecules. This energy is the total internal energy of the gas U if the molecules do not have rotational energy and if it can be assumed that no forces of attraction or repulsion exist which could give rise to molecular potential energy (ideal gas). By combining Eqs. (1–11) and (1–12), we obtain

$$pV = \tfrac{2}{3}U. \tag{1-13}$$

We compare this result with the ideal-gas law $pV = nRT$ and find that our calculations suggest

$$U = \tfrac{3}{2}nRT \tag{1-14}$$

for an ideal gas; that is, the temperature is a measure of the internal energy of the gas.* Let us now see how this result compares with measurements on real gases.

When a gas is heated at constant volume, the heat energy supplied causes a temperature change that must increase the energy of the gas since no work is done. The change in internal energy with respect to temperature is given by

$$dU/dT = \tfrac{3}{2}nR. \tag{1-15}$$

The change in internal energy with respect to temperature of one mole of an ideal gas at constant volume is called the *molar heat capacity* C_v. Therefore we obtain

$$C_v = \tfrac{3}{2}R, \tag{1-16}$$

and its value is

$$C_v = \frac{3}{2}R = \frac{3}{2} \times \frac{8.31 \text{ J}}{\text{mole} \cdot {}^\circ\text{K}} \times \frac{1 \text{ cal}}{4.18 \text{ J}} = 2.97 \text{ cal} \cdot \text{mole}^{-1} \cdot {}^\circ\text{K}^{-1}.$$

The experimental values of C_v for several gases at room temperature are given in Table 1–1. Note that three values agree very closely with the computed value but that the others are quite different. Both the agreements and the disagreements are interesting. The values which agree are those of monatomic gases, which come closest to the ideal gas. We shall have more to say about the apparent disagreements. The point here is to recall that in our discussion of kinetic theory we assumed that our molecules were isolated elastic spheres. Our result apparently does not apply to diatomic dumbbells or to more complicated molecules.

---

* Temperature can be defined by the aid of a constant-volume gas thermometer as being proportional to the pressure (from $pV = nRT$). This approach assumes that the medium is an ideal gas which, strictly speaking, does not exist, although some gases come close to it. A more satisfactory definition of temperature was given by Lord Kelvin in 1848. It is based on the heat transfers in the isothermic parts of the cycle of a Carnot engine and is independent of the working substance. (For example, see U. Ingard and W. L. Kraushaar, *Mechanics, Matter, and Waves.* Reading, Mass.: Addison-Wesley, 1960, p. 534.)

Table 1–1 C_v of gases

Gas		C_v, cal·mole^{-1}·°K^{-1}
Helium,	He	3.00
Argon,	A	3.00
Mercury,	Hg	3.00
Hydrogen,	H_2	4.82
Oxygen,	O_2	4.97
Chlorine,	Cl_2	6.01
Ether,	$(C_2H_5)_2O$	30.8

1–8   EQUIPARTITION OF ENERGY

The agreement we have observed for monatomic molecules would not have been possible had there not been the number 3 in the expression $C_v = 3R/2$. Looking back over our derivation, we find that the 3 entered into the calculation from the statement $\overline{v^2} = 3\overline{v_x^2}$, that is, because the molecule was free to move in three-dimensional space. The expression for the average kinetic energy of translation of the molecules of a gas is composed of three equal parts, $R/2$ per degree of absolute temperature associated with each coordinate. The principle of *equipartition of energy* states that if a molecule can have energy associated with several coordinates, the average energy associated with each coordinate is the same. Because of this principle, the number of coordinates necessary to specify the position and configuration of a body is called the number of its *degrees of freedom*.

A monatomic molecule requires three coordinates to specify its position. A rigid diatomic molecule requires three position coordinates and two more are necessary to specify its configuration. If we assume the second atom is at a fixed distance from the first, its location is specified as being on a sphere with the first atom at its center. It requires but two additional coordinates to specify where on this sphere the second atom lies. Thus the addition of a second atom adds two degrees of freedom to the molecule. If our derivation for molar heat capacity had been based on diatomic instead of monatomic molecules, we would have obtained $5R/2$ instead of $3R/2$. We find that $5R/2 = 4.95$ cal mole^{-1}·°K^{-1}, which agrees closely with the measured molar heat capacities of such diatomic molecules as hydrogen and oxygen, as shown in Table 1–1. Six coordinates are enough to specify the position of any *rigid* molecule, however complex, but if the molecules are composed of vibrating atoms, then the number of degrees of freedom may become very large. This accounts for the large molar heat capacity of ether. A fuller discussion of heat capacities requires the introduction of quantum theory but classical kinetic theory reveals much, both qualitatively and quantitatively.

With the help of independent data from molar-heat capacities, we have found that the kinetic theory of matter provides a quantitative mechanical model for both the ideal-gas law and molar-heat capacities. The qualitative result, Eq. (1–14), applies only for the ideal gas, as demonstrated in the subsequent discussion of specific heat. However, Eq. (1–11) has more general validity. Using $pV = nRT$, we find from Eq. (1–11) that

$$\tfrac{1}{2}M\overline{v^2} = \tfrac{3}{2}RT. \tag{1-17}$$

Substituting for the molecular mass $M = N_A m$, where m is the mass of one molecule, we get

$$\tfrac{1}{2}m\overline{v^2} = \tfrac{3}{2}(R/N_A)T = \tfrac{3}{2}kT. \tag{1-18}$$

The new constant $k = R/N_A$ is called Boltzmann's constant or the gas constant per molecule. Its value is $k = 1.38062 \times 10^{-23}$ J·°K^{-1}. Equation (1–18) shows that the average kinetic energy of translation of the molecules of a gas depends only on the absolute temperature. The average energy per degree of freedom is clearly $\tfrac{1}{2}kT$.

At a given temperature, the lighter molecules have the greater speeds. As calculated from Eq. (1–18), the root-mean-square speed of hydrogen molecules at room temperature is about 1800 m s^{-1}, or more than 1 mi s^{-1}.

1-9 MAXWELL'S SPEED DISTRIBUTION LAW

We have found that $\overline{v^2}$ can be computed from the temperature of a gas. The speed thus determined is one of the important average properties of a gas. But the average doesn't tell the whole story. For many physical and chemical problems, it is important to know the *speed distribution* of the molecules. For instance, we may ask how many molecules have more than twice the root-mean-square speed $v_{rms} = (\overline{v^2})^{1/2}$ or how many have speeds in the interval $0.79\, v_{rms}$ to $0.80\, v_{rms}$. This can be found from Maxwell's distribution law, which we shall proceed to derive. Figure 1–2 is a plot of this distribution function as applied to N_2 gas at a temperature of $T = 273$°K (0°C).

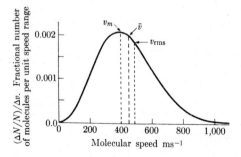

Fig. 1–2 Distribution of speeds for nitrogen molecules at 0°C.

The derivation of Maxwell's distribution law is based on the following assumptions:

Assumption 1. Space is isotropic. Therefore the x-components of velocity exhibit the same distribution as the components along any other axis (including the negative x-axis).

Assumption 2. The distribution of x-velocities is independent of the velocity components v_y and v_z.

Assumption 3. The average energy of the molecules is given by Eq. (1–18).

We start by writing the distribution function for the x-components of velocity as

$$\Delta N(v_x) = Nf(v_x^2)\, \Delta v_x. \qquad (1\text{--}19)$$

Here $\Delta N(v_x)/N$ is the fraction of the total number of molecules N with velocity in the small interval v_x to $v_x + \Delta v_x$. This fraction, divided by Δv_x, is the distribution function f, which is written in terms of v_x^2 instead of v_x. This will simplify the following derivation and does not introduce any new restrictions on the function beyond what is included in assumption no. 1.

Further, because of assumption no. 1, we can write

$$\Delta N(v_y) = Nf(v_y^2)\, \Delta v_y, \qquad (1\text{--}20)$$

$$\Delta N(v_z) = Nf(v_z^2)\, \Delta v_z, \qquad (1\text{--}21)$$

where the function f is the same as in Eq. (1–19), but with different arguments.

By writing the distribution function for x-velocity as a function of v_x^2 only and not also of v_y^2 or v_z^2, we have used assumption no. 2. (Other parameters, as for inⁿtance the temperature, may of course enter into the arguments of these functions.)

Figure 1–3 illustrates the velocity distribution of a sample gas. Note that the figure represents *velocity space* with coordinates v_x, v_y, and v_z, and that the *locations* of the particles (x, y, z) are not depicted. The gas can be enclosed for instance in a cubical container and in thermal equilibrium with its walls. Every time a molecule bounces off a wall, the corresponding velocity component changes sign and the corresponding point in Fig. 1–3 changes position. The overall picture, however, remains the same.

According to Eq. (1–19), the product $f(v_x^2)\, \Delta v_x$ can be interpreted as the probability for finding a given molecule in the velocity interval v_x to $v_x + \Delta v_x$. The probability for finding that the same molecule at the same instant of time also has y-velocity in the interval v_y to $v_y + \Delta v_y$ and z-velocity in the interval v_z to $v_z + \Delta v_z$ is clearly

$$\frac{\Delta N(v_x, v_y, v_z)}{N} = f(v_x^2)\, f(v_y^2)\, f(v_z^2)\Delta V, \qquad (1\text{--}22)$$

where $\Delta V = \Delta v_x\, \Delta v_y\, \Delta v_z$.

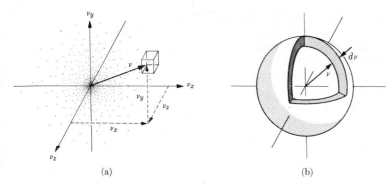

Fig. 1–3 (a) Velocity distribution of the molecules in a sample of gas. (b) Volume element in velocity space for speeds between v and $v + dv$.

The volume element in velocity space $\Delta v_x \, \Delta v_y \, \Delta v_z$ is shown in Fig. 1–3 at the tip of the velocity vector v. We now imagine a new coordinate system placed with the x-axis along v and with the new y- and z-axes perpendicular to it. In this new system, the fraction of molecules in a volume element ΔV of the same size as $\Delta v_x \, \Delta v_y \, \Delta v_z$ but oriented differently will be

$$\frac{\Delta N(v, 0, 0)}{N} = f(v^2) \, f(0) \, f(0) \Delta V. \qquad (1\text{–}23)$$

In the rotated system $v_y = 0$ and $v_z = 0$ and the functions $f(0)$ can be replaced by a constant A. Since Eqs. (1–22) and (1–23) describe the same fraction expressed in two different coordinate systems, we can write

$$A^2 f(v^2) = f(v_x^2) \, f(v_y^2) \, f(v_z^2), \qquad (1\text{–}24)$$

with $v^2 = v_x^2 + v_y^2 + v_z^2$.

We shall now prove that the only type of function f that satisfies Eq. (1–24) is the exponential. We denote with f' the derivative of f with respect to its argument and take the partial of (1–24) with respect to v_x. We obtain

$$A^2 f'(v^2) = f'(v_x^2) \, f(v_y^2) \, f(v_z^2).$$

Dividing by Eq. (1–24), we obtain

$$\frac{f'(v^2)}{f(v^2)} = \frac{f'(v_x^2)}{f(v_x^2)}.$$

By a similar procedure, including taking partial derivatives with respect to v_y and v_z^2, we obtain

$$\frac{f'(v^2)}{f(v^2)} = \frac{f'(v_x^2)}{f(v_x^2)} = \frac{f'(v_y^2)}{f(v_y^2)} = \frac{f'(v_z^2)}{f(v_z^2)}. \qquad (1\text{–}25)$$

Now comes an argument that is used very often in solving separable differential equations. The function $F(v_x^2) = f'(v_x^2)/f(v_x^2)$ depends only upon v_x^2, meaning that it does not vary if v_x^2 is fixed and v_y^2 of v_z^2 varies. The only way in which Eq. (1-25) can be fulfilled for *all* possible values of v_x^2, v_y^2, and v_z^2 is then that each fraction is equal to the same constant (call it $-\beta$), so that

$$\frac{f'(v_x^2)}{f(v_x^2)} = \frac{1}{f}\frac{df}{d(v_x^2)} = -\beta.$$

The solution of this is

$$\ln f = -\beta v_x^2 + \text{const},$$

which gives

$$f = f(0)e^{-\beta v_x^2} = Ae^{-\beta v_x^2}. \tag{1-26}$$

The reason why we chose a negative real number, $-\beta$, for separation constant is now apparent. A positive number would make $f \to \infty$, which is not realistic, and an imaginary constant will give an imaginary answer, which also is nonphysical.

We can now write the form of the distribution function for the x-component of velocity:

$$\frac{\Delta N(v_x)}{N} = Ae^{-\beta v_x^2}\Delta v_x, \tag{1-27}$$

where A and β remain to be determined. We postpone the determination of β and find A by imposing the obvious condition that the probability that the molecule has *some* velocity between $-\infty$ and ∞ is unity. We therefore write

$$\int_{-\infty}^{\infty} Ae^{-\beta v_x^2}\,dv_x = 1.$$

This procedure, which is called *normalization*, yields $A = (\beta/\pi)^{1/2}$. (The integral of the Gaussian function $\exp(-\beta x^2)$ can be found in any table of definite integrals.)

The velocity distribution function Eq. (1-22) combined with Eq. (1-24) gives

$$\frac{\Delta N(v_x v_y v_z)}{N} = \left(\frac{\beta}{\pi}\right)^{3/2} e^{-\beta v^2}\Delta V, \tag{1-28}$$

where we have replaced A with $(\beta/\pi)^{1/2}$. This exponential function shows that the most probable (or "fullest") volume element $\Delta V = \Delta v_x\,\Delta v_y\,\Delta v_z$ of specified velocity "size" is at the origin where $v = 0$. If we move the same velocity volume element away from the origin, fewer velocity vectors will terminate within it. One reason for this is that as we move the volume element away from the origin, we are becoming specific concerning the direction of motion of the molecules.

If we move from the distribution of *velocities* to the distribution of *speeds*, we can drop the restriction on direction of motion. Molecules with *speeds* between V and $V + \Delta V$ lie in a spherical shell in velocity space. To get the speed distribution function, we replace $\Delta V = \Delta v_x \, \Delta v_y \, \Delta v_z$ by $\Delta V = 4\pi v^2 \, \Delta v$, where v now means speed rather than velocity. We then find Maxwell's distribution of speeds to be

$$\Delta N(v)/N = 4\pi(\beta/\pi)^{3/2} \, v^2 e^{-\beta v^2} \, dv. \tag{1-29}$$

The distribution of speeds is no longer maximum at the origin. The reason is that for a given ΔV, our speed volume element at the origin is small and includes more velocity space as the speed V increases.

It remains to determine the constant β. For this purpose we use assumption no. 3 and write

$$\int_0^\infty (\tfrac{1}{2}mv^2)4\pi(\beta/\pi)^{3/2}v^2 e^{-\beta v^2} \, dv = \tfrac{3}{2}kT.$$

Again by using a table of integrals, we find that

$$\beta = \frac{m}{2kT}. \tag{1-30}$$

Inserted into Eq. (1–29), this gives

$$\frac{\Delta N(v)}{N} = 4\pi \left(\frac{m}{2\pi kT}\right)^{3/2} v^2 e^{-mv^2/2kT}\Delta v. \tag{1-31}$$

This is Maxwell's distribution law, which is illustrated by one example in Fig. 1–2.

The most probable speed v_m and the average speed v can be found very simply by the aid of Eq. (1–31); they are

$$v_m = \sqrt{2/3} \, v_{\text{rms}} = 0.817 \, v_{\text{rms}} \tag{1-32}$$

and

$$\bar{v} = \sqrt{8/3\pi} \, v_{\text{rms}} = 0.921 \, v_{\text{rms}}, \tag{1-33}$$

with $v_{\text{rms}} = (3kT/m)^{1/2}$ from Eq. (1–18).

Maxwell's distribution of speeds was employed to calculate other gas properties and was indirectly verified in terms of these secondary properties. A direct experimental verification was obtained by Zartman and Ko in 1930. They used an oven, shown in Fig. 1–4, containing bismuth vapor at a known high temperature (827°C). Bismuth molecules streamed from a slit in the oven into an evacuated region above.* The beam was made unidirectional by

---

* Fast-moving molecules escape from the oven more often than slow ones. Computation shows that if the oven is at a temperature T, the root-mean-square speed of escaping molecules is the same as the root-mean-square speed within an oven at a higher temperature, $4T/3$.

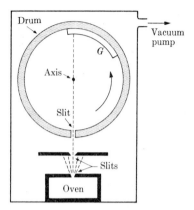

Fig. 1-4 Diagram of apparatus used by Zartman and Ko.

another slit, which admitted only properly directed molecules. Above the slit was a cylindrical drum that could be rotated in the vacuum about a horizontal axis perpendicular to the paper. A slit along one side of the drum had to be in a particular position to enable the beam of molecules to enter it. When the drum was stationed so that the beam could enter, the beam moved along a diameter of the drum and was deposited on a glass plate G mounted on the inside surface of the drum opposite the slit. During the experiment, the drum was rotated at a constant angular velocity so that short bursts of molecules were admitted on each rotation. Because the speeds of the molecules varied, some crossed the diameter quickly and others took much more time, and since the drum was turning while the molecules were moving across it, they struck the glass plate at different places. Thus the distribution of speeds was translated by the apparatus into a distribution in space around the inside of the drum, as indicated by the variation in the darkening of the glass where the bismuth was deposited. The thickness of the deposit was measured optically, and comparison of the experimental distribution of speeds with Maxwell's theoretical distribution expression showed excellent agreement.

1-10 COLLISION PROBABILITY; MEAN FREE PATH

If molecules were truly geometrical points, no collisions would take place between them. Actual molecules, however, are of finite size, and for the purposes of this discussion we are assuming that a molecule is a rigid, perfectly elastic sphere. A collision between two molecules is considered to take place whenever one molecule makes contact with another. Let us refer to one of the colliding molecules as the target molecule, of radius r_t, and to the other as the bullet molecule, of radius r_b. Then a collision occurs whenever the distance between the centers of the molecules becomes equal to the sum of their radii, $r_t + r_b$, as in Fig. 1–5(a).

When we are considering collisions of molecules of a given gas with other molecules of the same gas, the radii r_t and r_b are equal and there is no difference between target molecules and bullet molecules. In many instances, however, we wish to consider collisions between different kinds of particles, and so we shall speak of the target molecules as though they differed from the bullet molecules.

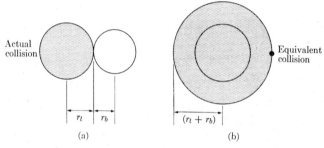

Actual collision

Equivalent collision

r_t r_b

$(r_t + r_b)$

(a)   (b)

Fig. 1–5 For mathematical convenience, the actual collision depicted in part (a) may be represented by the equivalent collision shown in (b).

Since it is only the center-to-center distance that determines a collision, it does not matter whether the target is large and the bullet is small, or vice versa. We may therefore replace an actual collision with the equivalent collision shown in Fig. 1–5(b), in which the bullet molecule has been considered to shrink to a geometrical point and the target molecule to expand to a sphere of radius $r_t + r_b$.

Now consider a thin layer of material of dimensions l, l, and dx. The layer contains (equivalent) target molecules only, and to begin with we assume that these are at *rest*. We then imagine that a very large number N of bullet molecules are incident normally on the face of the layer like a blast of pellets from a shotgun, in such a way that they are distributed over the face. If the thickness of the layer is so small that no target molecule can *hide* behind another, the layer presents to the bullet molecules the appearance shown in Fig. 1–6, where the shaded circles represent the target molecules and the black dots the bullet molecules.

Most of the bullet molecules will pass through the layer, but some will collide with target molecules. The ratio of the number of collisions, dN, to the total number of bullet molecules, N, is equal to the ratio of the area presented by the target molecules to the total area presented by the layer:

$$\frac{dN}{N} = \frac{\text{target area}}{\text{total area}}.$$

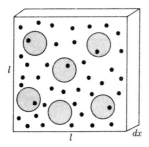

Fig. 1–6 Target with equivalent target molecules (shaded) and bullet molecules (dots).

The target area σ of a single (equivalent) molecule is

$$\sigma = \pi(r_t + r_b)^2. \tag{1-34}$$

This area is called the *collision cross section* of one (equivalent) molecule. The total target area is the product of this and the number of molecules in the layer. If there are n target molecules per unit volume, this number is $nl^2\, dx$, so the total target area is

$$nol^2\, dx.$$

The total area of the layer is l^2, so

$$\frac{dN}{N} = \frac{n\sigma l^2\, dx}{l^2} = n\sigma\, dx. \tag{1-35}$$

In the preceding equation the quantity dN/N is the fractional number of molecules that undergo collisions and therefore this ratio is simply the probability of a collision. (Strictly, this should have a negative sign because dN molecules are removed from the stream of bullets.) In the beginning of this discussion the cross section was thought of as an actual area presented by target molecule, but this was soon replaced by an equivalent area. As we shall see later in quantum mechanical systems, e.g., atoms and molecules, we cannot accept the concept of a sharp boundary as shown in Fig. 1–5. However, we can use Eq. (1–35) to *define the cross section σ,* which then becomes *a measure of the probability for collision.*

If N_0 bullet molecules per unit area are incident normally on the face of a layer of material containing *stationary* molecules having the macroscopic cross section $n\sigma$, then N, the number transmitted undeflected per unit area through a finite thickness x, can be found by integrating Eq. (1–35). We then have

$$\int_{N_0}^{N} -\frac{dN}{N} = \int_0^x n\sigma\, dx, \tag{1-36}$$

and obtain

$$\ln \frac{N}{N_0} = -n\sigma x$$

or

$$N = N_0 e^{-n\sigma x}. \tag{1-37}$$

This exponential equation is plotted as a solid line in Fig. 1-7.

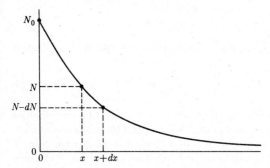

Fig. 1-7 Number of molecules N passing through a target layer undeflected versus thickness x of layer.

Let us next follow in imagination a single bullet molecule as it makes its way through a very thick target along the zigzag path shown in Fig. 1-8. We wish to obtain an expression for the average distance traveled between collisions, known as the *mean free path*, L. This can be deduced from the results above by a type of reasoning that is common and useful in problems of this sort.

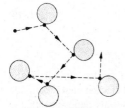

Fig. 1-8 Molecular free paths.

When molecules are passing through the thin layer of material in Fig. 1-6, the number removed from the beam by collisions is small compared with the original number, and we can say that N molecules have each traversed a thickness dx of material and that in the process a number dN of collisions have taken place. The total distance traveled by all of the N molecules is then $N\,dx$. We now make the hypothesis that the number of collisions made by a single molecule in traversing the same total distance $N\,dx$ is equal to the number of collisions made by N molecules, each traversing a distance dx. Then from Eq. (1–35), the total number of collisions made by the single molecule in a total path length $N\,dx$ is

$$dN = Nn\sigma\,dx. \qquad (1\text{–}38)$$

The mean free path of the molecule is equal to the total path length divided by the number of collisions, or

$$L = \frac{\text{total path length}}{\text{total number of collisions}}.$$

From the expressions above for the total path length and the total number of collisions, we have

$$L = \frac{N\,dx}{Nn\sigma\,dx} = \frac{1}{n\sigma}. \qquad (1\text{–}39)$$

The concept of mean free path may be visualized by thinking of a man shooting a rifle aimlessly into a forest. Most of the bullets will hit trees, but some bullets will travel much farther than others. It is easy to see that the average distance the bullets go will depend inversely on both the denseness of the woods and the size of the trees.

In the above analysis, we assumed that the target molecules were at rest. This assumption is valid for a bullet molecule going through a solid. If, however, we consider a gas in which both the target and the bullet molecules are moving randomly, the mean free path will decrease because now there are not only head-on collisions as before, but also "sideswipes" with targets moving across the line of travel of the bullet. It is found that the mean free path of a molecule of an ideal gas having a Maxwellian distribution of speeds is

$$L = \frac{0.707}{n\sigma}. \qquad (1\text{–}40)$$

1–11 FARADAY'S LAW OF ELECTROLYSIS—SKEPTICISM

Another line of argument supporting the atomic view of matter came from the work of Faraday. In 1833 he observed that if the same electric charge is made to traverse different electrolytes, the masses of the materials deposited on the electrodes are proportional to the chemical equivalent mass of the materials. The quantity of electricity required to deposit a mole of univalent ions in electrolysis is called the Faraday constant, F, and is equal to 9.64867×10^4 coulombs. Like the law of multiple proportions proposed by Dalton, this also implied atomicity of matter. Faraday's law, however, brings electricity into the picture and implies that both electricity and matter are atomic.

We have traced a few highlights of the development of the atomic view of matter through most of the nineteenth century, but since no one had ever seen a molecule, the entire theory was still regarded with skepticism. Maxwell, who proposed the distribution of speeds already discussed, did his greatest work in electrical theory. It was he who found the relationship between electricity and light, and it is because of his work that we often call light "electromagnetic radiation." In his comprehensive book on electricity and magnetism (1873), after explaining Faraday's laws of electrolysis on the basis of the atomic theory of matter and electricity, Maxwell says, "It is extremely improbable that when we come to understand the true nature of electrolysis we shall retain in any form the theory of molecular charges, for then we shall have obtained a secure basis on which to form a true theory of electric currents and so become independent of these provisional theories."

As late as 1908 the physical chemist Wilhelm Ostwald and the physicist Ernst Mach opposed the atomic theory of matter. Their skepticism is an interesting question in epistemology. These scientists were unwilling to accept purely indirect evidence. Mach makes their position clear in the following analogy: A long elastic rod held in a vise may be made to execute slow, perceivable vibrations. If the rod is shortened, the vibrations become a blur in which individual motions of the rod cannot be followed. If the rod is shortened further, the blur may be visually unobservable but a tone is heard. If the rod is made so short that we no longer experience a physical sensation from its behavior, we may still think of it as vibrating when struck. This, according to Mach, is a safe extrapolation of our ideas because it proceeds from the *directly* observable to the *indirectly* observable. Those who were skeptical about the atomic theory objected to the fact that the evidence was *entirely indirect*. The experiments described in the next section provided the observable events which made the indirect evidence we have given acceptable to everyone.

1–12 PERRIN'S VERIFICATION OF THE ATOMIC VIEW OF MATTER

Credit for removing the remaining skepticism of atomic theory goes to the French physical chemist Perrin. He tested the hypothesis that the suspended particles which dance about in a stationary liquid in Brownian movement behave like large gas molecules. For his experiments, Perrin prepared a water suspension of particles which met a stringent set of requirements. They had to be large enough to be seen individually, but small enough to have an appreciable thermal motion which could be measured; and they had to be of known uniform size and mass. Further, the concentration of the particles in the suspension had to be so low that the force effects between them could be neglected. In short, the particles had to be directly observable and conform to the assumptions of the kinetic theory of gases. Perrin was able to obtain a suspension of particles that met these requirements by centrifuging a water mixture of powdered gamboge, a gum resin more dense than water. The centrifuge separated the particles according to size. After drawing off a portion of the mixture where the magnitude of the particle size was suitable for his experiments, he could centrifuge again and again until the size of the remaining particles was nearly uniform. Although gamboge is more dense than water, Perrin observed that the particles did not settle out of still water. They assumed a distribution in height, with more particles per unit volume near the bottom of the container than at the top. He measured this distribution as a function of height.

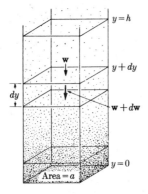

Fig. 1–9 Density distribution in a long column of gas in a gravitational field.

To derive the distribution equation, consider for the moment, instead of a water suspension, a vertical column of gas (Fig. 1–9) with cross-sectional area a and at a uniform temperature. Through this column, let us take a horizontal slice of thickness dy. If the weight of the gas above this slide is w, then the weight of the gas above the bottom of the slice will be $w + dw = w + mgna\,dy$, where mg is the weight of a molecule, n is the average number of molecules per unit volume, and $a\,dy$ is the volume of the slice. (Note that we are employing an atomic view of the gas.)   The difference of these weights per unit area, $mgn\,dy$ is the pressure difference due to the gas in the slice, that is, $dp = -mgn\,dy$. The minus sign denotes that the pressure decreases as the height increases. Since the molecules in the column of gas have weight, the number of molecules per unit volume at a low level is greater than at a higher one. Because of this difference in concentration, there is a corresponding difference in the number of molecular collisions per unit time at the two levels, and the column of gas comes to dynamic equilibrium.   In this state, the weight of the molecules in any layer is just balanced by the net upward force caused by the difference between the number of molecular impacts per unit time on the lower and upper horizontal surfaces of the layer. We shall next obtain an expression for the difference in pressure between two levels produced by a difference in molecular concentrations.

The equation $pV = RT$ holds for one mole of any gas that can be regarded as ideal. According to atomic theory, the number of molecules in a mole is the Avogadro constant N_A. We can obtain an expression that contains the concentration of the molecules by dividing the ideal-gas law equation by the Avogadro constant. Thus we have

$$pV/N_A = RT/N_A \quad \text{or} \quad p = nkT,$$

where $n = N_A/V$ is the molecular concentration. This concentration is a function of the pressure and therefore, since k and T are constant, $dp = kT \, dn$. When this expression for the difference of pressure due to the difference in molecular concentrations in the layer of height dy is equated to the difference caused by the weight of the layer, we obtain

$$kT \, dn = -mgn \, dy \quad \text{or} \quad \frac{dn}{n} = -\frac{mg}{kT} \, dy. \tag{1–41}$$

Here m is the mass of a single molecule.

The relation between the molecular concentration n_0 at $y = 0$ and n at $y = h$ can be found by integrating Eq. (1–41). We have

$$\int_{n_0}^{n} \frac{dn}{n} = \int_{0}^{h} -\frac{mg}{kT} \, dy,$$

which gives

$$n = n_0 e^{-mgh/kT}. \tag{1–42}$$

Since the pressure of a gas is directly proportional to the number of molecules per unit volume, Eq. (1–42) can be rewritten in terms of pressures. The resulting equation is then called the *law of atmospheres*, since it gives the distribution in height of the pressure in a column of gas at constant temperature and subject to the force of gravity.

Equation (1–42) must be modified slightly to make it applicable to water suspensions. The effective weight of a particle suspended in a fluid is the resultant of its weight and Archimedes' buoyant force. The volume of a particle of mass m and density ρ is m/ρ and the mass of an equal volume of liquid having a density ρ' is $\rho'm/\rho$. Therefore, the buoyant force on this particle when submerged in the liquid is $mg\rho'/\rho$, and its effective weight becomes

$$mg - mg \frac{\rho'}{\rho} = mg \left(\frac{\rho - \rho'}{\rho} \right).$$

When we replace the actual weight mg in Eq. (1–42) by the effective weight and reinsert instead of the Boltzmann constant $R/N_A = k$, we obtain

$$n = n_0 \exp \left[-\frac{N_A mg(\rho - \rho')h}{\rho RT} \right]. \tag{1–43}$$

This is the equation for *sedimentation* equilibrium of a suspension as a result of Brownian movement.

Perrin measured a series of n's at a series of h's in a very dilute suspension. The results verified the sedimentation equation. Equally important, his measurements yielded a value for N_A, since all other quantities in the equation were known. The very existence of the Avogadro constant implies the correctness of the atomic theory.

It is interesting that Einstein, the greatest contributor to the development of modern physics, also had a part in the final establishment of the atomic theory. In 1905 he derived an equation which describes how a suspended particle should migrate in a random manner through a liquid. His expression involved the Avogadro constant, and Perrin's verification of the Einstein formula confirmed the value of this constant. The results showed that small particles suspended in a stationary liquid do move about in the manner predicted by the molecular-kinetic theory of gases.

Altogether, Perrin used four completely independent types of measurements, each of which was an observable verification of atomic theory and each of which gave a quantitative estimate of the Avogadro constant. Since the publication of his results in 1908, no one has seriously doubted the atomic theory of matter.

1-13 BOLTZMANN'S DISTRIBUTION LAW

Maxwell's speed-distribution law (Eq. 1-21) and the law of atmospheres (Eq. 1-42) have something in common. In both formulas the factor $\exp(-E/kT)$ appears, where E in one case is the kinetic energy $\frac{1}{2}mv^2$ of a molecule and in the other is the potential energy mgh of a molecule in a gravitational field. The similarity is by no means accidental. Both formulas referred to can be derived from a general law of statistical mechanics called *Boltzmann's distribution law*:

$$n = n_0 e^{-(E-E_0)/kT}. \qquad (1-44)$$

The law deals with the distribution of molecules or other particles over different *energy states* with $E - E_0$ being the difference in energies between these states. The *a priori* distribution over the states, i.e., the distribution that would exist without any energy difference, must be uniform.

Let us consider the example of the law of atmospheres. Assume that the molecules in Fig. 1-9 are in an enclosed box with walls at temperature T. In the absence of a gravitational field, the distribution of molecules would be uniform (on the average). This means that there would be the same number in the *state* identified by a position between $y = 0$ and dy as in the state identified by a position in the equally large volume element between h and $h + dy$. If we now "turn on" the gravitational field and maintain the temperature T on all walls, the difference in potential energy between the two states defined above will be $E - E_0 = mgh$. Inserting this into Eq. (1-44), we obtain Eq. (1-42). Strictly speaking, the kinetic energy should also have been included in the description of the energy states. In the particular example discussed, the kinetic energy distribution is the same in the two volume elements. (The temperature is the same.) Therefore we need not consider the kinetic energy. Maxwell's speed-distribution law can be derived from Eq. (1–44) by postulating that the *a priori* distribution of molecules in velocity space is uniform. This means that the density of dots in Fig. 1–3(a) would be uniform, without the influence of the kinetic-energy difference on the exponential of Eq. (1–44).

Boltzmann's distribution law can be derived by maximizing the entropy of a system of particles with a constant total energy.* It is beyond the scope of this book to include this derivation.

PROBLEMS

1–1 An early chemist wishes to determine the atomic weight of nitrogen. He assumes that the atomic weight of oxygen is exactly 16, and he prepares four oxides of nitrogen which are distinctly different compounds (see data below).

Nitrogen, parts by weight	Oxygen, parts by weight	Product oxide
86.3	197	A
500	285	B
300	343	C
108.2	186	D

a) Show that these data demonstrate the law of multiple proportions. (*Hint:* First find the masses of one of these elements that unite with a unit mass of the other.) b) The chemical formulas of the products cannot be determined completely from the above data, but, by assuming that nature is simple, one may propose several possible sets of product formulas. Write out several possible sets of product formulas. c) Calculate the atomic weight of nitrogen for each set.

1–2 Compute the molar heat capacity at constant volume of a gas composed of molecules that are rigid three-dimensional structures.

1–3 Given that ρ represents the density of a gas, show that

$$v_{\text{rms}} = \sqrt{3p/\rho}.$$

1–4 a) Compute the arithmetic mean speed and the root-mean-square speed for each of the following distributions of the speeds of eight particles:
1. All eight have speeds of 10 ms^{-1}.
2. Two have speeds of 3 ms^{-1}, four have speeds of 6 ms^{-1}, and two have speeds of 10 ms^{-1}

---

* See, for instance, D. L. Livesey, *Atomic and Nuclear Physics.* Waltham, Mass.: Blaisdell, 1966, p. 13.

3. One has a speed of 3 ms^{-1}, three have speeds of 6 ms^{-1}, and four have speeds of 10 ms^{-1}.

4. Four are at rest and four have speeds of 10 ms^{-1}.

b) In each case decide whether the shape of the graph of the speed distribution would be the same as that of the translational kinetic-energy distribution, assuming that each particle has the same mass.

1-5 The speed distribution function of a group of N particles is given by $dN_v = av\, dv$, where dN_v is the number of particles that have speeds between v and $v + dv$, and a is a constant. No particle has a speed greater than V, and the speeds range from 0 to V. a) Draw a graph of the distribution function, that is, plot (dN_v/dv) versus v. b) Find the constant a in terms of N and V. c) Compute the average speed, the root-mean-square speed, and the most probable speed in terms of V. d) What percent of the particles have speeds between the average speed and V? between the root-mean-square speed and V?

1-6 a) Show from Eq. (1–31) that the most probable speed in a Maxwellian distribution is given by

$$v_m = \sqrt{2kT/m} = \sqrt{2RT/M},$$

and b) then show from Eq. (1–18) that $v_m = \sqrt{2/3}\, v_{rms}$. (*Hint:* Determine the condition for which the ordinate quantity in Fig. 1–2 is maximum.)

1-7 Show from Eq. (1–31) that the average speed in a Maxwellian distribution is

$$\bar{v} = \int_0^\infty (\Delta N_v)v\, dv \Big/ \int_0^\infty (\Delta N_v)\, dv = \sqrt{8kT/m}.$$

Some definite integrals are

$$\int_0^\infty x^2 e^{-ax^2}\, dx = (\sqrt{\pi}/4)a^{-3/2},$$

$$\int_0^\infty x^3 e^{-ax^2}\, dx = 1/2a^2,$$

$$\int_0^\infty x^4 e^{-ax^2}\, dx = (3\sqrt{\pi}/8)a^{-5/2}.$$

1-8 Show from Eq. (1–31) that the root-mean-square speed in a Maxwellian distribution is

$$v_{rms} = \left[\int_0^\infty (\Delta N_v)v^2\, dv \Big/ \int_0^\infty (\Delta N_v)\, dv \right]^{1/2} = \sqrt{3kT/m}.$$

1-9 The speed of propagation of a sound wave in air at 27°C is about 348 ms^{-1}. Find the ratio of this speed to the rms speed of nitrogen molecules at this temperature.

1-10 The drum of a Zartman-Ko apparatus (Fig. 1–4), has a radius of 8 cm and rotates at 6000 rpm. The oven contains mercury atoms at a temperature of 600°K. Two atoms of mercury, one with the most probable speed at oven temperature and the other with the rms speed at the same temperature, leave the oven and enter the rotating drum. These two atoms are then deposited on the glass plate at the far side of the drum. What is the separation of these two atoms on the glass plate? (Atomic weight of mercury = 200.6.)

1-11 An object can escape from the surface of the earth if its speed is greater than $\sqrt{2gR}$, where g is the acceleration caused by gravity and R is the radius of the earth. a) Using a radius of 6.4×10^6 m, calculate this escape speed. b) Explain why oxygen and nitrogen remain in the earth's atmosphere while hydrogen does not.

1-12 a) At what temperature will the rms speed of oxygen molecules be twice their rms speed at 27°C? b) At what temperature will the rms speed of nitrogen molecules equal the rms speed of oxygen molecules at 27°C?

1-13 a) To what temperature would an ideal gas in which the "particles" are baseballs have to be heated so their rms speed in a Maxwellian distribution would equal that of a fast ball having a speed of 30.5 ms^{-1}? (The mass of a baseball is 144 g.)

1-14 Find the rms speed, the average speed, and the most probable speed of the molecules of gaseous hydrogen at a temperature of (a) 20°C and (b) 120°C.

1-15 Assuming that the energy E of a molecule is only translational kinetic energy, a) show from Eq. (1-31) that the fractional number of molecules which have energies in the range ΔE is

$$\frac{\Delta N}{N} = \frac{2}{\sqrt{\pi}} \left(\frac{1}{kT}\right)^{3/2} E^{1/2} e^{-E/kT} \Delta E.$$

b) From the energy distribution of part a), show that the *most probable energy* is kT. c) What is the ratio of the average translational kinetic energy to the most probable translational kinetic energy?

1-16 Show that the kinetic energy of translation of a molecule having the *most probable speed* in a Maxwellian distribution is equal to kT.

1-17 A neutron is a fundamental particle. Like ordinary gas molecules, neutrons have a distribution of speeds, and this distribution is of prime importance in the theory of nuclear reactors. Quantitatively, a thermal neutron is usually defined as one having the most probable speed of a Maxwellian distribution at 20°C. Find a) the kinetic energy of translation and b) the speed of a thermal neutron. c) A thermal neutron is sometimes called a "kT neutron." Why? (The mass of a neutron is 1.0087 u.)

1-18 Assume that hydrogen atoms in the atmosphere of the sun obey the Maxwellian speed distribution. a) Given that the temperature is 6000°K, calculate the kinetic energy of one of these atoms moving with the most probable speed in the distribution. b) Calculate the speed of this atom.

1-19 When the atoms in a deuterium gas have an average translational kinetic energy of 12×10^{-14} J, they can approach one another so closely that nuclear fusion will occur. a) What is the speed of a deuterium atom having this kinetic energy? b) To what temperature would the deuterium gas have to be heated so that the rms speed of the atoms would equal the speed in the preceding part? (Deuterium is hydrogen having an atomic weight of 2.014.)

1-20 a) What is the total kinetic energy of translation of the atoms in 4 moles of helium at a temperature of 27°C? b) What would be the answer for the same amount of another ideal gas?

1-21 The microscopic cross section for a certain bullet and particle is σ when they are electrically neutral. Would the effective value of σ increase or decrease if the bullet and particle carried electric charges a) of like sign, b) of unlike sign?

1-22 a) Show that n, the number of molecules per unit volume of an ideal gas, is given by $n = pN_A/RT$, where N_A is the Avogadro constant. b) Find the number of molecules in 1 m^3 of an ideal gas under standard conditions. c) What is the number of molecules in 1 m^3 of an ideal gas at a pressure of two atmospheres and a temperature of 47°C? (1 atmosphere = 1.013×10^5N m^{-2}).

1-23 a) If the pressure is kept constant, at what temperature will the mean free path of the molecules of a given mass of an ideal gas be twice that at 27°C? b) If the temperature is kept constant, at what pressure in millimeters of mercury will the mean free path of the molecules of a given mass of an ideal gas be 1000 times greater than that at a pressure of 1 atm?

1-24 The molecular diameter of all diatomic gases is approximately 2×10^{-10} m. a) Find the mean free path for a Maxwellian distribution of speeds of the molecules of hydrogen gas when at a pressure of 1 atm and a temperature of 20°C. (Data for calculating the macroscopic cross section are given in Problem 1-22.) b) How many collisions per second would a molecule that is always moving with the average speed in a Maxwellian distribution make in the preceding case? (The time of contact during collisions is negligible.) c) What is the ratio of the mean free path in part a) to the wavelength of green light, $\lambda = 5500 \times 10^{-10}$ m?

1-25 A beam of bullet particles is incident normally on a layer of material containing stationary target particles. Find a) the fraction of the incident beam transmitted and the fraction which experienced collisions in a layer whose thickness equals the mean free path and b) the thickness of the layer in terms of the mean free path required to reduce the transmitted beam to one-half the intensity of the incident beam.

1-26 In one of his experiments, using a water suspension of gamboge at 20°C, Perrin observed an average of 49 particles per unit area in a very shallow layer at one level and 14 particles per unit area at a level 60 μ higher. The density of the gamboge was 1.194 g cm^{-3} and each particle was a spherical grain having a radius of 0.212 μ. (1 μ = 10^{-6} m.) Find a) the mass of each particle, b) the Avogadro constant, and c) the molecular weight of a particle if each grain is regarded as a single giant molecule. Use the results from parts a) and b) to calculate c).

CHAPTER 2

The Atomic View
of Electricity

2-1 ELECTRICAL DISCHARGES

We have already considered how Faraday's law of electroylsis implies that both matter and electricity are atomic. In spite of Maxwell's skepticism, it is very difficult to explain the fact that the passage of one faraday of electricity through an electrolyte liberates or deposits an equivalent weight of a substance, except by assuming that both matter and electricity exist in units which preserve their identity throughout the process.

In order to learn more about "particles of electricity," we turn to another line of investigation and consider the passage of electricity through gases. Although Benjamin Franklin's very dangerous experiment with kite and key was not a particularly convincing one, it nevertheless led to the correct conclusion that lightning is the discharge of electricity through a gas (air). Every electric spark is an example of this process. Since sparks are one of the most dramatic electric effects, it is natural that they should have been a subject of early study.

The passage of electricity through gases is a very complicated process and a great deal has been learned from it. There are many ways in which the character of an electrical discharge can be altered, but here we shall direct our attention to the effect of gas pressure. A typical discharge tube is shown in Fig. 2-1. This system has a gauge which measures the gas pressure and a pumping system which varies the pressure. Electrodes are sealed into the ends of the tube so that an electric field can be established between them.

When the pressure in the tube is atmospheric, a very large electric field is required to produce a discharge (about 3×10^6 Vm^{-1} for air). The discharge is a violent spark as the gas suddenly changes from being an excellent insulator to being a good conductor. As the pressure is reduced, the discharges are more easily established (Fig. 2-2), until, at very low pressures, they again become

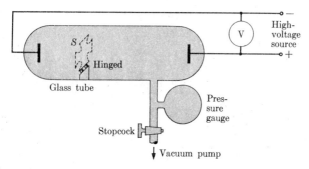

Fig. 2–1   Gas discharge apparatus.

difficult to start.   Discharges start most easily at a pressure of about 2 mm of mercury (although this will depend upon the kind of gas and the geometry of the electrodes).   As the pressure is reduced, the discharge changes in character. With air in the tube, the bright spark changes to a purple glow filling the whole tube, and with neon, one obtains the red glow seen in many advertising signs. On further lowering of the pressure, the glow assumes a remarkable and complicated structure, with striations and dark spaces.   At very low pressures the glow of the gas becomes dim and a new effect appears—the glass itself begins to glow.   If the bulb has within it a device which is hinged so that it can be made

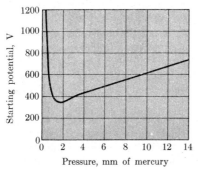

Fig. 2–2   Typical starting potential curve of gaseous discharge.

to move into or out of the region between the electrodes by tipping the entire bulb (S in Fig. 2–1), then another effect may be seen.   The greenish glow of the glass, which appears everywhere between the electrodes when the object S is out of the way, is partly obliterated when S is swung between the electrodes.   If the object S has some distinctive shape, it may be seen clearly that it is casting a shadow.   The shadow is on the side of S that is away from the negative electrode or cathode. If the cathode is small, the shadow is rather sharp. It is a simple deduction that the greenish glow is caused by some kind of rays from the cathode that cannot penetrate the obstruction S. These rays are called *cathode rays*. Many years ago it was observed that these rays could be deflected by both electric and magnetic fields, and the direction of these deflections showed that the rays were negatively charged.

Sir J. J. Thomson undertook a quantitative study of cathode rays in 1897. He was able to show that all cathode rays or corpuscles possess a common property. He showed that the ratio of their charge to their mass, q/m, was a constant. His measurements did not establish that all the rays have identical charges or identical masses, although this is the simplest interpretation of his results. He did, however, discover a unique characteristic of these rays and he is regarded as the discoverer of a fundamental particle of electricity, the electron.

2–2 NONRELATIVISTIC CHARGED-PARTICLE BALLISTICS

Before discussing one of the methods by which q/m can be measured, let us review some basic facts about the motion of charged particles in electromagnetic fields. When a particle having charge $+q$ is in an electric field of intensity E, the particle experiences a force in the direction of the field, of magnitude

$$F = qE. \qquad (2\text{–}1)^*$$

If all other forces on the particle are negligible compared with this one, the particle will undergo accelerated motion, and we have by Newton's second law

$$\frac{d\boldsymbol{p}}{dt} = qE, \qquad (2\text{–}2)$$

where $\boldsymbol{p}$ is the momentum of the particle. Unless the velocity of the particle is very high, we can in practice use nonrelativistic mechanics and write $d\boldsymbol{p}/dt = m\boldsymbol{a}$, yielding

$$m\boldsymbol{a} = qE. \qquad (2\text{–}3)$$

When a particle of charge q moves in a magnetic field of induction $\boldsymbol{B}$ with a velocity $\boldsymbol{v}$, it experiences a force that is perpendicular to the plane formed by the vectors $\boldsymbol{B}$ and $\boldsymbol{v}$:

$$F = q\boldsymbol{v} \times \boldsymbol{B}. \qquad (2\text{–}4)$$

---

* This equation and those following are valid in any consistent system of units. No conversion factors for units need be introduced provided *all* are electrostatic units, *all* are electromagnetic units, or *all* are meter-kilogram-second-ampere units. This will be true of all equations in this book except in cases where units peculiar to atomic physics, such as angstrom units or electron volts, are specified.

If the velocity vector is parallel to the magnetic field, clearly no force results and therefore there is no change in the motion. When the velocity vector points in any other direction, we can break it up into two components, one parallel to the field $v_{\parallel}$, and one perpendicular to the field $v_{\perp}$. The component $v_{\perp}$ gives rise to a force $F = qv_{\perp}B$, perpendicular to $v_{\perp}$, and this force therefore produces a circular motion. If the component $v_{\parallel}$ is nonzero, the result is a helix rather than a circular orbit. Both components and the total speed are numerically constant, but $v_{\perp}$ continuously changes direction. By use of Newton's second law, we find

$$qv_{\perp}B = mv_{\perp}^2/R, \qquad qBR = mv_{\perp}. \tag{2–5}$$

We have here used the formula for the centripetal acceleration $a_c = v^2/R$. Equation (2–5) is valid also in relativistic mechanics (Appendix 3), when m is taken as the relativistic mass. This is true because the speed does not change and therefore the mass is constant.

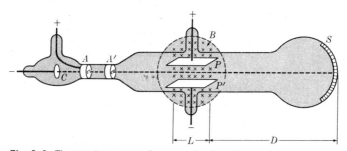

Fig. 2–3 Thomson's apparatus for measuring the ratio q/m for cathode rays.

2–3 THOMSON'S MEASUREMENT OF q/m

We are now ready to consider how Thomson measured the ratio of charge to mass, q/m, for what he called "cathode corpuscles." His apparatus (Fig. 2–3) consisted of a highly evacuated glass tube into which several metal electrodes were sealed. Electrode C is the cathode from which the rays emerged. Electrode A is the anode, which was maintained at a high positive potential so that a discharge of cathode rays passed to it. Most of the rays hit A, but there was a small hole in A through which some of the rays passed. These rays were further restricted by an electrode A' in which there was another hole. Thus a narrow beam of the rays passed into the region of the two plates P and P'. After passing between the plates, the rays struck the end of the tube, where they caused fluorescent material at S to glow.

The deflection plates P and P' were separated a known amount, so that when they were at a known difference of potential the electric field between

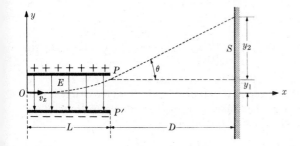

Fig. 2-4 Electrostatic deflection of cathode rays.

them could be computed. We shall assume that the field was uniform for a distance L between the plates and zero outside them. When the upper plate P was made positive, the electric field deflected the negative cathode rays upward.

In Fig. 2-4, the cathode rays are assumed to enter the region between the plates at the origin O with a velocity v_x. Because there is no force component in the x-direction, v_x remains constant.* The general equation for displacement in uniformly accelerated motion is

$$s = s_0 + v_0 t + \tfrac{1}{2}at^2. \tag{2-6}$$

Applying Eq. (2-6) to the horizontal direction, we obtain

$$x = v_x t. \tag{2-7}$$

Between the plates the rays experience an upward acceleration,

$$a_y = \frac{qE}{m}, \tag{2-8}$$

obtained from Eq. (2-3). The electric field E is constant, since the fringing-field zone is neglected, and it is equal to the potential difference between the deflection plates divided by their separation. Hence the general displacement equation in the vertical direction becomes

$$y = \frac{qEt^2}{2m}. \tag{2-9}$$

Elimination of t between Eqs. (2-7) and (2-9), yields the equation for the

---

* Strictly speaking, this is not true. When the particles leave the region of the plates with a y-displacement as shown, they will experience a decelerating force in the x-direction. (The field lines in the fringing field bulge out rather than being vertical as shown.) The effect is of the exact magnitude required to conserve the energy of the particles; that is, the speed after the deflector equals the speed before the deflector. If $v_y \ll v_x$, we can neglect this effect for the present discussion.

parabolic trajectory,

$$y = \frac{qEx^2}{2mv_x^2}.$$ (2–10)

The quantity y_1, defined in Fig. 2–4, is the value of y when $x = L$.

Beyond the plates, the trajectory is a straight line because the charge is then moving in a field-free space. The value of y_2 is $D \tan \theta$, where D and θ are defined as in Fig. 2–4. The slope of this straight line is

$$\tan \theta = \left(\frac{dy}{dx}\right)_{x=L} = \left(\frac{qEx}{mv_x^2}\right)_{x=L} = \frac{qEL}{mv_x^2}.$$ (2–11)

The total deflection of the beam, y_E, is $y_1 + y_2$, so that

$$y_E = y_1 + y_2 = \frac{qEL^2}{2mv_x^2} + \frac{qELD}{mv_x^2} = \frac{qEL}{mv_x^2}\left(\frac{L}{2} + D\right).$$ (2–12)

If q/m is regarded as a single unknown, then there are two unknowns in this equation. The initial velocity of the rays, v_x, must be determined before q/m can be found. We need another equation involving the initial velocity v_x, so that this unknown velocity can be eliminated between the new equation and Eq. (2–12).

Thomson obtained another equation by applying a magnetic field perpendicular to both the cathode-corpuscle beam and the electric field. It is represented in Fig. 2–3 as being into the page and uniform everywhere within the x-marked area. Thus the electric and magnetic forces acted on the cathode rays in the same geometric space.

Figure 2–5 shows the situation when the magnetic field alone is present. The negatively charged rays experience a force that is initially downward. This force is not constant in direction, but is always normal to both the field and the direction of motion of the rays. Therefore the cathode corpuscles move in a circular path according to Eq. (2–5). The center of curvature of the trajectory is at C, and the radius of curvature of the path is

$$R = mv_x/qB,$$ (2–13)

where v_x is the initial velocity of the rays in the x-direction. Referred to the origin O, the equation of this circular path is

$$x^2 + (R + y)^2 = R^2.$$ (2–14)

Solving for R, we get

$$R = -\frac{x^2 + y^2}{2y} \approx -\frac{x^2}{2y}.$$ (2–15)

The approximation is good if the deflection is small compared with the distance the rays have moved into the magnetic field, that is, when $y^2 \ll x^2$.

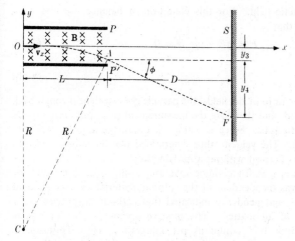

Fig. 2–5 Magnetic deflection of cathode particles.

Since the radius of curvature is difficult to measure, we eliminate R between Eqs. (2–13) and (2–15), and obtain

$$y = -\frac{qBx^2}{2mv_x}.\tag{2–16}$$

Therefore, for small deflections, the circular path may be approximated by the parabolic path of Eq. (2–16). The minus sign indicates that the curve is concave downward.

Just as in the electric case, we find that y_3 is the value of y for $x = L$. The rays again move in a straight line through the field-free region, so that

$$y_4 = D \tan \phi = D \left(\frac{dy}{dx}\right)_{x=L} = -\frac{D_q BL}{mv_x}.\tag{2–17}$$

For the total magnetic deflection y_B, we have

$$y_B = y_3 + y_4,$$

or

$$y = -\frac{q}{m}\left(\frac{BL^2}{2v_x} + \frac{BLD}{v_x}\right) = -\frac{qBL}{mv_x}\left(\frac{L}{2} + D\right).\tag{2–18}$$

Equation (2–18) is very similar to Eq. (2–12). It contains q/m and v_x together with measurable quantities, so that v_x can be eliminated and q/m found. It is interesting, however, to follow Thomson's procedure for determining v_x by considering the simultaneous application of the electric and the magnetic fields. If these are adjusted so that there is no deflection on the screen, then the force of the electric field on the charged particle is balanced by that of the magnetic field. For this condition of balance, we find from Eqs. (2–1) and (2–3) that

$$F = qE - qv_x B = 0, \qquad (2\text{–}19)$$

or, in terms of v_x,

$$v_x = E/B. \qquad (2\text{–}20)$$

For this particular ratio of the fields, the particle goes straight through both fields. It is undeflected, and therefore the measurement of v_x does not depend on the geometry of the tube. Since $y = 0$ at all times, the approximation in Eq. (2–15) is avoided. The velocity thus determined may be substituted into Eq. (2–12), which was derived without approximation.

Thomson measured q/m for cathode rays and found a unique value for this quantity which was independent of the cathode material and the residual gas in the tube. This independence indicated that cathode corpuscles are a common constituent of all matter. The modern accepted value of q/m is (1.758803 ± 0.000005) × 10^{11} coulombs per kilogram. Thus Thomson is credited for the discovery of the first subatomic particle, the electron. Because it was shown later that electrons have a unique charge e, the quantity he measured is now denoted by e/m_e. He also found that the velocity of the electrons in the beam was about one-tenth the velocity of light, much larger than any previously measured material particle velocity.[*]

The electrons Thomson studied had nearly equal velocities. If this had not been the case, the spot on the end of his experimental tube would have been seriously smeared. The reason why the velocities were nearly equal is, of course, that they had been accelerated through the same potential difference, starting from practically zero velocity. Let V be the potential difference between the cathode and the anode, and let the average potential of P and P' and the potential of A' and S be the same as that of A (Fig. 2–3). We then get by conservation of energy:

$$qV = \frac{m}{2} v_x^2,$$

or

$$q/m = e/m_e = v_x^2/2V. \qquad (2\text{–}21)$$

This is another equation relating e/m_e and v_x. It could have been used with Eq. (2–18) to give e/m_e. Thomson could have measured the potential difference between the cathode and anode and been spared either the electric or magnetic deflection of the beam in the vicinity of P and P'. Indeed, other methods of measuring e/m_e utilize this principle.

---

[*]   As shown in Appendix 3, relativistic effects are important when v^2/c^2 is not negligibly small, with c being the velocity of light. The errors introduced here (in Eq. 2–12) by using classical mechanics are of the order of magnitude of v^2/c^2, or about 1 percent.

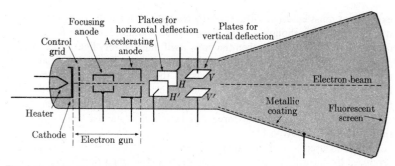

Fig. 2–6 Basic elements of a cathode-ray tube.

Cathode-ray tubes such as Thomson used have been developed into important modern electronic components. Electrostatic deflection of an electron beam is used in the cathode-ray tube of modern oscilloscopes. Such tubes usually have two sets of deflecting plates (Fig. 2–6), so that the electron beam can be deflected right and left as well as up and down. These tubes utilize the fact that the deflection is proportional to the electric field between the plates, as shown by Eq. (2–12). Television tubes, on the other hand, commonly utilize magnetic deflection to cause the beam to sweep over the face of the picture area.

Anyone can demonstrate for himself that electric and magnetic fields deflect electron beams. Holding a strong permanent magnet near the face of a television picture produces weird distortions. Rubbing the face of a picture tube or even the plastic protective window with wool, silk, or nylon will produce strong electric fields when the humidity is low. Neither the magnetic nor electric fields thus produced are uniform or perpendicular to the beam, and the deflections they produce are striking in their unpredictability.

2–4 ELECTRONIC CHARGE

Although the measurement of e/m_e indicated the identity of electrons, another measurement was required before e and m_e could be known separately. This was first made with precision in 1909 by R. A. Millikan, who perfected a technique suggested by J. J. Thomson and H. A. Wilson.

Both the charge e and the mass m_e of an electron are incredibly small quantities. The mass of any body can be determined from the measurement of the force acting on it when it is accelerated. Even if a single electron could be isolated for study, no instrument could measure its mass directly. Similarly, the charge on a body can be determined by measuring the force it experiences in an electric field. This method does not require the isolation of a single electron and, since very intense electric fields can be created, a measurable force can be produced.

An experiment to measure e must be carried out with a body having so few charges that the change of one charge makes a noticeable difference. Since the experiment must be done with very little charge, the force the body experiences will be small even though a large electric field is utilized. If the force on the charged body is very small, then the body itself must be very light. The force of gravity is always with us, and if the small electric force is not to be masked by a large gravitational force, then the mass of the body must be both small and known. If the body is small enough that the electric force on its charges is of the same order of magnitude as the gravitational force it experiences, then it may be that the gravitational force will be a useful standard of comparison rather than an annoying handicap.

Millikan used a drop of oil as his test body. It was selected from a mist produced by an ordinary atomizer. The drop was so small that it could not be measured optically, but with a microscope it could be seen as a bright spot because it scattered light from an intense beam, like a minute dust particle in bright sunlight.

When such a drop falls under the influence of gravity, it is hindered by the air it passes through. The way in which the fall of a small spherical body is hindered by air had been described by Stokes, who found that at low velocities such a body experienced a resisting force R proportional to its velocity, or

$$R = kv. \tag{2–22}$$

The proportionality constant k was found by Stokes to be

$$k = 6\pi\eta r, \tag{2–23}$$

where η is the coefficient of viscosity of the resisting medium and r is the radius of the body. (This law assumes that the resisting medium is homogeneous. A more complicated law must be used if the size of the body is of the same order of magnitude as the mean free path of the molecules of the medium.) This is a friction equation very different from that introduced in mechanics to describe the force between two sliding bodies. In that case we assumed that the friction force depended only on the nature of the sliding surfaces and the normal force pressing the surfaces together. Hence in mechanics we discussed a force which did not depend on the speed of the motion. In the problem of a box sliding against friction down an inclined plane, the friction produced a constant force opposing the motion, but the acceleration was constant and the velocity increased continuously. A body subject to a frictional force like that given by Stokes' law will behave very differently.

A falling droplet of oil is acted on by its weight w, the buoyant force B of the air, and the resisting force $R = kv$ (Fig. 2–7). The resultant downward force F is

$$F = w - B - kv. \tag{2–24}$$

Initially, the velocity v is zero, the resisting force is zero, and the resultant downward force equals $w - B$. The drop therefore has an initial downward

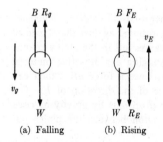

(a) Falling   (b) Rising

Fig. 2-7 Forces acting on an oil drop (equilibrium conditions).

acceleration. As its downward velocity increases, the resisting force increases and eventually reaches a value such that the resultant force is zero. The drop then falls with a constant velocity called its *terminal velocity*, v_g. Since $F = 0$ when $v = v_g$, we have from Eq. (2-24),

$$w - B = kv_g. \tag{2-25}$$

Let ρ be the density of the oil and ρ_a the density of the air. Then

$$w = \tfrac{4}{3}\pi r^3 \rho g, \qquad B = \tfrac{4}{3}\pi r^3 \rho_a g, \tag{2-26}$$

and inserting the value of k from Eq. (2-23), we get.

$$\tfrac{4}{3}\pi r^3 (\rho - \rho_a)g = 6\pi \eta r v_g. \tag{2-27}$$

All of the quantities in this equation except r are known or measurable. We can therefore solve for the drop radius r and hence can express the proportionality constant k in terms of known or measurable quantities. The result is

$$k = 18\pi \left[\frac{\eta^3 v_g}{2g(\rho - \rho_a)} \right]^{1/2}. \tag{2-28}$$

With this constant known, we can use velocity measurement to determine forces. In the experiment, the oil drop is situated between two horizontal plates where a known strong electric field may be directed upward or downward or may be turned off (Fig. 2-8). The droplet has a small electric charge q

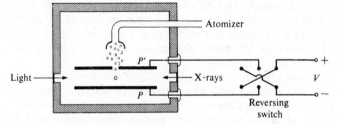

Fig. 2-8 Millikan's oil-drop experiment.

which may be minus or plus, depending on whether it has an excess or deficiency of electrons. The droplet gets this charge from rubbing against the nozzle of the atomizer and from encounters with stray charges left in the air by cosmic rays, deliberately produced by x-rays, or by bringing a radioactive material nearby. In the electric field the drop will experience a force qE, which can always be directed upward by the proper choice of the direction of E. The experimenter can turn E on and off so that the drop falls by gravity or rises because of a dominating electric force in the region between the plates but never touches either.

The microscope with which the drop's movements are followed is equipped with two horizontal hairlines whose separation represents a known distance along the vertical line in which the drop travels. By timing the trips of the drop over this known distance, the terminal velocities of the drop are found. The velocities of fall, v_g (positive down), are all the same, since oil does not evaporate noticeably, and therefore the weight of the drop is constant. The velocity of rise, v_E (positive up), however, depends on the charge q and upon E. The resultant force on the drop while it is rising (Fig. 2–7(b)) is

$$F = qE + B - w - kv. \tag{2–29}$$

When the terminal velocity v_E is reached, the resultant force is zero, so

$$qE = w - B + kv_E. \tag{2–30}$$

But from Eq. (2–25), $w - B = kv_g$, so finally

$$q = \frac{k}{E}(v_g + v_E). \tag{2–31}$$

Since these terminal velocities are constant, they are relatively easy to measure.

Equation (2–31) permits the evaluation of q, the charge on the drop. In the oil-drop experiment, the value of v_g is determined for a particular drop with the electric field off, and a whole series of v_E's for the same drop is observed with the field on. If we knew that the electronic charge was unique and that there was only one charge on the drop, then Eq. (2–31) would give the value of this charge at once. Since the nature of the electronic charge was not known, Millikan repeated the experiment with many different charges on the drop. This provided a set of q's *which he found to be integral multiples of one charge* which he took to be the ultimate unit of charge, e. Thus he established the *law of multiple proportions* for electric charges and concluded from it that electricity must be atomic in character.

Millikan made observations on oil drops of different sizes and also on drops of mercury. In one instance a drop was watched continuously for eighteen hours. The sets of observations always gave the same value of the electronic charge or "atom" of electricity. The best modern determination of e is $(1.602192 \pm 0.000007) \times 10^{-19}$ C.

2–5 MASS OF THE ELECTRON; AVOGADRO CONSTANT

Since e/m_e and e are now known, it is only simple arithmetic to find the mass of the electron to be

$$m_e = (9.10956 \pm 0.00005) \times 10^{-31} \text{ kg.}$$

Still another basic atomic constant may now be calculated with precision by using the value of the electronic charge. The Faraday constant is the amount of charge required to transport one atomic (molecular) mass of a univalent ion of a material through an electrolyte. Dividing the Faraday constant by e gives the number of electrons which have participated in this transport, or the Avogadro constant. The result agrees with Perrin's value, which had finally established the atomic view of matter.

2–6 POSITIVE RAYS

After the particle of negative electricity, the electron, had been identified, it was reasonable to ask about positive electricity. The search was made in a discharge tube very similar to that which disclosed cathode rays. In 1886, Goldstein observed that if the cathode of a discharge tube had slots in it, there appeared streaks of light in the gas on the side away from the anode. These channels of light, first called "canal rays," were easily shown to be due to charged particles. They moved in the direction of the electric field which was producing the discharge, and they were deflected by electric and magnetic fields in directions that proved that their charge was positive. Attempts were made to measure q/m, the ratio of the charge to the mass, of these *positive rays*. It was soon discovered that q/m for positive rays was much less than for electrons and that it depended on the kind of residual gas in the tube. The velocities of these positive rays were found to be nonuniform and much less than electron velocities.

Thomson devised a different method for measuring q/m of these positive rays having nonuniform velocities. Figure 2–9 shows the apparatus he used. The main discharge took place in the large bulb A at the left, where K is the cathode and D is the anode. The gas under study was slowly admitted through the tube at L and was simultaneously pumped out at F. Thus a very low gas pressure was maintained. Most of the positive rays produced in the bulb hit the cathode and heated it. The cathode had a "canal" through it, so that some of the positive rays passed into the right half of the apparatus. Just to the right of the cathode are M and N, the poles of an electromagnet. The pole pieces of this magnet were electrically insulated by sheets, I, so that the magnetic pole pieces could also be used as the plates of a capacitor for the establishment of an electric field. With neither electric nor magnetic fields, the positive rays passed straight through the chamber C to the sensitive layer at S. This layer was either the emulsion on a photographic plate or a fluorescent screen. The beam was

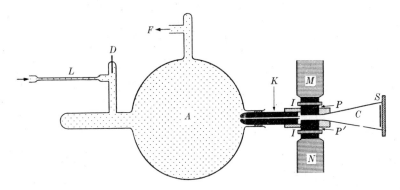

Fig. 2–9 Diagram of Thomson's apparatus for positive-ray analysis.

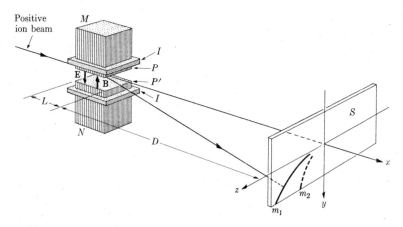

Fig. 2–10 Formation of positive-ray parabolas.

well defined because of the narrow tunnel in the cathode through which it had to pass. Instead of crossed fields as in the electron apparatus, this apparatus has its fields perpendicular to the rays but parallel to each other. The electric field is directed downward and the magnetic induction is upward, so that in Fig. 2–10 the electric force is toward the bottom of the page along the y-axis and the magnetic force is out of the page toward the reader along the z-axis.

Let a positively charged particle of unknown q/m enter the region between P and P' in Fig. 2–10 with an unknown velocity v_x along the x-axis. Then, according to Eq. (2–12), the deflection of the particle on the screen S due to the electric field is

$$y = \frac{qEL}{mv_x^2} \left(\frac{L}{2} + D\right), \qquad (2\text{–}32)$$

and, according to Eq. (2–18), the deflection at S caused by the magnetic field is

$$z = \frac{qBL}{mv_x} \left(\frac{L}{2} + D\right). \qquad (2\text{–}33)$$

These two equations together are the parametric equations of a parabola, where v_x is the parameter. Since v_x is different for different particles of the same type, the pattern on the screen is not a point but a locus of points. Elimination of v_x between these equations leads to

$$z^2 = \frac{q}{m} \frac{B^2 L}{E} \left(\frac{L}{2} + D\right) y, \qquad (2\text{–}34)$$

which is the equation of a parabola.

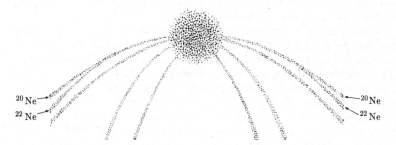

Fig. 2–11 The parabolas of neon.

Some actual parabolas obtained by Thomson's method are shown in Fig. 2–11. Examination of the figure reveals several things: Positive rays have distinct values of q/m, as is shown by the fact that the traces are clearly parabolas. That a single-experiment discloses several values of q/m is evident from the fact that there are several parabolas. It is apparent that the method is not capable of great precision because the parabolas are not sharp.

Thomson assumed that each particle of the positive rays carried a charge equal and opposite to the electronic charge, and he attributed the divergent parabolas to differences in mass. He assumed that the positive rays were positive because each had lost one electron. Thomson could identify particular parabolas with particular ions (charged atoms or molecules are called *ions*). Thus for atomic hydrogen, he could verify that the q/m he measured was equal to the

value one would expect from dividing the electronic charge by the mass per
atom (the atomic mass of hydrogen divided by Avogadro's number). The
reason that positive rays move more slowly than electrons and have lower values
of q/m than electrons is now clear: The positive rays are much more massive.
The largest q/m for positive rays is that for the lightest element, hydrogen.
From the value of q/m it was found that the mass of the *hydrogen ion* or *proton*
is 1836.2 times the mass of an electron. Electrons contribute only a small
amount to the mass of material objects.

2–7 ISOTOPES

The most striking thing that was shown by the Thomson parabolas was that
certain chemically pure gases had more than one value of q/m. Most notable
was the case of neon, of atomic mass 20.2. Neon exhibited a parabola situated
to correspond to a particle of atomic mass 20, but it also had a parabola which
indicated an atomic mass of 22. Since the next heavier element, sodium, has
an atomic mass of 23.0, efforts to explain away the unexpected value of q/m
failed at first. Finally, it was concluded that there must be two kinds of neon,
with different masses but chemically identical. The proof of this interpretation
was given by Aston, one of Thomson's students.

Aston used a principle which we discussed in Chapter 1. We pointed out
there that the average kinetic energy of a molecule in a gas is $3kT/2$. Different
gas molecules mixed together in a container must be at the same temperature,
and hence the average kinetic energy of each kind of molecule must be the
same. If the two gases have different molecular masses, the lighter molecules
must have the higher average velocity, and these will make more collisions per
unit time with the walls of the container than the heavier molecules. Therefore
if these molecules are allowed to diffuse through a porous plug from a container
into another vessel, the lighter molecules will have a higher probability of
passing through than the heavier, slower ones. Aston took chemically pure
neon gas and passed part of it through such a plug. Since one such pass accom-
plishes only a slight separation, the process had to be repeated many times.
He ended with two very small amounts of gas. One fraction had been through
the plug many times and the other had been "left behind" many times. He
measured the atomic mass of each fraction and found values of 20.15 for the
former and 20.20 for the latter. The difference was not great, but it was enough
to show that there are indeed two kinds of neon (at least). Many other elements
have since been shown to exist in forms that are chemically identical but
different in mass. Such different forms of an element are called *isotopes* of the
element. Thus Dalton's belief that all the atoms of an element were physically
identical in every way was not correct.

The discovery of isotopes solved several problems. It explained the two
parabolas observed by Thomson. It also gave a logical explanation of the fact

that the previously measured atomic mass of neon, 20.2, departs so far from an integral value. If chemical neon is a mixture of neon of atomic mass 20 (symbol Ne^{20}) and of neon of atomic mass 22 (Ne^{22}), then there is some proportion of the two that will mix and have an average atomic mass of 20.2.

2–8 MASS SPECTROSCOPY

A detailed search for the isotopes of all the elements required a more precise technique. Aston built the first of many instruments called mass spectrographs or mass spectrometers in 1919.* Aston introduced the idea of velocity focusing, which is explained below. His first instrument could separate ions with a difference in q/m of about 1 percent, and he could determine the magnitude of the mass to about 0.1 percent. In later work, he improved considerably upon these figures.

A modern mass spectrometer has directional focusing as well as velocity focusing. These terms can best be explained with reference to a specific instrument. As an example, Fig. 2–12 shows an instrument built by A. O. Nier and collaborators.†

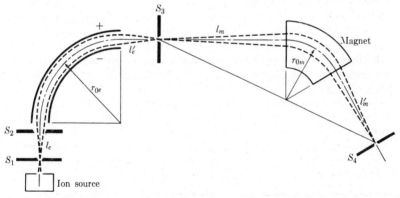

Fig. 2–12 Principle of operation of Nier's spectrograph.

Positive ions are produced in an ion source by impact from electrons emitted by an incandescent filament. The ions are accelerated through a potential difference of about 40 kV and focused by an electrostatic lens (similar to those operating in a television tube) upon slit S_1, which is normally set to an opening of 0.0005 in. The diverging bundle of rays (particle orbits) converge after passing through an electrostatic deflector to slit S_3 and again after passing

---

* F. W. Aston, *Phil. Mag.* **38** (1919), p. 707.
† A. O. Nier and T. R. Roberts, *Phys. Rev.* **81** (1951), p. 507.

through a magnetic deflector to slit S_4, behind which is a sensitive current detector (electron multiplier).

In the magnetic deflector, one can show by simple geometry why directional focusing takes place. Starting from S_3 and following the ray that goes to the left of the central ray, we see that it goes a longer distance through the magnetic field than the central ray does. It is therefore deflected through a larger angle and consequently converges with the central ray. The electrostatic deflector operates similarly, but the effect is stronger because the ray moving closest to the positive plate has higher potential energy, and therefore lower kinetic energy (inside the deflector), and is deflected more.

Directional focusing, as explained above, is vital in the operation of a mass spectrograph. Good resolving power (ability to separate different masses) can be obtained only if all particles of the same mass converge to a sharp line on slit S_4 and all particles of a different mass converge to another line spatially separated from the first.

We have assumed in the discussion of directional focusing that all particles have the same energy. This is approximately so, because they have been accelerated through the same potential (≈ 40 kV). For simplicity we assume that all have unit charge. In Aston's ion source, which was a gas-discharge tube, there was quite a difference in ion energy. In a modern spectrometer extreme care is taken to produce ions of as nearly the same energy as possible. However, with the extremely high resolving power of a modern instrument, it would still be possible to see considerable broadening of the image lines if velocity focusing were not used.

We shall not discuss the details of velocity focusing, but shall give an outline of the principle. The electrostatic deflector separates particles of different kinetic energy or mv^2 (compare Eq. 2–12). The magnetic deflector separates particles of different momenta or mv (compare Eq. 2–18). For the instrument in Fig. 2–12, the final position or point of impact of a particle on the plane of the detector slit S_4 can then be expressed as

$$\Delta y = -a\,\frac{\Delta(mv^2)}{m_0 v_0^2} + b\,\frac{\Delta(mv)}{m_0 v_0}. \tag{2–35}$$

Here $m = m_0 + \Delta m$ and $v = v_0 + \Delta v$, and a and b are constants, characteristic for the instrument. We assume that the electric and magnetic fields have been set such that a particle with mass m_0 and velocity v_0 will go through the center of S_4 ($\Delta y = 0$). The first term in Eq. (2–35) arises from the electrostatic deflector, and the second term is caused by the magnet. By partial differentiations, we get from Eq. (2–35):

$$\frac{\Delta y}{\Delta v} = -\frac{2a}{v_0} + \frac{b}{v_0}, \tag{2–36}$$

$$\frac{\Delta y}{\Delta m} = -\frac{a}{m_0} + \frac{b}{m_0}. \tag{2–37}$$

The deflecting powers (a and b) for the two deflectors are chosen such that $\Delta y/\Delta v = 0$; that is, $b = 2a$. This is the condition for velocity focusing. Clearly, the total deflecting power for a change of mass (mass dispersion) is still nonzero so that the different masses are separated.

In Fig. 2–12, slit S_2 is used to limit the angle of divergence of the bundle of rays accepted by the spectrograph, and S_3 is used to limit the range of velocities accepted for a given mass. Both slits have much wider openings than S_1 and S_4.

With the mass spectrometer discussed above, ions with mass differences of less than one-hundredth of 1 percent ($\Delta m/m = 10^{-4}$) could be separated, and the differences could be measured to an accuracy of about one per million. Newer and larger spectrographs have since been made in which both resolving power and accuracy have been increased by almost a factor of 100.*

The atomic masses determined in a mass spectrograph are always measured relative to other ions of nearly equal mass. Since ^{12}C is the standard (see the next section), one always attempts to measure the mass difference between an unknown mass and a hydrocarbon compound of the same mass number.† This is called the *doublet method* of mass spectroscopy. An example is‡

$$^{12}C\,H_4 - \,^{16}O = 36381.5 \pm 0.9 \ \mu\text{u (micro-mass units)}.$$

This is an equation with two unknowns, the mass of H^1 and the mass of O^{16}. (The mass of ^{12}C is 12.0000 by definition.) By measuring other doublets with different combinations of the same isotopes, possibly also involving others, one can determine the masses of these isotopes on the ^{12}C scale, often to within a few micro-mass units, that is, with a precision of better than one point per million.

PROBLEMS

2–1 What is the ratio of the electric force on a charged particle in an electric field of 20 V cm^{-1} to the force of gravity on the particle if it is a) an electron? b) a proton? c) Is the weight negligible compared with the electric force?

2–2 An electron moving in a vertical plane with a speed of 5.0×10^7 m s^{-1} enters a region where there is a uniform electric field of 20 V cm^{-1} directed upward. Find the electron's coordinates referent to the point of entry and the direction of its motion at a time 4×10^{-8} s later if it enters the field a) horizontally, b) at 37° above the horizontal, and c) at 37° below the horizontal.

---

*   See, for instance, H. Matsuda, S. Fukumoto, and T. Matsuo, *Proceedings of the Third International Conference on Atomic Masses*, R. C. Barber, editor. University of Manitoba Press (1967), p. 733.

†   The superscript 12 on the isotope symbol ^{12}C is the mass number, which is equal to the number of nucleons (protons and neutrons) in the nucleus. The mass number of a molecule is the sum of the mass numbers of its constituent atoms.

‡   K. S. Quisenberry, T. T. Scolman, and A. O. Nier, *Phys. Rev.* **102** (1956), p. 1071.

2–3 If the charged particle in Problem 2–2 were a proton instead of an electron, what must be the magnitude and direction of the electric field so that the answers for the proton would be the same as they were for the electron?

2–4 The dimensions of some parts of a typical commercial cathode-ray tube are given in Fig. 2–13. If electrons start from rest at the cathode, what is their velocity v_x at the origin O for an accelerating voltage of 1136 V between the anode and cathode?

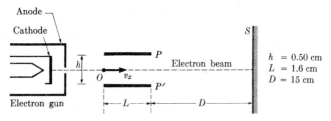

Figure 2–13

2–5 Given that the potential difference between the deflecting plates P and P' is 50 V in the cathode-ray tube in Problem 2–4, a) find the y-coordinate and the direction of motion of the electrons when $x = L$. b) What is the total deflection on the screen S?

2–6 A large, plane metal plate is mounted horizontally at a distance of 0.80 cm above another similar horizontal plate. They are charged to a potential difference of 40 V, the upper plate being positive. An electron is projected horizontally with a velocity of 10^6 m s^{-1} from a point O which is midway between the plates. a) Find the x-coordinate of the point at which the electron strikes a plate. b) Compute the tangent of the angle that gives the direction of the electron's motion as it strikes the plate. c) What is the change in kinetic energy of the electron in going from O to the plate? d) What would the answer to part c) be if the electron had no initial velocity at O?

2–7 a) Through what potential difference would a deuterium ion have to be accelerated from rest in a vacuum so that it would have a speed of 8.47×10^6 m s^{-1} b) What would have to be the magnitude and direction of the smallest magnetic induction that would constrain the moving deuterium ion to a circular path in an evacuated toroidal tube 1 m in diameter?

2–8 A uniform electric field of intensity 40×10^4 V m^{-1} is perpendicular to a uniform magnetic field of flux density 2×10^{-2} T. (A tesla T is a weber per square meter, Wb m^{-2}.) An electron moving perpendicularly to both fields experiences no net force. a) Show in a diagram the relative orientation of the electric field vector, the magnetic induction vector, and the velocity of the electron. b) Calculate the speed of the electron. c) What is the radius of the electron orbit when the electric field is removed?

2–9 A charged particle enters the region between two very large parallel metal plates, the particle's velocity being parallel to the plates when the particle enters. The plates are separated a distance of 2 cm and the potential difference between the plates is 2000 V. When the particle has penetrated 5 cm into the space between the plates, it is found that the particle has been deflected 0.6 cm. If a perpendicular magnetic field of flux density 0.1 T is impressed simultaneously with the electric field, the particle is found to undergo no deflection at all. Calculate the charge-to-mass ratio for this particle.

2–10 A cathode-ray tube is placed in a uniform magnetic induction B with the axis of the tube parallel to the lines of force. Given that electrons emerging from the gun with a velocity v make an angle θ with the axis as they pass through the origin O, show a) that their trajectory is a helix, b) that they will touch the axis again at the time $t = 2m_e/Be$, c) that the coordinate of the point touching is $x = 2m_ev$ cos θ/Be, and d) that for small values of θ, the coordinate of the point of crossing or touching the axis is independent of θ. e) The arrangement in this problem is called a magnetic lens. Why? f) How do the trajectories of the electrons passing through the origin at an angle θ above the axis differ from those directed at an angle θ below the axis?

2–11 Electrons are accelerated through a potential difference of 1000 V in an electron gun and leave the narrow hole in the anode as a narrow diverging beam. What magnitude of axial magnetic induction is required to focus the beam on a screen 50 cm from the hole. (*Hint:* See Problem 2–10.)

2–12 What is the final velocity of an electron accelerated through a potential difference of 1136 V if it has an initial velocity of 10^7 m s^{-1}?

2–13 Two positive ions having the same charge q but different masses, m_1 and m_2, are accelerated horizontally from rest through a potential difference V. They then enter a region where there is a uniform electric field E directed upward. a) Show that, if the ion beam entered the field along the x-axis, then the value of the y-coordinate for each ion at any time t is $y = Ex^2/4V$. b) Can this arrangement be used for isotope separation?

2–14 Two positive ions having the same charge q but different masses, m_1 and m_2, are accelerated horizontally from rest through a potential difference V. They then enter a region where there is uniform magnetic induction B normal to the plane of the motion. a) Show that, if the beam entered the magnetic field along the x-axis, the value of the y-coordinate for a small deflection of each at time t is

$$y = Bx^2(a/8mV)^{1/2}.$$

b) Can this arrangement be used for isotope separation?

2–15 Particles with charge q and mass m are injected into a homogeneous magnetic field having induction B. When their velocities are initially perpendicular to the field, the particles travel in circular orbits. Derive an expression for the frequency of revolution of the particles and show that the frequency is independent of the velocity.

2–16 A charged oil drop falls 4.0 mm in 16.0 s at constant speed in air in the absence of an electric field. The relative density of the oil is 0.80, that of the air is 1.30×10^{-3}, and the viscosity of the air is 1.81×10^{-5} N s m^{-2}. Find a) the radius of the drop and b) the mass of the drop. c) If the drop carries one electronic unit of charge and is in an electric field of 2000 V cm^{-1}, what is the ratio of the force of the electric field on the drop to its weight?

2–17 When the oil drop in Problem 2–16 was in a constant electric field of 2000 V cm^{-1}, several different times of rise over the distance of 4.0 mm were observed. The measured times were 36.1, 11.5, 17.4, 7.55, and 23.9 s. Calculate a) the velocity of fall under gravity, b) the velocity of rise in each case, and c) the sum of the velocity in part a) and each velocity in part b). d) Show that the sums in part c) are integral multiples (two significant figures) of some number and interpret this result. e) Calculate the value of the electronic charge from these data.

2–18 In an experiment to count and "weigh" atoms, it is found that a current of 0.800 A flowing through a copper sulfate solution for 1800 s deposits 0.473 g of copper. The atomic mass of copper is 63.54, its valence is 2, and the electronic charge is 1.60×10^{-19} C. Using only the data *given in this problem*, find a) the number of electronic charges carried by the ions which deposited as copper atoms, b) the number of copper atoms deposited, c) the mass of a copper atom, d) the number of atoms in a gram-atomic mass of copper, e) the number of electronic charges carried by a gram-equivalent mass of copper ions, f) the number of Coulombs required to deposit a gram-equivalent mass of copper, and g) the mass of a hydrogen atom, given that its atomic weight is 1.008.

2–19 What must be the direction of the electric field E and the magnetic induction B in Fig. 2–10 so that the segment of the positive-ion parabola will be in a) the lower right quadrant, b) the upper right quadrant, and c) the upper left quadrant, as viewed from the right of the diagram?

2–20 a) If the ion beam in Fig. 2–10 contains two types of ions having equal charges but different masses, which of the two parabolic segments will have those of greater mass? b) If the masses are equal but the charges different, which segment will contain those having the larger charge?

2–21 For a particular parabola in Thomson's mass spectrograms, what physical quantity is different for the ions that land close to the origin than for those landing farther away? Why does this difference exist, in spite of the fact that a constant voltage was used for the gas discharge?

2–22 In a mass spectrometer, ions having the same charge q but different masses m_1 and m_2 are accelerated from rest through a potential difference V. A narrow beam of these ions then enters a magnetic field having a magnetic induction B which is perpendicular to the motion of the particles. Derive a simple expression in terms of the *given* quantities for the *ratio* of the radii of the trajectories of the two types of ions in the magnetic field.

2–23 Copper has two isotopes whose masses are 62.9 and 64.9, respectively. What is the percent of abundance of each in ordinary copper having an atomic mass of 63.5?

2–24 Uranium hexafluoride, UF_6, is a gaseous compound at 100°C. Given a mixture of two such hexafluorides, one of the isotope ^{235}U and the other of ^{238}U, find the root-mean-square speed of each molecule. Comment on the possibility of separating these by a diffusion process.

CHAPTER 3

The Atomic View
of Radiation

3–1 INTRODUCTION

All sources of light consist of matter which is excited in one way or another.
The firefly excites his body matter by some obscure chemical process; the
matter of the sun is excited by heat. But ever since Heinrich Hertz demonstrated
the validity of Maxwell's theory of electromagnetic radiation, we have known
that the ultimate source of radiation is an accelerated electric charge. We cannot
begin the story of radiation with Maxwell, however, if we are to appreciate one
of the most dramatic demonstrations of the scientific method.

3–2 PARTICLES OR WAVES

Certain Greeks of ancient times argued that since a blind man reaches out to
feel his way about, the seeing man must reach out with his eyes. They thought
of light as a kind of tentacle emitted by the eye yet retaining contact with the
eye so that information about objects touched was conveyed to the mind. Such
a view obviously fails to explain why a man cannot see at night unless there
is an outside source of illumination.

It was realized long ago that light consists of something which goes out
from certain "sources," bounces off objects, and may finally enter the eye.
In the seventeenth century there were two views on the nature of the "something" that was bouncing about. Newton defended the premise that light
consists of a stream of fast-moving elastic particles of very small mass. His
view accounted for the law of reflection, which states that the angle of incidence
is equal to the angle of reflection. (This is the way perfectly elastic balls bounce
from the sidewalk.) He accounted for the law of refraction by arguing that
when particles of light are very near any optically dense medium like glass, they
are attracted to it, and this attraction increases the component of the velocity
of light in a direction perpendicular to the surface. Thus, according to Newton,

the light travels through the medium *faster* than it does in free space and has its direction altered *toward* the normal. Christian Huygens, on the other hand, supported the view that light consists of waves. The most impressive argument in his favor at that time was that two light beams can cross through each other without "colliding." He too explained reflection and refraction. His explanation of refraction was that when a wave front penetrates an optically dense medium at an angle, the wave moves more *slowly*. This slowing of the wave front causes the wave's direction of advance to be altered *toward* the normal.

3–3 ELECTRICITY AND LIGHT

After a century of neglect, the undulatory theory of light was revived by the versatile English scientist Thomas Young. In 1801, he showed that only the principle of interference of waves could explain the colors of thin films and of striated surfaces. During the next half century, further experimental work, especially by the French physicists Fresnel, Arago, Malus, Cornu, Fizeau, and Foucault, showed that the particle theory of light was not tenable. This work reached its culmination in 1864 when James Clerk Maxwell announced the results of his efforts to put the laws of electricity into good mathematical form. He had succeeded in this formulation and found in addition an important by-product: the laws could be combined into the mathematical form of the wave equation for electromagnetic waves. He showed, furthermore, that the velocity of these waves is the *velocity of light*! Thus in one dramatic move he put the theory of electricity in order and incorporated all optics into that theory.

Huygens' view completely displaced Newton's when Foucault found the velocity of light in an optically dense medium *less* than its velocity in free space, and Maxwell's theory was verified in 1888 when Hertz demonstrated that oscillating currents in an electric circuit can radiate energy through space to another similar circuit. Hertz used a circuit containing inductance and capacitance, hence capable of oscillating. Whenever a spark jumped across a gap in the active (transmitting) circuit, electromagnetic waves were radiated from the region in which the electric discharge occurred. (Modifications of this first transmitter were used for radio communication until the advent of vacuum tubes.) The passive or receiving circuit was a loop of wire containing a gap. When energy was transferred from one circuit to the other, sparks jumped across the receiver gap. Hertz's experiments showed that the radiation generated by electric circuits obeyed the known laws of optics. It thus appeared that the theory of light was in a satisfactory and elegant state.

Yet the last word on this subject had not been said. Hertz noted that the induced spark was more easily produced when the terminals of the receiving gap were illuminated by light from the sparks in the transmitter gap. This effect was studied more fully by one of Hertz's students, Hallwachs, who showed that a negatively charged clean plate of zinc loses its charge when illuminated by ultraviolet light. Thus Hertz's verification of Maxwell's wave theory of light led almost simultaneously to the discovery of the photoelectric effect which, as we shall see, led in turn to a profound reinterpretation of the wave theory of radiation.

3–4 ELECTRODYNAMICS

Maxwell's equations and the theory of propagation of electromagnetic waves are given in all texts on electricity and magnetism and will not be treated in detail here. A brief review is in order, however.

Consider a charged particle executing sinusoidal motion with angular frequency ω, for instance, by being forced to move up and down in a vertical antenna. The charge produces an electric field, $E = q/4\pi\varepsilon_0 r^2$, which can be measured near the antenna, but because of the r^{-2} dependence, diminishes rapidly as the distance increases. In addition to this electrostatic near field, the oscillating particle produces an electromagnetic field, the magnitude of which decreases only as r^{-1}. This field moves as a wave with a velocity which in free space is $c = (\varepsilon_0\mu_0)^{-1/2}$. Here $\varepsilon_0 = 8.85415 \times 10^{-12}$ Fm^{-1} is the permittivity of free space and $\mu_0 = 4\pi \times 10^{-7}$ Hm^{-1} is the permeability of free space. This wave moves out from the antenna in all directions but with an intensity that varies from zero in the direction of the antenna to maximum in the direction perpendicular to the antenna.

The electric and magnetic field intensities in the electromagnetic wave are perpendicular to each other, and both are perpendicular to the direction of propagation of the wave. This is illustrated in Fig. 3–1, in which the source, the antenna, is to the far left in the xy-plane and is centered on the x-axis.

In considering atomic radiations, we replace the antenna currents with electrons revolving in atomic orbits. However, as we shall see later, the classical theory of radiation has to be modified in the atomic case.

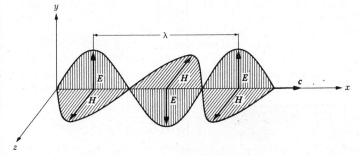

Fig. 3–1 A plane-polarized electromagnetic wave of wavelength λ showing the relation of the vectors **E**, **H**, and **c**.

The energy transmitted by the electromagnetic waves in a radiation field may be specified either in terms of the intensity or of the energy density of the wave motion. The intensity of the radiation is defined as the energy transmitted in unit time through a unit area normal to the direction of propagation of the waves. This is Poynting's vector. The MKSA unit of intensity is watts per square meter. The *energy density* or volume density of the radiation is defined as the amount of radiant energy in a unit volume of space. The MKSA unit of energy density is joules per cubic meter. It is evident that the energy density is equal to the intensity divided by the velocity of propagation of the wave. The term *energy density* is particularly useful in discussing the radiation within a heated enclosure.

3–5 THE UNITY OF RADIATION

From previous studies, the readers of this book are aware that the many forms of radiation, heat, light, radar, radio, etc., differ from one another in frequency

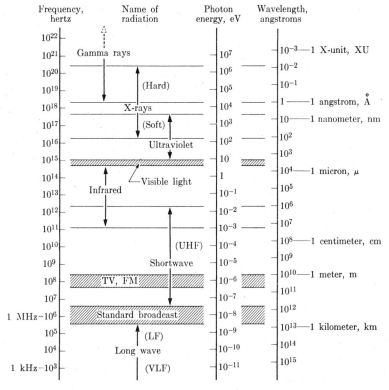

Fig. 3–2 The spectrum of electromagnetic radiation.

but not in kind. The so-called "kinds" of radiation are characterized by the techniques used to produce and detect them; actually, they all travel through free space with the same velocity and should all be understood in terms of the same theory. The tremendous range of the electromagnetic spectrum is shown in Fig. 3–2 (photon energy, mentioned in the figure, will be discussed later in this chapter). The classical theory of Maxwell applies to all these radiations and all are due ultimately to the acceleration of electrical charges. Except for differences of frequency, an observation made on one "kind" of radiation must also be true of all other kinds.

3–6 THERMAL RADIATION

Information about the nature of all radiation may be obtained from a study of any of the "kinds" of radiation. We now consider the radiation from heated bodies, since that investigation has proved particularly fruitful. We all know that a body will emit visible radiation if it is hot enough. A close relation between temperature and radiation is further implied by the fact that a white-hot body is hotter than a red-hot one. We might explore this matter further by passing the radiation from a hot body through some dispersive instrument such as a prism or grating spectrometer. If we measure the radiant energy emitted by a hot body (No. 1) for a whole series of radiant frequencies, we might obtain a graph similar to the dashed curve in Fig. 3–3. The ordinate of this curve is called the *monochromatic emittance*, W_λ, which is the amount of energy radiated per unit time per unit area of emitter in a wavelength range $d\lambda$; the abscissa is the wavelength rather than the frequency. Repeating the same experiment for another body (No. 2) of a different material but at the same temperature, we might now obtain the dotted curve of Fig. 3–3. It is clear from the figure that at most wavelengths the first body is a more efficient emitter at the given temperature than the second. Although the two curves differ, they have the same general character. They come to their highest points at about

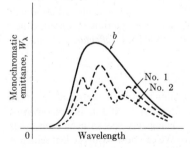

Fig. 3–3 The radiation spectrum of several hot bodies.

the same wavelength. Upon studying a great variety of substances all at the same temperature, we would obtain a great variety of emission curves, but none of these would ever have a greater monochromatic emittance, $W_{\lambda b}$, than the envelope curve, shown as a solid line in Fig. 3–3. It appears that this curve may have a significance which does not depend on the nature of the emitting material. Let us attempt to find or make an emitter which has an emission curve identical to the solid curve of Fig. 3–3.

3–7 EMISSION AND ABSORPTION OF RADIATION

It may be wondered why it is, if the surfaces of all bodies are continually emitting radiant energy, that all bodies do not eventually radiate away all their internal energy and cool down to a temperature of absolute zero. The answer is that they would do so if energy were not supplied to them in some way. In the case of the filament of an electric lamp, energy is supplied electrically to make up for the energy radiated. As soon as this energy supply is cut off, these bodies do, in fact, cool down very quickly to room temperature. The reason that they do not cool further is that their surroundings (the walls, and other objects in the room) are also radiating, and some of this radiant energy is intercepted, absorbed, and converted into internal energy. The same thing is true of all other objects in the room—each is both emitting and absorbing radiant energy simultaneously. If any object is hotter than its surroundings, its rate of emission will exceed its rate of absorption. There will thus be a net loss of energy and the body will cool down unless heated by some other method. If a body is at a lower temperature than its surroundings, its rate of absorption will be larger than its rate of emission and its temperature will rise. When the body is at the same temperature as its surroundings, the two rates become equal, there is no net gain or loss of energy, and no change in temperature.

Figure 3–3 shows that the emittance of a surface W is different at different wavelengths and the paragraph above implies that it is greater for higher temperatures. To simplify our next discussion consider an infinitesimal band of wavelengths and several opaque bodies in thermal equilibrium with each other and their surroundings. Because the bodies are opaque they will not transmit radiation and therefore, in general, part of the incident radiation will be reflected and the remainder will be absorbed. The fraction absorbed, called the *absorptance a*, plus the fraction reflected, called the *reflectance r*, must be unity or, since the surfaces may be different,

$$a_1 + r_1 = 1, \qquad a_2 + r_2 = 1, \quad \text{etc.} \tag{3–1}$$

Since the bodies are in thermal equilibrium with their surroundings, they will be "bathed" in radiation of uniform intensity, I. If this is not obvious, it may be helpful to think of the bodies as being tiny specks near each other but too small to cast shadows on each other. We can now write the last sentence quantitatively. The total radiation in a time Δt from body No. 1, which has an area ΔA_1 and a radiant emittance W_1, is $W_1 \Delta A_1 \Delta t$. The absorption by the same body in the same time is $a_1 I \Delta A_1 \Delta t$. For the condition of thermal equilibrium to exist these must be equal. Therefore we have

$$W_1 \Delta A_1 \Delta t = a_1 I \Delta A_1 \Delta t, \tag{3–2}$$

and similarly for another body,

$$W_2 \Delta A_2 \Delta t = a_2 I \Delta A_2 \Delta t, \quad \text{etc.} \tag{3–3}$$

Dividing Eq. (3–2) by Eq. (3–3), we obtain

$$\frac{W_1}{W_2} = \frac{a_1}{a_2} \quad \text{or} \quad \frac{W_1}{a_1} = \frac{W_2}{a_2}, \quad \text{etc.} \tag{3–4}$$

Since the number of specks or kinds of surface has not been restricted, it becomes evident that W/a for any substance must be a constant (which may, of course, still depend on wavelength and temperature).

We have just proved that a body or surface which is a good emitter (high value of W) must be a good absorber (high value of a) and conversely. If we could find a perfect absorber, we would necessarily have found the best possible emitter, the graph of which is shown as b in Fig. 3–3.

3–8 BLACK-BODY RADIATION

In acoustics, an open window is taken to be a perfect absorber of sound, since an open window reflects virtually no sound back into the room. In optics, there are few things darker than the keyhole of a windowless closet, since what little light gets into the closet bounces around against absorbing surfaces before it is redirected out the keyhole. Painting the inside of the closet black may increase the darkness of the keyhole, but the essential darkness of the hole is due to the geometry of the cavity rather than to the absorptivity of its surfaces. A small hole in a cavity of opaque material is the most perfect absorber of radiant energy man has found. Conversely, a small hole in a cavity is the most perfect emitter man has devised. We can conclude this from the proof above or we can understand it more thoroughly from the following. If we look into a hole in a heated cavity, we can see the radiation from the inside wall just opposite to the hole. In addition, we see some radiation from other parts of the inside of the cavity which was directed toward the spot of wall we are looking at and is reflected to us by that spot. The absorption and emission of radiation by a hole in a hollow tungsten cylinder is shown in Fig. 3–4. The light streak across the center of the figure is an incandescent filament maintained at a constant color temperature for comparison purposes. When the cylinder is cold, the hole is darker than any other part and actually appears black, but when the cylinder is heated sufficiently, the hole is brighter than the body of

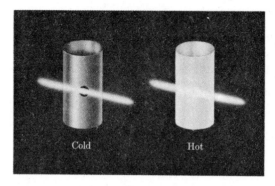

Fig. 3-4 Radiation from a hollow tungsten cylinder.

the tube and matches the reference filament. Such a hollow absorber-emitter is called a black body. Since a is equal to unity for black body, from Eq. (3-4) we obtain

$$\frac{W_1}{a_1} = \frac{W_2}{a_2} = \frac{W_b}{1} = W_b. \qquad (3-5)$$

This relation is called Kirchhoff's law of radiation: *The ratio of the radiant emittance of a surface to its absorptance is the same for all surfaces at a given temperature and is equal to the radiant emittance of a black body at the same temperature.*

We now discuss the multiple-reflection situation of a radiant cavity quantitatively. Consider the radiation traveling back and forth in an isothermal cavity formed between two plane parallel sheets of different materials, as shown in Fig. 3-5. Let us now follow the history of the radiation emitted from a unit

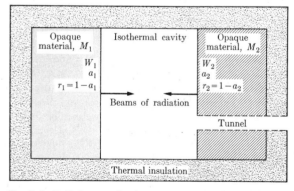

Fig. 3-5 Radiation traveling between two different materials.

area of each face in a time interval Δt, which is just long enough to permit the radiation to travel across the space to the other face. It is reflected there with some loss of energy, returns to the first face, is reflected there with further loss, and so on. Table 3-1 gives the values and the direction of travel of the com-

Table 3-1

Initially emitted by M_1	Initially emitted by M_2
$\rightarrow W_1 \Delta t$	$\leftarrow W_2 \Delta t$
$\leftarrow (1 - a_2)W_1\Delta t$	$\rightarrow (1 - a_1)W_2\Delta t$
$\rightarrow (1 - a_1)(1 - a_2)W_1\Delta t$	$\leftarrow (1 - a_1)(1 - a_2)W_2\Delta t$
$\leftarrow (1 - a_1)(1 - a_2)^2W_1\Delta t$	$\rightarrow (1 - a_1)^2(1 - a_2)W_2\Delta t$
$\rightarrow (1 - a_1)^2(1 - a_2)^2W_1\Delta t$	$\leftarrow (1 - a_1)^2(1 - a_2)^2W_2\Delta t$
$\leftarrow (1 - a_1)^2(1 - a_2)^3W_1\Delta t$	$\rightarrow (1 - a_1)^3(1 - a_2)^2W_2\Delta t$
$+ \cdots$	$+ \cdots$

ponents in the radiation streams per unit area between the walls after several intervals of Δt have elapsed.

While these successive traverses of the initial radiation from each face are occurring, both faces continue to emit. Therefore, when the steady state has been reached, there are simultaneous columns of thermal radiation going back and forth in the space between the faces. The total radiation streaming in one direction, say to the right, is simply the sum of all the components in the direction $\rightarrow$. Therefore, the total effective emittance toward the right is given by

$$W_r \Delta t = W_1 \Delta t + (1 - a_1)(1 - a_2)W_1 \Delta t + (1 - a_1)^2(1 - a_2)^2W_1 \Delta t$$
$$+ \cdots + (1 - a_1)W_2 \Delta t + (1 - a_1)^2(1 - a_2)W_2 \Delta t$$
$$+ (1 - a_1)^3(1 - a_2)^2 \Delta t + \cdots \qquad (3-6)$$

Let $x = (1 - a_1)(1 - a_2)$. Then substituting this in the preceding equation we obtain

$$W_r = W_1[1 + x + x^2 + \cdots] + W_2(1 - a_1)[1 + x + x^2 + \cdots]. \qquad (3-7)$$

The series within the pairs of brackets is a simple geometric progression whose limit, since $0 < x < 1$, is $1/(1 - x)$. In terms of the absorptances, this limit is

$$\frac{1}{1 - x} = \frac{1}{1 - (1 - a_1)(1 - a_2)} = \frac{1}{1 - (1 - a_1 - a_2 + a_1a_2)}$$

$$= \frac{1}{a_1 + a_2 - a_1a_2}. \qquad (3-8)$$

Because the system is isothermal, we can obtain the following relations from Kirchhoff's radiation law (Eq. 3–5):

$$W_1 = a_1 W_b \qquad \text{and} \qquad W_2 = a_2 W_b. \tag{3–9}$$

Substituting the values from Eq. (3–8) and Eq. (3–9) in Eq. (3–7), we have

$$W_r = \frac{a_1 W_b + a_2 W_b (1 - a_1)}{a_1 + a_2 - a_1 a_2} = \frac{W_b (a_1 + a_2 - a_1 a_2)}{a_1 + a_2 - a_1 a_2} = W_b. \tag{3–10}$$

This equation shows that the radiation to the right (it could just as well have been in any other direction) is effectively radiated from the left surface as though from a black body. If a tunnel, which is so small it does not subtract a significant portion of the radiation in the cavity, is bored through the right-hand face, then *the leakage radiation will be black body-radiation.* It is to be noted that the derivation contained no assumptions about either the nature of thermal radiation or of the kinds of surfaces inside the enclosure.

We now know how to make a black body and have achieved the goal we set at the end of Section 3–6.

The reader can demonstrate for himself that black bodies can even be made from bright objects. A bundle of sewing needles held with their points directed toward the eye looks remarkably black. A pile of razor blades at least $\frac{1}{16}$-inch thick also looks black when viewed from the sharp side. In these cases the incident radiation is completely absorbed as a result of all the partial absorptions experienced at the many successive partial reflections it undergoes in traveling down into the relatively deep, narrow spaces between the needles or the blades.

We now return to the question of the spectrum of the radiation emitted by a hot body. If we take a black body as our sample, we can measure the emission from the hole as we did the material samples in getting the data for Fig. 3–3. This experiment shows that the emission of the black body gives at once the smooth solid curve of Fig. 3–3, which, unlike the other curves in the figure, is independent of the material used to make the emitter. This confirms what we might have suspected before, that the solid curve portrays a general characteristic of thermal radiation at a given temperature. A study of this curve should give information about radiation itself. With consideration of the material composing the cavity eliminated, the remaining important variable is the temperature of the radiation source. Mathematically, the total energy radiated per unit time per unit area of emitter is proportional to the area under the curve, and Stefan found empirically that this area is directly proportional to the fourth power of the absolute temperature,

$$W_b = \sigma T^4, \tag{3–11}$$

where σ is called the *Stefan-Boltzmann's constant.* Its value is

$$\sigma = (5.6696 \pm 0.0010) \times 10^{-8} \, \text{W} \cdot \text{m}^{-2} \cdot {}^\circ K^{-4}.$$

Equation (3–11) was first derived theoretically by Boltzmann and is therefore called Stefan-Boltzmann's law. In the following two sections, we shall derive the equation giving the spectral distribution of black-body radiation (Planck's law). Equation (3–11) can then be found by integration (Problem 3–5). Boltzmann derived the law by a thermodynamic argument* before Planck's work.

A body that is not black will radiate less energy than the black body. Combining Eqs. (3–5) and (3–11), we get, in general,

$$W = a\sigma T^4. \tag{3-12}$$

The coefficient a, called *total emissivity* or absorptance, is tabulated in all standard handbooks of physics.

The thermodynamic method employed by Boltzmann can be pushed a little further in predicting properties of the spectral distribution of black-body radiation. Wien found that as the temperature of any black body is changed the curve retains its general shape, but that the maximum of the curve shifts with temperature so that the wavelength of the most intense radiation is inversely proportional to the absolute temperature, or λ_{max} = const$/T$. This is a special case of *Wien's displacement law*, which states that at corresponding wavelengths the monochromatic energy density of the radiation in the cavity of a black body varies directly as the fifth power of the absolute temperature. The relation defining corresponding wavelengths at temperatures T_1 and T_2 is $\lambda_1 T_1 = \lambda_2 T_2$. The displacement law enables us to predict the entire curve at *any* temperature, given the entire curve at *one* particular temperature. Neither of these radiation laws, however, treats the basic problem of why the energy radiated from a black body has this particular wavelength distribution.

3-9 WIEN AND RAYLEIGH-JEANS' LAWS

A comparison of the experimental black-body radiation curves of Fig. 3–6 and the Maxwell distribution of speeds in a gas shown in Fig. 1–2 shows a remarkable similarity. Wien noted this similarity and tried to fit a function such as Maxwell had derived for the speed distribution to the black-body wavelength distribution. There is more than the similarity of the curves to justify this approach. If the molecules of the black body are thermally agitated, then their distribution of speeds may be somewhat like that derived by Maxwell. The accelerations of these molecules should be related to their velocities. These molecules contain charges which are therefore thermally accelerated, and we have shown that classical electrodynamics indicates that radiation results from accelerated charges. This argument is hardly rigorous, but it is a plausible explanation of the relationship between the similar curves. The expression that Wien obtained

---

* See, for instance, F. K. Richtmyer, E. H. Kennard, and T. Lauritsen, *Introduction to Modern Physics*. New York: McGraw-Hill, (1955).

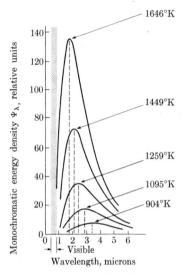

Fig. 3-6 The distribution of energy in the spectrum of the radiation from a black body at different temperatures.

for the monochromatic energy density ψ_λ within an isothermal black-body enclosure in the wavelength range λ to $\lambda + d\lambda$ is

$$\psi_\lambda \, d\lambda = \frac{c_1 \lambda^{-5}}{e^{c_2/\lambda T}} \, d\lambda, \qquad (3\text{--}13)$$

where λ is the wavelength, T is the absolute temperature, and e is the base of natural logarithms. This formula is essentially empirical and contains two adjustment constants c_1 and c_2, called the first and second radiation constants, respectively. Wien chose these constants so that the fit he obtained was rather good except at long wavelengths. The graph of Wien's law is shown dashed in Fig. 3-7. The points represent the experimental data of Lummer and Pringsheim.* But a "pretty good fit" is not good enough, and a formula which is essentially empirical tells us nothing about the nature of radiation.

Lord Rayleigh set out to derive the radiation distribution law in a rigorous way. He argued that the law of equipartition of energies (Section 1-8) should apply to the electromagnetic field in an enclosure. A standing wave of a given frequency interacts with oscillating atoms in the wall. Energy can flow in either direction from the wall to the field or conversely. The "temperature" of the field is therefore the same as the temperature of the walls. A one-dimensional harmonic oscillator has one degree of freedom representing its

---

* Lummer and Pringsheim, *Verhandl. Deut. Physik. Ges.* **1** (1899), pp. 23 and 215; **2** (1900), p. 163.

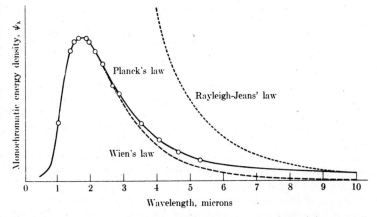

Fig. 3-7 Graphs of the radiation laws. Points represent experimental data.

kinetic energy, and, since the average potential energy equals its average kinetic energy ($\frac{1}{2}kT$), the total average energy is kT. A standing wave of electromagnetic radiation with a given direction of polarization represents a one-dimensional oscillator and should therefore have an average energy of kT. This is the basis for the derivation of Rayleigh-Jeans' radiation law. The law gives the energy content in an isothermal enclosure in a wavelength interval λ to $\lambda + d\lambda$. To derive it, we need to know how many *different* standing waves, called *modes* of radiation, there are in this wavelength interval. Each mode is then assumed to have an average energy of kT.

Let us first look at the simpler problem of calculating the number of modes of oscillations in a given frequency interval on a vibrating string. The x-axis is along the string, which is clamped at $x = O$ and $x = L$. We know from mechanics that standing transverse waves can be expressed as

$$y = A \sin kx \sin \omega t, \tag{3-14}$$

with

$$kL = n\pi, \tag{3-15}$$

where n is a positive integer. The *wave number* k, the wavelength λ, the angular frequency ω, the frequency v, and the wave velocity c on the string are related by the following equations:

$$k = 2\pi/\lambda, \qquad \omega = 2\pi v, \qquad c = \omega/k = \lambda v. \tag{3-16}$$

A mode of oscillation is by definition a standing wave with a given value of n. Our objective now is to count the number of possible values of n in a given frequency interval. We simply differentiate Eq. (3-15) and find

$$dn = \frac{L}{\pi} dk = \frac{L}{\pi c} d\omega. \tag{3-17}$$

By substituting $dk = -(2\pi/\lambda^2)\,d\lambda$ and neglecting the minus sign, we can also write

$$dn = \frac{2L}{\lambda^2}\,d\lambda. \qquad (3\text{-}18)$$

For example, if the string is $L = 100$ cm, Eq. (3-18) states that there can be 20 standing waves of different wavelengths in the interval $\lambda = 1$ cm to $\lambda + d\lambda = 1.1$ cm.

Let us now attack the three-dimensional problem, which, in principle, is very like the one we have discussed. We shall assume that the walls are perfectly reflective. If this were strictly true, there would be no exchange of energy between the wall and the electromagnetic field. However, we can imagine that the walls are almost perfectly reflective, and this modification will not change our calculation of the number of modes. Assume that the cavity is cubical with sides L. We can then find solutions of Maxwell's equation of the form

$$E_x = E_0 \cos k_x x \, \sin k_y y \, \sin k_z z \, \sin \omega t, \qquad (3\text{-}19)$$

with

$$\omega = c(k_x^2 + k_y^2 + k_z^2)^{1/2}. \qquad (3\text{-}20)$$

The expressions for E_y, E_z, H_x, H_y, and H_z are similar to Eq. (3-19). This is the three-dimensional version of Eq. (3-14). The x-dependence is a cosine function in Eq. (3-19) but will be a sine function with the same wave number k_x in the expression for E_y and E_z. The boundary conditions are now such that the components of the E-vector parallel to a given surface must be zero at that surface. This gives

$$\begin{aligned} k_x L &= n_x \pi, \\ k_y L &= n_y \pi, \\ k_z L &= n_z \pi, \end{aligned} \qquad (3\text{-}21)$$

where n_x, n_y, and n_z are positive integers. Combined with Eq. (3-20), this gives

$$\omega = \frac{\pi c}{L}\,(n_x^2 + n_y^2 + n_z^2)^{1/2}. \qquad (3\text{-}22)$$

A given set of integral values of n_x, n_y, and n_z represents a mode of electromagnetic oscillation with a given set of node planes. Another set of integers n_x, n_y, n_z corresponds to a different set of node planes. For each set there can be two independent directions of polarization. There are therefore two independent modes for each set n_x, n_y, and n_z.

We now ask how many different sets of n_x, n_y, and n_z result in an angular frequency below a given value ω (Eq. 3-22). The answer can be found most easily by plotting in a cartesian coordinate system the values of n_x, n_y, and n_z

along the three axes (Fig. 3–8). Each volume element in the first quadrant of this coordinate system contains one point corresponding to two modes of electromagnetic radiation. The positive numbers n_x, n_y, and n_z are components of a vector n, the maximum length of which is limited when there is a limit for the angular frequency ω. The relationship between the two is given by Eq. (3–22) as

$$n_{max} = \omega L/\pi c. \tag{3–23}$$

The total number of points, each of which represents two modes of radiation, can then be found by counting the number of unit volumes in the first quadrant within the distance n_{max} from the origin. This is equal to one-eighth the volume

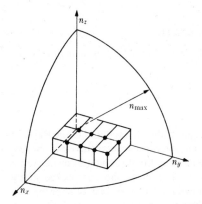

Fig. 3–8 Each point in this diagram represents a possible set of integers n_x, n_y, and n_z.

of a sphere with radius n_{max}. The number of states with angular frequency lower than ω is therefore

$$N = 2\,\frac{1}{8}\,\frac{4}{3}\,\pi\left(\frac{\omega L}{\pi c}\right)^3 = \frac{\omega^3 V}{3\pi^2 c^3} = \frac{8\pi V}{3\lambda^3}, \tag{3–24}$$

where $V = L^3$ is the volume of the box. The number of modes in the wavelength interval between λ and $\lambda + d\lambda$ is found by differentiation. Neglecting the minus sign, we find that

$$dN = \frac{8\pi V}{\lambda^4}\,d\lambda. \tag{3–25}$$

The energy density is now simply the number of modes per unit volume multiplied by kT:

$$\psi_\lambda\,d\lambda = \frac{8\pi kT}{\lambda^4}\,d\lambda. \tag{3–26}$$

This is Rayleigh-Jeans' law, which is plotted in Fig. 3–7 for comparison with the experimental data. At first glance this law appears vastly inferior to Wien's. Although it fits well for long wavelengths, at short wavelengths or high frequencies it heads toward infinity in what has been dramatically called the "ultraviolet catastrophe." Theoretically, however, the Rayleigh law must be taken far more seriously than Wien's. It was derived rigorously on the basis of classical physics. It involves no arbitrary constants, and where it does fit the experimental curve, it fits exactly. Whereas the failure of the Wien law was "too bad," the failure of the Rayleigh law presented a crisis. It indicated that classical theory was unable to account for an important experimental observation. This was the situation to which Max Planck directed himself.

3–10 PLANCK'S LAW; EMISSION QUANTIZED

Planck's first step was essentially empirical. He found that by changing Wien's formula slightly to

$$\psi_\lambda \, d\lambda = \frac{c_1 \lambda^{-5}}{e^{c_2/kT} - 1} \, d\lambda, \tag{3–27}$$

and by adjusting Wien's constants, he got a formula that reduced to the Rayleigh formula at long wavelengths and that fitted the experimental curve everywhere. He knew that he had found a correct formula and that it ought to be derivable. Planck's position was a little like that of a student who has peeked at the answer in the back of the book and is now faced with the task of showing how that answer can be logically computed. Planck tried by every method he could conceive to derive this correct formula from classical physics. He was finally forced to conclude that there was no flaw in Rayleigh's derivation and that the flaw must lie in classical theory itself.

Planck had to eliminate the "ultraviolet catastrophe" which came into Rayleigh's derivation because of the assumption that the radiation standing waves had an infinite number of modes of vibration (Eq. 3–24 with $\lambda \to 0$). Each of these was assumed to have an average energy kT and therefore the total energy content of the radiation field would be infinite. This is clearly unreasonable. Perhaps the high-frequency modes are not excited, or are they harder to excite? Let us take another look at the assumption of equipartition.

In effect, Rayleigh assumed that the energy content in one mode of oscillation could have any value from zero up and that the probability of finding an oscillator with energy E is given by Boltzmann's formula (Eq. 1–44). This gives an average energy

$$\bar{E} = \frac{\int E e^{-E/kT} \, dE}{\int e^{-E/kT} \, dE} = kT. \tag{3–28}$$

Another way of expressing this is to say that the modes can be in different *energy states*. Rayleigh assumed a continuum of states with a population proportional to the probability given by Boltzmann's law (see Fig. 3–9a).

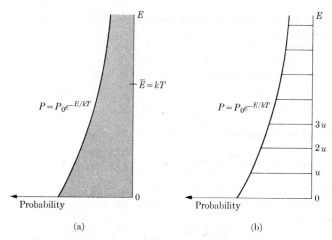

(a)   (b)

Figs. 3–9a and 3–9b (a) Probability P of finding an energy content E in a given mode of oscillation according to classical theory (Rayleigh). (b) Same as (a), but energy content can only take on discrete values, $E = mu$ (Planck). As drawn, this is an *energy-level diagram* with the horizontal coordinate indicating *relative population* in each level.

Planck postulated that each mode could only receive energy from the walls in discrete steps u. The energy content of one mode would then be 0, u, $2u$, $3u$, etc., or in general mu, where m is an integer. Let us see what this line of reasoning leads to. (The method at this point is following a procedure used by Boltzmann in 1877 to determine the distribution of kinetic energy among the molecules in a gas.) The number of oscillators having the energy m_u is

$$n_m = n_0 e^{-mu/kT}. \tag{3-29}$$

The energy contributed by the n_m oscillators is obviously

$$mun_m = mun_0 e^{-mu/kT}. \tag{3-30}$$

Therefore the average energy $\bar{E}$ of an oscillator is

$$\bar{E} = \frac{\sum_{m=0}^{\infty} mun_0 e^{-mu/kT}}{\sum_{m=0}^{\infty} n_0 e^{-mu/kT}}. \tag{3-31}$$

Since m is an integer, Eq. (3–16) becomes

$$\bar{E} = \frac{0 + ue^{-u/kT} + 2ue^{-2u/kT} + 3ue^{-3u/kT} + \cdots}{1 + e^{-u/kT} + e^{-2u/kT} + e^{-3u/kT} + \cdots}. \tag{3-32}$$

Let $x = e^{-u/kT}$. Then Eq. (3–17) can be written

$$\bar{E} = ux \frac{1 + 2x + 3x^2 + \cdots}{1 + x + x^2 + \cdots}. \tag{3–33}$$

The limits of these convergent series can be found by the usual methods (note that $x < 1$). The convergence limit of the series in the numerator is $1/(1 - x)^2$. This can be checked by expanding $(1 - x)^2$ according to the binomial theorem. The denominator is a simple geometric progression converging to $1/(1 - x)$. Substituting these limits in Eq. (3–33), we have

$$\bar{E} = ux \frac{1/(1 - x)^2}{1/(1 - x)} = \frac{ux}{1 - x} = \frac{u}{(1/x) - 1}. \tag{3–34}$$

When x is replaced by its equivalent, the result is

$$\bar{E} = \frac{u}{e^{u/kT} - 1}. \tag{3–35}$$

If we now multiply Eq. (3–35) by the number of modes of vibration in a unit volume of cavity space, from Eq. (3–25), we obtain the energy density in a wavelength range $d\lambda$,

$$\Psi_\lambda = \frac{8\pi}{\lambda^4} \frac{u}{e^{u/kT} - 1} \, d\lambda. \tag{3–36}$$

Recall that in this derivation the energy of an oscillator has been assumed to be an integer, m, times some small energy, u. Classical physics says the energy may have any value. This is equivalent to saying u may be exceedingly small and, in the limit, approach zero. If we set $u = 0$, Eq. (3–35) is indeterminate, 0/0. If we apply l'Hospital's rule, differentiating both numerator and denominator with respect to u before letting $u = 0$, we find that

$$\bar{E} = kT, \tag{3–37}$$

which is in complete agreement with Rayleigh's classical assumption of continuous energy. As we have seen, however, this assumption does not lead to the correct radiation law.

The relation given in Eq. (3–36) begins to look like Planck's empirical law (Eq. 3–27), if u is not zero. Indeed, the denominators of these two equations become identical (except for the minus one) if a value of u is chosen so that the powers of the exponential terms are the same. To obtain this value of u, we let

$$\frac{c_2}{\lambda T} = \frac{u}{kT}, \tag{3–38}$$

or

$$u = \frac{c_2 k}{\lambda} = \frac{c_2 k}{c} v. \tag{3–39}$$

In this last equation, c is the free-space velocity of light and v is the frequency of the oscillator and therefore also the frequency of the radiation it emits. If we replace the constants $(c_2 k/c)$ by another constant h, we have

$$u = \frac{hc}{\lambda} = hv. \tag{3–40}$$

When the value of u from Eq. (3–40) is substituted in Eq. (3–36), we obtain Planck's law for the energy density of black-body or cavity radiation. This law is

$$\psi_\lambda d\lambda = \frac{8\pi ch\lambda^{-5}}{e^{ch/\lambda kT} - 1} \, d\lambda. \tag{3–41}$$

This equation does agree with the experimental results. It is plotted in Fig. 3–7 (solid curve) for a temperature $T = 1646\,°K$.

When we introduced the idea of discrete energy steps u, we did not indicate that u would be different for the different modes. However, this is what our analysis has shown to be the case. Going back to Fig. 3–9(b), we can now explain qualitatively how Planck avoids the ultraviolet catastrophe. For small wavelengths, high frequencies, the distance from $E = 0$ to the first discrete energy level u is so large that the probability for a mode to exist in that state of excitation becomes diminishingly small. All modes of very high frequency therefore have $E = 0$. This is also immediately evident from Eq. (3–35).

The new constant h is called the *Planck constant*. We have seen that it could be determined from Wien's constant c_2 but it can also be evaluated from the photoelectric effect discussed later in this chapter. Its value is $h = (6.62620 \pm 0.00005) \times 10^{-34}$ J·s. (Note that the units are those of angular momentum.)

Thus Planck was led to his startling, nonclassical assumption that the energy states of an oscillator must be an *integral* multiple of the product of the constant h and the frequency v of the electromagnetic radiation it emits. If E represents the smallest permissible energy change, Planck's famous quantum* equation is

$$E = hv. \tag{3–42}$$

Planck introduced the quantum concept in 1900, and it eventually led to the conclusion that radiation is not emitted in continuous amounts but in discrete bundles of energy each equal to hv. These bundles or packets of radiant energy are now called *quanta* or *photons*. This was the beginning of the atomic theory of radiation, which has grown to become the quantum theory. It is obvious, however, that quanta of radiation of different frequencies have different "sizes" (energies), and that they are atomic only in the sense that they are

---

* Quantum is the Latin word for *how much* or *how great*.

discrete. Planck thought at first that his *ad hoc** hypothesis applied only to the oscillators and, possibly, to the emitted radiation in their immediate neighborhood and that, at most, it was a slight modification of Maxwell's theory of radiation. However, we shall see that he initiated a series of events which have changed our whole concept of the interaction of electromagnetic radiation with matter.

3–11 PHOTOELECTRIC EFFECT

We now turn from thermal radiation to another portion of the electromagnetic spectrum and consider an effect which is due to radiation of higher frequency. We mentioned earlier that even before the discovery of the electron, Hallwachs observed that zinc irradiated with ultraviolet light lost negative charge. He proposed that somehow the radiation caused the zinc to eject negative charge. In 1899 Lenard showed that the radiation caused the metal to emit electrons.

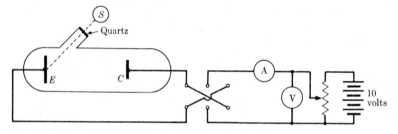

Fig. 3–10 Apparatus for investigating the photoelectric effect.

This phenomenon, called the photoelectric effect, can be studied in detail with the apparatus shown in Fig. 3–10. In this figure, S is a source of radiation of variable and known frequency v and intensity I, E is an emitting electrode of the material being studied, and C is a collecting electrode. Both electrodes are contained in an evacuated glass envelope with a quartz window that permits the passage of ultraviolet and visible light. The electric circuit allows the electrodes to be maintained at different known potentials and permits the measurement of any current between the electrodes. We first make the collecting electrode positive with respect to the emitting electrode, so that any electrons ejected will be quickly swept away from the emitter. About 10 V is enough to do this but not enough to free electrons from the negative electrode by positive-ion bombardment as was the case in the early cathode-ray tubes. If the tube is dark, no electrons are emitted and the microammeter indicates no current. If ultraviolet light is allowed to fall on the emitting electrode, electrons

---

* *Ad hoc* means literally *to this*, and is used to describe a hypothesis which is applicable to but one (this) situation.

are liberated and the current is measured by the microammeter. It is found that the rate of electron emission is proportional to the light intensity. By holding the frequency v of the light and the accelerating potential V constant, we can obtain data like that represented in Fig. 3–11.

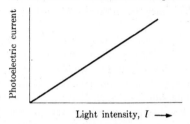

Fig. 3–11 Photoelectric current as a function of the intensity of the light. The frequency of the light and the accelerating potential are kept constant.

It is hardly surprising that if a little light liberates a few electrons, then more light liberates many. If we vary either the frequency of the light or the material irradiated, only the slope of the line changes.

We can now experiment by keeping the light intensity constant and varying the frequency. The graphs of these data are shown in Fig. 3–12, where A and B represent two different irradiated materials. The significant thing about these curves is that for every substance irradiated there is a limiting frequency below which no photoelectrons are produced. This frequency, called the *threshold frequency*, v_0, is a characteristic of the material irradiated. The wavelength of light corresponding to the threshold frequency is the *threshold wavelength*, λ_0. No photoelectrons are emitted for wavelengths greater than this.

The existence of a threshold frequency is difficult to explain on the basis of the wave theory of light. If we think of light as consisting of a pulsating electromagnetic field, we can imagine that that field is sometimes directed so as to tend to eject electrons from a metallic surface. We might even feel it

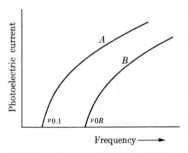

Fig. 3–12 Photoelectric current for two materials as a function of the frequency of the light. The intensity of the light and the accelerating potential are kept constant.

reasonable that certain frequencies of light would resonate with the electrons of the metal so that, for a particular metal, there might be preferred light frequencies which would cause emission more efficiently. The striking thing about these data is that for each material there is a frequency below which no photoelectrons are emitted and above which they are emitted. This effect is independent of the intensity of the light.

In 1905 Einstein proposed a daring but simple explanation. He centered attention on the energy aspect of the situation. Whereas Planck had proposed that radiation was composed of energy bundles only in the neighborhood of the emitter, Einstein proposed that these energy bundles *preserve their identity throughout their life*. Instead of spreading out like water waves, Einstein conceived that the emitted energy bundle stays together, and carries an amount of energy equal to hv. For Einstein, the significance of the light frequency was not so much an indication of the frequency of a pulsating electric field as it was a measure of the energy of a bundle of light called a *photon*. His interpretation of the data of Fig. 3–12 would be that a quantum of light below the threshold frequency just does not have enough energy to remove an electron from the metal, but light above that frequency does.

The threshold frequency is dependent on the nature of the material irradiated because there is for each material a certain minimum energy necessary to liberate an electron. The *photoelectric work function* or *threshold energy*, W_0, of a material is the *minimum* energy required to free a photoelectron from that material.

In a third photoelectric experiment let us hold both the frequency and intensity of the light constant. The variable is the potential difference across the photoelectric cell. Starting with the collector at about 10 volts positive, we reduce this potential to zero and then run it negative until the photocurrent stops entirely. Curve I_1 of Fig. 3–13 shows the type of curve we might expect for this particular substance. This curve requires careful interpretation.

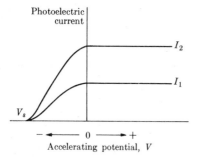

Fig. 3–13 Photoelectric current as a function of the accelerating potential for light of different intensities having a two-to-one ratio. The frequency of the light is constant.

When the potential difference across the tube is about 10 V or more, *all* the emitted electrons travel across the tube. This stream of charges is called the *saturation current*, and it is obvious that an increase in the potential of the collector cannot cause an increase in current. As the accelerating potential is reduced from positive values through zero to negative values, the tube current reduces because of the applied retarding potential. Eventually this potential is large enough to stop the current completely.

The *stopping potential* V_s is the value of the retarding potential differen , that is just sufficient to halt the *most energetic* photoelectron emitted. Therefore the product of the stopping potential and the electronic charge, $V_s e$, is equal to the maximum kinetic energy that an emitted electron can have. Since this stopping potential has a definite value, it indicates that the emitted electrons have a definite upper limit to their kinetic energy. Doubling the intensity of the light doubles the current at each potential, as in I_2 of Fig. 3–11, but the stopping potential is *independent* of the intensity.

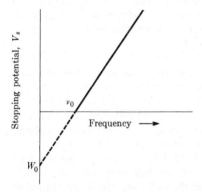

Fig. 3–14 Stopping potential as a function of the frequency of the light. Results are independent of intensity.

If, however, the experiment is repeated with a series of different light frequencies, it is found that the stopping potential increases linearly with the frequency. This is best shown by plotting the stopping potential against the frequency, as shown in Fig. 3–14. Below the threshold frequency no electrons are emitted and the stopping potential is of course zero; however, as the frequency is increased above the threshold, the stopping potential increases linearly with the frequency.

To see how fully the data of Fig. 3–14 confirm the Einstein photon interpretation of the photoelectric effect, we now interpret the graph of Fig. 3–14 as he would have. For light frequency between zero and the threshold frequency there are no photoelectrons produced, since the incident photons have less energy than the work function of the material. For light above the threshold frequency, photoelectrons are emitted. The energy of these emitted electrons may vary greatly. According to the Einstein view, however, there must be an upper limit to the energy of the emitted photoelectrons. No photoelectrons can have energy in excess of the energy of the incoming photon less the minimum energy to free an electron, the work function. Since the photon energy is proportional to frequency and since the stopping potential is a measure of the maximum kinetic energy of the emitted photoelectrons, the graph of stopping potential against frequency should be a straight line. This is precisely what Fig. 3-14 shows. The quantitative check of the Einstein interpretation is that the slope of the straight line provides a method of determining the way in which photon energy depends on photon frequency, which is the Planck constant.

A final and decisive experiment consists of making the irradiating light extremely weak. In this case, the number of photoelectrons is very small and special techniques are required to detect them. The significant result of this experiment is that dim light causes emission of photoelectrons which, however few, are emitted instantaneously and with the same maximum kinetic energy as for bright light of the same frequency.

According to the wave theory of light, pulsating electromagnetic fields spread out from their source. Dim light corresponds to waves of small amplitude and small energy. If dim light spreads over a surface, conservation of energy requires that either no photoelectrons should be emitted or the electrons must store energy over long periods of time before gathering enough energy to become free of the metal. The fact that high-energy photoelectrons appear immediately can be explained only by assuming that the light energy falls on the surface in concentrated bundles. According to Einstein, the dim light consists of a few photons each having energy depending only on the light frequency. This energy is not spread over the surface uniformly as required by the wave theory. A photon that is absorbed gives all its energy to one electron, and that electron will be emitted violently even though the number of such events is small.

If a man dives into a swimming pool, his energy is partly converted into waves which agitate other swimmers in the pool. If it were observed that when a man dives into a pool another swimmer is suddenly ejected from the pool onto a diving board, we would be forced to conclude that the energy provided by the diver did not spread out in an expanding wavefront, but was somehow transferred in concentrated form to the ejected swimmer. A swimming party held in such a superquantum pool would be a very odd affair compared with one in a classical pool.

To summarize Einstein's interpretation of the photoelectric effect, we equate the energy of an incident photon of frequency v to the sum of the work function of the emitter ($W_0 = hv_0$) and the maximum kinetic energy that an ejected photoelectron can acquire. We then have

$$hv = hv_0 + \tfrac{1}{2}m_e v_{max}^2, \quad \text{or} \quad \tfrac{1}{2}m_e v_{max}^2 = hv - hv_0,$$

or

$$V_s e = hv - W_0. \tag{3–43}$$

This is a linear equation. It is the equation of the graph in Fig. 3–14. It is evident that the slope of the curve V_s plotted as a function of v is equal to h/e, that v_0 is the v-axis intercept, and that W_0/e is the intercept of the extrapolated curve on the V_s-axis. Einstein's photoelectric equation was first verified with precision in 1916, eleven years after it was proposed, by Millikan, who made careful measurements of the photoemission from many different substances.

3–12 SUMMARY OF THE ATOMIC VIEW OF RADIATION

We introduced this chapter by outlining the disagreement between Newton and Huygens over the nature of light. We described how Maxwell strengthened Huygens' wave theory when he showed that electromagnetic waves were a consequence of the laws of electricity and magnetism. We reported that Hertz demonstrated that electric circuits could be made to produce the electromagnetic waves Maxwell predicted. But we also mentioned that Hertz observed that he could produce sparks more easily when his spark gap was illuminated. Thus Hertz's work, which supported Maxwell's theory, also contained the first observation of the photoelectric effect. Although the wave theory of light accounts beautifully for many optical phenomena, it fails to account for either the black-body radiation or the photoelectric effect, where light appears to possess marked particle aspects. It is hardly satisfactory to regard light as a wave motion part of the time and a particle phenomenon at other times. We shall return to the question of the resolution of this conflict of viewpoint in Chapter 5. At this point it is clear, however, that the resolution of this paradox can never eliminate the idea that light is emitted and absorbed in bundles of energy called photons, and that now radiation must join matter and electricity in having a basically atomic character. *The fact that radiant energy is quantized is a radical departure from classical physics and will require us to re-examine the whole energy concept from the quantum point of view.* Establishing this fact has been the main business of this chapter. Before closing the chapter, however, we shall consider some related topics.

3–13 THE ELECTRON VOLT; PHOTON ENERGIES

In the Einstein equation, we measured the maximum kinetic energy of the emitted electrons by noting the potential energy difference (eV_s), which was equivalent to the electron kinetic energy. This method of determining and expressing electron energies is a particularly convenient one, and it suggests a new unit of energy. This new unit of energy is called the *electron volt*, eV, which is defined as the amount of energy equal to the change in kinetic energy of one electronic charge when it moves through a potential difference of one volt. Since the electron volt is an energy unit, it is in the same category as the joule, the foot-pound, the British thermal unit, and the kilowatt-hour.

Energies in joules can be converted to electron volts by dividing by $e_c = 1.60 \times 10^{-19}$. In this case e_c is *not a charge* but a *conversion factor* having the units of joules per electron volt. The Einstein equation, Eq. (3–43), is valid in any consistent system of units. If we choose MKSA units and divide Eq. (3–43) by the factor e_c, we obtain the same relation in electron volts:

$$E_{k(\text{max})} \ (numerically \ \text{equal to } V_s) = \frac{h\nu}{e_c} - \frac{W_0}{e_c}. \qquad (3\text{–}44)$$

In words, this equation states that the maximum kinetic energy of a photo-electron in electron volts equals the energy of the photon in electron volts minus the work function in electron volts.

When the electron volt is too small a unit, it is convenient to use 10^3 eV = 1 keV (kilo-electron-volt), and 10^6 eV = 1 MeV (million-electron-volt).

It is also useful to express photon energies in electron volts. In terms of photon frequency,

$$E = \frac{h\nu}{e_c} = \frac{6.63 \times 10^{-34}}{1.60 \times 10^{-19}} \nu \ \text{eV} = 4.14 \times 10^{-15}\nu \ \text{eV}. \qquad (3\text{–}45)$$

Or, since $\nu = c/\lambda$, we get

$$E = \frac{4.14 \times 10^{-15} \times 3 \times 10^8}{\lambda} \ eV$$

$$= \frac{1.24 \times 10^{-6}}{\lambda} \ \text{eV}, \qquad (3\text{–}46)$$

with λ in meters. If the wavelength is expressed in angstroms instead of meters, we have

$$E = \frac{1.24 \times 10^4}{\lambda} \ \text{eV}. \qquad (3\text{–}47)$$

We shall use Eq. (3.47) *frequently*.

Example. Light having a wavelength of 5000 Å falls on a material having a photoelectric work function of 1.90 eV. Find (a) the energy of the photon in eV, (b) the kinetic energy of the most energetic photoelectron in eV and in joules, and (c) the stopping potential.

Solution.

a) From Eq. (3–47),

$$E = \frac{12400}{5000} = 2.47 \text{ eV.}$$

b) The law of conservation of energy gives

maximum kinetic energy = photon energy − work function

or

$$E_k = 2.47 \text{ eV} - 1.90 \text{ eV} = 0.57 \text{ eV.}$$

Also

$$E_k = 0.57 \times 1.60 \times 10^{-19} = 9.11 \times 10^{-20} \text{ J.}$$

(c)

$$V_s = \frac{0.57 \text{ eV}}{1 \text{ electronic charge}} = 0.57 \text{ V.}$$

3–14 THERMIONIC EMISSION

The subjects discussed in this and the next section are, strictly speaking, not parts of "The Atomic View of Radiation," but their relations to the topics discussed earlier in this Chapter are such that, pedagogically as well as historically, they belong here.

We have already considered two ways in which electrons can be released from a metal. In Chapter 2 we discussed the discharge of electricity through gases. The electrons that participate in cold-cathode discharges are obtained from the cathode while it is bombarded by the positive ions produced in the residual gas in the tube. In this chapter we have considered another emission process, called photoelectric emission. There is still another kind of electron emission, which we shall now discuss briefly.

If a metal is heated, the thermal agitation of the matter may give electrons enough energy to exceed the work function of the material. Thus the space around a heated metal is found to contain many electrons. A study of this effect shows that the *thermionic work function* is very nearly the same as the photoelectric work function—a most satisfying result.

Since a fine wire can be heated easily by passing an electric current through it, thermionic emission is one of the most convenient electron sources. Most radio-type vacuum tubes use a heated cathode as their electron source. Thermal emission of negative charges from a hot wire in a vacuum was first observed by Edison in 1883 when he was making incandescent lamps, and such thermal emission is called the *Edison effect*. In 1899, J. J. Thomson, showed that the thermions in this effect are electrons.

3–15 SPECIFIC HEAT OF SOLIDS

In Section 1–4, we mentioned an experimental law discovered by Dulong and Petit in 1819 stating that the product of the atomic mass and specific heat is the same for all elementary (solid) substances. It can be restated to read: "The specific heat per mole is the same for all solid substances." This law was based on early measurements of the specific heat for a series of substances. All these measurements were taken at room temperature. The value found for the specific heat per mole was approximately 6 cal·mole^{-1} °C.

As discussed in Section 1–7, the temperature of a gas is a direct measure of its translation kinetic energy. Similarly, the temperature of a solid is a measure of the kinetic energy of the atoms as they perform vibrations about the equilibrium positions in the lattice structure. At the interphase between the solid and the gas there will exist an equilibrium of no net energy flow if the temperature of the solid is the same as the temperature of the gas. Since the gas molecules and the atoms in the solid are constantly colliding with each other, they have, in equilibrium, the same average kinetic energy. This means that each atom in the solid has an average kinetic energy of $\frac{3}{2}kT$. Since these atoms are vibrating as harmonic oscillators, they will also on the average have potential energy. It is well known from mechanics that, in the harmonic oscillator, the average potential energy equals the average kinetic energy. Therefore the total energy per atom is $3\,kT$. The total energy content per mole is therefore

$$E = 3kN_AT = 3\,RT, \tag{3–48}$$

with $R = kN_A$ being the gas constant. The specific heat per mole is therefore

$$c_v = dE/dT = 3R = 5.94 \text{ cal·mole}^{-1} \text{ °K}^{-1}, \tag{3–49}$$

in agreement with Dulong and Petit's law.

In this simple derivation we have assumed that the substances undergo no change in phase, that is, change of the crystalline structure of the solid, during heating. We have also disregarded any effect resulting from changes of energy of the so-called "free" electrons in metals. As further discussed in Chapter 11, only a very small fraction of these free electrons increase their energy as the solid is heated. Therefore the effect on the specific heat of this energy increase is negligibly small.

It was very soon shown that Dulong and Petit's law for some substances failed quite badly at room temperature and that for all substances the specific heat decreases with the absolute temperature. Figure 3–15 shows as examples the specific heats of diamond, silicon, aluminum, and lead as functions of the absolute temperature. As the temperature increases, the specific heat for all these substances approaches approximately the value $3R$ predicted above. However, our simple derivation fails to account for the decrease towards absolute zero. Einstein in 1907* was able to explain the basic features of the curves shown in Fig. 3–15. He assumed that the energy of oscillations of the vibrating atoms is quantized in exactly the same way as the modes of electro-

---

*   A. Einstein, *Ann. Physik* **22** (1907), p. 180.

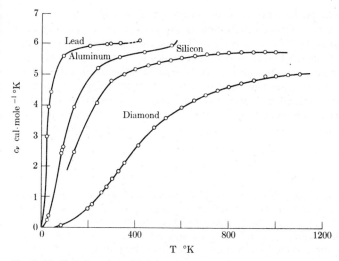

Fig. 3-15 Variation of specific heat at constant volume with temperature. Reproduced by permission from Richtmyer, Kennard, and Lauritsen, *Introduction to Modern Physics*, New York: McGraw-Hill © 1955, p. 410.

magnetic oscillation in an isothermal enclosure (Section 3-10). Accordingly, the average energy per oscillator is not $3\,kT$ but

$$\bar{E}_0 = \frac{3h\nu}{e^{h\nu/kT} - 1} \tag{3-50}$$

(compare Eq. 3-35). The frequency ν is now the vibrational frequency of the atom in the lattice of the crystal. We find the total energy E per mole by multiplying $\bar{E}_0$ by Avogadro's constant N_A. The specific heat per mole is then

$$c_v = \frac{dE}{dT} = 3R\,\frac{e^{h\nu/kT}}{(e^{h\nu/kT} - 1)^2}\left(\frac{h\nu}{kT}\right)^2. \tag{3-51}$$

The frequency of vibration of an atom in a solid can be estimated in various ways. For instance, by measuring the compressibility of the solid, one can estimate the "spring constant" for the restoring forces; and, of course, the mass of the atom is known. By using such techniques, one was able to show that Einstein's theory was in qualitative agreement with experimentally observed specific heats.

The assumption of one single vibrational frequency is an oversimplification. Debye* improved Einstein's formula by assuming that the vibrational frequencies had a broad spectrum up to a maximum value and that there are two

---

* P. Debye, *Ann. Physik* **39** (1912), p. 789.

types of vibrations, one transverse and one longitudinal. However, of central importance also in Debye's derivation is the average energy per degree of freedom as given by Planck's formula. Thus Einstein and Debye showed that the concept of quantization of energy is not limited to electromagnetic radiation in an isothermal cavity, but also to mechanical harmonic oscillators. In the next chapter, we shall see how Niels Bohr found that the energies of electrons in atoms are quantized and also that their angular momenta are quantized. It fell on Erwin Schrödinger (Chapter 6) with some help of others to tie all these loose ends together in a neat theory that we call *wave mechanics*.

PROBLEMS

3-1 The displacement x at time t of mass m which is moving with simple harmonic motion of amplitude A and frequency v is given by $x = A \sin 2\pi v t$. a) Show that its kinetic energy T is $2\pi^2 v^2 A^2 m \sin^2 2\pi v t$. b) Show that the time average of T over a whole cycle and the time average of V over a whole cycle are each equal to one-half the total energy of the oscillator, $2\pi^2 v^2 A^2 m$.

3-2 Show that Planck's radiation law, Eq. (3–41), reduces to Wien's law for short wavelengths and to the Rayleigh-Jeans' law for long ones. (*Hint:* Express the exponential term as a series to obtain the second of these laws.)

3-3 The cavity of a black-body radiator is in the shape of a cube measuring 2 cm on a side and the black body is at a temperature of 1500°K. a) Find the number of modes of vibration per unit volume in the cavity in the wavelength band between 4995 Å and 5005 Å. b) Calculate the radiant energy in the whole cavity in this wavelength band of 10 Å (1) by assigning an energy of kT to each mode of vibration and (2) from Planck's radiation law.

3-4 Show that the energy density of black-body radiation expressed in terms of frequency is

$$\psi_v = \frac{8\pi h v^3}{c^3(e^{hv/kT} - 1)} \, dv.$$

3-5 Show that the total energy density in black-body radiation over the whole range of frequencies from 0 to ∞ is identical in form to the Stefan-Boltzmann law for total radiation. A useful definite integral is

$$\int_0^\infty \frac{x^3 \, dx}{e^x - 1} = \frac{\pi^4}{15}.$$

3-6 a) Show that the maximum energy density in the spectrum of black-body radiation occurs at a wavelength λ_m which can be found from the equation $(1 - x/5)e^x = 1$, where $x \equiv ch/\lambda_m kT$. b) Find the roots of this equation, and then show that $\lambda_m T = 2.90 \times 10^{-3}$ m °K.

3-7 At the surface of the earth a 1-cm^2 area oriented at right angles to the sun's rays receives about 0.13 J of radiant energy each second. Assume that the sun is a black-body radiator. What is the surface temperature of the sun? (The radius of the sun is about 7×10^8 m and the earth is about 1.49×10^8 km from the sun.)

3-8 A tungsten sphere 0.5 cm in radius is suspended within a large evacuated enclosure whose walls are at 300°K. Tungsten is not a black body but has an average emissive power that is 0.35 that of a black body. What power input is required to maintain the sphere at a temperature of 3000°K if heat conduction along the supports is neglected?

3-9 Find the percent change in the total energy radiated per unit time by a black body if the absolute temperature of the black body is increased by a) 100 percent, b) 10 percent, c) 1 percent, and d) 0.1 percent.

3-10 At what wavelength does the maximum intensity of the radiation from a black body occur at a temperature of 300°K? 1000°K? 6000°K?

3-11 If 5 percent of the energy supplied to an incandescent light bulb is radiated as visible light, how many visible quanta are emitted per second by a 100-watt bulb? Assume the wavelength of all the visible light to be 5600 Å.

3-12 In order that an object be visible to the naked eye, the intensity of light entering the eye from the object must be at least 1.5×10^{-11} J · m^{-2} · s^{-1}. What is the minimum rate at which photons must enter the eye so that an object is visible, given that the diameter of the pupil is 0.7 cm? Assume a wavelength of 5600 Å.

3-13 What is the energy in eV of a photon having a wavelength of 912 Å?

3-14 Show that Planck's constant h has the same physical units as angular momentum.

3-15 A mass of 10 g hangs from a spring with a force constant of 25 N m^{-1}. Assume that this oscillator is quantized just as the radiation oscillators are. a) What is the minimum energy that can be supplied to the mass? b) If the mass at rest absorbs the minimum energy of part a), what is the resulting amplitude? c) How many quanta must the mass absorb in order to have an amplitude of 10 cm?

3-16 Particles of a certain system can have energies of E, $2E$, or $3E$, where $E = 0.025$ eV. a) What are the ratios of the number of particles in each of the upper states to the number of particles in the lowest state when the system is in equilibrium at 290°K? b) What is the average energy of a particle in the equilibrium distribution of these states?

3-17 In a problem in Chapter 1, it was found that a thermal neutron has a velocity of 2200 m s^{-1}. a) What is a thermal neutron's kinetic energy in eV? b) What is the increase in kinetic energy in eV of each water molecule in a stream that goes down a 450-ft (137.1 m) waterfall?

3-18 The fissioning of a ^{235}U atom yields 200 MeV of energy. How many such atoms must fission to provide an amount of energy equal to that required to lift a mosquito one inch? The mass of an average mosquito is 0.90 mg.

3-19 The visible light from a 40-watt incandescent bulb is incident normally on a potassium surface 50 cm from the bulb. a) How long will it take a potassium atom to absorb 2.0 eV of energy which is its photoelectric work function? Consider the bulb a point source that radiates 7.5 percent of the input power as visible light. Assume that the absorbing area of the potassium atom is equivalent to a circular disk having a diameter of 5.0 Å. b) How long would it take the potassium atom to absorb 2.0 eV of energy if it is illuminated by full moonlight? The illumination at 50 cm from a 40-watt bulb is about 740 times greater than full moonlight.

3-20 The light-sensitive compound on most photographic films is silver bromide, AgBr. We shall assume that a film is exposed when the light energy absorbed dissociates this molecule into its atoms. (The actual process is more complex, but the quantitative result does not differ greatly.) The energy or heat of dissociation of AgBr is 23.9 kcal $\cdot$ mole^{-1}. Find a) the energy in eV, b) the wavelength, and c) the frequency of the photon that is just able to dissociate a molecule of silver bromide. d) What is the energy in eV of a quantum of radiation having a frequency of 100 MHz? e) Explain the fact that light from a firefly can expose a photographic film, whereas the radiation from a television station transmitting 50,000 watts at 100 MHz cannot. f) Will photographic films stored in a light-tight container be ruined (exposed) by radio waves constantly passing through them? Explain.

3-21 When a certain photoelectric surface is illuminated with light of different wavelengths, the following stopping potentials are observed:

λ, Å	3660	4050	4360	4920	5460	5790
V_s, V	1.48	1.15	0.93	0.62	0.36	0.24

Plot the stopping potential as ordinate against the frequency of the light as abscissa. Determine a) the threshold frequency, b) the threshold wavelength, c) the photoelectric work function of the material, and d) the value of the Planck constant h (the value of e being known).

3-22 The photoelectric work function of potassium is 2.0 eV. If light having a wavelength of 3600 Å falls on potassium, find a) the stopping potential, b) the kinetic energy in eV of the most energetic electrons ejected, and c) the velocities of these electrons.

3-23 What will be the change in the stopping potential for photoelectrons emitted from a surface if the wavelength of the incident light is reduced from 4000 Å to 3980 Å? (Assume that the decrease in wavelength is so small that it may be considered a differential.)

3-24 The threshold wavelength for photoelectric emission from a certain material is 6525 Å. Find the stopping potential when the material is irradiated with a) light having a wavelength of 4000 Å, and b) with light having twice the frequency and three times the intensity of that in the previous part. c) If a material having double the work function were used, what would be the answers to parts a) and b)?

3-25 Light of wavelength 4000 Å liberates photoelectrons from a certain metal. The photoelectrons now enter a uniform magnetic field having an induction of 10^{-4} T. The electrons move normal to the field lines so that they travel circular paths. The largest circular path has a radius of 5.14 cm. Find the work function for the metal.

3-26 A surface is irradiated with monochromatic light of variable wavelength. Above a wavelength of 5000 Å, no photoelectrons are emitted from the surface. With an unknown wavelength a stopping potential of 3V is necessary to eliminate the photoelectric current. What is the unknown wavelength?

CHAPTER 4

The Atomic Models
of Rutherford
and Bohr

4-1 INTRODUCTION

We have traced how matter, electricity, and radiation came to be regarded as atomic in character. We have established the existence of some elementary particles that are more fundamental than the chemical elements. Electrons, for example, are common to all elements and are a common building block of all matter. Our discussion of positive rays and mass spectroscopy showed that matter also has positive constituents which are much more massive than electrons. Thomson, who made the first quantitative measurements on electrons and positive rays, assumed that a normal chemical atom consists of a mixture of constituents. This mixture came to be called the "plum-pudding" atomic model: The atom was regarded as a heavy positive sphere of charge seasoned with enough electron plums to make it electrically neutral.

4-2 PROBING THE ATOM WITH ALPHA PARTICLES

A very different atomic model was indicated by experiments performed by Rutherford and his associates in 1911.

We shall discuss radioactivity at some length in Chapter 12, but in order to be able to discuss the Rutherford experiments a few observations need to be made now. Certain atoms are unstable and fly apart of their own accord. The nature of these disintegrations depends on the element that is disintegrating, but in every case the fragments ejected consist either of electrons, here called beta rays, or of doubly ionized helium atoms, called alpha particles. These disintegration fragments usually are ejected with high energies from a radioactive substance and are often accompanied by very short-wavelength photon radiation called gamma rays. Radium, for example, is an excellent source of high-energy alpha particles. These alpha particles can travel through a few centimeters of air before they are stopped, and in a vacuum they travel long distances without losing energy. When they strike certain materials, they cause visible fluorescent light flashes.*

Rutherford studied how these alpha particles from radium were absorbed by matter. He found they were absorbed by sheets of metal a few hundredths of a millimeter thick, but that they could readily pass through gold foil several ten-thousandths of a millimeter thick. Rutherford's apparatus is shown schematically in Fig. 4–1. Radium was placed in a cavity at the end of a narrow tunnel in a lead block. Alpha particles were emitted in random directions by this source and the lead absorbed all except those emitted along the axis of the tunnel. In this way Rutherford obtained a collimated beam of alpha particles which streamed toward the gold foil. Particles deflected by an angle θ by passage through the foil produced flashes on a ZnS fluorescent screen, and these flashes were observed in a low-power microscope.

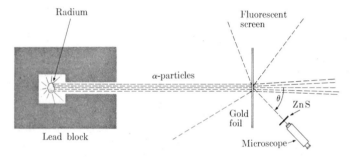

Fig. 4–1 Schematic diagram of Rutherford's alpha-particle scattering apparatus.

Many of the alpha particles did go straight through the foil or were deflected only by very small amounts. Amazingly, however, some alpha particles were deflected through very large angles. A few even returned to the side of the gold foil from which they came. Rutherford's astonishment at this is evident in his comment, "It was quite the most incredible event that has ever happened to me in my life. It was almost as incredible as if you fired a 15-inch shell at a piece of tissue paper and it came back and hit you." This observed scattering through large angles was contrary to predictions based on

---

*   Radiolight watch dials are painted with a paste containing fluorescent material and a trace of radium. Under a microscope the glow of the dial can be seen to be a multitude of flashes, called scintillations, which remind one of the twinkling of the stars on a immer night. The effect may be seen through a 4-power magnifier, but it is better to use two or three times this magnification. The light is less likely to appear continuous if there is very little radioactive material on the dial. Observations must be made in a completely darkened room and it may be necessary to wait about five minutes for the eyes to become dark-adapted. This time delay will also permit any phosphorescence to fade and eventually die out.

the Thomson model of the atom. Let us examine these predictions in some detail.

Assume that an alpha particle of charge ze (with $z = 2$) collides with a Thomson atom of radius R. Can it be turned around in its path if the forces acting are only electrostatic forces? Before it starts on its way back, it must be momentarily at rest, and this means that the kinetic energy has been converted into potential energy. (Since the alpha particle is much lighter than the atom it is colliding with, we neglect the kinetic energy resulting from center-of-mass motion.) The potential energy for a particle of charge ze at the surface of a uniform-charge cloud of radius R and charge Ze is $V_c = zZe^2/4\pi\varepsilon_0 R$. At the center of the charge cloud the potential energy is

$$V_c = \frac{3zZe^2}{8\pi\varepsilon_0 R}. \qquad (4\text{-}1)$$

Inserting $z = 2$, $Z = 80$ (for example), $R \approx 1\text{Å} = 10^{-10}$ m, and the known values for e and ε_0, we get after converting to electron volts $V_c = 3456$ eV. We have completely neglected the effect of the electrons, which, of course, neutralize the positive charge and therefore substantially reduce its effect. Indeed, only local fluctuations of charge within the atom can produce the forces we are looking for. Since the kinetic energy of the alpha particles used in the experiments by Rutherford and his associates was about 5 MeV, it is clear that a single collision with a Thomson atom could not result in anything but a very small angle of deflection. A collision with an electron cannot produce much deflection either, because of the fact that the electron is 7000 times lighter than the alpha particle. What about multiple collisions?

A simple but adequate theory of multiple collisions predicts that the number of particles deflected into a small solid angle centered about an angle of deflection θ should be

$$N(\theta) = N(0) \cdot e^{-\theta^2/2\sigma^2}. \qquad (4\text{-}2)$$

This is a Gaussian distribution, or standard distribution with σ being the standard deviation determining the width of the curve. Two of Rutherford's associates, Geiger and Marsden, measured the angular distribution of alpha particles scattered from a 0.4 μ thick gold foil. They found that about 1 in 20,000 was scattered through an angle of more than 90 degrees. Geiger later determined the probable angle of deflection as $\theta_p = 0.87$ degree. The probable angle θ_p, defined as the angle which has a 50 percent likelihood of being exceeded, relates to the standard deviation as $\theta_p = 0.6745\sigma$. This gives $\sigma = 1.29°$ for the experiment described above.* By inserting $\theta = 90°$ and

---

*   It is amusing to note that Rutherford in his very famous paper on scattering of alpha particles by matter refers to the probable angle as "the *most* probable angle of deflexion." The most probable angle, that is, the maximum in the standard distribution, is clearly $\theta = 0$. Thus even great scientists err, and sometimes worse than this! The reference is E. Rutherford, *Phil. Mag.* **21** (1911), p. 669.

$\sigma = 1.29°$, we find from Eq. (4–2), $N(90) = N(0) \times 10^{-1060}$. This is such an incredibly small number that it clearly is not worth the effort to work out the integrals to determine the fraction of the beam of particles deflected by more than 90 degrees.

4–3 RUTHERFORD'S NUCLEAR ATOM

Rutherford concluded that the large deflections must come about by *single* encounters between alpha particles and atoms and that therefore the atoms must be seats of much more intense electric fields than those that would seem to be consistent with the Thomson model. He assumed that the positive massive part of the atom was concentrated in a very small volume at the center of the atom. This core, now called the *nucleus*, is surrounded by a cloud of electrons, which makes the entire atom electrically neutral. Because the atom is mostly empty space, many of the alpha particles go through the foil with practically no deviation. But an alpha particle that passes close to a nucleus experiences a very large force exerted by the massive positive core and is deflected through a large angle in a single encounter. From Eq. (4–1) and the example following it, it is clear that the radius of the nucleus must be more than 1000 times smaller than the radius of the atom if this is to stop an alpha particle and turn it around in its path. Collisions with electrons result in but very small deflections and can therefore be neglected.

We shall study the mechanics of a single encounter between an alpha particle and a nucleus, with the objective of finding a formula to replace Eq. (4–2) for the angular distribution of alpha particles scattered by a foil.

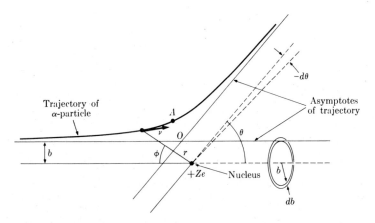

Fig. 4–2 Scattering of an alpha particle by the Rutherford nuclear atom.

Figure 4-2 shows the trajectory of an alpha particle approaching the nucleus with an impact parameter b. This is the distance between the nucleus and the straight-line path the alpha particle would have taken in the absence of an interaction. We use a polar coordinate system (r, ϕ), as indicated in Fig. 4-2, and write the law of conservation of energy,

$$\frac{1}{2} m \left(\frac{dr}{dt}\right)^2 + \frac{1}{2} mr^2 \left(\frac{d\phi}{dt}\right)^2 + \frac{zZe^2}{4\pi\varepsilon_0 r} = \frac{1}{2} mv_0^2, \qquad (4\text{-}3)$$

where v_0 is the initial asymptotic velocity of the alpha particle. We have assumed that the nucleus is so much heavier than the alpha particle that we can neglect recoil.

The law of conservation of angular momentum yields

$$mr^2 \frac{d\phi}{dt} = mv_0 b$$

or

$$\frac{d\phi}{dt} = \frac{v_0 b}{r^2}. \qquad (4\text{-}4)$$

We now introduce for convenience a parameter $2q$ which is equal to the distance of closest approach in a *head-on* collision:

$$2q = \frac{zZe^2}{2\pi\varepsilon_0 mv_0^2}. \qquad (4\text{-}5)$$

Combining Eqs. (4-3), (4-4), and (4-5), we get

$$\frac{dr}{dt} = \mp v_0 \left(1 - \frac{2q}{r} - \frac{b^2}{r^2}\right)^{1/2}. \qquad (4\text{-}6)$$

The double sign arises from the square root. The radial velocity dr/dt is clearly first negative, then changes sign to positive at the position of minimum distance to the nucleus (Fig. 4-2). By again combining Eq. (4-6) with Eq. (4-4), we obtain

$$\frac{d\phi}{dr} = \mp \frac{b}{r^2} \left(1 - \frac{2q}{r} - \frac{b^2}{r^2}\right)^{-1/2}. \qquad (4\text{-}7)$$

This is a differential equation describing the orbit in polar coordinates (r, ϕ). Using a table of integrals, we find for the first part of the orbit from $r = \infty$ to point A in Fig. 4-2

$$\phi = \text{Arc cos} \left[\frac{b}{(b^2 + q^2)^{1/2}} \left(1 - \frac{2q}{r} - \frac{b^2}{r^2}\right)^{1/2}\right]$$

$$- \text{Arc cos} \frac{b}{(b^2 + q^2)^{1/2}}. \qquad (4\text{-}8)$$

We have integrated from ∞ to r and used the minus sign in Eq. (4–7). At the point of minimum r, we have $dr/dt = 0$, which inserted into Eq. (4–6) gives

$$1 - \frac{2q}{r} - \frac{b^2}{r^2} = 0$$

at point A. The angle ϕ corresponding to this point is, by Eq. (4–8),

$$\phi_A = \frac{\pi}{2} - \text{Arc cos} \frac{b}{(b^2 + q^2)^{1/2}} . \tag{4–9}$$

The orbit is symmetric about point A, since $d\phi/dr$ numerically depends upon r only and not upon ϕ as well (Eq. 4–7). The radius vector r therefore sweeps through a total angle $2\phi_A$. From Fig. 4–2, we see that the total angle of deflection is

$$\theta = \pi - 2\phi_A = 2 \text{ Arc cos} \frac{b}{(b^2 + q^2)^{1/2}} . \tag{4–10}$$

From this we find

$$\cos \frac{\theta}{2} = \frac{b}{(b^2 + q^2)^{1/2}} , \tag{4–11}$$

and easily

$$\sin \frac{\theta}{2} = \frac{q}{(b^2 + q^2)^{1/2}} . \tag{4–12}$$

Combining Eqs. (4–11) and (4–12), we get

$$b = q \cot \frac{\theta}{2} . \tag{4–13}$$

This, then, is a simple relationship between the impact parameter b and the total angle of deflection θ.

Our objective was to find a formula for the angular distribution of particles scattered by a foil representing a large number of scattering centers (nuclei). We can best do that by calculating the collision cross section (Section 1–10) for the process. First we shall modify this concept slightly. In Section 1–10, the cross section for a collision process represented a target area. A hit in this area resulted in deflection of the "bullet" particle. Nothing was said about the direction of the scattered particle after the collision. Figure 4–2 indicates a ring, displaced to the right for clarity, representing a target area for all alpha particles with impact parameters between b and $b + db$. This area is

$$d\sigma = 2\pi b \, db. \tag{4–14}$$

All particles aimed at that area will have a scattering angle between θ and $\theta + d\theta$, where θ is given by Eq. (4–13), and $d\theta$ by the differential of same:

$$db = -\frac{q}{2}\frac{d\theta}{\sin^2 \theta/2}. \qquad (4\text{–}15)$$

The angles θ and $\theta + d\theta$ define two cones with the horizontal line through the nucleus as their axis (Fig. 4–2). The solid angle between the two cones is $d\Omega = 2\pi \sin \theta\, d\theta$, and this is therefore the solid angle into which particles aimed at the target area $d\sigma$ will be scattered. By substitution we now get from Eq. (4–14), neglecting the minus sign,

$$d\sigma = \frac{\pi q^2 \cos \phi/2\, d\theta}{\sin^3 \theta/2} = \frac{q^2 2\pi \sin \theta\, d\theta}{4 \sin^4 \theta/2} = \frac{q^2\, d\Omega}{4 \sin^4 \theta/2}. \qquad (4\text{–}16)$$

Finally, we insert q from Eq. (4–5) and get the Rutherford cross-section formula

$$\frac{d\sigma}{d\Omega} = \frac{z^2 Z^2 e^4}{64\pi^2 \varepsilon_0^2 m^2 v_0^4 \sin^4 \theta/2}. \qquad (4\text{–}17)$$

The interpretation of this equation is that each nucleus represents a target area $d\sigma$ for deflecting a particle by an angle θ into a solid angle $d\Omega$. Let the target foil have n atoms per unit volume and a thickness Δx, and let the detector be at an angle θ subtending a solid angle $\Delta\Omega$ with the target. By using Eq. (1–35), we find the fraction of alpha particles from the beam scattered to the detector to be

$$\frac{\Delta N}{N} = n \left(\frac{d\sigma}{d\Omega}\right) \Delta\omega\, \Delta x, \qquad (4\text{–}18)$$

with the differential cross section $d\sigma/d\Omega$ given by Eq. (4–17).

Rutherford's formula gives infinite cross section for $\theta = 0$. This corresponds to $b \to \infty$ and in reality, of course, we do not have infinite impact parameters. Indeed, we could have set an upper limit for b as approximately the radius of the atom, because outside the atom the electric field from the nucleus is shielded by the electrons.

Neglecting the region close to $\theta = 0$, we see that the angular distribution of alpha particles is described by the factor $(\sin \theta/2)^{-4}$. This term does not vary nearly so fast with θ as does Eq. (4–2). Rutherford found that all available data agreed with his predictions and thus was the nuclear model of the atom born. The year: 1911.

In 1913, Geiger and Marsden[*] published the results of a very exhaustive test of Rutherford's theory. They used silver and gold foils as targets for the alpha particles and recorded the rate of scintillations as a function of angle

---

[*]   H. Geiger and E. Marsden, *Phil. Mag.* **25** (1913), p. 605.

over a very wide angular range. Fig. 4–3 shows their result. In this graph, according to Rutherford's formula, all points for a given experiment should fall on a straight line with a slope of 45°. The agreement is very good, considering in particular the fact that the counting rate, measured by eye, varied over almost four decades.

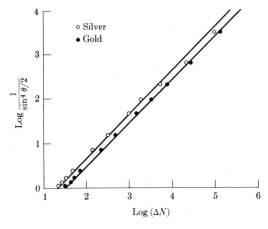

Fig. 4–3 Number ΔN of scattered alpha particles versus scattering angle θ (logarithmic). Reproduced by permission from Richtmyer, Kennard, and Lauritsen, *Introduction to Modern Physics,* New York: McGraw-Hill © 1955, p. 146.

Geiger and Marsden, and later Chadwick, also attempted to measure absolute values for the scattering rate (i.e., the cross section) such that they could thereby determine the nuclear charge Z. They concluded that Z was approximately half the atomic mass number. Much more accurate measurements of Z for a large number of elements were made about this time by Moseley. His experiments with x-rays emitted by the various elements showed that Z is identical with the atomic number; that is, the number giving the place of the element in the Periodic Table. This will be discussed in more detail in Chapter 10.

4–4 SIZE OF THE NUCLEUS

The detailed studies of alpha scattering carried out in Rutherford's laboratory on many elements soon revealed that the simple $(\sin \theta/2)^{-4}$ law does not always hold. The discrepancies occur for light elements, particularly for large angles of deflection. This was immediately interpreted as a breakdown of the r^{-2} force law at small distances. Put differently, it revealed that the nucleus is not a point charge and that at small distances forces other than the Coulomb force are acting. It was possible to estimate that the radius at which these forces affected the motion of the alpha particles was of the order of 5×10^{-15}m for medium-mass atoms.

We now know that the nucleus consists of protons and neutrons held together by very short-range but very strong forces. An alpha particle approaching the nuclear surface experiences these forces and may be scattered or broken up into its components, two protons and two neutrons. The study of these processes is a part of nuclear physics, discussed briefly in Chapter 12.

4–5 SPECTRA

Most readers of this book have studied light and know that spectrographs are instruments which analyze light according to its distribution of frequency or color. These instruments always have an entrance slit, a dispersive component that may be a prism or grating, and a detector that is usually a photographic plate. The instrument forms an image of the slit on the detector, the focusing being accomplished with a system of lenses, or in the case of a reflective-grating spectrometer by the curvature of the grating. Separated images are formed for each frequency of light present, so that light which is continuous in its frequency distribution forms a wide image that is a continuous succession of slit images. Light which is discontinuous in frequency distribution forms a discrete set of slit images that are called *spectral lines*.

Figure 4–4(a) depicts a reflective grating made by scribing fine lines in a highly reflective metallic surface. A parallel beam of light falling in on the mirror at an angle θ_i with the normal will be reflected—to zeroth order—such that it leaves at an angle θ_i, as shown. A first-order maximum in the diffraction

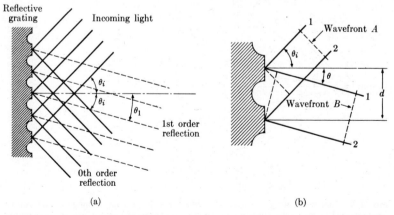

Fig. 4–4 (a) Reflection of parallel light from a grating. (b) Detail of the 1st-order reflection. Path 2 one wavelength longer than 1.

pattern will occur at some angle θ_1 and if the grating has a large number of lines, this maximum will be sharp.

Figure 4–4(b) shows in more detail two rays falling in on the grating. The points where these rays hit the grating are sources of light radiating in all directions. To get constructive interference when the two rays later are focused to one point on the detector, the wave fronts must be perpendicular to the direction of motion. This will be the case if the difference in path length from wave front A to wave front B is a whole number of wavelengths; that is,

$$d(\sin \theta_i - \sin \theta) = n\lambda, \tag{4–19}$$

where n is an integer. For $n = 0$, we get $\theta = \theta_i$, independent of λ. For $n = 1$ or higher, we see that $\sin \theta$ depends on λ. The grating therefore disperses light according to the wavelengths of its components.

Figure 4–5 shows the layout of a concave grating spectrometer. The reflective grating is bent with a radius of curvature $2R$. The entrance slit for the light and detector plates are placed on a circle with radius R. It can then be shown that sharp images of the slit will be produced, by the focusing action of the mirror grating, on the detector.

Spectroscopy with prism spectrometers, as well as with grating spectrometers, was a well-developed science in the latter part of the last century. It was found that the light from any element in gaseous form produces a discontinuous line spectrum. Each element has its own characteristic frequency distribution

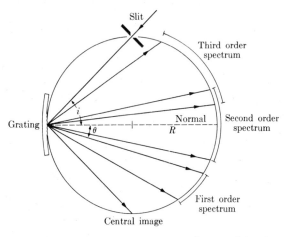

Fig. 4–5 Concave grating spectrometer. Images of the slit are formed on the curved photographic plates by the curvature of the grating (radius $2R$) acting as a concave mirror. Reproduced by permission from Jenkins and White, *Fundamentals of Optics*, New York: McGraw-Hill © 1957, p. 348.

or spectrum, so that each element can be identified by the light that it emits. The most dramatic instance of such identification occurred when the element helium was "discovered" in the spectrum of the sun before it was chemically isolated here on earth.

The emission of a spectral line by gas atoms could presumably be explained somewhat as follows on the basis of the Thomson model of the atom: An electron is bound to the atom by electric and possibly other forces and is normally at rest in an equilibrium position. Displaced from that position by a collision between two atoms it will execute oscillations. Since it is charged, it will radiate energy of frequency equal to the frequency of oscillations. If the oscillations are not strictly harmonic (i.e., proportional to sin ωt), it will also radiate higher harmonics. The puzzle is that no atom radiates spectral lines with frequencies being simple harmonics of a fundamental. All elements display a great multitude of lines spread over a very large frequency spectrum. Certain regularities are found (next section) but nothing that supports the above picture.

After Rutherford's discovery of the nucleus, it was immediately suggested that the electrons move in orbits about the nucleus and that the electrostatic attraction provided the centripetal force. The difficulty with this model is that the electron is continuously accelerating (centripetal acceleration), and according to classical electromagnetic theory an accelerating charge e radiates power at a rate $P = e^2 a^2 / 6\pi\varepsilon_0 c^3$ watts, where a is the acceleration. A simple calculation shows that the electrons in orbits about the nucleus would lose energy and spiral in towards the nucleus so fast that in about 10^{-8}s all matter would have collapsed

This set the stage for one of the most brilliant natural philosophers of modern times, Niels Bohr (Section 4-7). Before we present his simple, yet revolutionary, theory, we shall discuss in some detail the experimental data on which it was based.

4-6 THE HYDROGEN SPECTRUM

The obvious place to start the study of spectra is with the spectrum of hydrogen. It is not surprising that this lightest element has the simplest spectrum and probably the simplest structure. Part of the hydrogen spectrum is shown in Fig. 4–6. The regularity of these spectral lines is immediately evident, and it appears obvious that there is some interrelationship among them. In 1884, a Swiss high-school mathematics teacher by the name of Balmer took the wavelengths of these lines as a problem in numbers. He set out to find a formula which would show their interrelation. He hit upon a formula which could be made to give these wavelengths very precisely. The Balmer formula is

$$\lambda \text{ (angstroms)} = \frac{3645.6n^2}{n^2 - 4}. \tag{4-20}$$

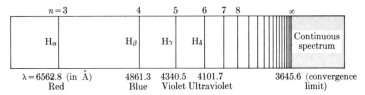

Fig. 4–6 Diagram of the Balmer series of atomic hydrogen. (The wavelengths are the values in air.)

Each different wavelength is obtained by putting into the formula different values of the running integers n, which are $n = 3$, $n = 4$, $n = 5$, etc.

The success of the Balmer formula led Rydberg to attempt a formulation which would apply to heavier elements. He proposed an equation of the form

$$\bar{\nu} = \frac{1}{\lambda} = A - \frac{R}{(n + \alpha)^2} , \tag{4–21}$$

where $\bar{\nu}$ is the *wave number*,* R is the *Rydberg constant* which is equal to $1.09737 \times 10^7 \text{ m}^{-1}$, and n is a running integer. A and α are adjustment constants which depend on the element and the part of the spectrum or spectral series to which the formula is applied. Rydberg found that this formula, which can be regarded as a generalization of the Balmer formula, could be fitted to many spectral series, and further that the value of R was nearly the same when the formula was applied to different elements.

In 1908, Ritz noted that the wave numbers of many spectral lines are the differences between the wave numbers of other spectral lines, and that the A term of the Rydberg formula was really a particular value of a term, like the second term of the Rydberg formula. Using this "combination principle," Ritz rewrote the Rydberg formula as

$$\bar{\nu} = \frac{R}{(m + \beta)^2} - \frac{R}{(n + \alpha)^2} , \tag{4–22}$$

---

*   The wave number $\bar{\nu}$, as used in spectroscopy, is the number of waves per unit length, and differs from the more conventional wave number k used in Chapter 3 by a factor 2π. One might suppose that the logical quantity to use for the reciprocal form of wavelength would be the frequency, c/λ. In spectroscopy, the wave number is used because in order to compute the frequency without losing the remarkable precision of wavelength measurements, it would be necessary to know the velocity of light to an equal precision. Wave numbers can be computed without knowing the velocity of light and so they retain all the accuracy of spectroscopic wavelength measurements. However, the wave number is not an absolute constant for a given spectral line because its wavelength depends upon the index of refraction of the medium in which the measurements are made. The wavelength in air is corrected to vacuum by means of the relation $\lambda_{\text{vac}} = \mu\lambda_{\text{air}}$, where μ is the index of refraction of air for the particular wavelength. In the visible region, λ_{vac} is approximately 2.5×10^{-2} percent greater than λ_{air}.

where α and β are adjustment constants which depend on the element. For different spectral series of a given element, m takes on different integral values. The different lines within a series are computed by changing the running integer n. It is easily shown that when $\alpha = \beta = 0$ and $m = 2$, Eq. (4–22) reduces to the Balmer formula for hydrogen.

In the same year, 1908, Paschen found another hydrogen series of lines in the infrared region to which Eq. (4–22) could be fitted by making $\alpha = \beta = 0$, $m = 3$, and $n = 4, 5, 6$, etc. Thus, both the then-known hydrogen series could be represented by

$$\bar{\nu} = R \left(\frac{1}{m^2} - \frac{1}{n^2} \right) . \tag{4–23}$$

This gives the Balmer series when $m = 2$ and $n = 3, 4, 5$, etc., and correctly predicts the Paschen series for $m = 3$ and $n = 4, 5, 6$, etc.

4–7 THE BOHR MODEL AND THEORY OF THE ATOM

Equation (4–23) represented the entire known hydrogen spectrum with great precision, but it was an empirical formula. In spite of many attempts, it defied derivation on the basis of known physical laws. In 1913, Niels Bohr succeeded in deriving this important relation, but only by breaking with concepts of classical physics believed to be well established.

Bohr extended Rutherford's model of the atom. He retained the small core or nucleus of the atom and proposed that the electrons, known to be a part of the atom, move in orbits around the nucleus. In the case of hydrogen, Bohr proposed that the nucleus consisted of one proton with one electron revolving about it. This is a planetary model of the atom where the heavy positive nucleus is like the sun and the light, negative electron is like the planet earth. In this model, hydrogen is a tiny, one-planet solar system with the gravitational force of the solar system replaced by the electrostatic force of attraction between the oppositely charged particles. The general equations for the gravitational force and the electrostatic force are, respectively,

$$F = G \frac{MM'}{r^2} \quad \text{and} \quad F = \frac{1}{4\pi\varepsilon_0} \frac{qq'}{r^2} . \tag{4–24}$$

Both forces are inversely proportional to the square of the distance between the particles. The planets of the solar system have elliptical orbits which are nearly circular. Bohr assumed that the planetary electron of hydrogen moves in a circular orbit, which makes the analysis of the classical aspects of the problem straightforward. Let v be the tangential speed of a mass M' that is revolving around a very large mass M in a circular orbit or radius r. Revolution occurs around the center of mass of the system which, in effect, is at the center of the large, massive body. The centripetal force acting on M' is the gravitational force of attraction due to M. Thus we have

$$F = G\frac{MM'}{r^2} = M'a = \frac{M'v^2}{r}, \qquad (4\text{–}25)$$

from which we obtain

$$v^2 = \frac{GM}{r}. \qquad (4\text{–}26)$$

In Bohr's model of the atom, an electron of charge e, mass m_e, and tangential speed v revolves in a circular orbit of radius r around a massive nucleus having a positive charge Ze. In this case, too, the center of the orbit is essentially at the center of the heavy nucleus. The centripetal force acting on the orbiting electron is the electrostatic force of attraction of the nuclear charge, and therefore the force equation is

$$F = \frac{1}{4\pi\varepsilon_0}\frac{Ze \cdot e}{r^2} = m_e a = \frac{m_e v^2}{r}. \qquad (4\text{–}27)$$

From this equation we find that

$$v^2 = \frac{Ze^2}{4\pi\varepsilon_0 m_e r}. \qquad (4\text{–}28)$$

(For hydrogen, the atomic number Z equals one. We include Z for generality.) Each of the equations (4–26) and (4–28) provides a relationship between the variables v and r. If one is known, the other can be found. In the gravitational case, any pair of values of v and of r which satisfy Eq. (4–26) may actually occur. In the electrical case, classical physics imposes no limitation on the number of solutions there can be for Eq. (4–28). For the case of the hydrogen atom, Bohr introduced a restrictive condition which is known as the first Bohr postulate. He assumed that not all the possible orbits that can be computed from Eq. (4–28) are found in hydrogen. Bohr's *first postulate* is that *only those orbits occur for which the angular momenta of the planetary electron are integral multiples of $h/2\pi$*, that is, $nh/2\pi$. Here n is any integer and h is Planck's constant. Bohr's first postulate introduces the integer idea that appears in the Ritz formula and also introduces Planck's constant, which we have seen plays an important role in the atomic view of radiation. Stated mathematically, this first postulate is

$$m_e vr = \frac{nh}{2\pi} = n\hbar, \qquad (4\text{–}29)$$

where $n = 1, 2, 3, \ldots$ and $\hbar$, called "h-bar" is Planck's constant divided by 2π.

The orbiting electron in hydrogen must simultaneously satisfy the conditions expressed by Eqs. (4–28) and (4–29). After eliminating v between these two equations, we find that the orbits which exist or are "permitted" in the hydrogen atom are only those that have radii

$$r = \frac{\varepsilon_0 h^2 n^2}{\pi m_e Z e^2} .$$ (4-30)

With numerical values inserted, this gives

$$r = 0.529 \, n^2 \times 10^{-8} \text{m} = 0.529 \, n^2 \text{Å}.$$ (4-30a)

Thus, the "first Bohr orbit" has a radius of 0.529 Å; the second has a radius of 2.116 Å, etc.

In discussing the energy of a planetary electron, we shall use the usual convention that the electron has no potential energy when it is infinitely far from its nucleus. The potential energy of a negative electronic charge at a distance r from the nucleus of positive charge Ze is then

$$E_p = - \frac{Z e^2}{4\pi\varepsilon_0 r} .$$ (4-31)

Note that the potential energy of the electron in this case is zero at infinity and negative elsewhere. We can use Eq. (4-28) to find its kinetic energy:

$$E_k = \frac{1}{2} m_e v^2 = \frac{Z e^2}{8\pi\varepsilon_0 r} .$$ (4-32)

The total energy of the planetary electron is the sum of the potential and kinetic energies:

$$E = E_k + E_p = \frac{Z e^2}{8\pi\varepsilon_0 r} - \frac{Z e^2}{4\pi\varepsilon_0 r} = - \frac{Z e^2}{8\pi\varepsilon_0 r} .$$ (4-33)

We have computed the total energy as a function of r. But we have seen that r can have only those values given by Eq. (4-30). Using this equation to eliminate r, we find that

$$E_n = - \frac{m_e e^4 Z^2}{8\varepsilon_0^2 h^2 n^2} ,$$ (4-34)

where $n = 1, 2, 3, \ldots$ for the energy states that it is possible for the electron*

---

* In calling E the energy of the electron, we are not precise. We have assumed that the electron does all the moving while the nucleus remains at rest. Since the mass M of the proton is 1836 times the mass m_e of the electron, the latter has most of the kinetic energy of the atomic system. A detailed treatment would require us to consider the movement of all particles about their common center of mass. There is a theorem in mechanics which states that in a two-body problem such as this, the motion of one body may be neglected if the mass of the other body is taken to be the "*reduced mass*," which is the product over the sum of the two masses, $m_e M/(m_e + M) = m_e/(1 + m_e/M)$. If, in Eq. (4-34) and elsewhere, we *replace* the electron mass m_e by the reduced mass, then our equations correctly describe the atomic system *as a whole* (Problem 4-7).

to have. The integer n is called the *total* or *principal* quantum number and it can have any of the series of values, 1, 2, 3, ... The values of n determine the energies of the states. When n is large, the energy is large, that is, less negative than for small integers. The energy required to remove an electron from a particular state to infinity is called the *binding energy* of that state. It is numerically equal to E_n.

Figure 4–7 shows the potential energy and the total energy as a function of r (Eq. 4–33). The allowed orbit radii (Eq. 4–30) are indicated, and the corresponding values of the total energy are shown. The energies are given in electron volts, found by inserting numerical values for the constants in Eq. (4–34) and converting from joules to eV. In general, we get

$$E_n = -\frac{13.6}{n^2} \text{ eV.} \qquad (4\text{--}34\text{a})$$

We now consider how Bohr used this set of energies to account for the hydrogen spectrum. In Chapter 3 we described how classical electrodynamics predicts that energy will be radiated whenever a charged particle is accelerated. We were careful to point out that the acceleration could be due to a change of direction of motion as well as due to a change of speed. According to classical theory, an orbital electron should radiate energy because of its centripetal acceleration. In order to preserve his atomic model of planetary electron orbits, Bohr had to devise a theory which would violate this classical prediction since, according to it, any electron that separated from the nucleus would soon radiate away its energy and fall back into the nucleus. Bohr's second break with classical physics is contained in his *second postulate*, which states that *no electron radiates energy so long as it remains in one of the orbital energy states;*

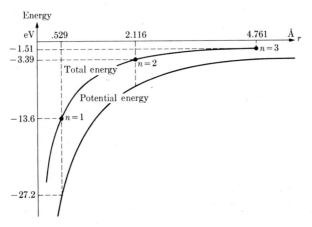

Fig. 4–7 Energy relations in the hydrogen atom.

and that radiation occurs only when an electron goes from a higher energy state to a lower one, the energy of the quantum of radiation, hν, being equal to the energy difference of the states. Let the quantum number $n = n_2$ represent a higher energy state and $n = n_1$ represent a lower energy state $(n_1 < n_2)$, then the second Bohr postulate can be written as

$$hν = E_{n_2} - E_{n_1}. \tag{4-35}$$

Substituting for the energies from Eq. (4–34), we have for the frequency of the emitted radiation

$$ν = \frac{m_e e^4 Z^2}{8\varepsilon_0^2 h^3} \left(\frac{1}{n_1^2} - \frac{1}{n_2^2} \right) \tag{4-36}$$

or, in terms of the wave number,

$$\bar{ν} = \frac{1}{\lambda} = \frac{ν}{c} = \frac{m_e e^4 Z^2}{8\varepsilon_0^2 h^3 c} \left(\frac{1}{n_1^2} - \frac{1}{n_2^2} \right) \tag{4-37}$$

where c is the speed of light in a vacuum. Comparing Eq. (4–37) with Eq. (4–23) shows that both have the same form.

Equally impressive is the fact that the constant factor of the Bohr formula is the Rydberg constant, R. Again comparing Eqs. (4–37) and (4–23), we find that, since $Z = 1$ for hydrogen,

$$R = \frac{m_e e^4}{8\varepsilon_0^2 h^3 c} = 1.0973731 \times 10^7 \text{ m}^{-1}. \tag{4-38}$$

The R given here is R_∞, which would be correct if the mass of the nucleus were infinite compared with the mass of an electron. If the motion of the nucleus is taken into account, m_e must be replaced by the reduced mass. Therefore, in general, $R = R_\infty/(1 + m_e/M)$. This accounts for the slight variation of R from element to element noted by Rydberg. It is a triumph of the Bohr model and theory that the slight differences between the spectra of ordinary hydrogen and its isotope, heavy hydrogen (deuterium), can be attributed to the influence of the nuclear mass. In fact, heavy hydrogen was discovered spectroscopically by Urey in 1932.

The Bohr formula gives the Balmer series for $n_1 = 2$ and the Paschen series for $n_1 = 3$, as we have seen before. But the Bohr theory places no restrictions on n_1 and his result suggested that there might be additional hydrogen series not yet found experimentally. In 1916 Lyman found a series in the far ultraviolet, in 1922 Brackett found a new series in the infrared, and in 1924 Pfund located another in the same region. Table 4–1 summarizes the five hydrogen series.

Table 4–1   The spectral series of hydrogen

Values of n_1	Name of series	Values of n_2
1	Lyman	2, 3, 4, etc.
2	Balmer	3, 4, 5, etc.
3	Paschen	4, 5, 6, etc.
4	Brackett	5, 6, 7, etc.
5	Pfund	6, 7, 8, etc.

4–8 HYDROGEN ENERGY LEVELS

The discovery of sharp energy states of the hydrogen atom was a finding that had very far-reaching consequences in physics. All atomic, molecular, and nuclear systems have discrete energy levels; indeed, macroscopic systems can exist only in states of discrete energies, but these energy levels are so closely spaced that they cannot be experimentally resolved. Because of the general interest of this subject, we shall here look at the energy levels of hydrogen in some detail.

These levels can be represented graphically as shown in Fig. 4–8. The quantum numbers are shown at the left and the corresponding energies of hydrogen in electron volts are given at the right. In this array of energies, the higher (less negative) energies are at the top, while the lower (more negative) are toward the bottom. In a normal unexcited hydrogen atom, the electron is in its lowest energy state at the bottom, with $n = 1$. An electron in this *ground state* is stable and remains in this state continuously without emitting or absorbing energy. The "excitement" begins when the electron absorbs energy in some way. There are a variety of ways in which this may be brought about. If the hydrogen is in an electric discharge, a free electron which has been accelerated by the electric field may hit* it. If the hydrogen is heated, the electron may be excited by a thermal-motion collision. If the hydrogen is illuminated, it may absorb energy from a photon. Suppose the electron in hydrogen absorbs about 20 eV of energy in one of these ways. This is enough energy to lift the electron to $n = \infty$ (13.6 eV) with 6.4 eV left over. In this case, the electron is made entirely free of its home nucleus and is given 6.4 eV of kinetic energy besides. If the electron absorbs just 13.6 eV, it is merely freed from its home nucleus and drifts about with only its thermal kinetic energy. In either of these cases the remaining nucleus is an ion. If the energy of a bombarding electron is less than that required for ionization but equal to or

---

* We use the word "hit" loosely. We saw in the discussion of alpha-particle scattering that a collision between charged bodies does not involve physical contact in the usual sense.

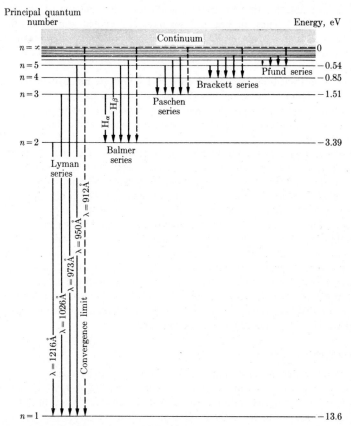

Fig. 4–8 Energy-level diagram of the hydrogen atom.

greater than that needed to raise an electron in an atom to one of its permitted energy levels, then the atomic electron will absorb just enough energy to put it into some higher energy state. After the bombarding electron has transferred enough energy to the atom to excite it, the electron will leave the encounter, carrying away any excess as kinetic energy. The *excitation energy* of any level in electron volts is *numerically* equal to the *excitation potential* of that state in volts.

After excitation, the atomic electron returns to its normal state. If it was excited to $n = 4$, it may jump from 4 to 1 in one step. It may also go 4, 2, 1 or 4, 3, 1 or 4, 3, 2, 1. In each step of the return trip, the electron must lose an amount of energy equal to the difference of the energy levels. The only mechanism available for this energy loss is through the emission of electromagnetic radiation. Thus, in Fig. 4–7 we have represented graphically the second Bohr postulate, given in Eq. (4–35). When we see the light from a hydrogen discharge, we are "seeing" the electrons go from exicted states to lower states.

The electron transitions which end on $n = 1$ constitute the Lyman series, on $n = 2$, the Balmer series, on $n = 3$, the Paschen series, etc. From the energy-level diagram we can see that the Lyman transitions involve the largest changes of energy, produce the highest frequencies, and provide the "bluest" (ultraviolet) light.

The shaded region at the top of Fig. 4–7 represents the fact that electrons at infinity may have kinetic energy, so that their energy there is not zero but positive. If the electron of hydrogen is completely removed from its nucleus, then one of these electrons at infinity having *any* energy may fall into any one of the energy levels. Such an electron undergoes a change of energy equal to its energy at infinity minus the negative energy of the level to which it falls. The "double negative" in the last sentence enables us to conclude that the energy radiated by such a transition is the sum of the electron's kinetic energy at infinity and that involved in the transition from $n = \infty$ to the final level. The energy radiated will have a value greater than that involved in the transition from $n = \infty$ to the final level. Since there is a wide distribution of the energies among the electrons at infinity, there is a continuous spectrum below the short-wavelength convergence limit of any series.

4–9 IONIZATION POTENTIALS

Confirmation of the energy level concept is convincingly given by a consideration of ionization potential. Consider first a radio-type tube, Fig. 4–9, which contains only a filament-heated cathode and a plate as anode. When the plate is positive with respect to the cathode, electrons will move across the tube to the anode. This current is limited by two factors. First, the number of electrons emitted per unit area from a cathode depends upon cathode composition and temperature. In the remainder of this discussion we shall assume that the cathode is operated hot enough so that the tube current is not significantly limited by cathode emission. The second factor is the effect of the electrons

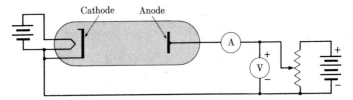

Fig. 4–9 Apparatus for determining ionization potential.

in the region between the electrodes upon those emerging from the cathode. The concentration of negative charge in the inter-electrode region is called *space charge*, and it lowers the potential in the vicinity of the emitting surface. Indeed, the potential in this region usually falls below the potential of the emitter. Thus, although the plate or accelerating potential is still positive, this decrease in potential due to space charge will reduce the electron current because the potential barrier will turn back electrons emitted with low kinetic energy. (The electrons in thermionic emission have a distribution of speeds similar to that of the molecules of a gas.) However, those high-energy electrons that get beyond this barrier caused by space charge arrive at the plate with the same energy they would have had if the space charge had been absent, since the total potential difference V between the electrodes is independent of the space charge. The space charge limited current is not a linear function of the potential difference as in the case of an ohmic resistor; it is found to be proportional to the three-halves power of the potential difference. This is known as the Child-Langmuir Law. In mathematical form, it is $I = kV^{3/2}$. The value of k depends upon the geometry of the tube and the volume density of the charges between the electrodes.

The ionization potential of a gas is determined by introducing some of the gas into a tube such as that shown in Fig. 4–9, and then measuring the plate current as a function of plate voltage. As the potential difference is increased, it is found that above some particular value of the potential the current increases much more rapidly than it does below that value, as shown in Fig. 4–10. When the plate potential reaches this critical value, the electrons arriving at the anode have acquired enough energy to knock electrons off the atoms of the gas close to this electrode. The positive ions produced when the voltage equals or exceeds the critical value neutralize some of the negative space charge. Thus ionization causes a marked increase in the tube current. If the gas under study is hydrogen, the ionization potential is found to be 13.6 V. It is a remarkable confirmation of the energy-level idea that there should be excellent agreement

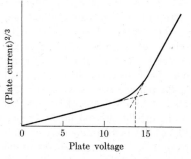

Fig. 4–10 Plate current in hydrogen-filled tube.

for the ionization potential as measured by the very different techniques of spectroscopy and electronics. Since the electrons are emitted from the cathode with an initial velocity distribution, some of them acquire enough energy to produce ionization at lower accelerating potentials than others. This accounts for the curved section joining the two straight-line portions of the graph in Fig. 4–10. Except for this short curved part, the break in the line is quite abrupt. This sudden change of slope would not occur if several low-energy electrons could combine in their "efforts" to ionize the atom of hydrogen.

4–10 RESONANCE POTENTIALS

The experiment just described was set up to measure the potential through which electrons must be accelerated before they can lift orbital electrons from their lowest energy state (ground state) to infinity. This ionization was detected by an increase in the current through the tube. But before the bombarding electrons have enough energy to take the atom apart by removing an electron, they have enough energy to lift an electron to an excited state. Orbital electrons in the gas can be transferred from their lowest energy state to any of the higher states. As implied earlier, the quantum conditions which require an orbital electron to emit only certain frequencies as radiation apply also to the absorption process. These electrons can absorb only energies represented by transitions between energy levels. If an orbital electron is hit by a bombarding electron with insufficient energy to produce an energy transition, the orbital electron absorbs no energy from the bombarding electron and *the collision is perfectly elastic*. If the orbital electron is hit by a high-energy bombarding electron, then the orbital electron can absorb energy by making a transition. This leaves the bombarding electron with that much less energy. *Such a collision is inelastic*, since the bombarding electron is left with less energy than it had before the collision. Such an inelastic collision puts the orbital electron in one of the excited states, and hence it can radiate energy in returning to a lower state.

Consider again the ionization experiment. As the potential difference across the tube is slowly increased, the electrons from the heated cathode are accelerated to higher and higher velocities. At low speeds, these electrons make completely elastic collisions with the electrons of the gas, so that they are deviated but not slowed by the collision process. As the potential difference across the tube is increased, however, a potential is reached where energy can be transferred to an orbital electron. For the purpose of discussion consider hydrogen, which has an ionization potential of 13.6 V. A look at Fig. 4–8 discloses that the least amount of energy the orbital electron in the ground state can absorb is 13.6 eV − 3.4 eV or 10.2 eV. A bombarding electron with 10.2 eV of energy can "resonate" with hydrogen and transfer its energy to the hydrogen. This produces no ionization, so the current through the tube is not changed, but after making such collisions, the bombarding electrons proceed more slowly and the hydrogen shows its "excitement" by radiating. The hydrogen will not glow visibly because this resonance radiation is one line of the Lyman series, which is in the ultraviolet region; however, ultraviolet spectroscopy confirms that the radiation is there.

In order to demonstrate the resonance phenomenon electronically, we need a more elaborate tube, such as that used by Franck and Hertz,* who first performed the experiment in 1913 using mercury vapor as the gas. Mercury has 80 electrons around its nucleus and has therefore a much more complex energy-level diagram than hydrogen. The important fact, however, is that it, like hydrogen, has discrete energy levels to which the atom can be excited by electron bombardment. Mercury vapor is chosen because it is monatomic whereas hydrogen is ordinarily a diatomic molecule whose dissociation energy is 4.5 eV. If the gas were hydrogen, most of the bombarding electrons would give up their energy to excite molecular energy states and also to dissociate the molecules after the accelerating potential reached 4.5V. This complex situation would conceal the effects of atomic hydrogen in this type of experiment.

The principal parts of such a tube are shown schematically in Fig. 4–11. From the standpoint of electronics, the effect of resonance is that the bombarding electrons are slowed down, so we need a device which will measure the energy of the bombarding electrons after they have made collisions. Suppose that the anode of the ionization tube is perforated or made of wire mesh. In this case, some of the bombarding electrons will pass through the electrode rather than hit it. We now need to know the energy with which the bombarding electrons arrive at the anode.

In our consideration of the photoelectric effect, we measured the energy of photoelectrons by making them move against the force action of an electric field, and the energy of the photoelectrons was given by the stopping potential. Here we use much the same technique and insert into the tube another electrode beyond the anode. This collector electrode is maintained less positive than the

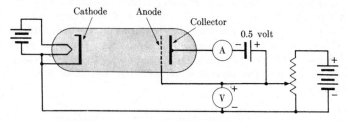

Fig. 4–11 Apparatus for determining resonance potential of gas.

---

* J. Franck and G. Hertz, *Verhandl. Deut. Phys. Ges.* **16** (1914), p. 512.

anode, say 0.5 V, so that any electrons that pass through the anode will be slowed by the field between the electrodes. Electrons which reach this last electrode must have passed the anode with an energy of at least 0.5 eV.

The experimental procedure consists of measuring the collector current as a function of the anode potential with respect to the cathode, and typical results are shown in Fig. 4–12. From $V = 0$ to $V = 0.5$ V, there is no collector current, since no electrons can reach the anode if they have less than 0.5 eV of energy. Above $V = 0.5$ V, the collector current rises because the number of electrons having at least this minimum energy increases. When V reaches the 4.9-eV resonance potential of the gas, the collector current begins to decrease because some of the bombarding electrons are slowed by inelastic collisions with orbital electrons in the gas. The current rises again as V is further increased since, in the stronger field, bombarding electrons can make inelastic collisions early and still undergo enough acceleration to surmount the 0.5-V barrier.

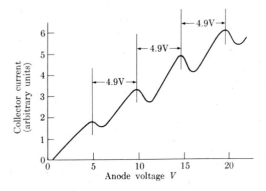

Fig. 4–12   Resonance potential curve for mercury.

The second dip is not due to a new energy transition, because very few electrons ever get enough energy to excite the next transition. The second dip occurs at twice the resonance potential and is caused by the bombarding electrons suffering two inelastic collisions of the same kind. Thus each peak of the curve signifies more collisions and each peak is an integral multiple of the resonance potential.   The separation of successive resonance peaks is 4.9 V for mercury*.

---

*   Since mercury ionizes at 10.4 V, the third resonance peak will be masked by other effects if the tube shown in Fig. 4–11 is used. Actually, a more complicated tube which differentiates the resonance and ionization effects is used. This important experimental detail does not in any way alter the principle discussed in this section.

Franck and Hertz studied the radiation given off by the mercury vapor bombarded by the electrons and found a well-known mercury line at $\lambda = 2537$ Å. The corresponding photon energy is given by Eq. (3–47) as

$$E = \frac{1.24 \times 10^4}{2537} = 4.9 \text{ eV}.$$

The radiation from the mercury vapor was detected only when the anode voltage exceeded 4.9 V. Clearly, the energy level in mercury at 4.9 eV cannot be excited by multiple hits from electrons; it has to be reached in one single step. This is clear evidence that mercury cannot exist with an intermediate energy content and is the strongest proof yet devised of Bohr's idea of discrete levels.

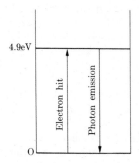

Fig. 4–13 Energy-level diagram illustrating absorption and emission of energy by mercury.

Figure 4–13 shows the ground state and first excited state of mercury in an energy-level diagram where the ground-state energy has been chosen as reference. The absorption and emission processes of the Franck-Hertz experiment are indicated by arrows.

4–11 PHOTON ABSORPTION

In the previous two sections we have discussed how an atom can absorb discrete amounts of energy from bombarding electrons. An atom may also absorb energy from photons, but there is an important difference. Absorbed photons disappear entirely. A photon with more energy than the ionization energy of an atom can always be absorbed because the excess energy will appear as kinetic energy of the photoelectron. A photon with less than the ionization energy cannot be absorbed unless its energy is equal to one of the excitation energies of the absorbing atom.* Consider hydrogen again. Ordinarily, the probability of finding a hydrogen atom in an excited state is very small; therefore, we assume that it is always in its ground state. Thus hydrogen can *only* absorb photons whose wavelengths correspond to those emitted in the far ultraviolet, the Lyman series. Hydrogen atoms are therefore transparent to visible and infrared light. If we pass radiation of all wavelengths through hydrogen and analyze the transmitted light by means of a spectrograph, we find the transmitted intensity *reduced* for the Lyman wavelengths. Such a spectrum, having a bright background and *dark lines*, is called an *absorption* spectrum. Because the atoms that have been excited by the absorption of radiation re-emit photons in *random* directions upon returning to the ground state, there is a decrease of intensity along the direction of the transmitted radiation. The absorption lines observed are actually very faint bright lines that appear dark by contrast.

There are certain advantages of studying absorption spectra. For many atoms, as for hydrogen, the absorption spectrum is simpler than the emission spectrum. For hydrogen, as mentioned above, one can observe absorption for the Lyman series only. From these lines, one can directly construct an energy-level diagram. According to our present simple theory, this energy-level diagram appears to be complete. It is not, because selection rules (see below) do not allow absorptive transitions to all states, in particular for many-electron atoms. However, absorption spectra give the most direct information on the levels that do connect with the ground state by photon emission or by absorption.

The determination of elements on the sun is a dramatic example of absorption spectroscopy. The sun is a hot body which emits a continuous spectrum of photons. As these photons pass through the outer atmosphere of the sun, wavelengths which are characteristic of the gases present are absorbed. Thus the continuous spectrum of the light from the sun is crossed with (relatively) dark lines which were first observed by Fraunhofer in 1815. Most of the Fraunhofer lines correspond to the wavelengths of elements found on the earth. The absorption lines of the Balmer series of hydrogen are especially prominent in the spectrum of the sun. The Balmer lines of hydrogen and the visible-region lines of other elements have rather long wavelengths and can be absorbed *only* by excited atoms of the respective elements. These higher energy states are produced in the following way. Although the gaseous atmosphere of the sun is cooler than its surface, the temperature of the gas is still so high that a large number of atoms have sufficient kinetic energy to excite

---

* This statement is only approximately true. First, an excited state has a certain width, so that the energy of the incident photon can vary within some narrow limits, and absorption still takes place (see Chapter 8). Secondly, in a process called the Raman effect, a photon of energy higher than a given energy level can with finite but low probability excite the atom to that state, with the excess energy being carried off in the form of a reduced-energy photon.

many other atoms by collision. Thus these atoms are raised above the lowest energy level to states where they can absorb wavelengths longer than the ultraviolet. For many years one set of Fraunhofer lines in the visible region could not be associated with any known element. It was presumed to be due to a new "sun element" which was appropriately named helium. This hypothesis was confirmed when helium was isolated on the earth and its emission spectrum was found to correspond with the previously unidentified Fraunhofer lines.

Many of the spectral series that are characteristic of molecular structure are in the infrared region. Absorption spectroscopy is the only feasible way of investigating the structure of these molecules that would be dissociated by being excited in an electric arc in an attempt to produce emission lines. Molecular spectra are further discussed in Chapter 11.

4-12 A CRITICISM OF BOHR'S THEORY

Max Planck discovered that energy was exchanged between a heated body and the surrounding electromagnetic field in quantized steps. Niels Bohr discovered quantization of angular momentum and quantization of the energy content of the atom. He interpreted the observed discrete frequencies of emitted radiation as arising from "quantum jumps" between discrete atomic energy levels with the frequency v given by $hv = \Delta E$. Bohr's theory, or parts of it, has been superseded by *wave mechanics*, in which the quantization of angular momentum and energy is shown to result from the wave nature of matter. The principal shortcomings of Bohr's theory are the following:

1. The emission spectrum from the hydrogen atom exhibits more details, i.e., splitting of the lines, when recorded in a spectrograph with high resolving power. By assuming elliptic orbits in addition to circular ones, and by separately quantizing the angular motion and the radial motion, Sommerfeld[*] contributed substantially to the resolution of this problem. Uhlenbeck and Goudsmit[†] postulated that the electron has an intrinsic angular momentum, called the *spin* of the electron. With these modifications, Bohr's theory comes close to predicting the exact position of the energy levels of the hydrogen atom. However, modern precise measurements show discrepancies and can only be explained by a refined theory of wave mechanics (see Chapter 7 and the references given there).

2. The quantization of the angular moment, $mvr = n\hbar$ of an individual electron applies only if the electron moves in a pure central-force field. This is not the case when there is more than one electron in the atom because of the mutual repulsion between them. Therefore Bohr's theory is strictly a

---

[*]   A. Sommerfeld, *Ann. Physik* **51** (1916), p. 1.

[†]   G. E. Uhlenbeck and S. A. Goudsmit, *Naturwiss.* **13** (1925), p. 593.

one-electron theory, although most of the concepts are valid also for many-electron atoms. Wave mechanics applies equally well to any atom or molecule. However, mathematical complexities make it difficult in practice to calculate with precision anything more complex than the structure and energy levels of the helium atom (see Chapter 9).

3. The quantum jumps were introduced by Bohr as a postulate. Using the refined theories of Sommerfeld and others, it was also found that quantum jumps occurred from a given level only to certain selected other levels. *Ad hoc selection rules* were found, but not in any way understood. There was no way of calculating or even of estimating the length of time an electron would stay in a given orbit. All this was resolved very naturally by wave mechanics (see Chapter 8).

After studying wave mechanics of the hydrogen atom, the student will realize that Bohr's picture of it is too naïve, and that some of his ideas will have to be discarded (notably the sharp orbits). Some purists with the hindsight of wave mechanics call Bohr's theory a "historic accident". Most physicists, however, agree that Bohr laid the foundation for the theory of the atom.

PROBLEMS

4–1 Assuming that the nucleus has a well-defined spherical boundary, find the electric-field intensity at the surface of a) a hydrogen nucleus which has a radius of 0.8×10^{-15} m, and b) a gold nucleus which has a radius of 7.0×10^{-15} m.

4–2 An alpha particle having a kinetic energy of 7.68 MeV is projected directly toward the fixed nucleus of a copper atom. What is their distance of closest approach?

4–3 a) Calculate n, the number of atoms per unit volume for aluminum and for gold. (The relative densities for aluminum and for gold are 2.70 and 19.3, respectively.) b) When a parallel beam of 4.80-MeV alpha particles is incident normally on gold foil having a thickness of 4.0×10^{-15} cm, then 2.0×10^4 particles per second are recorded by a detector at 20°. How many will be recorded at 60°? c) How many would be recorded at 20° if the alpha-particle energy were reduced to 2.40 MeV? d) How many would be recorded at 20° if the initial beam of 4.80-MeV alpha particles had been incident on aluminum foil having a thickness of 6.0×10^{-5} cm instead of on the gold foil?

4–4 a) The probability that a stream of particles will be scattered through an angle θ *or more* is equal to the ratio of N_θ, the number of such scattered particles, to N, the total number of incident particles. a) Show that when a beam of particles having kinetic energy E_k undergoes Rutherford scattering in a piece of foil Δx thick and containing n nuclei per unit volume,

$$N_\theta N = \sigma n\Delta x = \pi b^2 n\Delta x = \pi \left(\frac{1}{4\pi\varepsilon_0} \frac{zZe^2}{2E_k} \cot\frac{\theta}{2} \right)^2 n\Delta x.$$

b) What is the impact parameter when a 4.80-MeV alpha particle is scattered 20° by a gold nucleus and when it is scattered 60°? c) If a piece of gold foil is 4×10^{-5} cm thick, what fraction of a beam of 4.80-MeV alpha particles can be expected to be scattered more than 20° and more than 60°?

4–5 A narrow parallel beam of 4.80-MeV alpha particles striking a copper foil (density 8.9) 10^{-4} cm thick has an intensity of 10^6 particles per second. How many scintillations per minute will be produced by those scattered particles striking a 2 mm × 2 mm fluorescent screen which is 5 cm away from the point of incidence in a direction of 60° with the line of incidence?

4–6 a) Calculate the radii of the first, second, and third "permitted" electron orbits in hydrogen in Ångstroms. b) What is the diameter of the hydrogen atom in the ground state? c) Calculate the electric-field intensity at the first orbit due to the nuclear charge and compare the result with the answer to Problem 4–1.

4–7 Repeat the calculations of Eqs. (4–27) to (4–34), taking into account the finite proton mass; i.e., use the center of mass as center of rotation for the electron. In rewriting Eq. (4–29), note that the sum of the angular momenta of the two particles is $n\hbar$.

4–8 The Bohr model for hydrogen shows that the orbital electron can be found only at certain fixed distances from the proton, the larger radii corresponding to higher quantum numbers. Assume that the electron in a hydrogen atom moves outward to larger radii. Which of the following quantities increase and which decrease: angular momentum, total energy, potential energy, kinetic energy, frequency of rotation?

4–9 A particle of mass m moves in a circular orbit of radius r under the influence of a "spring" force kr directed toward the center (k is a constant). Assuming that Bohr's postulates apply to this system, derive the equation for a) the radii of the permissible orbits and b) the energies of these orbits in terms of the quantum number n. c) Show that the frequency radiated when the particle makes a transition from one orbit to the adjacent orbit is the same as the frequency of the circular motion.

4–10 Calculate the binding energy of the electron in hydrogen in joules and in eV when $n = 1, 2, 3$, and infinity.

4–11 Rearrange and alter the Balmer formula, Eq. (4–20), so that the left-hand side is wave number in reciprocal meters. Show that the result agrees with Eq. (4–37) when the Rydberg constant is substituted in the latter equation and when $n_1 = 2$ and $n_2 = n$.

4–12 Calculate a) the frequency, b) the wavelength, and c) the wave number of the H_β-line of the Balmer series of hydrogen. This line is emitted in the transition from $n_2 = 4$ to $n_1 = 2$. Assume that the nucleus has infinite mass.

4–13 An atom of tungsten has all of its electrons removed except one. a) Calculate the ground-state energy for this one remaining electron. b) Calculate the energy and wavelength of the radiation emitted when this electron makes a downward transition from $n = 2$ to $n = 1$. c) In what portion of the electromagnetic spectrum is this photon?

4–14 a) Calculate the first three energy levels for the electron in Li^{++}. b) What is the ionization potential of Li^{++}? c) What is the first resonance potential for Li^{++}?

4–15 Calculate the short wavelength limit of each of the series listed in Table 4–1, and find the energy of the quantum in eV for each.

4–16 Some of the energy levels of a *hypothetical* one-electron atom (not hydrogen) are listed in the table below:

n	1	2	3	4	5	∞
E_n, eV	-15.60	-5.30	-3.08	-1.45	-0.80	0

Draw the energy-level diagram and find a) the ionization potential, b) the short wavelength limit of the series terminating on $n = 2$, c) the excitation potential for the state $n = 3$, and d) the wave number of the photon emitted when the atomic system goes from the energy state $n = 3$ to the ground state. e) What is the minimum energy that an electron will have after interacting with this atom in the ground state if the initial kinetic energy of the electron was 1) 6 eV, 2) 11 eV?

4–17 a) What is the least amount of energy in eV that must be given to a hydrogen atom so that it can emit the H_β-line (see Problem 4–12 and Fig. 4–7) in the Balmer series? b) How many different possibilities of spectral line emission are there for this atom when the electron goes from $n = 4$ to the ground state?

4–18 The energy levels in eV of a *hypothetical* one-electron atom (not hydrogen) are given by

$$E_n = -18.0/n^2, \quad \text{where} \quad n = 1, 2, 3, \ldots$$

a) Compute the four lowest energy levels and construct the energy-level diagram. b) What is the excitation potential of the state $n = 2$? c) What wavelengths in angstroms can be emitted when these atoms in the ground state are bombarded by electrons that have been accelerated through a potential difference of 16.2 V? d) If these atoms are in the ground state, can they absorb radiation having a wavelength of 2000 Å? e) What is the photoelectric threshold wavelength of this atom?

4–19 The frequencies v of the spectral lines emitted by a certain *hypothetical* one-electron atom (not hydrogen) are given by the relation

$$v = 864 \times 10^{12} \left(\frac{1}{n_1^2} - \frac{1}{n_2^2} \right) \text{Hz},$$

where the n's are the principal quantum numbers. a) Find the wavelengths in angstroms of the first three lines of the series terminating on the ground state. b) What is the photoelectric threshold wavelength of this atom? c) Construct the energy-level diagram. Give the values of the energies in eV of the first four levels and show, with labeled arrows, the transitions that cause the emission of the wavelengths in parts a) and b). d) What is the binding energy of the electron when it is in the state $n = 3$? e) State and clearly explain the possible interactions when a large number of these hypothetical atoms in the ground state are bombarded by: 1) a beam of electrons having 2.90 eV of kinetic energy; 2) a beam of 2.90 eV photons.

4–20 A *hypothetical* one-electron atom (not hydrogen) has excited states at 5, 7, 8, and 8.5 eV above the ground state. A beam of radiation containing quanta having energies of 8, 6, 5, 3, and 0.5 eV passes into an atmosphere composed of the hypothetical atoms. Which of the quanta can be absorbed a) if all the atoms are in the ground state and b) if some are in the ground state and various others are in the various excited states?

4-21 What wavelengths will be emitted if a region containing atomic hydrogen in the ground state is a) bombarded by 9.60-V electrons, b) bombarded by 12.32-V electrons, c) irradiated with light of wavelength 1026 Å (second Lyman line), d) irradiated with light of wavelength 6563 Å (first Balmer line), and e) irradiated with light of wavelength 1127 Å?

4-22 The first ionization potential of helium is 24.6 V. a) How much energy in eV and in joules must be supplied to ionize it? b) To what temperature would an atmosphere of helium have to be heated so that an atom of it moving with the most probable speed in a Maxwellian distribution would have just enough kinetic energy of translation to ionize another helium atom by collision?

4-23 a) Show that the frequency of revolution of an electron in its circular orbit in the Bohr model of the atom is $v = mZ^2e^4/4\varepsilon_0^2 n^3 h^3$. b) Show that when n is very large, the frequency of revolution equals the radiated frequency calculated from Eq. (4-36) for a transition from $n_2 = n + 1$ to $n_1 = n$. (This problem illustrates Bohr's *correspondence principle*, which is often used as a check on quantum calculations. When n is small, quantum physics gives results that are very different from those of classical physics. When n is large, the differences are not significant, and the two methods then "correspond.")

4-24 A 10-kg satellite circles the earth once every 2 h in an orbit having a radius of 8000 km. a) Assuming that Bohr's angular-momentum postulate applies to satellites just as it does to an electron in the hydrogen atom, find the quantum number of the orbit of the satellite. b) Show from Bohr's first postulate and Newton's law of gravitation that the radius of an earth-satellite orbit is directly proportional to the square of the quantum number, $r = kn^2$, where k is the constant of proportionality. c) Using the result from part b), find the distance between the orbit of the satellite in this problem and its next "allowed" orbit. d) Comment on the possibility of observing the separation of the two adjacent orbits. e) Do quantized and classical orbits correspond for this satellite? Which is the "correct" method for calculating the orbits?

4-25 a) What would the temperature of the atmosphere of the sun have to be so that thermal agitation alone would put one millionth of the hydrogen atoms there into the necessary energy state for the absorption of the Balmer series wavelengths; that is, into the state $n = 2$? b) What other means would be available in the atmosphere of the sun for pumping up hydrogen to this higher energy state? c) Compare the answer to part a) with the actual temperature of the sun, 6000°K.

4-26 a) Show that the magnetic moment of a circular Bohr orbit in hydrogen is given by $n(h/4\pi)(e/m_e)$. (The magnetic moment of a current-carrying loop of wire is equal to the product of the current and the area bounded by the loop.) b) Calculate the magnetic moment of the orbit in hydrogen for which $n = 1$. (This particular value of the magnetic moment is called the *Bohr magneton*, μ_β.)

Waves and Particles

5-1 WAVE-PARTICLE DUALITY OF LIGHT; COMPTON SCATTERING

Electromagnetic radiation, which includes visible light, infrared and ultraviolet radiation, x-rays, and the gamma rays emitted by nuclei, is shown to be a wave motion by interference experiments. This type of experiment, which involves constructive and destructive interference, is considered to be a test for the existence of waves since interference patterns produced exhibit maxima and minima exactly as predicted by addition of two sinusoidal amplitudes with varying phase shift. It is difficult to conceive of a mechanism whereby particles without an associated wave nature could produce such results.

On the other hand, a host of experiments indicate that electromagnetic radiation behaves like corpuscles. The classical example that we have already studied is the photoelectric effect (Section 3–11). We shall now discuss an experiment in which electromagnetic radiations, in this case x-rays, behave both like waves and particles. The origin of and the techniques for producing x-rays are treated in Chapter 10 of this book. We shall therefore not go too deeply into the details of the experimental setup here.

The experiment to be discussed was performed by A. H. Compton* in 1923. An outline of the principle is shown in Fig. 5–1. X-rays, that is electro-magnetic radiations, of a wavelength of $\lambda = 0.71$ Å fall in from the left on a carbon target. The radiation scattered from the target at a scattering angle α is analyzed by a spectrometer. This spectrometer works on the same principle as a grating used in spectroscopy of visible light or ultraviolet (see Section 4–5), but because of the very short wavelength of x-rays it is impossible to scribe a grid fine enough to yield an appreciable deflection of the first-order maximum. Therefore, the grating is a crystal, and the regular lines of atoms in the crystal lattice replace the scribed lines of the grating. This will be discussed further in Chapter 10.

---

* A. H. Compton, *Phys. Rev.* **21** (1923), p. 715; **22** (1923), p. 409.

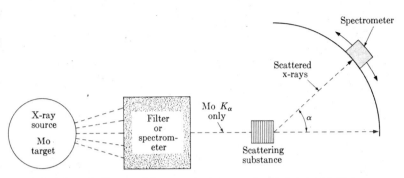

Fig. 5–1 Schematic diagram of the apparatus for measuring Compton scattering.

Figure 5–2 shows the result of Compton's experiment. The top peak at $\alpha = 0$ shows essentially the spectrum of the beam of light incident on the carbon target. It is virtually unchanged by passing through the target. At other scattering angles, we see the appearance of two peaks in the spectrum. One is called the unmodified line, having the same wavelength as the incident radiation; the other peak, which is broader, is called the modified line. It has a wavelength that is larger than that of the unmodified line, and the wavelength increment is increasing with increasing scattering angle α.

The unmodified peak is easy to understand in terms of classical electro-dynamics. This classical viewpoint is as follows. The electromagnetic field will exert forces on the charged particles of the atom and thereby perturb the electron orbits. The perturbations have to oscillate with the frequency of the driving force, that is, the frequency of the incident radiation. The oscillations of the electrons will, in turn, produce new electromagnetic radiation going out essentially in all directions, but with an intensity distribution similar to that from an antenna. Unless the incident radiation is polarized, however, this intensity distribution will not be observed. The frequency of the x-radiation of the wavelength used by A. H. Compton in his experiment is much higher than the orbital frequency of the electron in the carbon target. It is then possible to calculate the dynamics of the problem and the energy radiated by the electrons by considering them free particles. Since each electron in this way absorbs a certain amount of energy from the incident x-ray beam, it can be represented by a cross section. The scattering of x-rays without change of wavelength is called *Thomson scattering*, and the cross section referred to is the Thomson cross section. The calculation of this cross section for one "free" electron is rather straightforward and is left to one of the problems (problem 5–1). The result is

$$\sigma_T = \frac{e^4}{6\pi\varepsilon_0 m_e^2 c^4} = 6.66 \times 10^{-25} \text{ cm}^2. \tag{5–1}$$

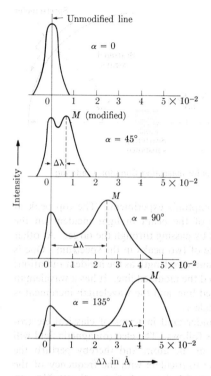

Fig. 5–2 Wavelength displacement of the modified line, M, of the K_α-radiation of molybdenum scattered from carbon, as a function of scattering angle.

This represents the target area for removal of energy from the electromagnetic wave by one electron. The cross section for one atom is simply Z times the one-electron cross section.

The unmodified peaks shown in Fig. 5–2 can be explained as discussed above without resorting to the concept of photons as carriers of the electromagnetic radiation. In the classical picture of the process outlined above, it is clear that an electron in forced oscillations by an external sinusoidal force can only reradiate the same frequency as the incident radiation. From where then do the modified peaks in Fig. 5–2 arise? Compton showed that the *corpuscular* theory of x-rays could explain this peak, and the scattering with modified wavelength is called *Compton scattering*. We shall proceed to calculate the wavelength of the modified peak by assuming that a photon collides elastically with a free electron at rest.

Figure 5–3(a) shows schematically a photon with energy $h\nu_0 = hc/\lambda_0$ approaching an electron at rest. The photon collides with the electron, and

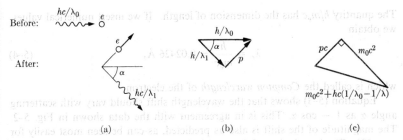

Before:

Fig. 5–3 (a) Compton scattering schematic. (b) Conservation of momentum. (c) Mnemonic triangle for electron.

after the collision the photon has been deflected by an angle α. It has given up some of its energy to the recoil energy of the electron, and therefore the frequency has been reduced to $h v_1 = hc/\lambda_1$. Figure 5–3(b) shows a triangle which illustrates the conservation of momentum. The photon is here treated as a relativistic particle with zero rest mass. Equation (A3–48) in Appendix 3 then gives for the momentum $p = E/c$. The same relationship between energy and momentum of an electromagnetic wave can be calculated from classical electrodynamics. With $E = hv$, we get $p = hv/c = h/\lambda$. The momentum of the incident photon is therefore h/λ_0, and the momentum of the scattered photon is h/λ_1. Finally, p is the momentum of the electron. Figure 5–3(c) shows a mnemonic triangle for the electron similar to Fig. A3–5. The total energy of the electron is the rest energy plus the energy lost by the photon, as indicated on the figure along the hypotenuse. In writing this expression for the total energy of the electron, we have used the law of conservation of energy. The momentum triangle in Fig. 5–3(b) of course represents conservation of momentum. We can now apply the cosine rule to both triangles to find expressions for p^2 and then equate the two expressions to eliminate p^2. Before doing this, we divide all terms in Fig. 5–3(c) by c. The result is

$$\frac{h^2}{\lambda_0^2} + \frac{h^2}{\lambda_1^2} - 2\frac{h}{\lambda_0}\frac{h}{\lambda_1}\cos\alpha = \left(m_e c + \frac{h}{\lambda_0} - \frac{h}{\lambda_1}\right)^2 - m_e^2 c^2. \quad (5\text{–}2)$$

After canceling the square terms and some rearrangement, we obtain

$$2\frac{h^2}{\lambda_0\lambda_1}(1 - \cos\alpha) = 2m_e c\left(\frac{h}{\lambda_0} - \frac{h}{\lambda_1}\right).$$

After multiplication with $\lambda_0\lambda_1/2hm_e c$, we obtain

$$\lambda_1 = \lambda_0 + \frac{h}{m_e c}(1 - \cos\alpha). \quad (5\text{–}3)$$

The quantity $h/m_e c$ has the dimension of length. If we insert numerical values, we obtain

$$\lambda_c = \frac{h}{m_e c} = 0.02426 \text{ Å}, \tag{5-4}$$

which is called the *Compton wavelength* of the electron.

Equation (5–3) shows that the wavelength shift should vary with scattering angle α as $1 - \cos \alpha$. This is in agreement with the data shown in Fig. 5–2. The magnitude of the shift is also as predicted, as can be seen most easily for $\alpha = 90°$. The broadening of the modified or Compton peaks seen in Fig. 5–2 is a result of the motion of the electron in the atom. The theory above was based on an electron initially at rest. If the motion of the electron is taken into account, the broadening of the modified peak can be completely explained.

The appearance of the modified peak is therefore further evidence for the view that electromagnetic radiation consists of photons; that is, packets of electromagnetic energy. We now return briefly to the unmodified line. This also is possible to understand in terms of the photon concept. The unmodified line can be thought of as arising from scattering by electrons that are not torn loose from the atom; they remain in their initial state, and the whole atom takes up the recoil energy. Compton scattering, or the modified line, arises from events in which the electrons are knocked out of the atom and therefore absorb momentum and energy. This energy can only come from a reduction in the energy of the incident photon; that is, in an increase in the wavelength of the photon involved in the process. In the corpuscular theory, then, one line represents elastic scattering with the atom; the other represents inelastic scattering in which the atom is disrupted. However, all scattered photons do reveal their wave structure in the spectrometer by which they are analyzed.

It appears that electromagnetic radiation must be considered as a wave in some processes and as a particle in others. This does not occur randomly, however; the processes can be sorted into the two following types: Those that require the wave nature are ones which may be called propagation processes. An important part of their explanation is the consideration of the path or paths traveled by the light, as in interference experiments where a path difference is determined. The processes that require the particle nature may be called interaction processes. The radiation interacts with matter to produce a resultant absorption or scattering.

This dual nature of light was not readily accepted. The main reason for this is the apparently contradictory aspects of the two natures. A wave is specified by a frequency ν, wavelength λ, phase velocity u, amplitude A, and intensity I. These are not all independent. Thus the velocity, frequency, and wavelength are related by $u = \nu\lambda$. A wave is necessarily spread out and occupies a relatively large region of space. Actually, a sinusoidal wave would have to have infinite length to have a sharp frequency or wavelength. It can be shown, theoretically or experimentally, by harmonic analysis to consist of a band spectrum. A particle, on the other hand, is specified by mass m, velocity v, momentum p, and energy E. The characteristic which seems in conflict with a wave is that a particle, for instance an electron, is very small and presumably occupies a definite position in space. It is difficult to accept the conflicting ideas that light is a wave that is spread out over space and also a particle that is at a "point" in space. This acceptance is necessary, however, to explain all the results of the experiments which can be performed with light. (We use the word "light" to include the entire electromagnetic spectrum.)

We do have connections between the wave and particle characteristics of light. As indicated in Chapter 3, Planck related the energy of the photon, E, and the frequency of the wave, v, by

$$E = hv. \tag{5–5}$$

In the treatment of Compton scattering above, we have used

$$p = h/\lambda \tag{5–6}$$

between the momentum of the photon, p, and the wavelength of the wave, λ. In addition, the intensity of the wave is related to the rate at which photons pass through a unit area. Consequently, the particle characteristics of light can be found from the wave characteristics, even though the concepts of wave and particle appear to contradict each other. We shall attempt to resolve this contradiction in Section 5–6.

5–2 THE DE BROGLIE HYPOTHESIS

The dual nature of light, made necessary by experimental results, was extended by deBroglie in 1924. He felt that nature was symmetrical and the dual nature of light should be matched by a dual nature of matter. His argument was that if light can act like a wave sometimes and like a particle at other times, then things like electrons, which were considered particles, should also act like waves at times.

To specify the wave properties, deBroglie proposed that the relation between the momentum and the wavelength of a photon (Eq. 5–6) is a general one, applying to photons and material particles alike. He therefore postulated that to any moving object there is associated a wavelength.

$$\lambda = \frac{h}{mv}. \tag{5–7}$$

This is called the deBroglie wavelength. These proposed waves were not electromagnetic waves but were a new kind of wave, which were called matter waves or *pilot* waves. The word *pilot* implies that these waves pilot or guide the particle. When deBroglie published his hypothesis, it was not supported by any experimental evidence. His only real argument was his intuitive feeling that nature must be symmetrical. He could make important deductions, however, from his postulate, the results of which were very suggestive, if not entirely convincing (see Sections 5–3 and 5–6).

At this point we may consider the fact that the wavelength is not sufficient to specify a wave completely. The frequency or velocity must also be known. We choose to define the frequency of the matter wave by extending the photon analogy, $\nu = E/h$, and by using the relativistic energy expression, $E = mc^2$. Since the phase velocity of any wave motion is $u = \nu\lambda$, we find the velocity of the waves associated with a particle to be $u = \nu\lambda = (E/h)(h/mv)$. Thus we have

$$u = \frac{mc^2}{h} \frac{h}{mv} = \frac{c^2}{v}. \tag{5–8}$$

In this equation, v is the speed of the material particle, which must be *less* than the speed of light, c; thus u is *greater* than the speed of light. The speed of the mass-energy of the particle does not exceed the speed of light in free space, but the phase velocity of its associated waves does. This result does not conflict with the concepts of relativity, since the speed of light is a limiting speed only for mass-energy. (See Appendix 3.) As it turns out, the deBroglie wavelength of a particle can be measured, but neither the frequency nor the phase velocity can.

5–3 BOHR'S FIRST POSTULATE

The theoretical implications of the deBroglie wavelength of matter are interesting. By making a very plausible assumption, we can relate this wavelength to the Bohr model of the atom.

A plucked guitar string will oscillate with transverse displacements in such a fashion that there will be a node at each end. Similarly, an acoustical resonator, an organ pipe, if closed at both ends and excited by a rapidly varying pressure through an inlet close to one end can resonate with displacement nodes at both ends. To get resonance, i.e., large displacements for only small driving pressures, the frequency of the driving pressure has to be chosen such that an integral number of wavelengths equals the length of the resonator.

If we bend the acoustical resonator into a circle, a doughnut, with no obstructing walls inside, resonance can be obtained for wavelengths satisfying the condition

$$2\pi r = n\lambda,$$

where r is the radius of the circle formed by the center line of the tube and n is an integer.

Let us now assume that the Bohr orbits correspond to standing electron waves, analogous to the circular resonator. If we use the above condition with the deBroglie wavelength, we have

$$2\pi r = \frac{nh}{m_e v} . \tag{5-9}$$

Recalling that the angular momentum of a particle moving in a circular orbit is $m_e vr$, we find that the angular momentum of the Bohr electron is

$$m_e vr = n \frac{h}{2\pi} , \tag{5-10}$$

which is precisely Bohr's first postulate. This discussion should not be interpreted as deriving Bohr's postulate, for essentially what we have done is replace Bohr's postulate with deBroglie's postulate, with the additional assumption that electrons in stationary states are represented by standing waves.

5–4 MATTER REFRACTION

Einstein pointed out that if the deBroglie hypothesis is valid, then it should be possible to diffract electrons. Schrödinger felt that if deBroglie were right, then the waves associated with matter should suffer refraction.

Light usually travels in straight lines, but when it goes from one medium to another it is refracted. Refractive bending is due to changes in the velocity of propagation of light, which is low in a medium of high refractive index. We are aware of abrupt refractions such as occur at the surfaces of a lens. However, the refractions at layers of air of differing temperatures are quite gradual. When the summer sun beats on a blacktop highway, the layers of air next to the road are expanded. Although the refractive index of air is very close to unity, the hot air over the highway has an index even nearer unity. Light coming down to the highway enters a region of lower index and is refracted away from the normal because of the refractive index gradient. If the light approaches this region of index gradient at a grazing angle, total reflection causes the familiar mirage effect. In this case, the bending of the path of light by refraction is not abrupt. The light rays form a continuous curve.

Schrödinger felt that the continuous curved paths of material objects might be such a continuous refraction of the associated matter waves. To see how this works out, we consider the following example. The parabolic flight of a baseball is a simple case of a material body moving in a curved path. At the top of the flight the path is concave downward, the instantaneous velocity v is horizontal, and the path may be regarded momentarily as the arc of a circle of radius of curvature R. The acceleration of the ball is the centripetal acceleration, v^2/R, which is the acceleration caused by gravity, g.

Equating these two expressions for the acceleration, we can solve for the radius of curvature of the path:

$$R = \frac{v^2}{g} . \tag{5–11}$$

To express this result in terms of energy, we note that the total energy E of the baseball is constant and that the gravitational potential energy is $E_p = m_0 g y$, where y is the height of the ball above the ground. The velocity of the ball is so small that we may use classical physics. Since the kinetic energy must be $(E - E_p)$, we have

$$E_k = \tfrac{1}{2} m_0 v^2 = E - E_p$$

or

$$v^2 = \frac{2(E - E_p)}{m_0} , \tag{5–12}$$

so that R, in terms of energy, becomes

$$R = \frac{2(E - E_p)}{m_0 g} . \tag{5–13}$$

Having found R by classical, nonrelativistic means, we next attempt to solve the same problem by considering the refraction of matter waves.

We apply Eq. (5–12) and $u = c^2/v$ to determine the phase velocity of the associated waves of the baseball, and obtain

$$u = c^2 \sqrt{m_0/2(E - E_p)} = c^2 \sqrt{m_0/2(E - m_0 g y)}, \tag{5–14}$$

where $E_p = m_0 g y$. It is evident that u is a function of the height y, and that u increases when y increases. This means that the higher the ball, the less is the "refractive index" of the space in which the associated waves move. Let us again compute the radius of curvature that this "refraction" imparts to the trajectory of the ball.

We assume, as before, that for an instant dt the ball moves on the arc of a circle of radius R. As in the study of optical refraction, we shall talk in terms of an infinitesimal wavefront of width dy perpendicular to the "ray". In Fig. 5–4 the phase waves move at a height y above the earth, and they curve concave downward because the top of the wavefront moves faster than the bottom. From the figure we find that

$$d\theta = \frac{u \, dt}{R} = \frac{(u + du) \, dt}{R + dy} ,$$

yielding

$$R = \frac{u}{du/dy} . \tag{5–15}$$

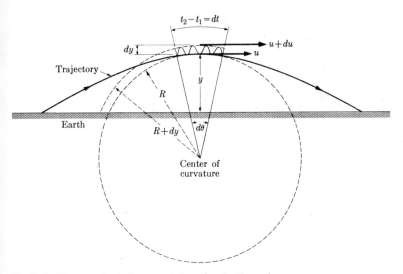

Fig. 5–4 Wave-mechanical representation of projectile motion.

To find du, we first put Eq. (5–14) in the form

$$u(E - m_0 g y)^{1/2} = c^2 \left(\frac{m_0}{2}\right)^{1/2}$$

and then differentiate u with respect to y. The result reduces to

$$du = \frac{1}{2} \frac{m_0 g}{E - m_0 g y} u \, dy. \qquad (5\text{–}16)$$

Substituting this expression for du in Eq. (5–15), we get a relation which simplifies to

$$R = \frac{2(E - E_p)}{m_0 g}. \qquad (5\text{–}17)$$

Agreement between Eqs. (5–13) and (5–17) supports Schrödinger's idea that it may be possible to devise a system of mechanics in which the paths of rays of matter waves replace the classical Newtonian trajectories. His great success in this respect is described in the next chapter.

Thus far we have presented no real experimental evidence, such as the observation of interference effects, that could provide convincing proof of the wave nature of light. However, in 1925 Elsasser deduced from deBroglie's theory that a beam of electrons diffracted by a crystal should show interference phenomena. This prediction eventually led to the experimental verification of the wave nature of matter.

5–5 THE DAVISSON AND GERMER EXPERIMENT

In 1927 Davisson and Germer* were studying the scattering of electrons by nickel. Their technique was reminiscent of both Rutherford alpha-particle scattering and Compton x-ray scattering. They directed a beam of electrons onto a block of nickel and measured the intensity of the electrons as they scattered from the nickel in different directions. In the course of the experiment, their vacuum system broke accidentally and had to be repaired.

When the vacuum system broke the nickel target was at a high temperature, and the air caused the nickel to acquire a heavy coat of oxide. To remove the oxide from the block of nickel, Davisson and Germer reduced the oxide slowly in a high-temperature oven. When their apparatus was reassembled, they began to get very different results. Whereas the number of scattered electrons had previously become continuously less as the scattering angle increased, they now found that the number of electrons went through maxima and minima. *The electrons were being diffracted.* Using the familiar techniques of x-ray diffraction by crystals, Davisson and Germer computed the wavelength their electrons must have, and they found that this wavelength agreed with the deBroglie formula.

The prolonged heating to clean the nickel block had caused it to become a single crystal, and the electron diffraction pattern was completely analogous to x-ray diffraction by the Bragg technique (see Chapter 10). This experiment verified the deBroglie hypothesis and indicated that material particles have wave properties.

To consider the Davisson and Germer experiment in more detail, we show their apparatus schematically in Fig. 5–5. At the right is an electron gun that provides a collimated beam of electrons whose energy is known from the accelerating potential. These electrons were scattered by the nickel target, which could be rotated about an axis perpendicular to the page. The movable electron collector could be swung about the same axis as the target, so that it

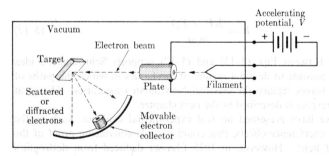

Fig. 5–5 Schematic diagram of the Davisson-Germer electron diffraction apparatus.

---

*   C. P. Davisson and L. H. Germer, *Phys. Rev.* **30** (1927), p. 705.

could receive the electrons coming from the target in any direction included in the plane of the diagram. Figure 5–6 shows the results obtained for two target orientations both before and after the target was heat-treated. Since Davisson and Germer used 75-eV electrons, they could obtain the electron velocity from the classical expression

$$E_k = Ve = \frac{m_e v^2}{2},$$ (5–18)

and substitute into the deBroglie relation, obtaining

$$\lambda = \frac{h}{m_e v} = \frac{h}{\sqrt{2Vem_e}}.$$ (5–19)

By inserting $V = 75$ V and the values of the other constants, we obtain $\lambda = 1.42$ Å. The distance between rows of atoms causing the diffraction in the nickel crystal was just a little larger, making the crystal an ideal grating for this kind of experiment. A quantitative check of the diffraction pattern showed that deBroglie's postulate is correct

The deBroglie hypothesis was further verified in Germany when Estermann and Stern diffracted helium atoms from a lithium fluoride crystal, and in the United States when Johnson diffracted hydrogen from the same kind of crystal. G. P. Thomson, son of J. J. Thomson, obtained excellent powder diffraction patterns (see Chapter 10) by sending a collimated beam of electrons through very thin sheets of various metals. Figure 5–7(a) shows an electron diffraction pattern of aluminum. For comparison an x-ray diffraction pattern of aluminum is shown in part (b) of the figure. The effective wavelengths for the two patterns

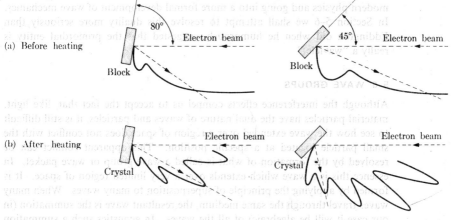

Fig. 5–6 (a) Electron scattering from a block of nickel, and (b) electron diffraction from a single crystal of nickel.

 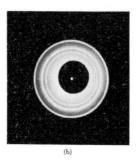

(a)   (b)

Fig. 5–7 (a) Electron diffraction pattern of aluminum, using electrons accelerated through 8000 volts. (b) X-ray diffraction pattern of aluminum, using K-radiation from copper. The wavelengths and geometry are different for the two photographs. A lead disk was placed over the center of the x-ray film for most of the exposure.

are different but the similarities are evident.   Davisson and Germer, using electrons instead of x-rays, repeated an experiment earlier carried out by A. H. Compton on diffracting soft x-rays from a man-made grating at grazing incidence.

With the complete verification of the deBroglie hypothesis, we have arrived at a point where our atomic world has strange aspects.   Compton scattering showed that waves have particle aspects and the deBroglie hypothesis shows that particles have wave characteristics.

In the following two sections we shall discuss the mathematical theory of wave groups and in the rest of the chapter some of the physical implications. We are now deviating from a description of the historical development of modern physics and going into a more formal development of wave mechanics. In Section 5–6 we shall attempt to resolve this duality more seriously than Eddington did when he humorously suggested that the primordial entity is really a "wavicle."

5–6 WAVE GROUPS

Although the interference effects compel us to accept the fact that, like light, material particles have the dual nature of waves and particles, it is still difficult to see how the wave extended over a region of space does not conflict with the small particle located at a specific position.   This apparent conflict can be resolved by the formation of what is called a wave group or wave packet.   In essence this is a wave which extends over a very limited region of space. It is formed by applying the principle of superposition to many waves.   When many waves travel through the same medium, the resultant wave is the summation (in our case it will be algebraic) of all the waves.   In acoustics such a summation of two waves of slightly different frequencies produces beats, which are fluctuations in the amplitude of the resultant wave. We shall see that when more and more frequencies are added, the regions where the amplitude is large can be made smaller.

To simplify the discussion of the superposition we will use a one-dimensional wave; that is, a wave whose displacement, y, depends on the position along a line, x, and the time, t. A sinusoidal wave with amplitude A may be written as

$$y = A \sin 2\pi \left(\frac{x}{\lambda} - vt\right) = A \sin (kx - \omega t), \qquad (5\text{-}20)$$

where we have introduced k, the propagation number which equals $2\pi/\lambda$, and the angular frequency $\omega = 2\pi v$. Even with one-dimensional conditions it is difficult to draw the wave, since there are two independent variables. What we usually do is hold one fixed and vary the other. Thus we either draw the displacement as a function of position at some fixed time (equivalent to a snapshot) or the displacement as a function of time at some fixed position. In the following development, we will use time as the variable. The results would be the same using the position as the variable if t were replaced by x and ω were replaced by k.

The time dependence of a sinusoidal wave with amplitude A can be considered as a component of a vector of length A which is rotating with a constant angular velocity ω, as shown in Fig. 5–8(a). Such a rotating vector is called a *phasor*. Since the sum of the components of many vectors is the component of the vector sum, we can get the time dependence of the sum of many waves by adding many phasors. Let us add n waves with angular velocities between ω_1 and ω_n. To simplify the addition we choose waves with the same amplitude and angular velocities which vary uniformly, so that $\omega_2 - \omega_1 = \omega_3 - \omega_2 = \cdots = \omega_n - \omega_{n-1} = \delta\omega$. Since there are $n - 1$ intervals beween ω_1 and ω_n, this interval is

$$\delta\omega = \frac{\omega_n - \omega_1}{n - 1}.$$

If all the phasors are parallel at $t = 0$, they will be spread out uniformly at time t, as indicated in Fig. 5–8(b). The angle between adjacent phasors will be given by

$$\delta\theta = (\delta\omega)t = \left(\frac{\omega_n - \omega_1}{n - 1}\right) t. \qquad (5\text{-}21)$$

The magnitude of the vector sum is the amplitude of the resulting wave, while the projection of the resultant on the vertical axis is the instantaneous displacement. We assume that $\delta\omega$ is so small that the amplitude does not change very much during one revolution. The amplitude represents the envelope of the oscillations and we will determine the general shape of this envelope. As

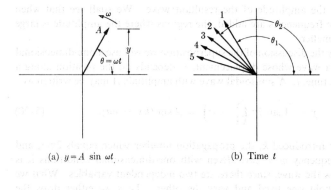

(a) $y = A \sin \omega t$ (b) Time t

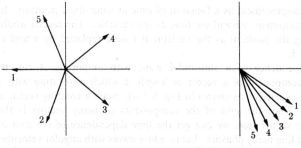

(c) Time t_1, resultant zero   (d) Just before time t_2

Fig. 5–8 (a) Single phasor. (b) Five phasors a short time after $t = 0$. (c) Five phasors with zero resultant. (d) Five phasors a short time before they become parallel.

the phasors fan out from $t = 0$, the magnitude of the resultant decreases to zero. This first zero occurs when the fan covers the entire angle 2π and the angle between adjacent phasors is $2\pi/n$, as shown in Fig. 5–8(c) for five phasors. If we call the time for the first zero t_1, Eq. (5–21) becomes

$$\frac{2\pi}{n} = \left(\frac{\omega_n - \omega_1}{n - 1}\right) t_1,$$

which can be solved for t_1 to give

$$t_1 = \left(\frac{2\pi}{\omega_n - \omega_1}\right) \frac{(n - 1)}{n}. \tag{5–22}$$

For a while after t_1 the magnitude of the resultant will be small, since the phasors will still be spread out. Eventually, however, the second phasor will catch up to the first and at this time all the other phasors will also be aligned with the first. The resultant will be the same magnitude that it was when $t = 0$. Fig. 5–8(d) shows the phasors just before this occurs. If we call the time when they are aligned t_2, the angle between adjacent phasors is 2π and Eq. (5–21) becomes

$$2\pi = \left(\frac{\omega_n - \omega_1}{n - 1}\right) t_2,$$

which gives for t_2:

$$t_2 = \left(\frac{2\pi}{\omega_n - \omega_1}\right) (n - 1). \tag{5–23}$$

After time t_2 has elapsed, the envelope will repeat the shape it took between $t = 0$ and $t = t_2$, so that we have the magnitude of the sum of the phasors as a function of time.

The quantitative variation of the envelope of the resulting wave will depend on the number of waves added together; however, the preceding qualitative discussion gives us some idea of how the resultant wave will appear. This is shown in Fig. 5–9(a). The wave has a large amplitude only in limited regions with sections of relatively low amplitude between. The regions of large amplitude are called the *wave groups* and the individual waves which are added together are called the *phase waves*. Remember that we chose to consider time as the variable. If we had varied x at a fixed time, the analysis would have been the same with ω replaced by k. The resultant wave as a function of position is shown in Fig. 5–9(b).

Although we have managed to produce wave groups, there are too many of them to reasonably represent a particle. For the wave to appear like a particle there should be only one group. This can be accomplished if we can get the time between the group maxima, t_2, to be infinite. A consideration of Eq. (5–23) shows that this can be done by having n become infinite. A *single* wave group can be formed by the addition of an infinite number of waves. Note that this does not mean that the frequency difference in the denominator of Eq. (5–23) must be infinite. An infinite number of frequencies can be contained in a finite frequency interval. The "size" of the group in time is $2t_1$, which we call the *time duration* of the group. For an infinite number of waves Eq. (5–22) for t_1 becomes

$$t_1(n = \infty) = \frac{2\pi}{\omega_n - \omega_1}.$$

If we call $\omega_n - \omega_1$ the frequency spread $\Delta\omega$, we have

$$2t_1 = \Delta t = 4\pi/\Delta\omega; \tag{5–24}$$

the time duration of the wave group is determined by the frequency spread. In the same way the spatial size of the group, Δx, is given by

$$\Delta x = 4\pi/\Delta k; \tag{5–25}$$

the spread of propagation numbers determines the size of the group.

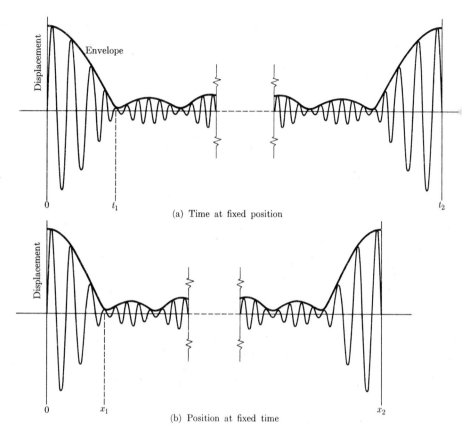

(a) Time at fixed position

(b) Position at fixed time

Fig. 5–9 A resultant wave produced by summation of many waves with different frequencies (a) as a function of time, (b) as a function of position.

Although we have been able to construct a wave group which has the particle-like characteristic of extending over a very limited region of space, there is still the question of the propagation velocity of the group. Each of the phase waves has a phase velocity $u = v\lambda = \omega/k$. In a nondispersive medium all the phase waves have the same velocity and consequently the group will move with this velocity. In a dispersive medium the phase velocities differ and the question of the group velocity is more complicated.

Let us consider two of the phase waves, which can be written as

$$y_1 = A \cos (k_1 x - \omega_1 t)$$

and

$$y_2 = A \cos (k_2 x - \omega_2 t),$$

for which the phase velocities are $u_1 = \omega_1/k_1$ and $u_2 = \omega_2/k_2$. The functions have been chosen such that the two waves are in phase and maximum at $x = 0$ and $t = 0$. The addition of these two waves can be done by using the trigonometric identity

$$\cos a + \cos b = 2 \cos \tfrac{1}{2}(a - b) \cos \tfrac{1}{2}(a + b).$$

The resultant wave becomes

$$y = y_1 + y_2$$
$$= 2A \cos \tfrac{1}{2}[(k_2 - k_1)x - (\omega_2 - \omega_1)t] \cos \tfrac{1}{2}[(k_1 + k_2)x - (\omega_1 + \omega_2)t].$$

If the propagation numbers and frequencies differ only by differential amounts, we have

$$k_2 - k_1 = dk, \qquad \omega_2 - \omega_1 = d\omega,$$
$$\tfrac{1}{2}(k_1 + k_2) \approx k_1 \qquad \text{and} \qquad \tfrac{1}{2}(\omega_1 + \omega_2) \approx \omega_1.$$

The resultant wave is then

$$y = 2A \cos \tfrac{1}{2}[dk\, x - d\omega\, t] \cos (k_1 x - \omega_1 t). \qquad (5\text{--}26)$$

The second cosine function times A is one of the original waves. The cosine function in front modulates this wave with another cosine function of wavelength π/dk and a frequency $(d\omega/\pi)$. From the product of these we can get the velocity of propagation of the modulation, which is the group velocity v_g:

$$v_g = \left(\frac{\pi}{dk}\right)\left(\frac{d\omega}{\pi}\right) = \frac{d\omega}{dk}. \qquad (5\text{--}27)$$

The group velocity depends on the way in which the frequency varies with the propagation number. Since we have considered only two phase waves, it is possible that v_g will differ for different pairs of phase waves; that is, the group velocity may be a function of frequency. When many waves are added, the derivative of Eq. (5-27) is evaluated for the central frequency of those used in the summation.

If the wave group is to represent a particle, then it is necessary that the speed of the group and the speed of the particle be the same. If these speeds differed, the particle would soon be in a region where the amplitude of the wave is negligible and the wave would not give a useful indication of the position of the particle. Using the mass-energy relation from relativity, we can find the particle velocity in terms of its momentum and energy:

$$v = p/m = pc^2/mc^2 = pc^2/E. \qquad (5\text{--}28)$$

To get the group velocity in the same terms we use $p = h/\lambda$ and $E = h\nu$ which are written as

$$k = \frac{2\pi p}{h} \qquad \text{and} \qquad \omega = \frac{2\pi E}{h}. \qquad (5\text{--}29)$$

The group velocity can then be written as

$$v_g = \frac{d\omega}{dk} = \frac{dE}{dp}. \qquad (5\text{-}30)$$

To evaluate this we need the energy-momentum relationship from relativity, Eq. (A3–48);

$$E^2 = p^2c^2 + m_0^2c^4.$$

Differentiating this, we obtain

$$2E \, dE = 2pc^2 \, dp.$$

The group velocity becomes

$$v_g = \frac{dE}{dp} = \frac{pc^2}{E}. \qquad (5\text{-}31)$$

The particle velocity (Eq. 5–28) thus equals the group velocity (Eq. 5–31). We therefore see that the choices that were made for the frequency and wavelength to be associated with the particle also lead to the satisfying result that the wave group and the particle have the same speed.* Thus it is possible to have a wave motion which has the particle characteristic of being in a small region of space and which will move with the particle's speed.

5-7 FOURIER ANALYSIS; ORTHOGONALITY

Most readers will be familiar with the mathematics of Fourier series used to describe periodic functions. For instance, a function of x with a period L can be expanded in a Fourier series as follows:

$$f(x) = \sum_{n=0}^{\infty} \left(A_n \cos \frac{2\pi nx}{L} + B_n \sin \frac{2\pi nx}{L} \right). \qquad (5\text{-}32)$$

For example, the transverse displacement of the plucked guitar string mentioned in Section 5–3 can be described by this function. We then think of the guitar string as continuing indefinitely, and the simplest description is obtained by making the period L equal to twice the length of the string. Thus the length of the string is half the wavelength of the *fundamental* (lowest frequency) for which $n = 1$. We further have $A_n = 0$ for all values of n because the cosine functions do not satisfy the boundary requirement that the displacement is zero for $x = 0$ and $x = L$. Therefore B_1 is the amplitude of the fundamental, B_2 is the amplitude of the second harmonic, B_3 is the amplitude of the third harmonic, etc.

---

* It is a curious fact that if we had used the classical expression $E = E_k = \frac{1}{2}mv^2 = p^2/2m$, we would also have found agreement between group and particle velocities.

Equation (5–32) can be written as

$$f(x) = \sum_{n=-\infty}^{n=\infty} C_n e^{i2\pi nx/L}. \qquad (5\text{--}33)$$

The proof of this statement is left to one of the problems. Note that the integer n now runs from $-\infty$ to $+\infty$. We thereby get positive and negative exponentials under the summation sign as needed to produce cosine and sine functions. Assuming that the coefficients A_n and B_n in Eq. (5–32) are real, as required for instance in the case of a plucked string, the coefficient C_n will be complex.

In order to find the coefficients C_n, we assume that the function $f(x)$ is given, for instance, in tabular form or in analytic forms broken up over several parts of the period. Examples of the latter are sawtooth functions and square waves well known in electronics. If $f(x)$ is known in such a form that it can be integrated, we find the coefficients C_n in the following way. We multiply each side of Eq. (5–33) with $e^{-i2\pi mx/L}$ and integrate over x from $-L/2$ to $+L/2$:

$$\int_{-L/2}^{L/2} f(x)e^{-i2\pi mx/L}\,dx = \sum_{n=-\infty}^{\infty} C_n \int_{-L/2}^{L/2} e^{i2\pi(n-m)x/L}\,dx. \qquad (5\text{--}34)$$

The function in the integrand on the right-hand side of Eq. (5–34) is a sum of a sine function and a cosine function, both with periods equal to $L/(n-m)$, except when $n = m$, in which case the function is unity. For $n \neq m$, the integrals from $-L/2$ to $+L/2$ are integrals over a whole number of wavelengths, and they therefore vanish. We can then write

$$C_m = \frac{1}{L} \int_{-L/2}^{L/2} f(x)e^{-i2\pi mx/L}\,dx. \qquad (5\text{--}35)$$

We have here transposed the two sides of Eq. (5–34) and written C_m instead of C_n, because only the term in the series for which $n = m$ remains on the right-hand side of Eq. (5–34).

Equation (5–33) can be used to describe any periodic function with period of length L and with the coefficients C determined by the aid of Eq. (5–35). For instance, this analysis can be used to describe the transverse displacements of a plucked guitar string, as described above, because the function is defined over a limited range in x and we can therefore arbitrarily call this range half the period. The function (5–33) can also be used, for instance, to describe the pressure oscillation in air near a piano in which middle C has been struck. The independent variable x is then time, and L is the period. The coefficients

C will be slowly decaying functions of time with a different decay rate for the various harmonics.*

The functions $e^{i2\pi nx/L}$, with n being an integer running from $n = -\infty$ to $n = +\infty$, are *orthogonal* functions in the interval $x = -L/2$ to $x = +L/2$. Two functions $\phi_n(x)$ and $\phi_m(x)$ are orthogonal in the interval $x = a$ to $x = b$ if

$$\int_a^b \phi_m^* \phi_n \, dx = 0, \qquad \text{for} \qquad n \neq m. \tag{5–36}$$

Here ϕ_m^* is the complex conjugate of ϕ_m, that is, ϕ_m^* is produced by changing the sign of all terms containing $i = \sqrt{-1}$.

The orthogonality of the functions used in Fourier analysis is, of course, necessary for Eq. (5–34) to reduce to Eq. (5–35). It is not only sine and cosine functions and complex exponentials that form orthogonal sets of functions. In later chapters we shall discuss further the fact that the solutions of Schrödinger's wave equation in general form orthogonal sets, and that arbitrary functions can be expanded in terms of these functions in a similar manner as that expressed by Eq. (5–32) or (5–33).

Another feature of the trigonometric functions or complex exponentials is that they form a *complete* set. This means that an infinite series, such as Eq. (5–33), can always be found to describe $f(x)$ exactly, provided $f(x)$ is finite and has a limited number of discontinuities in the interval $x = -L/2$ to $x = +L/2$. For the proof of this statement, we have to refer to a textbook in mathematics.

In the discussion above, we have defined the function $f(x)$ in an interval $-L/2$ to $+L/2$, and it is clear from the formula that the function will repeat itself in successive intervals of length L. Now we see that we can increase the length L of the interval to include any region that we may be interested in, and it would not matter if $f(x)$ repeated itself outside these limits. Indeed, there is no reason why we should not let L go to infinity. In order to do so, we first write Eq. (5–33) as

$$f(x) = \sum_{n=-\infty}^{n=\infty} \frac{LC_n}{2\pi} e^{ikx}\Delta k, \tag{5–37}$$

where we have introduced a new variable

$$k = 2\pi n/L, \tag{5–38}$$

---

* We are oversimplifying a bit. The middle C key strikes not one but three strings in the piano. The three strings are intentionally tuned to slightly different resonance frequencies (fundamentals): otherwise, the piano would sound dull. Also, the "harmonics" do not have exactly two or three times the frequency of the fundamental because of stiffness of the strings.

which we recognize as being the propagation number $k = 2\pi/\lambda$. We further obtain $\Delta k = 2\pi\Delta n/L$ with $\Delta n = 1$.

For an expression such as Eq. (5–33) to be meaningful, the series must converge. This means that the coefficients C_n, in general, will decrease as n increases. However, one can get an arbitrarily good description of $f(x)$ with a truncated series, that is, with a finite number of terms. The longer the interval L, the more terms are needed, and each individual C_n will then be smaller. Coming back to Eq. (5–37), we see that for $f(x)$ to remain finite, the product of L and C_n must remain finite, so C_n approaches zero as L goes to infinity. We therefore introduce a new function to replace the product LC_n:

$$g(k) = (2\pi)^{-1/2} LC_n. \tag{5–39}$$

The factor $(2\pi)^{-1/2}$ is included for symmetry reasons, as will be immediately evident. Making this substitution in Eq. (5–37) and converting the sum to integrals, we obtain

$$f(x) = (2\pi)^{-1/2} \int_{-\infty}^{\infty} g(k)e^{ikx} \, dk. \tag{5–40}$$

This is a Fourier series, in which the wavelength does not change in discrete jumps as in Eq. (5–33) or (5–32) but rather varies continuously (or stated differently, the wavelength changes by infinitesimal steps). The amplitude function $g(k)$ is found very simply by substituting Eq. (5–39) into Eq. (5–35), changing the subscript from m to n. The result is

$$g(k) = (2\pi)^{-1/2} \int_{-\infty}^{\infty} f(x)e^{-ikx} \, dx. \tag{5–41}$$

The function $g(k)$ is called the Fourier transform of $f(x)$, and the two functions $f(x)$ and $g(k)$ are called Fourier inverse functions.

As an example, consider the Gaussian distribution function

$$f(x) = \pi^{-1/4}\sigma^{-1/2}e^{-x^2/2\sigma^2}, \tag{5–42}$$

where σ is the standard deviation or root-mean-square deviation from the mean value $\bar{x} = 0$. This function is plotted in Fig. 5–10. We find the Fourier transform from Eq. (5–41) to be

$$g(k) = 2^{-1/2}\pi^{-3/4}\sigma^{-1/2} \int_{-\infty}^{\infty} e^{-x^2/2\sigma^2}e^{-ikx} \, dx$$

$$= 2^{1/2}\pi^{-3/4}\sigma^{-1/2} \int_{0}^{\infty} e^{-x^2/2\sigma^2} \cos kx \, dx. \tag{5–43}$$

We have here written $e^{-ikx} = \cos kx - i \sin kx$ and made use of the fact that an antisymmetric function (i.e., the one containing $\sin kx$) integrates out to zero. The last integral can be found in a table of definite integrals*. Inserted into Eq. (5–43), it gives

$$g(k) = \pi^{-1/4}\sigma^{1/2}e^{-k^2\sigma^2/2}. \tag{5–44}$$

This transform is also plotted in Fig. 5–10.

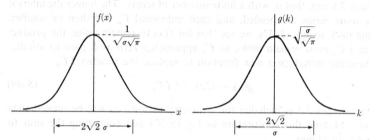

Fig. 5–10 The Gaussian function $f(x)$ and its Fourier transfer $g(k)$ which is also Gaussian.

We can write the exponential in Eq. (5–44) as $e^{-k^2/2\sigma_k^2}$. The standard deviation σ_k for the transform can be found by comparing Eqs. (5–42) and (5–44). We find that

$$\sigma_k = 1/\sigma. \tag{5–45}$$

Consider the Gaussian (Eq. 5–42) as an example of a deBroglie pilot wave. The transform (Eq. 5–44) then represents the spectrum of propagation numbers k necessary to describe this wave or the wavelength spectrum with $\lambda = 2\pi/k$. If we use the standard deviations as measures of the width of the wave train and its transform, we find from Eq. (5–45) that

$$\Delta x\,\Delta k \approx 1. \tag{5–46}$$

Using the widths $2\sqrt{2}\,\sigma$ and $2\sqrt{2}/\sigma$ indicated under the curves in Fig. 5–10, we obtain

$$\Delta x\,\Delta k = 8, \tag{5–47}$$

which can be compared with Eq. (5–25).

5–8 WAVE-PARTICLE DUALITY

The wave-group idea is an attempt to resolve the conflict contained in the fact that some explanations of experiments require the use of waves while others require the use of particles. This interpretation means that an electron is a group of matter waves and a photon is a group of electromagnetic waves,

---

* For instance, in *Handbook of Chemistry and Physics*, Chemical Rubber Publishing Company, Cleveland (any year).

that is, there are only waves in nature but they form wave packets which we call particles. As indicated in Section 5–4, the trajectories of the particles are due to the refractions of the waves. Macroscopic objects consist of many of these wave goups and the interactions between objects are simply interactions of waves.

Although this "reality" of the waves seems reasonable, there are some difficulties associated with it. When a wave is incident on a boundary between two media, it generally splits into a reflected wave and a refracted wave. The incident wave group becomes two groups. If the wave group is to be an electron, where the boundary would be produced by a change in electric potential energy, we know that the electron does not split. It is difficult to see how the two wave groups, one reflected and one refracted, can be the single electron. In addition, the Coulomb force, which is stated for point charges and acts between electrons, cannot be handled conveniently with this interpretation.

Another possible interpretation was presented by deBroglie. In this the particles are "real" and the associated waves are pilot waves which guide the particle and are to be looked upon as probability waves. The amplitude of these probability waves at a certain position is a measure of the probability of the particle being at that position. The pilot waves are abstract quantities and the word "wave" is used as it is, for instance, in the phrases "wave of enthusiasm" and "crime wave." Since the waves are not directly observable, there is no necessity for a medium. This interpretation removes the difficulty of the wave group concept when the wave is partially reflected and partially refracted. For the probability waves, the amplitude of the reflected wave determines the probability that the particle reflects from the boundary and the amplitude of the refracted wave determines the probability that the particle penetrates the boundary. A single particle will do *only* one or the other, but a large number of particles will divide according to the probabilities.

This pilot wave interpretation, which means that a light beam is a stream of photons, also runs into difficulty. Suppose that we pass a light beam through a pair of slits separated by a small distance, as in the interference experiments of Young. The interference pattern produced on a screen consists of alternate light and dark bands. The positions of these bands are determined by the differences of the paths of the two waves proceeding from the slits to the screen. The alternate light and dark bands represent alternate large and small probabilities of a photon arriving at the respective positions on the screen. If one of the slits is covered, the interference pattern changes, which means the probabilities of where the photon will arrive at the screen changes. For example, the photon may now have a large probability of arriving at a position where the previous probability was very small. If the photons are real, however, they *must* go through one slit or the other. Consequently, as the photon goes through one slit, its motion is influenced by the other slit and the photon is able to know whether the slit through which it did not pass is open or not.

This gives some "intelligence" to the particles which does not seem reasonable. We will return to this problem in Section 5–10.

The resolution of the conflict between waves and particles lies in an appraisal of what we mean by a wave and a particle. Both of these terms, when applied to the fundamental entities, are abstractions of the human mind which are arrived at by extrapolation from the macroscopic world of grains of sand and waves on strings. The following is another very clever and useful trick of the human mind. A hollow rubber ball has its center of gravity at its center. Discussion of most, but not all, of the motion of the ball can be greatly facilitated by regarding the ball as a point mass with all its mass at the center of gravity. The center of gravity has no objective reality, and if someone cuts the ball open, points to the center and says, "Ha! You see, there is no mass there," we reply that the center of gravity makes a poor description of what is at the center of the ball, but that it continues to be useful in describing the motion of the ball. No one description of the ball can ever completely represent what the reality of the ball is. In the same way the particle description and the wave description are each incomplete in attempting to describe physical reality.

The mistake of those who say that interference shows that light *is* a wave phenomenon is a verbal mistake that is made every day. We point to a map and say this *is* the United States. What we mean is that this diagram on a piece of paper is a scale representation of many of the physical and political features of the United States. We know that the real United States cannot be folded, rolled up, or burned. We know that the states are not different in color, only a few square inches in area, and completely flat. The map is a clever, useful, elegant model invented by the human mind. More may be learned about some aspects of the United States in one hour of map study than in a lifetime of looking at the real United States. We do not scoff at maps because they are unreal, we admire them as useful descriptions.

Both the wave and the particle are models we have constructed in attempting to describe matter. Quite naturally, we do not expect either model to give a complete description. Some properties, such as interference, are contained in one model, the wave, while other properties, such as mass, are contained in the other model, the particle. The two models complement each other in that together they give a description of matter. Thus we should say that the electrons are waves *and* particles, not waves *or* particles. The same statement can be made about electromagnetic radiation. During an experiment the particular model which is used is determined by the apparatus used.

Even though we admit that waves and particles are not "real," it is very awkward to talk about experimental procedures and results in such a way as to indicate this. Consequently, we will still make statements which seem to imply that particles exist; for example, we say that the intensity of the wave is a measure of the probability of the location of the particle. This is for convenience only. Both the wave and the particle are incomplete models and both are necessary for a description of all the properties of matter which are experimentally determined. With this interpretation, there is no conflict in the dual nature of matter or electromagnetic radiation.

5–9 THE HEISENBERG UNCERTAINTY PRINCIPLE

An important consequence of the wave-particle duality can be developed from the wave group analysis of Sections 5–6 and 5–7. In an attempt to get a wave that had a limited extent, we added many waves to form a wave group. If we correlate the wave model to the particle model by assuming that the amplitude of the group measures the probability of the particle being at that position, we see that there is still no certainty in knowing the location of the particle. It could be anywhere in the group.

To decrease the uncertainty in location of the particle, we have to reduce the size of the group, Δx. If we rearrange Eq. (5–25) into

$$\Delta x \, \Delta k = 4\pi, \tag{5–48}$$

the size of the group can be reduced by increasing the spread of propagation numbers, Δk. It appears that we may eliminate the uncertainty in position of the particle by using an infinite spread of propagation numbers. We see from $k = 2\pi p/h$ that the momentum of the particle is determined by the propagation number of the wave. If we use an infinite spread of propagation numbers, we will have an infinite spread in the momentum of the particle. When we decrease the uncertainty of the particle's position, we increase the uncertainty of the particle's momentum. If we put Eq. (5–48) in terms of momentum, we have

$$\Delta x \, \Delta p = 2h.$$

The coefficient of h in this expression was obtained through our simplification of using waves with the same amplitudes and with a uniform spread of frequencies. A different choice of these would give a different number for this coefficient. If we choose to characterize the uncertainties Δx and Δp by root-mean-square deviations rather than the widths of the central maximum as in Fig. 5–9, we find

$$\Delta x \, \Delta p_x \simeq \hbar. \tag{5–49}$$

Compare Eq. (5–46) with Eq. (5–49).

The subscript is added to the momentum to indicate that it is the momentum associated with the x-displacement. Equation (5–49) is interpreted as indicating that the uncertainty in position of the particle times the uncertainty in the associated momentum is approximately $\hbar$. The words *associated momentum* are used because in the three-dimensional case there are also momentum components in the y- and z-directions and with the x-position we use the *x*-component of momentum. There are equivalent equations for the other directions:

$$\Delta y \, \Delta p_y \simeq \hbar, \tag{5–50}$$

$$\Delta z \, \Delta p_z \simeq \hbar. \tag{5–51}$$

These uncertainties are involved with the nature of matter and are not the same as the uncertainties introduced by the limited precision of some measuring device. In a practical experiment the uncertainties introduced by the equipment will usually be much larger than the ones associated with the wave-particle duality.

We can perform the same analysis with Eq. (5–24), $\Delta t = 4\pi/\Delta\omega$, where the frequency spread determined the time duration of the group as it passed a given position. Using $E = h\nu = h\omega/2\pi$, we obtain $\Delta t \, \Delta E \simeq h$, or when using root-mean-square deviations,

$$\Delta t \, \Delta E \simeq \hbar. \tag{5–52}$$

This relationship can be interpreted as meaning that the uncertainty of the energy of the particle is dependent on the time interval used for measuring the energy.

This result throws light on a question not considered in the Bohr theory of atomic energy states. The excited states have finite lifetimes Δt and therefore an associated energy uncertainty, $\Delta E \approx \hbar/\Delta t$. Spectral lines emitted from a short-lived state are broader than lines emitted from long-lived states, and the widths can actually be observed with precision instruments.

The equations concerning uncertainties, that is, Eqs. (5–49) to (5–51), (5–31) and (5–32) are variant statements of the *Heisenberg Uncertainty Principle*. We look upon these statements as indicative of the inherent nature of the physical world. Thus it is impossible for us to know an exact position and an exact momentum of a photon or an electron. A precise knowledge of one can be obtained only at the expense of the precision of the other. Frequently, the uncertainty principle is introduced as being due to the act of measurement. For example, when the position of an electron is determined, the measurement introduces the uncertainty in position and momentum because of an interaction between the apparatus and the electron. This implies that the electron had an exact position and momentum before the measurement. We prefer the interpretation that the uncertainties are inherent in the nature of the things we do experiments with. Admittedly, this choice cannot be made on the basis of any physical result. Physics deals with the results of measurements and either interpretation leads to the same uncertainties in measured quantities.

As anticipated in Chapter 1, another philosophical idea affected by the uncertainty principle was that of causality. According to classical theory, the path of a particle is determined by its initial position and momentum and by the forces acting on it. If the forces between the particles of the universe were known and if it were possible to measure, at a given time, the exact position and momentum of every particle, then the past and future positions and momenta of every particle could be calculated. The past and future are completely determined by the information known at an instant of time. The uncertainty principle indicates that we cannot know an exact position and momentum for each particle; we can only determine what the particles will probably do. For macroscopic objects the uncertainties are so small that the probable motion does not differ significantly from classical motion. However, for photons and electrons, the classical prediction of their motion gives a poor idea of the experimental results.

5–10 THE DOUBLE-SLIT EXPERIMENT

To crystallize the ideas we have been discussing about the wave-particle duality and to emphasize the limits on our ability to describe the behavior of the basic entities of the physical world, we take the double-slit diffraction experiment mentioned in Section 5–8 for an example. A schematic diagram of the experiment is shown in Fig. 5–11. The source emits a beam which is incident on two slits separated by a distance D. The beam could be electromagnetic, that is, a stream of photons, or a beam of cathode rays, that is, a stream of electrons. The following analysis applies to either, but for convenience we shall consider the stream to be photons. At a distance from the slits which is large, compared to D, we have a detector, which could be a photographic film or a series of photoelectric cells.

If the detector is a film, it will show, after exposure, the characteristic interference pattern indicated by the curve labeled intensity on the figure. The positions of the maxima and minima are found by considering the superposition

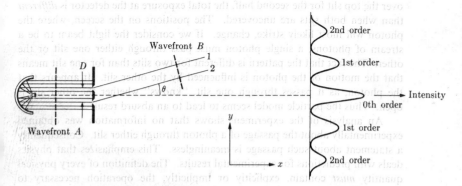

Fig. 5–11 A double-slit diffraction experiment. The distance to the screen is very long compared to the slit separation D.

of the wave from one slit with the other; that is, the interference pattern is a prediction of the wave model.

Rays 1 and 2, which converge to a point on a screen and therefore can interfere with each other, can be considered on the left-hand part of Fig. 5–11 to be virtually parallel, because of the distances involved. From wavefront A to wavefront B is a difference in distance between the two rays of $D \sin \theta$. The angular separation of the central maximum and the adjacent minimum is therefore

$$D \sin \theta = \lambda/2 = h/2p_x,$$

where λ is the wavelength of the light and p_x is the associated momentum of the photon.

When angle θ is small, it becomes

$$\theta = h/2p_x D, \tag{5–53}$$

and θ is the angle between any adjacent maximum and minimum.

If the detector is a series of photoelectric cells, the light will release photo-electrons and the maxima will indicate those cells where many electrons are emitted. Each photoelectron represents the arrival at the detector of a photon and thus more photons strike the detectors around the maxima in the pattern than around the minima. The pattern gives very little information pertaining to a single photon but only the effect produced by many photons. The cor-relation between the wave model and the particle model is statistical. The maxima of the wave pattern represent regions of greatest probability for the arrival of a photon.

If one of the slits is covered during the experiment, the resulting single-slit pattern will differ from the preceding one. If a cover is placed over the bottom slit for the first half of the experiment and then the cover is placed over the top slit for the second half, the total exposure at the detector is *different* than when both slits are uncovered. The positions on the screen, where the photon will most likely strike, change. If we consider the light beam to be a stream of photons, a single photon must pass through either one slit or the other. The fact that the pattern is different for two slits than for one slit means that the motion of the photon is influenced by the other slit. It appears that the photon, as it passes through one slit, "knows" whether the other slit is open. Thus the particle model seems to lead to an absurd result.

An analysis of the experiment shows that no information was obtained experimentally about the passage of a photon through either slit. Consequently a statement about such passage is meaningless. This emphasizes that physics deals with predictions for experimental results. The definition of every physical quantity *must* contain, explicitly or implicitly, the operation necessary to measure the physical quantity. It makes *no sense* to talk about results which cannot be observed. If we want to know through which slit the photon passes, we must revise the experiment so that we can determine this. To detect the passage of a photon we place many small particles just to the right of the slits. After passing through a slit, the photon will collide with one of these particles. Observation of the recoil of the small particle will allow us to determine the slit used by the photon. In this ideal experiment the only uncertainties introduced will be those predicted by the uncertainty principle; we will assume that the precision achieved in constructing the apparatus was so high that there are no uncertainties in dimensions, such as the separation of the slits.

To be certain of the slit from which the small particle recoiled, the uncertainty in its y-position must be much smaller than the separation of the slits; we must have

$$\Delta y \ll D.$$

There will be an exchange of momentum during the collision, but there is an uncertainty in the amount since we don't know the details of the collision. The uncertainty in the y-component of the momentum of the photon, Δp_y, must not be great enough to cause it to deviate from the interference pattern. This means that we must have

$$\Delta p_y / p_x \ll \theta = h/2p_x D,$$

or

$$\Delta p_y \ll h/2D.$$

Since momentum is conserved, Δp_y is also the uncertainty in the y-component of the momentum of the small particle. If we multiply the uncertainty in the y-position of the small particle with the uncertainty in its y-component of the momentum, we obtain

$$\Delta y \, \Delta p_y \ll Dh/2D = h/2. \tag{5–54}$$

If we compare this with the prediction of the uncertainty principle, $\Delta y \, \Delta p_y \simeq \hbar$, we see that the small uncertainties necessary in Eq. (5–54) are not possible. If Δy is small enough that we can determine through which slit the photon passes, Δp_y is so large that we do not get the interference pattern at the detector. *We cannot detect both the particle nature, as indicated by the collision with the small particle, and the wave nature, as indicated by the interference pattern.* This example also illustrates how the uncertainty principle is used to resolve apparent conflicts between the wave model and the particle model.

5–11 SUMMARY

The wave-particle duality of matter is substantiated by experiment. Neither the wave model nor the particle model is sufficient alone to include all of the properties of the physical world. The two models are synthesized to complement each other in providing a description for all experimental results. This synthesis is contained in the relations between the wave properties of wavelength and frequency and the particle properties of momentum and energy.

The predictions of the two models seem to be correlated statistically; a large wave amplitude means a large probability of the particle being at that position. For material particles like electrons, the particle model has been developed so that, for example, we can calculate electron trajectories in magnetic fields. The corresponding wave model for material particles requires further elaboration. Although we can find the associated wavelength and frequency, we have no method for calculating the amplitude of the "electron wave." Our experience with previous wave motions, such as sound waves, indicates that a wave equation is needed. The solution of this equation would give the amplitude of the wave, which we can correlate with the particle model. A *complete* acceptance of the dual nature of matter requires a further development of the wave model.

PROBLEMS

5-1 Show that the cross section for Thomson scattering is

$$\sigma_T = \frac{e^4}{6\pi\varepsilon_0 m_e^2 c^4} = 6.66 \times 10^{-25} \text{ cm}^2.$$

5-2 X-ray photons of wavelength 0.712 Å undergo Compton collisions in carbon. What is the wavelength change of the line scattered at 90° if the scattering particle is a) an electron and b) the whole carbon atom?

5-3 Each of three quanta of radiation undergoes a 90° Compton scattering in a block of graphite. Assuming that the ejected electron had no binding energy in carbon, compute the fractional change in wavelength ($\Delta\lambda/\lambda$) for the scattered radiation when the incident quantum is: a) a gamma ray from cobalt, $\lambda = 1.06 \times 10^{-2}$ Å; b) x-rays from molybdenum, $\lambda = 0.712$ Å; and c) visible light, $\lambda = 5000$ Å. d) The binding energy of an electron in carbon is actually 4.0 eV. If this is taken into account, what would be the answers to the preceding parts? e) Comment on the feasibility of resolving the two waves in a beam composed of the incident and scattered radiation in each of the preceding cases.

5-4 An x-ray quantum having a wavelength of 0.15 Å undergoes a Compton collision and is scattered through an angle of 37°. a) What are the energies of the incident and scattered photons and of the ejected electron? b) What is the magnitude of the momentum of each photon? c) Find the momentum of the electron both graphically and analytically using the values found in the preceding part.

5-5 Using the data and results of Problem 5-2 for Compton scattering of $\lambda = 0.712$ Å photons by carbon, find the energy of the recoil particle given that it is a) an electron and b) the whole carbon atom. c) What is the direction of motion of the recoil particle in each case with respect to the direction of incidence of the photon?

5-6 A photon of energy E undergoes a Compton collision with a free particle of rest mass m_0. a) Show that the maximum recoil kinetic energy of the particle is

$$E_{k_{max}} = \frac{E^2}{E + m_0 c^2/2}.$$

b) What is the maximum energy that can be transferred to a free electron by Compton collision of a photon of violet light ($\lambda = 4000$ Å)? c) Could violet light eject electrons from a metal by a Compton collision?

5-7 When a hydrogen atom goes from the state $n = 2$ to the state $n = 1$, the energy of the atom decreases by 10.2 eV. In Chapter 4 it was stated that all of this energy is radiated as a single photon. Actually, the energy of the photon must be slightly less than 10.2 eV, since a small part of the energy is needed to provide the kinetic energy of the recoiling atom. a) What is the recoil momentum of the hydrogen atom? b) What fraction of the 10.2 eV is taken by the recoil of the atom?

5-8 The apparatus for a Compton-scattering experiment is arranged so that the scattered photon and the recoil electron are detected only when their paths are at right angles to one another. Show that under these conditions a) the scattered wavelength is given by $\lambda' = \lambda/\cos \alpha$ and b) the energy of the scattered photon is $m_e c^2$.

5-9 Show that the deBroglie wavelength in angstroms for an electron accelerated from rest through a potential difference V in volts is a) classically $\lambda = 12.27/V^{1/2}$ and b) relativistically

$$\lambda = \frac{12.27}{V^{1/2}} \left(\frac{Ve}{2m_e c^2} + 1 \right)^{-1/2}.$$

5-10 What is the deBroglie wavelength of the waves associated with an electron that has been accelerated from rest through a potential difference of a) 100 V? b) 8000 V?

5-11 Show that the deBroglie wavelength for a particle of mass m moving with the rms speed of a Maxwellian distribution at temperature T is $\lambda = h/(3mkT)^{1/2}$, where k is Boltzmann's constant.

5-12 An alpha particle (doubly ionized helium) is ejected from the nucleus of a radium atom with 5.78 MeV of kinetic energy. a) What is the deBroglie wavelength of this particle? b) How does this wavelength compare with the nuclear diameter, which is about 3×10^{-15} m for the alpha particle?

5-13 a) What is the momentum of a photon of wavelength 0.02 Å? b) What is the momentum of an electron that has the same total energy as a 0.02 Å photon? c) What is the deBroglie wavelength of the electron in part b)?

5-14 Using the rotation vector idea of Section 5-6, add four waves with equal amplitudes and different frequencies to obtain the resultant amplitude as a function of time. Assume that $\omega_1 = 2\pi$ rad s^{-1} and $\delta\omega = \pi$ rad s^{-1}. Plot the amplitude as a function of time for every $\frac{1}{8}$ s and show that the time between groups is 2 s and the time duration of the group is 1 s.

5-15 A wave group is formed by the addition of an infinite number of waves. The ratio of the angular frequency and propagation number is the phase velocity. a) Given that the phase velocity is constant, show that the group velocity is equal to the phase velocity b) Given that the phase velocity is proportional to the propagation number, show that the group velocity is twice the phase velocity.

5-16 Show that the group velocity v_g can be obtained from the phase velocity u by the relation

$$v_g = u - \lambda \frac{du}{d\lambda}.$$

5-17 Neglecting surface tension, the velocity of deep-water waves having the wavelength λ is given by $u = (g\lambda/2\pi)^{1/2}$, where g is the acceleration from gravity. Show that the group velocity for such waves is one-half the phase velocity.

5-18 a) Show from Eqs. (5-7) and (5-8) that the phase velocity in free space of the deBroglie waves associated with a moving particle having a rest mass m_0 is given by

$$u = c \sqrt{1 + \left(\frac{m_0 c\lambda}{h}\right)^2}.$$

b) According to this equation, which wavelengths will have the greater phase velocity, the long ones or the short ones? Will each exceed c? c) Does the equation indicate that there is dispersion of deBroglie waves in free space?

5-19 Prove that Eq. (5-33) is equivalent to Eq. (5-32).

5-20 Compute the minimum uncertainty in the location of a 2-g mass moving with a speed of 1.5 m s^{-1} and the minimum uncertainty in the location of an electron moving with a speed of 0.5×10^8 m s^{-1}, given that the uncertainty in the momentum is $\Delta p = 10^{-3} p$ for both.

5-21 Assume that the uncertainty in the location of a particle is equal to its deBroglie wavelength. Show that in this case the uncertainty in its velocity is approximately equal to its velocity.

5-22 The electron in a hydrogen atom moves into the excited state $n = 2$ and remains there for 10^{-8} s before making a downward transition to the ground state. Calculate the uncertainty of the energy in the state $n = 2$. Is this a significant fraction of the Bohr theory prediction of -3.39 eV?

5-23 We wish to measure simultaneously the wavelength and position of a photon. Assume that our measurement of wavelength gives $\lambda = 6000$ Å and that our equipment allows an accuracy of one part in a million in the measurement of λ. What is the minimum uncertainty in the position of the photon?

CHAPTER 6

Wave Mechanics

6–1 INTRODUCTION

In the last chapter we discussed deBroglie's speculations about wave properties of particles. We also described briefly the experiments of Davisson and Germer, experiments that showed interference phenomena for electron beams, and at the same time verified deBroglie's formula for the wavelength. The more formal description of wave mechanics that we shall give in this chapter is due primarily to Erwin Schrödinger* but with significant contributions also coming from other great physicists, notably Albert Einstein, Max Born, and Werner Heisenberg.

We are going to introduce Schrödinger's wave mechanics here as a series of postulates. In this respect, the teaching of wave mechanics differs from the teaching of classical mechanics. The latter can be understood by following simple deductive steps based on certain fundamental experimental laws, such as Newton's laws. These deductions are carried out with the use of a certain amount of mathematics, but usually of a simple kind. It is not possible to develop wave mechanics by using these well-established methods, because wave mechanics cannot be deduced directly from the results of simple experiments. Involved in the understanding of wave mechanics are certain definite inductive jumps, and it is least confusing to introduce them as postulates, with no background, no plausibility arguments, but simply taken out of thin air. We then use the postulates to build up a theory of atomic matter, a theory that predicts the outcome of certain experiments. If the experiments are carried out and agree with the theory, we are satisfied and go on to predict the outcome of other experiments. Again, if we are successful, we become more confident and start to believe that the theory is right. The skeptical reader is asked to

---

* E. Schrödinger, *Ann. Physik.* **79**, pp. 361, 489, 734; **80** p. 437; **81** (1926), p. 109.

take stock after having read the rest of this book and then to decide whether he is a believer or a nonbeliever in wave mechanics.

Of course, we have taken a similar approach several times earlier in this book; for instance, when we discussed Planck's black-body radiation, we postulated that the energy in the cavity could only increase or decrease by units of the quantum energy hv. Based on this postulate and well-known physical principles, we developed a theory that fitted the experimental facts. The same was the case, for instance, with the photoelectric effect and Bohr's atom.

Simultaneously with Schrödinger's development of the theory of wave mechanics, Werner Heisenberg* succeeded in writing his theory of matrix mechanics, which is equivalent to Schrödinger's theory but most often more cumbersome. We are here going to stick with Schrödinger's description.

In the following three chapters we are going to discuss the wave mechanics of a single particle. This single particle will be moving in force fields described by the potential energy for the particle as a function of its position. In practice, of course, these force fields are produced by other particles. For the moment, however, we shall pay no attention to how the fields are produced but only that they do exist and that they are stationary. We are going to introduce four postulates, one concerning the existence of two wave functions Ψ and Φ and their meaning. The second postulate gives a prescription for finding Φ when Ψ is known and conversely. The third postulate concerns the existence of differential operators representing measurable physical quantities, and the fourth postulate is Schrödinger's equation, which shows how to find the wave function Ψ or Φ, given the energy interactions of the particle with its surroundings (e.g., the potential energy). In a later chapter these postulates will be extended to systems with more than one particle.†

6–2 THE MEANING OF Ψ

Postulate 1a. *The motion of a particle is described by a wave function in real space* $\Psi(x, y, z, t)$, *which contains all the information that can be obtained experimentally by performing measurements relating to this motion. The numerical square of the wave function expresses the probability density of finding the particle at a given position in space.*

Thus we write

$$P(x, y, z, t) \, dx \, dy \, dz = |\Psi|^2 \, dx \, dy \, dz. \tag{6–1}$$

This equation expresses the probability for finding the particle at time t within

---

* W. Heisenberg, *Z. Physik.* **33** (1925), p. 879.

† The introduction to the principles of wave mechanics given here for one particle follows essentially the general treatment in Robert B. Leighton, *Principles of Modern Physics,* New York: McGraw-Hill (1959).

the volume element $d\tau = dx\,dy\,dz$ at the point x, y, z. The wave function Ψ can, for instance, be a sinusoidal function such as the one described in Eq. (5–20). The use of the absolute value implies that Ψ may be imaginary or complex, and indeed it is. We must therefore immediately reject the notion that the wave function itself is measurable as a wave displacement, for instance, in some medium similar to water waves, acoustical waves, or other known waves. The theory of wave mechanics is thus a very abstract theory and would certainly be rejected if it were not for the precise agreement between experimental results and the theoretical predictions based on this theory.

What we have given here in the first postulate is a formal interpretation of the deBroglie's pilot waves. We still cannot say that we know what the wave function is, but we have given the square of its numerical value a definite meaning. We have also implied that the wave function contains information about physical quantities other than the position, quantities such as momentum, angular momentum, and energy.

If we know that a particle is inside a specified volume in space, for instance, a closed box, then the probability for finding the particle inside the box is 1. Thus we write

$$\int |\Psi|^2 \, d\tau = \int \Psi^* \, \Psi \, d\tau = 1, \tag{6–2}$$

where the integral is taken over the box. This "box" may be microscopic or sometimes all space. We have written the square of the absolute value as a product of the wave function and its own complex conjugate.*

As we shall see later, the wave function for a given problem is found by solving a linear differential equation. A solution of such an equation is always undetermined by a constant factor. The normalizing integral (Eq. 6–2) is therefore used to find this normalizing factor.

In Chapter 5 we discussed the band widths or, more specifically, the wavelength spectrum, of wave trains. This wavelength spectrum is equivalent to a momentum spectrum since, according to deBroglie, $\lambda = h/p$. In our more formal description, we introduce the equivalent of the wave length spectrum as a wave function $\Phi(p_x, p_y, p_z, t)$ in momentum space.

Postulate 1b. *The motion of a particle is described by a wave function in momentum space, $\Phi(p_x, p_y, p_z, t)$, which contains all the information that can be obtained experimentally by performing measurements relative to this motion. The numerical square of the wave function expresses the probability density in momentum space for the particle to be observed with a given momentum.*

Thus we write

$$P(p_x, p_y, p_z, t) \, dp_x \, dp_y \, dp_z = |\Phi|^2 \, dp_x \, dp_y \, dp_z. \tag{6–3}$$

---

* The complex conjugate of $a + ib$ is $a - ib$. The product of these is $a^2 + b^2$, which is equal to $|a + ib|^2$.

The wave function Φ must satisfy the normalizing integral

$$\int |\Phi|^2 \, d\tau_p = \int \Phi^*\Phi \, d\tau_p = 1, \tag{6–4}$$

where $d\tau_p = dp_x \, dp_y \, dp_z$ is the volume element in momentum space.

6–3 DEDUCTIONS FROM THE FIRST POSTULATE

A consequence of the interpretation we have given the wave function in the previous section is that the outcome of an experiment cannot, in general, be predicted exactly. For instance, there is an uncertainty involved in the measurement of the position of a particle, and if we repeat an experiment over and over again and at a given instant of time measure the position coordinates, the results will differ. However, wave mechanics gives us a simple formula for determining the average result of a large number of such measurements. We find the average value, also called the *expectation value*, for the position coordinates for x by multiplying a given value of x with the probability of finding the particle at that point within the volume element $d\tau$ and then integrating overall space in which the wave function is nonzero:

$$\langle x \rangle = \int |\Psi|^2 x \, d\tau = \int \Psi^* x \Psi \, d\tau. \tag{6–5}$$

The angle brackets around x are commonly used in wave mechanics as a symbol for the expectation value, although some textbooks use $\bar{x}$. In Eq. (6–5), we have split up the product of the complex conjugate Ψ^* and Ψ itself and have put x in between. Thus far, this has no important consequences. The integrand is simply a product of these functions, and the order of the factors irrelevant. Later on, however, we shall introduce differential operators to represent physical variables, and then the order of the factors will be all important.

It is clear that we can expand the description for calculating the expectation value to any physical quantity that is a function of the space coordinates and time. For instance, take the potential energy V. This is a function of space coordinates only, $V = V(x, y, z)$. Again, we find the average value or expectation value of the potential energy by calculating V for a given point, multiplying by the probability for finding the particle at that point within the volume element $d\tau$, and then integrating over space:

$$\langle V \rangle = \int \Psi^* V \Psi \, d\tau. \tag{6–6}$$

In general, we write for the expectation value of a function $f(x, y, z, t)$

$$\langle f(t) \rangle = \int \Psi^* f(x, y, z, t) \Psi \, d\tau. \tag{6–7}$$

Note that the space coordinates x, y, and z are integrated out but that the expectation value may be a function of t. For instance, a particle trajectory in classical mechanics represents a series of loci of a point particle over a given time interval. In wave mechanics, a sharp well-defined trajectory can also be defined, but this is not to be regarded as the actual trajectory of the particle, but as the loci of the expectation value of x, y, and z over a given time interval.

We can now write similar expressions for the expectation value of a momentum or for any function of momentum and time. For instance, for the x-component of momentum, we have the equivalent of Eq. (6–5),

$$\langle p_x \rangle = \int \Phi^* p_x \Phi \, d\tau_p. \tag{6-8}$$

The kinetic energy can be written in terms of the momentum components and the mass m as

$$E_k = \frac{1}{2m} (p_x^2 + p_y^2 + p_z^2). \tag{6-9}$$

Hence the expectation value for the kinetic energy is

$$\langle E_k \rangle = \frac{1}{2m} \int \Phi^* (p_x^2 + p_y^2 + p_z^2) \Phi \, d\tau_p. \tag{6-10}$$

In general, any function of p_x, p_y, p_z and t has an expectation value given by

$$\langle f_p(t) \rangle = \int \Phi^* f_p(p_x, p_y, p_z, t) \Phi \, d\tau_p. \tag{6-11}$$

The integral is taken over all of momentum space or of the part of momentum space in which the particle is known to exist.

As mentioned above, the wave function Ψ is deBroglie's pilot wave, and the wave function Φ is the momentum- or wave-number spectrum of the pilot wave (see Fig. 5–10). In the analysis in Chapter 5, it is seen that the momentum spectrum or wave-number spectrum of the pilot wave is the Fourier transform of the pilot wave. This leads up to the next postulate.

6–4 RELATIONSHIP BETWEEN Ψ AND Φ; OPERATORS

Postulate 2. *The wave functions Ψ and Φ are Fourier inverse functions.*

For simplicity, let us here work with a one-dimensional set of wave functions, $\Psi(x, t)$ and $\Phi(p_x, t)$. In accordance with postulate 3, we then write

$$\Phi(p_x, t) = h^{-1/2} \int_{-\infty}^{\infty} \Psi(x, t) e^{-ik_x x} \, dx, \tag{6-12}$$

$$\Psi(x, t) = h^{-1/2} \int_{-\infty}^{\infty} \Phi(p_x, t) e^{ik_x x} \, dp_x, \tag{6-13}$$

where $k_x = p_x/\hbar$. The reason why $h^{-1/2}$ appears in front of the two integrals instead of $(2\pi)^{-1/2}$ as in Eqs. (5–40) and (5–41) is that the function Φ is written in terms of and integrated over p_x rather than k_x. This technique gives us a recipe for finding the wave function Φ in momentum space when we know the function Ψ in ordinary space. We can then find the expectation values for physical quantities depending upon momentum coordinates by using the wave function Φ. We shall now show that it is not necessary to make the transformations, because we can find a quite simple technique by which the expectation values of the momentum or any power thereof can be obtained directly from Ψ.

We write the expectation value for the x-component of momentum in the form given by Eq. (6–8) and substitute Eq. (6–12) to get

$$\langle p_x \rangle = h^{-1/2} \int_{-\infty}^{\infty} \left[\Phi^* p_x \int_{-\infty}^{\infty} \Psi e^{-ip_x x/\hbar}\, dx \right] dp_x. \qquad (6\text{–}14)$$

We now use partial integration on the integral in the brackets to obtain

$$\int_{-\infty}^{\infty} \Psi e^{-ip_x/\hbar}\, dx = -\frac{\hbar}{ip_x} \Psi \bigg|_{-\infty}^{\infty} + \frac{\hbar}{ip_x} \int_{-\infty}^{\infty} \frac{\partial \Psi}{\partial x} e^{-ip_x x/\hbar}\, dx. \qquad (6\text{–}15)$$

In all cases of practical interest, the wave function is bounded; that is, Ψ is zero for $x = \pm\infty$. The first term on the right-hand side of Eq. (6–15) therefore disappears. Substituting into Eq. (6–14), we then get

$$\langle p_x \rangle = -i\hbar h^{-1/2} \int_{-\infty}^{\infty} \left[\Phi^* \int_{-\infty}^{\infty} \frac{\partial \Psi}{\partial x} e^{-ip_x x/\hbar}\, dx \right] dp_x. \qquad (6\text{–}16a)$$

Since the final result is independent of the order of integration, we can rewrite this as

$$\langle p_x \rangle = -i\hbar \int_{-\infty}^{\infty} \left[h^{-1/2} \int_{-\infty}^{\infty} \Phi^* e^{-ip_x x/\hbar}\, dp_x \right] \frac{\partial \Psi}{\partial x}\, dx. \qquad (6\text{–}16b)$$

By comparing with Eq. (6–13), we see that the expression in brackets is Ψ^*. Inserting this, we get

$$\langle p_x \rangle = \int_{-\infty}^{\infty} \Psi^* \left[\frac{\hbar}{i} \frac{\partial}{\partial x} \right] \Psi\, dx. \qquad (6\text{–}17)$$

We have shown here that we can find the expectation value for momentum by working with the space wave function Ψ rather than with the momentum wave function Φ. Equation (6–17) is very similar to Eq. (6–7). In fact, we have found that we can find the expectation value of the momentum by exactly the same formula as for a function of the coordinate, except that instead of the momentum itself, we insert a differential operator $(\hbar/i)\, \partial/\partial x$. We can easily prove by the same method as used above that the expectation value for the nth power of p_x is given by

$$\langle p_x^n \rangle = \int_{-\infty}^{\infty} \Psi^* \left(\frac{\hbar}{i} \right)^n \left(\frac{\partial}{\partial x} \right)^n \Psi \, dx. \tag{6–18}$$

Note carefully that the prescription is to take the nth derivative with respect to x of the wave function Ψ and not the nth power of the first-order derivative.

We have developed these formulas for expectation values of momenta by using one-dimensional wave functions. The extension to three-dimensional wave functions is actually trivial, and we state without proof that the results are identical to Eqs. (6–17) and (6–18), only that dx has to be replaced by $d\tau$, the volume element. Similar expressions apply, of course, to the y- and z-components of momentum, only that the differential operator is then a partial derivative of y or z, respectively.

To summarize, in this formalism we have found that we can find the expectation value for any component of the momentum of a particle or any power thereof by using Eqs. (6–7) and by making the following substitutions:

$$p_x \rightarrow \frac{\hbar}{i} \frac{\partial}{\partial x},$$

$$p_y \rightarrow \frac{\hbar}{i} \frac{\partial}{\partial y}, \tag{6–19}$$

$$p_z \rightarrow \frac{\hbar}{i} \frac{\partial}{\partial z}.$$

The next question that naturally arises is: How do we find the expectation value for a physical quantity for which the classical expression is a mixture of space and momentum coordinates? For instance, the total energy $p^2/2m + V$ or the z-component of angular momentum $L_z = xp_y - yp_x$. This question is dealt with in the third postulate.

6–5 THE USE OF OPERATORS

Postulate 3. *The expectation value of a physical quantity $F(\mathbf{r}, \mathbf{p})$ is given by*

$$\langle F \rangle = \int \Psi^* F_{op} \Psi \, d\tau, \tag{6–20}$$

where F_{op} is a linear Hermetian operator obtained by replacing the momentum components in $F(\mathbf{r}, \mathbf{p})$ with Eqs. (6–19).

In the last section, we proved that this technique is valid when F is a function of momentum coordinates only. In the third postulate we have extended these techniques to the situation in which F is a function of both space and momentum coordinates.

A linear operator is an operator for which the distributive law

$$F_{op}(\Psi_1 + \Psi_2) = F_{op}\Psi_1 + F_{op}\Psi_2 \qquad (6\text{–}21)$$

holds and which simultaneously satisfies

$$F_{op}(C\Psi) = CF_{op}\Psi, \qquad (6\text{–}22)$$

where C is a constant. A Hermetian operator is defined as an operator that satisfies

$$\int \Psi_1^* F_{op}\Psi_2 \, d\tau = \int \Psi_2 (F_{op}\Psi_1)^* \, d\tau. \qquad (6\text{–}23)$$

The integral is as usual taken over all space, and the two functions Ψ_1 and Ψ_2 are arbitrary integrable functions.

It is necessary to specify that the operators be Hermetian, because in some instances it is possible to form more than one differential operator from a classical expression containing space and momentum coordinates. For instance, consider the product xp_x. When p_x is replaced by the first of Eqs. (6–19), it is clear that it makes a difference whether p_x is pre- or post-multiplied by x. In cases such as this, a linear combination of products in which the factors are interchanged can be translated into a Hermetian operator. In all examples that we are going to consider in this book, this problem does not occur; the operators are independent of the order of the factors in the classical expression, and they do satisfy Eq. (6–23).

The Hermetian property of the differential operators is a sufficient condition for making the expectation value of the physical quantity real. We take the complex conjugate of Eq. (6–20) and find that

$$\langle F \rangle^* = \int \Psi (F_{op}\Psi)^* \, d\tau = \int \Psi^* F_{op}\Psi \, d\tau = \langle F \rangle. \qquad (6\text{–}24)$$

We have found that the complex conjugate of the expectation value is equal to the expectation value itself. This can be the case only if the expectation value is a real number.

We can now write down the most important operators that we shall need in our further work in atomic physics. First the operator for the total energy expressed as the sum of the kinetic energy and potential energy can be constructed from the classical expression

$$E = \frac{1}{2m}(p_x^2 + p_y^2 + p_z^2) + V(x, y, z). \qquad (6\text{–}25)$$

The corresponding operator is

$$H = -\frac{\hbar^2}{2m}\left(\frac{\partial^2}{\partial x^2} + \frac{\partial^2}{\partial y^2} + \frac{\partial^2}{\partial z^2}\right) + V(x, y, z). \qquad (6\text{–}26)$$

This is called the Hamiltonian operator, H, because in classical physics the energy expressed as in Eq. (6–25) as a function of momentum and position coordinates is called the Hamiltonian function. We can abbreviate expression (6–26) by introducing the Laplacian operator

$$\nabla^2 \equiv \frac{\partial^2}{\partial x^2} + \frac{\partial^2}{\partial y^2} + \frac{\partial^2}{\partial z^2} \,, \tag{6–27}$$

thus giving for the Hamiltonian,

$$H = -\frac{\hbar^2}{2m} \nabla^2 + V. \tag{6–28}$$

The classical expression for angular momentum is

$$L = r \times p. \tag{6–29}$$

The components of this equation can be written as

$$\begin{aligned} L_x &= yp_z - zp_y, \\ L_y &= zp_x - xp_z, \\ L_z &= xp_y - yp_x. \end{aligned} \tag{6–30}$$

The corresponding quantum mechanical operators are therefore

$$\begin{aligned} L_{x\text{op}} &= \frac{\hbar}{i} \left(y \frac{\partial}{\partial z} - z \frac{\partial}{\partial y} \right), \\ L_{y\text{op}} &= \frac{\hbar}{i} \left(z \frac{\partial}{\partial x} - x \frac{\partial}{\partial z} \right), \\ L_{z\text{op}} &= \frac{\hbar}{i} \left(x \frac{\partial}{\partial y} - y \frac{\partial}{\partial x} \right). \end{aligned} \tag{6–31}$$

It is also possible to form the operator for the square of the total angular momentum by taking the sum of the squares of Eqs. (6–31).

6–6 SCHRÖDINGER'S EQUATION

Postulate 4. *The wave function ψ must satisfy the equation*

$$H\Psi = \hbar i \frac{\partial \Psi}{\partial t}. \tag{6–32}$$

This is called Schrödinger's time-dependent equation.*

---

*   The wave function Φ satisfies an equation identical to Eq. (6–32), except that the Hamiltonian operator is then written with the classical expression for the momentum components unchanged and ·with the space coordinates x, y, and z substituted by expressions of the form $(-\hbar/i)(\partial/\partial p_x)$. However, we are not going to use the momentum wave function Φ further in this book.

All wave motion in physics is governed by a differential equation involving second-order derivatives with respect to space coordinates and a second-order derivative with respect to time. This applies to the motion of transverse waves on a string, acoustical waves, electromagnetic waves, etc. Schrödinger's equation has on the left-hand side, in addition to the potential, the Laplacian operator, which is of second order in spatial coordinates, and on the right-hand side an imaginary constant times the *first-order derivative* with respect to time. The operator H on the left-hand side of the equation is the operator for total energy written in terms of momenta and position coordinates. We see that the postulate in Eq. (6–32) is equivalent to postulating that there is another operator for total energy of the form

$$E_{op} = \hbar i \frac{\partial}{\partial t} \, . \tag{6–33}$$

Equation (6–33) is very similar to Eq. (6–19) for the momentum operators, and it is very plausible that there should be such a similarity. This we can see from the following discussion. A traveling wave is described by a sine function or a sum of sine functions or similar functions always with an argument of the form $(kx - \omega t)$. For instance, see Eq. (5–20). By applying the operator for p_x in Eq. (6–19) to any function in which x and t appear together in this combination, we get, in taking the derivative of the argument, a factor $k\hbar$, which according to deBroglie is the momentum of the particle. By performing the same operation with the operator in Eq. (6–33), we get out a factor $\hbar\omega$, which represents the energy of the particle. In other words, the operators (6–19) "pull out" the momentum components of the wave function, and Eq. (6–33) "pulls out" the total energy. This hint led Schrödinger to try the particular equation that bears his name. How successful he was we shall learn in the following chapters of this book.

In trying to solve an equation of the form (6–32), one can attempt to separate the variables. We therefore write the wave function Ψ as

$$\Psi = \psi(x, y, z)\, \eta(t). \tag{6–34}$$

By substituting this expression into Eq. (6–32), we obtain

$$\eta H\psi = \psi \hbar i \frac{d\eta}{dt} \, , \tag{6–35}$$

which, divided by Ψ yields

$$\frac{1}{\psi} H\psi = \frac{1}{\eta} \hbar i \frac{d\eta}{dt} \, . \tag{6–36}$$

This equation has on the left-hand side a function of the space coordinates and on the right-hand side a function of time only. The only way in which both sides can be equal for all possible values of x, y, z and for any value of t is that both sides are equal to the same constant. For reasons that will immediately be obvious, we call the separation constant E and obtain the following two equations:

$$H\psi = E\psi \tag{6-37}$$

and

$$\frac{d\eta}{\eta} = -\frac{iE}{\hbar} dt. \tag{6-38}$$

The last equation can be solved immediately to yield

$$\eta = e^{-i\omega t} = \cos \omega t - i \sin \omega t, \tag{6-39}$$

with $\omega = E/\hbar$. This is clearly the angular frequency of the wave, and we therefore recognize the separation constant E as the energy of the particle. For the time being, we are referring to deBroglie's work when making this statement. Our wave mechanics should, however, be developed independently of earlier work and be based only upon the four postulates. We shall therefore come back to Eq. (6-37) in Section 6-8, and there show that E is indeed the energy of the particle. In the mathematical separation of the wave equation we have implied that E is a constant. Clearly, the procedure is only valid when energy is conserved.

The time factor $e^{-i\omega t}$ has a numerical value of unity. The total wave function Ψ is therefore normalized if ψ is normalized. We can then rewrite the normalizing integral (Eq. 6-2) as

$$\int \psi^* \psi \, d\tau = 1. \tag{6-40}$$

Equation (6-37) is called Schrödinger's time-independent equation. It can be solved when we know the form of the potential energy appearing in the Hamiltonian operator (Eq. 6-28). As will be further discussed in Section 6-8, the time-independent equation is a type of differential equation called an eigenvalue equation. For a particle bound in a potential well, e.g., the electron in the hydrogen atom, physically acceptable solutions exist only for specific values of the constant energy E. The equation correctly produces the energy levels of the hydrogen atom, without any further arbitrary assumptions or postulates. For the moment, we shall tackle some mathematically simpler problems.

6-7 THE ONE-DIMENSIONAL SQUARE WELL OF INFINITE DEPTH

Assume that a particle is bouncing back and forth between two impenetrable walls, as shown in Fig. 6-1. We are concerned only with the motion of this particle in the x-direction. This motion will be described by a wave function

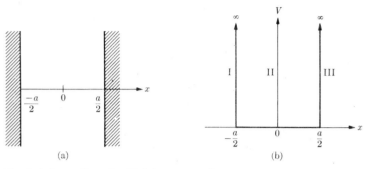

Fig. 6–1 A one-dimensional infinite square well.

that can be found from the one-dimensional Schrödinger equation with a potential as shown in Fig. 6–1(a). We write Schrödinger's time-independent equation in one dimension as

$$-\frac{\hbar^2}{2m}\frac{d^2\psi}{dx^2} + V(x)\psi = E\psi. \tag{6–41}$$

The function $V(x)$ shown in Fig. 6–1(b) is very difficult to express in terms of x as an analytic function, defined over the full range of x from $-\infty$ to $+\infty$. We therefore choose to solve Schrödinger's equation in steps. In regions I and III (Fig. 6–1b), the potential energy is infinite. From Eq. (6–41), we then see that unless the energy of the particle is also infinite, or $\psi = 0$, the second-order derivative of ψ with respect to x must be infinite. This does not lead to a physically acceptable solution, and therefore the only possible solution in regions I and III is $\psi = 0$. In region II, the potential energy is zero, and we get

$$\frac{d^2\psi}{dx^2} + k^2\psi = 0, \tag{6–42}$$

with

$$k = \frac{1}{\hbar}\sqrt{2mE}. \tag{6–43}$$

A general solution for Eq. (6–42) can be written as

$$\psi = A\sin kx + B\cos kx. \tag{6–44}$$

This solution must be matched to the solutions in regions I and III, because Schrödinger's equation must also be satisfied at the boundaries. So what are the boundary conditions? Let us look at this problem in general. In Fig. 6–2(a) is drawn a part of a hypothetical wave function with a break in the curve. At the break, the first derivative of the wave function has a discontinuity, and therefore the second-order derivative is infinite. By inspecting Eq. (6–41),

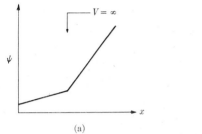 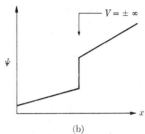

(a)   (b)

Fig. 6–2 (a) Wave function with discontinuous derivative requires $V = \infty$ at the break point. (b) Discontinuous wave function requires $V = \pm \infty$ at break point.

we see that this is permissible if the potential is infinite at this point. In part (b) of the figure another hypothetical wave function is drawn, this time with a discontinuity in the function itself. This implies that the second-order derivative is $+\infty$ and $-\infty$ at the same point, or at two points an infinitesimal distance apart. A real physical potential can be quite large, so that in an idealized case one can set it equal to infinity, as for instance in the case under discussion. A sharp break in the wave function is therefore allowed in certain cases. However, no practical physical situation can result in a wave function, with a discontinuity as depicted in Fig. 6–2(b).

Returning now to the one-dimensional well, we see that the wave function described by Eq. (6–44) must be zero at $x = -a/2$ and $x = +a/2$. We then get two breaks in the wave function but no discontinuity. The distance a between the two walls must be equal to a whole number of half wavelengths, so we can write

$$ka = n\pi, \quad \text{with} \quad n = 1, 2, 3, 4, \ldots . \tag{6–45}$$

The wave function takes the forms

$$\psi = A \sin kx \quad \text{for} \quad n = 2, 4, 6, \ldots \quad (B = 0),$$
$$\psi = B \cos kx \quad \text{for} \quad n = 1, 3, 5, \ldots \quad (A = 0). \tag{6–46}$$

The first set of functions is all antisymmetric about the origin, and the second set is symmetric about the origin. However, in both cases the probability density ψ^2 is symmetric. Figure 6–3(a) shows plots of the three wave functions corresponding to $n = 1, 2,$ and 3, and Fig. 6–3(b) shows the corresponding probability density ψ^2.

Equation (6–45) shows that the wave number k is quantized; that is, it can take on only certain discrete values. We have seen that this was a result of boundary conditions for the wave function. Since k is related to the energy,

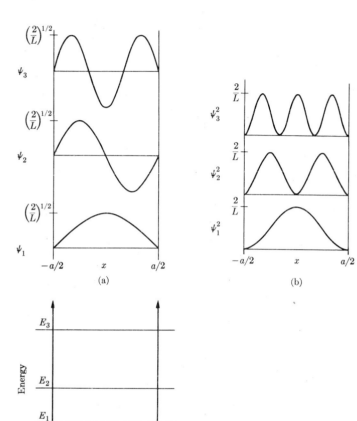

Fig. 6–3 (a) The three lowest wave functions for the infinite square well. (b) Probability density for the same three states. (c) Energy levels in the square well.

the particle can exist only between the two walls in certain discrete energy states found by combining Eqs. (6–43) and (6–45). This gives

$$E = \frac{\pi^2 \hbar^2}{2ma^2} n^2. \tag{6–47}$$

Figure 6–3(c) shows an energy-level diagram for this problem with $n = 1, 2,$ and 3.

The complete wave functions with the time factor included are

$$\Psi = Ae^{-i\omega t} \sin kx, \qquad n = 2, 4, 6, \ldots,$$
$$\Psi = Be^{-i\omega t} \cos kx, \qquad n = 1, 3, 5, \ldots \tag{6-48}$$

From now on, we shall leave out the time part of the wave function and only work with ψ, except in the treatment of time-dependent perturbations (Section 8–5). For stationary states, we can calculate all quantities of interest without including $e^{-i\omega t}$ because it is numerically equal to unity.

Let us calculate the energy for an example in which a is of atomic dimensions and the particle is an electron. Inserting numerical values, we find $E = 37.7 \, n^2/a^2$ eV, with a in angstroms. For instance, if a is 2 angstrom units, the energy of the lowest state ($n = 1$) is $E = 9.4$ eV. In the calculations, we have assumed zero potential energy in the allowed region. Consequently, $E = E_k$, and the kinetic energy for an electron between two impenetrable walls 2 angstroms apart is therefore 9.4 eV in this state.

Note that we have determined the energy of the particle without normalizing the wave function. This is an important observation. The energy depends only upon the wavelength or wave number k, and not upon the amplitude. In order to use the wave function to calculate expectation values, however, we have to normalize. We therefore write (from Eq. 6–2)

$$\int_{-a/2}^{a/2} A^2 \sin^2 kx \, dx = 1, \qquad n = 2, 4, 6, \ldots.$$

$$\int_{-a/2}^{a/2} B^2 \cos^2 kx \, dx = 1, \qquad n = 1, 3, 5, \ldots$$

The average of a $\sin^2$ function or a $\cos^2$ function over a whole number of half wavelengths is $\frac{1}{2}$; thus the first integral gives $A^2 a/2 = 1$, and the second $B^2 a/2 = 1$, so that in both cases the normalizing factor is

$$A = B = \sqrt{2/a}. \tag{6-49}$$

Let us pause for a moment here and consider the implications of the results we have arrived at. We have found that a particle between two impenetrable walls can exist in definite quantum states with wave functions given by Eqs. (6–46) and energies given by Eq. (6–47). The most important point is that we have demonstrated why energy is quantized. Schrödinger's equation does not give a solution which is finite everywhere and normalizable unless the energy is given by Eq. (6–47). As we shall see later in the discussion of the hydrogen atom, this is exactly the reason why atoms have quantized energy. The same is the case for nuclei.

It may have occurred to some readers that the boundary conditions can be fulfilled by a wave function which is a sum of terms of the form (6–46), that is, a Fourier expansion. This is true; however, this sum function is no longer a solution of the original time-independent wave equation (Eq. 6–41) with constant E (Problem 6–7). As we shall discuss further in Section 6–9, this means that such a sum function does not represent a *stationary state* for the particle between impenetrable walls with constant potential between the walls. We shall use expansions of the kind mentioned frequently in Chapter 8 in the discussions of perturbations.

We are now ready to calculate a few expectation values; first, the expectation value for position x. We use the first of the two equations (6–46) and write

$$\langle x \rangle = \int_{-a/2}^{a/2} \frac{2}{a} x \sin^2 kx \, dx = 0.$$

We see immediately that the integral is zero, because the integrand consists of an even function and an odd function, yielding as a product an odd function with opposite contributions from the two regions $-a/2$ to zero and zero to $a/2$. If we had used the second of Eq. (6–46), the results would have been the same. It is obvious that the average value of x should be zero, because of the symmetry of the problem.

Next, let us calculate the expectation for momentum. We find

$$\langle p_x \rangle = \int_{-a/2}^{a/2} \frac{2}{a} \sin kx \frac{\hbar}{i} k \cos kx \, dx = 0.$$

Again, the result is zero, because the integrand is a product of an even and an odd function. The expectation value for the square of the momentum is

$$\langle p_x^2 \rangle = \int_{-a/2}^{a/2} \frac{2}{a} \sin kx (-\hbar^2) k^2 (-\sin kx) \, dx = (\hbar k)^2 = \frac{n^2 \pi^2 \hbar^2}{a^2}.$$

We have here seen that the momentum itself has an expectation value of zero but that the square of the momentum has a nonzero value. This is logical, since the particle presumably is bouncing back and forth between the two walls with an average momentum of zero but with a definite value for the square of the momentum, since the kinetic energy has a nonzero value (Eq. 6–47). Finally, we calculate the expectation value for the square of the position. This is

$$\langle x^2 \rangle = \int_{-a/2}^{a/2} \frac{2}{a} x^2 \sin^2 kx \, dx = \frac{4}{ak^3} \int_0^{n\pi/2} y^2 \sin^2 y \, dy.$$

We have here introduced a new variable, $y = kx$, and because of symmetry, we can integrate over half the region and multiply by 2. The integral can be solved by integration by parts. The final result is

$$\langle x^2 \rangle \doteq a^2 \left(\frac{1}{12} - \frac{1}{2\pi^2 n^2} \right).$$

Solving the same problem with the second of Eq. (6–46) for all odd n solutions, we find that the result is identical.

6–8 THE ONE-DIMENSIONAL SQUARE WELL OF FINITE DEPTH

We shall now study an example similar to the one above, except that the potential does not go to infinity at the boundaries of the square well. The potential energy for a finite square well is shown in Fig. 6–4. We have chosen to set the potential energy equal to zero outside the well and to $-V_0$ inside the well. We shall assume that the particle is bound to the well, so that the total

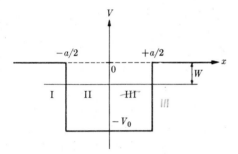

Fig. 6–4 A square well of finite depth.

energy is $E = -W$, where W is a positive number called the *binding energy*. It is the energy required to release the particle from the well. Inside the well, the particle has a kinetic energy of $V_0 - W$. Outside the boundaries $x = \pm a/2$, the particle cannot move classically because the kinetic energy would be negative, $E_k = -W$; that is, the velocity is imaginary. Quantum mechanically, we shall see that the situation is different.

It is again awkward to express the potential energy for the complete region of x from $-\infty$ to $+\infty$ as one analytic function. Instead, we choose to divide space into three regions, as shown in Fig. 6–4. We solve Schrödinger's equation in the three regions independently and then match the solutions at the boundaries. Unlike the case treated above, the potential energy is everywhere finite, and therefore the wave function itself *as well as the first-order derivative* of the wave function must be matched at the boundaries according to the discussion above with reference to Fig. 6–2.

The one-dimensional wave equation in region II can again be written in the form (6–42), but with the wave number k now given by

$$k = \frac{1}{\hbar} \sqrt{2m(V_0 - W)}. \tag{6–50}$$

Note that it is the kinetic energy that appears, together with $2m$, under the square-root sign and that another way of writing Eq. (6–50) is

$$E_k = (k\hbar)^2/2m,$$

where $(k\hbar)^2$ is p^2, the momentum squared. The solution of Schrödinger's equation in region II can again be written as (Eq. 6–44):

$$\psi_{\text{II}} = A \sin kx + B \cos kx. \tag{6–44}$$

In regions I and III, Schrödinger's equation takes the form

$$\frac{d^2\psi}{dx^2} - \gamma^2\psi = 0, \tag{6–51}$$

with

$$\gamma = \frac{1}{\hbar}\sqrt{2mW}. \tag{6–52}$$

A general solution of Eq. (6–51) is

$$\psi_{\text{I, III}} = Ce^{\gamma x} + De^{-\gamma x}. \tag{6–53}$$

We must now look at boundary conditions. First, we require that the wave function itself is finite everywhere. For region I, then, we see immediately that we must put $D = 0$; otherwise, the wave function would go to infinity when x goes to $-\infty$. Similarly, in region III, we must put $C = 0$ because otherwise the wave function would go to infinity when x goes to $+\infty$. We therefore write

$$\psi_{\text{I}} = Ce^{\gamma x},$$
$$\psi_{\text{III}} = De^{-\gamma x}. \tag{6–54}$$

We proceed to match the wave functions at the boundaries $x = -a/2$ and $x = +a/2$. First let us try to find solutions given that either A or $B = 0$. This was a necessary requirement in the example discussed previously, and we shall prove below that this is the case also for this example.

In the previous example, we found that the boundary conditions required that the wave number k could have only discrete values, as given by Eq. (6–45). The amplitudes for the wave functions A or B did not enter into the discussion of boundary requirements and could be determined afterwards by use of the normalizing integral. In the present case, we find that the amplitudes A or B and C or D enter into the matching equations, because now the wave function apparently does not go to zero at $\pm a/2$, but penetrates into the classically forbidden regions, as shown by Eqs. (6–54)*. For the moment, we are not so

---

* The previous example can be regarded as a special case of this example, in which γ goes to infinity.

much interested in the amplitudes as we are in finding the allowed values for the wave number k. This will give us the energy-level diagram for the finite well. The quickest way to this goal is to match at the boundaries not ψ and $d\psi/dx$, individually, but the ratio of the two, which is called the *logarithmic derivative*, $(1/\psi)\,d\psi/dx$. Since the amplitude coefficients appear both in the wave function itself and in the derivative, they will be divided out and will not appear in the matching equation for logarithmic derivatives. At the boundary $x = -a/2$, we then get

$$\frac{1}{\psi_\mathrm{I}}\frac{d\psi_\mathrm{I}}{dx} = \frac{1}{\psi_\mathrm{II}}\frac{d\psi_\mathrm{II}}{dx}. \tag{6–55}$$

With Eq. (6–54) and (6–44) inserted, this gives

$$\gamma = k\cot\left(-\frac{ka}{2}\right) \qquad \text{for} \qquad B = 0,$$
$$\gamma = -k\tan\left(-\frac{ka}{2}\right) \qquad \text{for} \qquad A = 0. \tag{6–56}$$

Proceeding in the same way at the second boundary, $x = +a/2$, we find

$$-\gamma = k\cot\left(\frac{ka}{2}\right) \qquad \text{for} \qquad B = 0,$$
$$-\gamma = -k\tan\left(\frac{ka}{2}\right) \qquad \text{for} \qquad A = 0. \tag{6–57}$$

These equations are identical with Eqs. (6–56).

Assuming that the depth and width of the potential well are given, the problem is to find a value, or several values of W, such that Schrödinger's equation is satisfied, not only in the three regions but also at the boundaries between them. Our analysis has led us to Eqs. (6–56). Since both γ and k depend upon W, we must solve these transcendental equations by trial and error, choosing a value for W, then calculate γ and k and insert the results into Eq. (6–56). If the well is deep enough, the resultant solutions produce a series of functions, as shown in Fig. 6–5. These wave functions are similar to those in Fig. 6–3, except that they penetrate into the classically forbidden region. This penetration gives a wave function with a given number of nodes more space; that is, the wavelength gets longer than for the corresponding wave function in the previous example. Therefore the energy is lower.

It remains to be proved that no solution exists unless either A or B is zero. If both are nonzero, we can write Eq. (6–44) as

$$\psi_\mathrm{II} = A_1\sin(kx - \alpha), \tag{6–58}$$

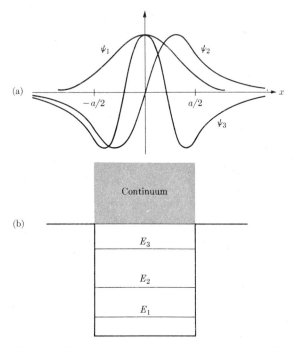

Fig. 6–5 (a) The three lowest wave functions for the finite square well. (b) Energy levels in the finite square well.

where α is a phase angle. The two boundary conditions can now be written as

$$\gamma = k \cot\left(-\frac{ka}{2} - \alpha\right),$$

$$-\gamma = k \cot\left(\frac{ka}{2} + \alpha\right). \tag{6-59}$$

Since there is only one free variable in this problem, W, the two equations must be simultaneously fulfilled. This requires

$$\cot\left(-\frac{ka}{2} - \alpha\right) = -\cot\left(\frac{ka}{2} - \alpha\right). \tag{6-60}$$

This is only fulfilled for $\alpha = j(\pi/2)$ with $j = 1, 2, 3$, etc. Selecting an even value for the integer j is equivalent to setting $B = 0$ in Eq. (6–44), and selecting an odd value is equivalent to making $A = 0$.

In the previous section we saw that the infinite square well had an infinite number of acceptable wave functions labeled with the integer $n = 1, 2, 3, \ldots,$

∞. The kinetic energy increases as n^2, but since the well is infinitely deep, the increasing energy will never enable the particle to escape from the well.

In the present example, clearly there is a limit to the kinetic energy of a particle that is bound to the well. Classically, as well as in wave mechanics, this limit is $E_k = V_0$. There are therefore only a finite number of bound states associated with such a well. So what happens when E_k in the well exceeds V_0? Classically, the particle will escape to infinity. In wave mechanics, the particle energy E is positive and therefore E_k is everywhere positive. Instead of solutions of the form (6–54) in regions I and III, we then get sine functions or solutions of the form $e^{\pm ikx}$ which have constant amplitudes from the boundary edge to infinity. We shall discuss these wave functions representing a free particle further in Section 6–10. It suffices here to say that, since there are no boundaries, there are no restrictions on the wave number k. Therefore the energy can take on any positive value. The energy-level diagram for this example thus has a continuum for $E > 0$ (Fig. 6–5b).

Now, one numerical example. In order to simplify the calculations, we turn the problem above around a little and ask: Given the width of a potential well and the binding energy W, what is the depth of the well? Assume $a = 2$ Å and $W = 2.5$ eV. By inserting numerical values in Eqs. (6–52), we find

$$\gamma = 0.512 \sqrt{W} \text{ Å}^{-1} = 0.810 \text{ Å}^{-1}.$$

The first part of the equation above is of general validity for an electron when W is inserted in electron volts. The equation gives the exponent γ in the forbidden region where the kinetic energy is $-W$. The same formula applies for k, the wave number in the classically allowed region, where under the square-root sign we then use the kinetic energy. We rewrite the second of Eqs. (6–56) as

$$\frac{ka}{2} \tan \left(\frac{ka}{2}\right) = \frac{\gamma a}{2} = 0.810.$$

The solution of this transcendental equation is $ka/2 = 0.795$, or $k = 0.795$ Å^{-1}. This corresponds to a kinetic energy

$$E_k = \left(\frac{k}{0.512}\right)^2 = 2.41 \text{ eV}.$$

Therefore the depth of the potential well is

$$V_0 = W + E_k = 4.91 \text{ eV}.$$

In the previous example, we found that the kinetic energy in the ground (lowest) state was 9.42 eV; this compares with 2.41 eV in the present example. The drastic reduction is the result of the longer wavelength the wave function has when it is allowed to penetrate into the classically forbidden regions. For this particular example, with a well depth of 4.91 eV and width $a = 2$ Å, there is only one bound state for the electron (Problem 6–8).

6–9 EIGENFUNCTIONS AND EIGENVALUES

In problems of classical mechanics, under certain circumstances, quantities such as energy, momentum, and angular momentum are conserved. This section deals with the wave-mechanical equivalent of the conservation laws.

Schrödinger's time-independent equation (Eq. 6–37) is an example of a type of differential equation called an *eigenvalue equation*. In general, we can write an eigenvalue equation as

$$F_{op}\,\psi = f\psi. \qquad (6\text{–}61)$$

The differential operator F_{op} operates on a function ψ, and this yields a constant f times the function. The function ψ is then called an *eigenfunction* of the operator F_{op}, and the corresponding value for f is called the *eigenvalue*. In general, such an equation has many solutions; that is, a set of eigenfunctions and associated eigenvalues. We now want to prove that the physical quantity associated with the operator F_{op} has the expectation value f, when the particle is in state ψ, and further that f is not only the expectation value or average value but that repeated measurements on the system in state ψ will yield identical results, namely, f. We also say that this physical quantity has a *sharp value f*, or that it is a constant of the motion, to use a classical expression. We first prove the first part of the statement, namely, that the expectation value for the operator F_{op} is f. We write

$$\langle F \rangle = \int \psi^* F_{op}\psi \; d\tau = \int \psi^* f\psi \; d\tau = f \int \psi^*\psi \; d\tau = f. \qquad (6\text{–}62)$$

We have here used the normalizing integral (Eq. 6–40).

To prove the second part of the statement made above, we start by defining a quantity called *variance*. This is a measure of how large the deviations are from the average value. We define it in the following way:

$$(\Delta F)^2 = \int \psi^*(F_{op} - \langle F \rangle)^2 \psi \; d\tau. \qquad (6\text{–}63)$$

Variance is as we see the expectation value for the square of the deviations from the average value $\langle F \rangle$. Multiplying out the parentheses, we get

$$(\Delta F)^2 = \langle F^2 \rangle - 2\langle F \rangle \int \psi^* F_{op}\psi \; d\tau + \langle F \rangle^2 = \langle F^2 \rangle - \langle F \rangle^2. \qquad (6\text{–}64)$$

We have here again used the normalizing integral ψ. We now need to prove that, if the operator for F satisfies the eigenvalue equation (6–61), the variance is zero. Combining Eqs. (6–61), (6–62), and (6–64), we obtain for this case

$$(\Delta F)^2 = \int \psi^* F_{op}^2\psi \; d\tau - \langle F \rangle^2 = \int \psi^* f^2\psi \; d\tau - f^2 = 0.$$

This proves that the physical quantity associated with F_{op} has a sharp value.

In the discussion following Eq. (6–39) in Section 6–6, deBroglie's work was invoked to show that the separation constant E is the energy of the particle. This can now be shown on the basis of the wave-mechanical postulates without resorting to previous work. Schrödinger's time-independent equation (Eq. 6–37) is an eigenvalue equation, and therefore E is an eigenvalue for the operator of the total energy H. This proves that E is the energy and reinforces the statement following Eq. (6–39) that Schrödinger's *time-independent* equation applies only when the total energy is conserved.

Problems in quantum mechanics most often consist of constructing a Hamiltonian and then finding a set of eigenvalues and eigenfunctions for this Hamiltonian. As mentioned above, and also as seen in the two examples treated in Section 6–7, Schrödinger's equation for a bound particle can have many solutions. We indicate that by writing Schrödinger's equation in the following way:

$$H\psi_n = E_n\psi_n. \tag{6–65}$$

The subscript n identifies the solution and the associated eigenvalue E_n for the energy. Sometimes two completely different solutions ψ_n and ψ_m may by accident have identical energies: $E_n = E_m$. In this case we say that the solutions are *energy degenerate*.

Wave functions that are eigenfunctions of a Hamiltonian may also simultaneously be eigenfunctions of another operator, for instance, the operator for a component of the angular momentum. In the discussion of the hydrogen problem in Chapter 7, we shall meet exactly such a situation. Consider, for instance, the eigenvalue equation

$$F_{op}\psi_n = f_n\psi_n, \tag{6–66}$$

together with Eq. (6–65). It is evident that

$$HF_{op}\psi_n = F_{op}H\psi_n,$$

because both sides are equal to $E_n f_n \psi_n$. In this case, then, the order of the two operators does not matter; i.e., the operators *commute*. It can be shown in general* that the *necessary and sufficient* condition that simultaneous eigenfunctions exist is that the corresponding operators commute.

6–10 MOMENTUM EIGENFUNCTIONS; FLUX

In Section 6–8, we mentioned briefly the free particle for which $E > V$ everywhere. We shall here first study the simple case of a constant potential, for simplicity, $V = 0$.

---

* For instance, see P. Fong, *Elementary Quantum Mechanics*. Reading, Mass.: Addison-Wesley (1962), p. 310.

Schrödinger's one-dimensional equation for $V = 0$ is

$$-\frac{\hbar^2}{2m}\frac{d^2\psi}{dx^2} = E\psi, \tag{6–67}$$

which for $E > 0$ can be written as

$$\frac{d^2\psi}{dx^2} + k^2\psi = 0, \tag{6–68}$$

with

$$k = \frac{1}{\hbar}\sqrt{2mE}. \tag{6–69}$$

The solution of Eq. (6–68) can be written in the following form:

$$\psi = A \sin kx + B \cos kx \tag{6–70}$$

or

$$\psi = Ce^{ikx} + De^{-ikx}. \tag{6–71}$$

To represent a particle with constant momentum, ψ must be an eigenfunction of the momentum operator (Eq. 6–19). It is easily shown that the function $A \sin kx$ or $A \cos kx$ is not a momentum eigenfunction. However, we find

$$\frac{\hbar\partial}{i\partial x}(Ce^{ikx}) = \hbar k Ce^{ikx} \tag{6–72}$$

and

$$\frac{\hbar\partial}{i\partial x}(De^{-ikx}) = -\hbar k De^{-ikx}. \tag{6–73}$$

In one case we have put $D = 0$ in Eq. (6–71), and in the other case we have put $C = 0$. This is the only way in which we can fulfill the eigenvalue equation (Eq. 6–61). Clearly, then, the wave function of the form e^{ikx} represents a particle or particles with momentum $p_x = \hbar k$, and a wave function of the form e^{-ikx} represents a particle or particles with momentum $p_x = -\hbar k$.

If we now try to normalize a momentum wave function Ce^{ikx} or De^{-ikx}, we run into some difficulty. Since these functions have constant amplitudes from $x = -\infty$ to $x = \infty$, the normalization condition gives $C = 0$ or $D = 0$. One usually gets around this problem by cutting off the wave function at $x = \pm L$, where L is a number that can be made arbitrarily large. Very often, however, we can work with unnormalized wave functions.

There is another way of looking at this problem; namely, we can let the wave function represent more than one particle. For example, in Section 6–11, we shall calculate the probability for a particle to penetrate a potential barrier If the probability is, say, one percent, then one particle in a hundred, on the average, will penetrate. Thus it does not matter if we calculate the probability by using a one-particle wave function or if we let the wave function represent many particles and calculate the fraction going through the barrier. If we use the latter approach, we have to reinterpret the meaning of the amplitude of the wave function. The absolute square will then represent the average number of particles per unit volume rather than the probability for finding a given particle in a unit volume.

Since the numerical value of the imaginary exponential is unity, the normalization of the momentum wave functions is very simple, and we find that for the function used in Eq. (6–72) the number of particles per unit volume is C^2, and for the function used in Eq. (6–73) the number of particles per unit volume is D^2. These particles are moving with a velocity $v = p_x/m = \hbar k/m$. From classical arguments we find easily that the number of particles passing through a unit area perpendicular to the direction of the beam per unit time is $C^2 v$ or $D^2 v$, respectively. These quantities are called the *flux* of particles in the beam. We shall now proceed to calculate this flux by using wave mechanical rather than classical arguments.

Consider again only one particle represented by the time-dependent wave equation

$$-\frac{\hbar^2}{2m}\frac{\partial^2 \Psi}{\partial x^2} + V\Psi = i\hbar \frac{\partial \Psi}{\partial t}. \tag{6–74}$$

The complex conjugate of this equation is

$$-\frac{\hbar^2}{2m}\frac{\partial^2 \Psi^*}{\partial x^2} + V\Psi^* = -i\hbar \frac{\partial \Psi^*}{\partial t}. \tag{6–75}$$

Multiplying the first of these equations with Ψ^* and the second with Ψ and subtracting, we obtain

$$-\frac{\hbar^2}{2m}\left[\Psi^* \frac{\partial^2 \Psi}{\partial x^2} - \Psi \frac{\partial^2 \Psi^*}{\partial x^2}\right] = i\hbar \frac{\partial}{\partial t}(\Psi^* \Psi). \tag{6–76}$$

This is integrated from x_1 to x_2. The two expressions inside the bracket on the left are integrated by parts, and of the resulting four terms, two cancel each other. The remaining expression is

$$-\frac{\hbar^2}{2m}\left(\Psi^* \frac{\partial \Psi}{\partial x} - \Psi \frac{\partial \Psi^*}{\partial x}\right)\Bigg|_{x_1}^{x_2} = i\hbar \frac{\partial}{\partial t}\int_{x_1}^{x_2} \Psi^* \Psi \, dx. \tag{6–77}$$

Aside from the factor $i\hbar$, the right-hand side is an expression that clearly is the buildup rate per unit time of probability density in the volume element between x_1 and x_2. Conservation of total probability then requires that the left-hand side must represent the flow of probability density into the region minus the flow of probability density out of the region. This leads us to the following expression for the flux of probability density:

$$S = -\frac{i\hbar}{2m}\left(\psi^* \frac{\partial \Psi}{\partial x} - \psi \frac{\partial \Psi^*}{\partial x}\right). \tag{6-78}$$

With this expression inserted, Eq. (6–77) becomes

$$S(x_1) - S(x_2) = \frac{\partial}{\partial t}\int_{x_2}^{x_1} \Psi^*\Psi \, dx. \tag{6-79}$$

We have here used one-dimensional wave functions and integrated over x only. In three dimensions, flux is a vector, and the derivatives with respect to x in Eq. (6–78) are replaced with the gradient of Ψ and Ψ^*, respectively.

Returning now to a wave function representing a beam of particles, we reinterpret the flux (Eq. 6–78) as the number of particles crossing the unit area per unit time. For the momentum wave function, Ce^{ikx}, we find that the flux is

$$S = -\frac{i\hbar}{2m}C^2(e^{-ikx}ike^{ikx} - e^{ikx}(-ik)e^{-ikx}) = \frac{\hbar k}{m}C^2 = C^2v.$$

This is the same result that we found by classical arguments above.

6–11 BARRIER PENETRATION

In the study of the particle in the finite potential well, we saw that the probability for finding the particle inside classically forbidden regions was nonzero. The wave function in these regions decayed as a negative exponential function of distance. Therefore, if such a region is of finite width, the wave function can actually leak through and have a nonzero value on the other side of this potential barrier. It is our objective in this section to calculate the probability that a particle will penetrate a potential barrier. However, instead of wave functions for bound particles, we shall use momentum wave functions representing a beam of particles.

Consider first the potential step shown in Fig. 6–6(a). Let a beam of particles represented by the plane wave e^{ik_1x} fall in on this potential step-up from the left. The momentum of each particle is $p_x = k_1\hbar$. Since the numerical value of the wave function is unity, there is one particle per unit volume in the beam, and the flux is $S_1 = k_1\hbar/m$ particles per unit area per unit time. When the beam hits the potential step-up, some particles are reflected and some are transmitted into the region $x > 0$ with reduced momenta. Classically, all particles will be transmitted, and they will all receive a reduction in kinetic energy equal to $\Delta E_k = -V_0$ at the potential step-up. In wave mechanics, however, we shall show shortly that the only way in which Schrödinger's equation can be satisfied at the step-up is by a partial reflection of the wave function. Each single particle then has a certain probability for being transmitted and a certain

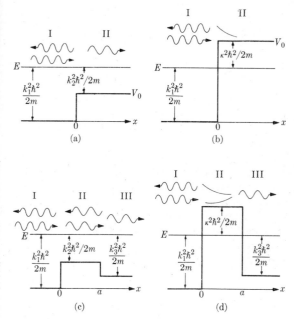

Fig. 6–6 Potential steps and barriers.

probability for being reflected. As we have seen in the previous section, the general solution of Schrödinger's equation for $E_k > 0$ is a sum of a term of the form e^{ikx} and a term of the form e^{-ikx}. For physical reasons, only the term with positive exponent will appear in region II of Fig. 6–6(a). This is because there is presumably no source of particles to the right in the diagram, and there is no further potential step-up or step-down that can reflect the particles that are moving towards the right. We can then write for the wave functions in the two regions:

$$\text{Region I,} \qquad \psi_1 = e^{ik_1 x} + R e^{-ik_1 x},$$
$$\text{Region II,} \qquad \psi_2 = T e^{ik_2 x}, \tag{6–80}$$

where

$$k_1 = \frac{1}{\hbar} \sqrt{2mE} \qquad \text{and} \qquad k_2 = \frac{1}{\hbar} \sqrt{2m(E - V_0)}.$$

The coefficients R and T are to be determined by using boundary conditions at $x = 0$. These conditions are $\psi_1 = \psi_2$ and $d\psi_1/dx = d\psi_2/dx$ for $x = 0$. Applying these boundary conditions to Eqs. (6–80), we obtain

$$1 + R = T, \qquad k_1 - k_1 R = k_2 T,$$

with solutions

$$T = \frac{2k_1}{k_1 + k_2},\qquad (6\text{--}81)$$

$$R = \frac{k_1 - k_2}{k_1 + k_2}.\qquad (6\text{--}82)$$

Equation (6–82) shows that, unless $k_1 = k_2$, that is, $V_0 = 0$, there will be reflection at the boundary. The fraction of particles reflected is simply R^2.

As a second example, consider the case in Fig. 6–6(b). It is similar to the example we have just discussed except that k_2 is now imaginary ($V > E$). The second equation in (6–80) will then be of the form $Ce^{-\kappa x}$. The wave function of the form $e^{\kappa x}$ is also a solution of Schrödinger's equation in this region, but this solution must be rejected for physical reasons because it will go to infinity when x goes to infinity. Since, for this case, the last equation of (6–80) can be changed to the desired form by replacing k_2 with $i\kappa$, the correct solution for the constants T and R can also be found by replacing k_2 in Eqs. (6–81) and (6–82) by $i\kappa$. The result is

$$T = \frac{2k_1}{k_1 + i\kappa},\qquad (6\text{--}83)$$

$$R = \frac{k_1 - i\kappa}{k_1 + i\kappa}.\qquad (6\text{--}84)$$

The numerical value of R given by Eq. (6–82) is clearly smaller than unity, indicating that only a fraction of the incident particles is reflected from the boundary. The numerical value of R, as given in Eq. (6–84), however, is unity, indicating that all particles are reflected. The wave function in Region II, $\psi_2 = Te^{-\kappa x}$ suggests that there is, on the average, a constant number of particles in the classically forbidden region.

Consider now the potential function shown in Fig. 6–6(c). If a plane wave strikes this stepup from the left, it will again be partially transmitted and partially reflected. We write the wave functions in the three regions as:

Region I, $\psi_1 = e^{ik_1x} + Re^{-ik_1x}$,

Region II, $\psi_2 = Ce^{ik_2x} + De^{-ik_2x}$,   (6–85)

Region III, $\psi_3 = Te^{ik_3x}$.

Using the boundary conditions requiring continuity of ψ as well as $d\psi/dx$ at $x = 0$ and $x = a$, we find

$$1 + R = C + D,$$
$$k_1 - k_1R = k_2C - k_2D,$$
$$Ce^{ik_2a} + De^{-ik_2a} = Te^{ik_3a},$$
$$k_2Ce^{ik_1a} - k_2De^{-ik_2a} = k_3Te^{ik_3a}.$$

$$(6\text{--}86)$$

The four equations (6–86) have four unknowns, C, D, T, and R. By solving for them, we find for the amplitude of the transmitted wave

$$T = \frac{4k_1 k_2 e^{ik_2 a}}{(k_1 + k_2)(k_2 + k_3) - (k_3 - k_2)(k_1 - k_2)e^{i2k_2 a}}. \qquad (6\text{–}87)$$

The number of particles per unit volume in region III is equal to $|T|^2$. Since we have assumed a density of one particle per unit volume in the incoming beam ($e^{ik_1 x}$), the ratio of densities is simply $|T|^2$. However, the probability B for transmission through the region of stepped-up potential is given by the ratio of the fluxes:

$$B = \frac{k_3}{k_1} |T|^2. \qquad (6\text{–}88)$$

This probability is called the *transmission coefficient*.

It is interesting to note that for $e^{i2k_2 a} = 1$ and $k_1 = k_3$, the transmission coefficient is unity. This occurs for $2k_2 a = 2n\pi$, where n is an integer. Stated differently, the barrier width must be a whole number of half wavelengths $\lambda = 2\pi/k_2$. This condition is well known in the theory of electrical transmission lines.

In the example of single step-ups and step-downs, we found that the calculations made for cases where $E > V$ in both regions could be carried over to cases where $E < V$ in one of the regions by replacing k with $i\kappa$. We make this substitution in region II and find from Eq. (6–87) the amplitude transmission factor T for the case of Fig. 6–6(d):*

$$T = \frac{4ik_1 e^{-\kappa a}}{(k_1 + i\kappa)(k_3 + i\kappa) - (k_1 - i\kappa)(k_3 - i\kappa)e^{-2\kappa a}}. \qquad (6\text{–}89)$$

The transmission coefficient, which in this case, also is called the *barrier penetration factor*, is still given by Eq. (6–88).

When the potential barrier has such dimensions that $2\kappa a \gg 1$, the second term in the denominator becomes negligible compared with the first term. We then get for the barrier penetration factor

$$\begin{aligned}
B = \frac{k_3}{k_1} |T|^2 &\approx \frac{16 k_1 \kappa^2 k_3}{(k_1^2 + \kappa^2)(k_3^2 + \kappa^2)} e^{-2\kappa a} \\
&= \frac{16}{(k_1/\kappa + \kappa/k_1)(k_3/\kappa + \kappa/k_3)} e^{-2\kappa a}.
\end{aligned} \qquad (6\text{–}90)$$

When $2\kappa a \gg 1$, the most important factor in Eq. (6–90) obviously is the exponential, which then will be extremely small. The factor in front of the exponential,

---

* For the benefit of the electrical engineer: This is a reasonably close analogy of two transmission lines joined over an attenuator.

which usually is of the order of magnitude of unity (its maximum value is 4), is then unimportant by comparison. For order-of-magnitude calculations, we can therefore write

$$B \approx e^{-2\kappa a}. \tag{6-91}$$

As an example, consider an electron beam with $e = 5$ eV being directed against a barrier of height $V_0 = 10$ eV, and with $a = 10$ Å. We find

$$k = \kappa = 0.512 \sqrt{5} = 1.145 \text{ Å}^{-1}.$$

Inserting this into Eq. (6-90), we find the transmitted fraction

$$B = \frac{16}{(1 + 1)(1 + 1)} \, e^{-22.9} = 4.05 \times 10^{-10}.$$

If we increase the electron energy to 9 eV, we find a barrier penetration factor of 5.15×10^{-5}.

One of the fi st important successes of Schrödinger's wave mechanics was the explanation of nuclear alpha decay as a phenomenon of barrier penetration. All heavy nuclei are alpha unstable, which means that energy can be gained by removing two protons and two neutrons bound together as a helium nucleus or alpha particle. The excess energy ranges from zero to about 9 MeV. It can be estimated that two protons and two neutrons get close enough together to form an alpha particle on the nuclear surface and make what we might call an escape trial about four times every 10^{-19} seconds, or 4×10^{19} escape trials per second. Figure 6-7 shows the potential barrier that such an alpha particle has to pass through. The example represents alpha decay of $^{234}_{92}\text{U}$ to $^{230}_{90}\text{Th}$ with a total disintegration energy $E = 4.76$ MeV. The shape of this barrier is found by adding the repulsive Coulomb potential and the attractive and very

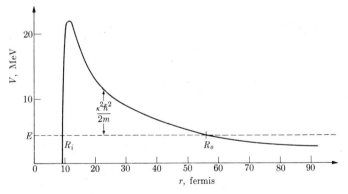

Fig. 6-7 Potential barrier between the nucleus $^{230}_{90}\text{Th}$ and an alpha particle. The total energy of decay is $E = 4.76$ MeV.

strong nuclear potential. For the example shown, the nuclear potential is very small outside—about 12 fermis. (One fermi $= 10^{-13}$ cm). The barrier penetration factor has been calculated to 2.3×10^{-33}. The probability for escape per second is therefore $2.3 \times 10^{-33} \times 4 \times 10^9 = 9.2 \times 10^{-14}$, giving a mean life of 1.1×10^{13} second, or about 3×10^5 years.

6–12 THE HARMONIC OSCILLATOR

The simple harmonic oscillator most often studied in classical physics consists of a "massless" spring fastened to a wall at one end and to a mass m gliding on a frictionless table at the other end. If the spring constant is β, the restoring force is $F = -\beta x$, and we find by classical calculations that the mass executes simple oscillations of the form

$$x = A \sin \omega t \qquad \text{(classical)}, \qquad (6\text{–}92)$$

with the frequency given by

$$\omega = \sqrt{\beta/m}. \qquad (6\text{–}93)$$

The potential energy stored in the spring is

$$V = \tfrac{1}{2}\beta x^2, \qquad (6\text{–}94)$$

and the total energy of the system is

$$E = \tfrac{1}{2}\,\beta A^2 \qquad \text{(classical)}. \qquad (6\text{–}95)$$

Classically, any value for the amplitude A is allowed, and therefore any value for the total energy is allowed.

Planck hypothesized that the energy exchange between the harmonic oscillators in the wall of an isothermic cavity and the electromagnetic modes of oscillations in the cavity could only take place with steps $\Delta E = \hbar\omega$. The main objective of the following exercise is to show that the energy levels of the harmonic oscillator, as calculated from wave mechanics, are separated by $\Delta E = \hbar\omega$. Assuming therefore that energy is absorbed and given off by quantum jumps between two neighboring levels, we shall thereby have derived the relationship used by Planck.

Schrödinger's equation for the one-dimensional harmonic oscillator is

$$-\frac{\hbar^2}{2m}\frac{d^2\psi}{dx^2} + \frac{1}{2}\beta x^2\psi = E\psi. \qquad (6\text{–}96)$$

We rewrite this as

$$\frac{d^2\psi}{dx^2} + \frac{2m}{\hbar^2}\left(E - \frac{1}{2}\beta x^2\right)\psi = 0. \qquad (6\text{–}96a)$$

It will prove convenient to make this equation dimensionless. We accomplish this by making the following substitutions:

$$\alpha^2 \equiv \omega m/\hbar,$$
$$\gamma \equiv 2mE/\hbar^2, \qquad (6\text{--}97)$$
$$\xi \equiv \alpha x$$

With these new constants and the new independent variable ξ inserted, we get

$$\frac{d^2\psi}{d\xi^2} + \left(\frac{\gamma}{\alpha^2} - \xi^2\right)\psi = 0. \qquad (6\text{--}98)$$

The double derivative of the wave function ψ is negative for $\xi^2 < \gamma/\alpha^2$. For larger values of ξ^2, the logarithmic derivative is positive, and we therefore have an exponential-type function. For very large values of ξ^2, we can neglect the term γ/α^2 in order to find the asymptotic behavior of ψ. We write

$$\frac{d^2\psi}{d^2\xi} - \xi^2\psi = 0 \qquad \text{for} \qquad \xi^2 \to \infty. \qquad (6\text{--}99)$$

The solution of this equation is

$$\psi_{\text{Asympt}} = Be^{-\xi^2/2} \qquad (6\text{--}100)$$

It is a commonly used trick in the treatment of differential equations to try a solution that is the asymptotic solution times another arbitrary function. We therefore try

$$\psi = e^{-\xi^2/2}\,H(\xi). \qquad (6\text{--}101)$$

Inserted in Eq. (6–94), this yields

$$H'' - 2\xi H' + \left(\frac{\gamma}{\alpha^2} - 1\right)H = 0, \qquad (6\text{--}102)$$

where H'' is the double derivative with respect to ξ and H' is the first-order derivative with respect to ξ. As a solution for H, we try a power series in ξ:

$$H = a_0 + a_1\xi + a_2\xi^2 + a_3\xi^3 + \cdots \qquad (6\text{--}103)$$

We insert this into the terms of Eq. (6–102) and obtain

$$H'' = 2a_2 \qquad + 2\cdot3a_3\xi \qquad + 3\cdot4a_4\xi^2 \qquad + 4\cdot5a_5\xi^3 \qquad + \cdots,$$
$$-2\xi H' = \qquad\qquad - 2\cdot1a_1\xi \qquad - 2\cdot2a_2\xi^2 \qquad - 2\cdot3a_3\xi^3 \qquad - \cdots,$$
$$(\gamma/\alpha^2 - 1)H = (\gamma/\alpha^2-1)a_0 + (\gamma/\alpha^2-1)a_1\xi + (\gamma/\alpha^2-1)a_2\xi^2 + (\gamma/\alpha^2-1)a_3\xi^3 + \cdots$$

We here arranged the three terms in Eq. (6–102) under one another in such a way that each column includes only terms of like power of ξ.

Of course, Eq. (6–102) must be fulfilled for any value of ξ. This means that the coefficient in front of each power of ξ must individually be equal to zero. This leads to the following equations:

$$1 \cdot 2a_2 + (\gamma/\alpha^2 - 1 - 2 \cdot 0)a_0 = 0,$$
$$2 \cdot 3a_3 + (\gamma/\alpha^2 - 1 - 2 \cdot 1)a_1 = 0,$$
$$3 \cdot 4a_4 + (\gamma/\alpha^2 - 1 - 2 \cdot 2)a_2 = 0,$$
$$4 \cdot 5a_5 + (\gamma/\alpha^2 - 1 - 2 \cdot 3)a_3 = 0.$$

It is evident from these equations that we can determine a_2 by knowing a_0 and a_4 by knowing a_2, etc. Similarly, we can determine a_3 by knowing a_1 and a_5 by knowing a_3, etc. In general, we find a recursion formula,

$$a_{l+2} = \frac{-(\gamma/\alpha^2 - 1 - 2l)}{(l + 1)(l + 2)} a_l, \tag{6–104}$$

where $l = 0, 1, 2, 3$, etc.

Clearly, we have found a solution to Eq. (6–102). This solution includes two independently adjustable integration constants a_0 and a_1 which we expect to find for a second-order differential equation. The question is: Does the power series converge? The answer is "No." It can easily be proved that for large values of ξ the power series increases as e^{ξ^2}. Therefore, multiplied by $e^{-\xi^2/2}$, as prescribed in Eq. (6–101), the complete wave function ψ diverges. However, the series can be truncated as follows. We demand that the coefficient γ/α^2 be an odd positive integer,

$$\gamma/\alpha^2 = 2n + 1, \tag{6–105}$$

where $n = 0, 1, 2, 3$, etc. We then see from Eq. (6–104) that one of the two series of coefficients a_l will stop at $l = n$. If n is an even number, this will truncate the series of even coefficients, and we can then make all terms in the series of odd coefficients zero by putting $a_1 = 0$. Conversely, if n is odd, we put $a_0 = 0$, and the series of odd coefficients will be truncated at $l = n$. When the values of γ and α are inserted from Eq. (6–97) into Eq. (6–105), we obtain

$$E = (n + \tfrac{1}{2})\hbar\omega. \tag{6–106}$$

The solutions that we have arrived at for Eq. (6–102) are called *Hermite polynomials*. With the help of Eq. (6–104), the coefficients in Eq. (6–103) can easily be calculated. This has been done for the first four values of n, and the results are presented in Table 6–1. The Hermite polynomials have here been

Table 6–1 Harmonic oscillator wave functions

n	E_n	ψ	Parity
0	$\tfrac{1}{2}\hbar\omega$	$\alpha^{1/2}\pi^{-1/4} \exp(-\alpha^2 x^2/2)$	$+1$
1	$\tfrac{3}{2}\hbar\omega$	$(2\alpha)^{1/2}\pi^{-1/4}(\alpha x) \exp(-\alpha^2 x^2/2)$	-1
2	$\tfrac{5}{2}\hbar\omega$	$(2\alpha)^{1/2}\pi^{-1/4}(\alpha^2 x^2 - \tfrac{1}{2}) \exp(-\alpha^2 x^2/2)$	$+1$
3	$\tfrac{7}{2}\hbar\omega$	$(4\alpha/3)^{1/2}\pi^{-1/4}(\alpha^3 x^3 - \tfrac{3}{2}\alpha x) \exp(-\alpha^2 x^2/2)$	-1

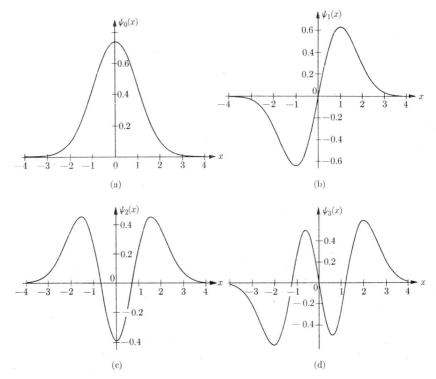

Fig. 6–8 Normalized harmonic-oscillator wave functions for the quantum numbers 0, 1, 2, and 3. [Cf. J. B. Russell, "A Table of Hermite Functions," *J. Math. Phys.* **12**, 291 (1933).]

combined with the exponential (Eq. 6–101), and the resulting wave functions have been normalized. Figure 6–8 shows plots of these first four functions. Figure 6–9 shows the probability density, that is, the square of the harmonic oscillator wave function, for $n = 0$, 1, 2, and 5, and on the same graph is shown the corresponding probability density calculated on the basis of the classical motion, that is, a pure sinusoidal motion with an amplitude given by Eq. (6–95) combined with Eq. (6–106).

6–13 PARITY

We have seen in the examples studied so far that bound-state wave functions are either odd functions or even functions; that is, they are either antisymmetric or symmetric about the origin. This property of symmetry or antisymmetry is called *parity*, defined as positive if $\psi(x) = \psi(-x)$ and negative if $\psi(x) = -\psi(-x)$. The parity for the harmonic oscillator wave functions is listed in

Relative probability of finding a moving particle in unit distance

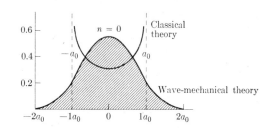

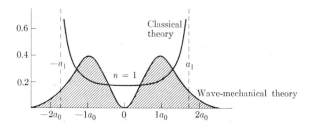

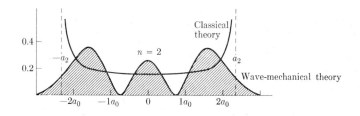

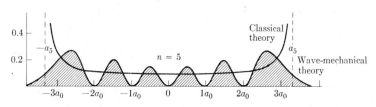

Displacement of the particle

Fig. 6–9 Each diagram shows the relative probability of finding a harmonic oscillator at various displacements both classically and wave-mechanically. Four different energies are shown, corresponding to quantum numbers $n = 0, 1, 2$, and 5. The classical amplitudes are a_2 for $n = 2$, etc. Thus $2a_0$ is twice the classical amplitude for $n = 0$. Reprinted with permission from Blackwood, Osgood, and Ruark, *An Outline of Atomic Physics*, 3rd ed.

Table 6-1. It can be proved in general that, if the potential is symmetric about the origin, the resulting eigenfunctions of the Hamiltonian will have definite parities; that is, they are odd and even functions. To prove this we write Schrödinger's equation

$$-\frac{\hbar^2}{2m}\frac{d^2\psi}{dx^2} + V(x)\psi = E\psi. \tag{6-107}$$

We now make the substitution $x' = -x$, and because $V(x') = V(x)$, we find

$$-\frac{\hbar^2}{2m}\frac{d^2\psi}{dx'^2} + V(x') = E\psi. \tag{6-108}$$

The first term in the equation does not change sign by the substitution because it is a double derivative.

Equations (6-107) and (6-108) are identical in form and therefore must have identical solutions. We shall assume that the solutions are not energy degenerate. Then, for a specific eigenvalue E there corresponds an eigenfunction ψ. The solutions of the two equations must then be the same, aside from a constant factor, so we can write

$$\psi(x') = C\psi(x) \tag{6-109}$$

or

$$\psi(-x) = C\psi(x). \tag{6-109a}$$

This equation can only be satisfied for all values of x if $C = \pm 1$. If C is $+1$, the function is even or symmetric in x; that is, it has positive (or even) parity. If C is -1, it is odd or antisymmetric in x, and we say that it has negative (or odd) parity.

In most cases concerning bound states that we deal with in atomic and nuclear physics, the potential function is symmetric, and therefore the energy eigenfunctions have definite parities. In nuclear physics, parity plays a very important role, and in most nuclear-decay processes or transmutations, parity is conserved. Indeed, until the work by Lee and Yang in 1956[*], the belief was that parity was always conserved. A popular way of expressing parity conservation is to say that, if it is possible to perform a certain experiment, it should also be possible to perform the mirror image of that experiment. Parity nonconservation in beta decay (see Section 12-11) was demonstrated by C. S. Wu and coworkers[†] following the suggestion by Lee and Yang. The experiment showed that a given beta-decay process for oriented nuclei was not equal to its own mirror image.

---

[*]   T. D. Lee and C. N. Yang, *Phys. Rev.* **104** (1956), p. 254.

[†]   C. S. Wu, E. Ambler, R. W. Hayward, D. D. Hoppes, and R. P. Hudson, *Phys. Rev.* **105** (1957), p. 1413.

PROBLEMS

6-1 Given the following one-dimensional wave function:

$$\psi = Ae^{-ax} \quad \text{for} \quad x > 0,$$

$$\psi = Ae^{ax} \quad \text{for} \quad x < 0.$$

a) Normalize this function. b) What is the probability for finding the particle between $x = 1/a$ and $x = 1/a + dx$? c) What is the probability for finding the particle between $x = 1/a$ and $x = 2/a$?

6-2 Given the wave function of Problem 6-1, a) Find the expectation values for x, p_x, x^2, and px^2. b) The wave function has a cusp at $x = 0$. Does that tell you anything about the potential?

6-3 Given the following one-dimensional wave function:

$$\psi = 0 \qquad \text{for} \quad x < -a$$

$$\psi = k(x + a) \quad \text{for} \quad -a < \ x < 0,$$

$$\psi = k(a - x) \quad \text{for} \quad 0 < \ x < a,$$

$$\psi = 0 \qquad \text{for} \quad x > \quad a.$$

a) Normalize this function. b) Find the expectation values for x^2 and p_x^2.

6-4 Given the wave function of Problem 6-3. a) Using Schrödinger's equation, find the potential energy everywhere and plot it. Assume $E = 0$. b) What is the kinetic energy in the region $0 < x < a$ (endpoints not included)?

6-5 Show that a sum of two wave functions of the type given in Eq. (6–46) is not a solution of Schrödinger's time-independent equation.

6-6 The functions ψ_n and ψ_m are eigenfunctions of a given Hamiltonian H, and the corresponding energies are E_n and E_m. Under what conditions is a linear combination $a\psi_n + b\psi_m$ also an eigenfunction of H?

6-7 The functions ψ_1, ψ_2, ψ_3, etc. are eigenfunctions of H with energies E_1, E_2, E_3, etc. The linear combination $\psi = a_1\psi_1 + a_2\psi_2 + a_3\psi_3 + \cdots$ is not an eigenfunction of H, but what is the expectation value $\langle H \rangle$ for the total energy?

6-8 Prove that the well treated in the example at the end of Section 6–8 has only one bound state. [*Hints:* In the limit $E = 0$, the boundary condition at $x = \pm a/2$ becomes $d\psi/dx = 0$. The second state ψ_2 must have one zero which would occur at $x = 0$.]

6-9 A particle of mass m is trapped in a cubical box with impenetrable walls. The origin is at one corner and the positions of the diametrically opposite corner are given by $x = a$, $y = a$, and $z = a$. Show that a function of the form $\psi = A \sin k_x x \sin k_y y \sin k_z z$ is a solution of Schrödinger's equation for this problem. Choose $V = 0$ inside the box. Find the quantization conditions for k_x, k_y, and k_z, using quantum numbers n_x, n_y, and n_z and a procedure similar to the one used in Section 6–7. Find the total energy E expressed by n_x, n_y, and n_z.

6-10 a) Normalize the wave function in Problem 6–9. b) Determine the expectation value for p_x^2. c) Is p_x^2 sharp?

6–11 Given the one-dimensional, one-particle wave function,

$$\psi = A(1 + ax)e^{-ax} \quad \text{for } x > 0,$$
$$\psi = A(1 - ax)e^{ax} \quad \text{for } x < 0,$$

where a is a constant.   a) Normalize.   b) Find the total energy E and the potential $V(x)$ assuming $V = 0$ at $x = \infty$. [*Hint:* Insert ψ into Schrödinger's equation.]

6–12 Consider the ground-state wave function $\psi = A \sin kx$ for a particle between impenetrable walls at $x = 0$ and $x = a$, $(ka = \pi)$.   a) Normalize this wave function.   b) Calculate the expectation values for the momentum p_x and for the coordinate x of the particle.

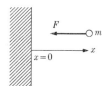

Fig. 6–10

6–13 A particle of mass m is attracted by a constant force F towards a perfectly reflective (impenetrable) wall at $x = 0$. See Fig. 6–10.   a) Sketch the potential energy of the particle $V(x)$, putting $V = 0$ to the immediate right of the wall.   b) Write Schrödinger's one-dimensional, time-independent equation for this problem. Do not attempt to solve it analytically.   c) Sketch, qualitatively but yet carefully, the one-dimensional wave functions for the ground state and for the first excited state. For both states draw in on the $V(x)$ diagram lines representing the total energies E_1 and E_2 for the two states. Pay attention to details, for instance, where the wave functions have inflection points $(d^2\psi/dxr^2 = 0)$.

6–14 Determine which of the following functions are eigenfunctions of the momentum p_x:

a) $A \sin kx$ b) $A \sin kx + A \cos kx$

c) $A \cos kx + iA \sin kx$ d) $Ae^{ik(x-a)}$

e) $Ae^{ikx} + Ae^{-ikx}$ f) $Ae^{ikx} + iAe^{-ikx}$

6–15 Given the wave function $\psi = \exp(iax - iby)$, show that this is an eigenfunction for momentum and find the particle's velocity.

6–16 A beam of electrons, each with total energy $E = 1.00$ eV, approaches a potential energy step from the left, traveling toward the right, as shown in Fig. 6–11. The potential energy of the electrons is $V = 0.75$ eV everywhere to the left of the step, zero everywhere to the right. What is the ratio of the particle flux on the right side of the step to the flux of incoming particles on the left side? (That is, what is the transmission coefficient?)

6–17 Find the barrier-penetration factor for electrons of kinetic energy 10 eV through a barrier 2 Å thick and with $V = 20$ eV, assuming $V = 0$ on both sides of the barrier.

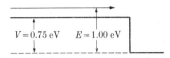

$V = 0.75\ \text{eV} \qquad E = 1.00\ \text{eV}$

Fig. 6–11

6–18 In the example at the end of Section 6–11, the barrier-penetration factor for alpha particles was found to be 2.3×10^{-33}. If the particles had been protons of the same energy, the penetration factor would have been much higher. Discuss.

6–19 A small object of mass 1 mg slides on a frictionless surface with velocity 1 cm s^{-1}. It encounters a potential step-up (barrier) 1 cm wide. The magnitude of the potential is such that, classically, the kinetic energy of the object inside the barrier is the negative of what it is outside. Find the barrier-penetration factor.

6–20 Using the harmonic-oscillator wave function for the lowest state ($n = 0$), calculate the variances $(\Delta x)^2$ and $(\Delta p_x)^2$ and show that the values are consistent with the uncertainty principle. (You need a table of definite integrals).

6–21 A mass of 1 mg is attached to a spring with spring constant 1 dyn · cm^{-1} (10^{-3} N · m^{-1}). Calculate the energy and the classical amplitude of the "zero-point" vibration ($n = 0$).

6–22 A one-dimensional harmonic oscillator ($V = \frac{1}{2}\alpha x^2$, mass $= m$) is in a state described by the wave function

$$\psi = Bx \cdot e^{-bx^2}.$$

a) Show that ψ satisfies Schrödinger's equation, and determine b and the energy E in the process. b) Is this the ground state, first excited state, or what? c) Write down an expression giving the probability for finding $x > A$, where A is the classical amplitude of the oscillator when the energy is E. Include formulas for A and B.

CHAPTER 7

Wave Mechanics of the Hydrogen Atom

7–1 THE TWO-BODY PROBLEM IN WAVE MECHANICS

The formulation of wave mechanics can be extended to a system of any number of particles N. The time-independent wave function is then a function of the $3N$ space coordinates representing the location of the N particles. In more formal and rigorous introductions to wave mechanics, it is customary to write immediately the postulates (Chapter 6), such as to include any number of particles. For pedagogic reasons, we have here started with one-particle systems and shall now extend the postulates to many-particle systems and reinterpret the meaning of the wave function. It is important to remember that this added technique, as well as the original formalism discussed in Chapter 6, is given in postulate form. The whole formalism cannot be deduced directly from any experimental laws or philosophical rules. But predictions can be made that can be tested by experiment. This is the only acceptable ultimate test of any theory of physics.

The many-body Hamiltonian is constructed very logically by adding the kinetic-energy operator for all particles to the potential-energy function that describes the interactions between all particles. It is clear that with this extension, Schrödinger's equation will again represent the wave-mechanical analogue of the classical equation for the conservation of energy. The meaning of the wave function, for instance for a two-particle system, is that the square of the absolute value, or $\psi^*\psi$, gives the probability density for finding particle 1 in a given position (x_1, y_1, z_1) within the volume element $d\tau_1 = dx_1 \, dy_1 \, dz_1$ and simultaneously particle 2 at position (x_2, y_2, z_2) within the volume element $d\tau_2 = dx_2 \, dy_2 \, dz_2$.

For the particular case of two particles interacting with each other via a potential energy that *depends only upon the distance between the particles,* the time-independent Schrödinger equation takes the form

$$\left(-\frac{\hbar^2}{2m_1} \nabla_1^2 - \frac{\hbar^2}{2m_2} \nabla_2^2 \right) \psi + V(r_{12})\psi = E\psi. \tag{7–1}$$

In this equation, ∇_1^2 depends upon the coordinates x_1, y_1, and z_1; ∇_2^2 depends upon the coordinates x_2, y_2, and z_2. It can be shown that Eq. (7–1) can be separated into two equations if one introduces the center-of-mass coordinates and relative coordinates given by

$$R = \frac{r_1 + r_2}{2}, \tag{7-2}$$

$$r_{12} = r_1 - r_2. \tag{7-3}$$

The total wave function is again written as a product,

$$\psi = \psi_{CM}\psi_{rel}. \tag{7-4}$$

Substitution into Eq. (7–1) yields, after rearrangement and separation,

$$-\frac{\hbar^2}{2M} \nabla_{CM}^2 \psi_{CM} = E_{CM}\psi_{CM} \tag{7-5}$$

and

$$-\frac{\hbar^2}{2\mu} \nabla_{12}^2 \psi_{rel} + V(r_{12})\psi_{rel} = E_{rel}\psi_{rel}. \tag{7-6}$$

Here M is the sum of the two masses $m_1 + m_2$, and μ is the *reduced mass*, equal to

$$\mu = \frac{m_1 m_2}{m_1 + m_2}. \tag{7-7}$$

The total energy is the sum of the energy of center-of-mass motion and the energy of the relative motion, exactly as in classical mechanics:

$$E = E_{CM} + E_{rel}. \tag{7-8}$$

Equation (7–5) gives as a solution a plane-wave motion

$$\psi_{CM} = \text{const } e^{i(k_x X + k_y Y + k_z Z)} = \text{const } e^{ik \cdot R}, \tag{7-9}$$

where the square of the wave number k is given by

$$k^2\hbar^2 = 2ME_{CM}. \tag{7-10}$$

Schrödinger's equation for the relative motion (Eq. 7–6) contains only as independent variables the components of the relative vector r_{12}. In many cases of practical interest, the center of mass is virtually at rest, or at least its motion is of no significance. We are then interested only in the solutions of Eq. (7–6), which is equivalent to a one-particle equation. By the procedure outlined above, we have reduced the number of independent variables from six (Eq. 7–1) to three (Eq. 7–6).

7–2 SCHRÖDINGER'S EQUATION IN SPHERICAL COORDINATES

The interaction between the proton and the electron in the hydrogen atom satisfies the condition mentioned in the previous section that the potential depends only upon the distance between the two particles. Strictly speaking, this is true only for the major part of the interaction, namely, the coulomb field. The interaction between the magnetic moment of the electron and the magnetic field caused by the orbital motion depends also on the orientation of the electron-spin axis, as discussed in Section 7–9. However, this is a minor perturbation that we will not yet consider. It is clear that the motion of the two particles in the hydrogen atom relative to each other can be described by Eq. (7–6). We drop the subscripts 1, 2, and rel and write

$$-\frac{\hbar^2}{2\mu}\left(\frac{\partial^2}{\partial x^2} + \frac{\partial^2}{\partial y^2} + \frac{\partial^2}{\partial z^2}\right)\psi - \frac{Ze^2}{4\pi\varepsilon_0 r}\psi = E\psi. \qquad (7\text{–}11)$$

The potential energy is, of course, the familiar coulomb potential. We have included in the expression Z, the charge number of the nucleus, which for hydrogen is 1. However, if Z is carried through in these calculations, the results are also applicable to other one-electron atoms, such as the He^+ ion and the Li^{++} ion, etc. The distance r appearing in the denominator of the potential term is equal to $(x^2 + y^2 + z^2)^{1/2}$. The insertion of this leads to a very ugly differential equation. The problem therefore is not easy to handle in Cartesian coordinates, and since r is one of the coordinates in a spherical coordinate system, it is natural to convert Schrödinger's equation into such a system. The relationship between the spherical coordinates r, θ, and ϕ and the Cartesian coordinates x, y, and z can be read directly from Fig. 7–1. They are

$$x = r \sin \theta \cos \phi,$$

$$y = r \sin \theta \sin \phi, \qquad (7\text{–}12)$$

$$z = r \cos \theta.$$

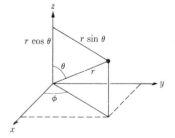

Fig. 7–1 Relationship between cartesian and spherical coordinates.

We use these transformation equations to find the Hamiltonian operator (6–26) in spherical coordinates. Schrödinger's time-independent equation in spherical coordinates then takes the form

$$-\frac{\hbar^2}{2\mu}\left[\frac{1}{r^2}\frac{\partial}{\partial r}\left(r^2\frac{\partial\psi}{\partial r}\right) + \frac{1}{r^2\sin\theta}\frac{\partial}{\partial\theta}\left(\sin\theta\frac{\partial\psi}{\partial\theta}\right) + \frac{1}{r^2\sin^2\theta}\frac{\partial^2\psi}{\partial\phi^2}\right] + V\psi = E\psi.$$
(7–13)

When the potential energy is spherically symmetric, we can write

$$V = V(r),$$
(7–14)

and we shall see that Eq. (7–13) is separable; that is, the angular dependence of the wave function can be found by solving one differential equation, and the radial dependence can be found by solving another. We write the total wave function as a product,

$$\psi = R(r)Y(\theta, \phi),$$
(7–15)

and substitute this into Eq. (7–13). After arranging the terms so that all quantities that are functions of r are on the left-hand side and all functions of θ and ϕ are on the right-hand side, we obtain

$$\frac{1}{R}\frac{d}{dr}\left(r^2\frac{dR}{dr}\right) + \frac{2\mu r^2}{\hbar^2}(E - V)$$
$$= -\frac{1}{Y}\left[\frac{1}{\sin\theta}\frac{\partial}{\partial\theta}\left(\sin\theta\frac{\partial Y}{\partial\theta}\right) + \frac{1}{\sin^2\theta}\frac{\partial^2 Y}{\partial\phi^2}\right]. \quad (7\text{–}16)$$

The only way in which this equation can be satisfied for all values of r, θ, and ϕ is to have both sides of the equation equal to the same constant called the *separation constant*. Concentrating first on the right-hand side, we obtain

$$\frac{1}{\sin\theta}\frac{\partial}{\partial\theta}\left(\sin\theta\frac{\partial Y}{\partial\theta}\right) + \frac{1}{\sin^2\theta}\frac{\partial^2 Y}{\partial\theta^2} = -CY,$$
(7–17)

where C is the separation constant. We note that Eq. (7–17) does not contain the total or the potential energy. It is therefore completely general. In other words, if we solve it once, we have solved it for all cases where V does not depend on θ or ϕ.

Again the approach is to try to separate the equation into the two variables θ and ϕ. We therefore write

$$Y = \Theta(\theta)\Phi(\phi)$$
(7–18)

and substitute this into Eq. (7–17). The result is, after some rearrangement,

$$-\frac{1}{\Theta}\sin\theta\frac{d}{d\theta}\left(\sin\theta\frac{d\Theta}{d\theta}\right) - C\sin^2\theta = \frac{1}{\Phi}\frac{d^2\Phi}{d\phi^2}.$$
(7–19)

The equation has been divided through once by the expression (7–18), and we have changed from partial to simple derivatives, because each function depends upon only one independent variable.

Again, Eq. (7–19) can be fulfilled for all values of θ and ϕ only if each side is equal to the same constant. For reasons that are obscure for the moment but will be clear later, the separate constant is called $-m^2$. The ϕ-equation then becomes

$$\frac{d^2\Phi}{d\phi^2} + m^2\Phi = 0, \tag{7–20}$$

with solutions of the form

$$\Phi = e^{im\phi}. \tag{7–21}$$

The ϕ-function must be cyclic and repeat itself after $\Delta\phi = 2\pi$. Equation (7–21) satisfies this requirement, provided m is an integer. It is now clear that if we had chosen a positive number for the separation constant instead of $-m^2$, the ϕ-function would have taken the form of a positive or negative exponential, which would not have satisfied the condition of continuity and single valuedness that must be imposed upon the wave function.

The next task is to solve the θ-equation

$$\sin\theta \, \frac{d}{d\theta}\left(\sin\theta \, \frac{d\Theta}{d\theta}\right) + (C\sin^2\theta - m^2)\Theta = 0. \tag{7–22}$$

It is advantageous to introduce a new variable

$$\xi = \cos\theta. \tag{7–23}$$

By substitution we obtain

$$\frac{d}{d\xi}\left[(1 - \xi^2)\frac{d\Theta}{d\xi}\right] + \left[C - \frac{m^2}{1 - \xi^2}\right]\Theta = 0. \tag{7–24}$$

If we make $m = 0$ and replace the constant C with another constant of the form $l(l + 1)$, Eq. (7–24) becomes Legendre's differential equation,

$$(1 - \xi^2)\frac{d^2P_l}{d\xi^2} - 2\xi\frac{dP_l}{d\xi} = -l(l + 1)P_l. \tag{7–25}$$

We have here carried out one differential operation on the first term and replaced Θ with P_l. The solutions $P_l(\cos\theta)$ for this equation are called *Legendre polynomials*. These solutions are found in exactly the same way as described for the Hermite polynomials that were used in the harmonic oscillator problem. Equation (7–25) is an eigenvalue equation, and again there is a restriction on the eigenvalue $l(l + 1)$. Unless l is made a positive integer, the polynomial solution becomes an infinite series that diverges for $\cos \theta = \pm 1$, that is, for $\theta = 0$ and π. The solutions for the first four values of l are

$$\Theta_0(m = 0) = P_0(\cos \theta) = 1 \qquad \text{for} \quad l = 0,$$
$$\Theta_1(m = 0) = P_1(\cos \theta) = \cos \theta \qquad \text{for} \quad l = 1,$$
$$\Theta_2(m = 0) = P_2(\cos \theta) = 3 \cos^2 \theta - 1 \qquad \text{for} \quad l = 2, \tag{7–26}$$
$$\Theta_3(m = 0) = P_3(\cos \theta) = 5 \cos^3 \theta - 3 \cos \theta \qquad \text{for} \quad l = 3.$$

These are the solutions for $m = 0$. Earlier we imposed the requirement on m that it be an integer, positive or negative. Since only m^2 appears in Eq. (7–24), the solutions for positive and negative values of m will be identical. It can be shown quite readily that the solutions for m different from zero can be obtained from the Legendre polynomials listed above by use of the following expression:

$$P_{l,m}(\xi) = (1 - \xi^2)^{m/2} \frac{d^m P_l(\xi)}{d\xi}. \tag{7–27}$$

The proof of this statement is left to one of the problems (Problem 7–3).

The functions defined by Eq. (7–27) are called *associated* Legendre's functions. They are solutions of Eq. (7–22), and we therefore write

$$\Theta_{l,m}(\theta) = P_{l,m}(\xi) = P_{l,m}(\cos \theta). \tag{7–28}$$

The Legendre polynomials are of the lth order in $\cos \theta$, and it is therefore clear from Eq. (7–27) that the associated Legendre functions will be zero for $|m| > l$.

The associated Legendre functions can be calculated in accordance with the prescription given above and combined with the Φ-function to form the function Y (Eq. 7–18). The combinations $Y_{l,m}(\theta, \phi)$ are called *spherical harmonic functions*. The integers l and m identifying these functions represent the eigenvalues $-l(l + 1)$ and $-m^2$ which appear in the eigenvalue equations (7–25) and (7–20). As we shall see in the next sections, these eigenvalues are associated with angular momentum.

A few of the spherical harmonic functions are listed below. Polar diagrams of the numerical squares of some functions with $m = 0$ are shown in Fig. 7–2.

$$Y_{0,0} = \frac{1}{\sqrt{4\pi}},$$
$$Y_{1,0} = \sqrt{3/4\pi} \cos \theta,$$
$$Y_{1,\pm 1} = \sqrt{3/8\pi} \sin \theta \, e^{\pm i\phi}, \tag{7–29}$$
$$Y_{2,0} = \sqrt{5/16\pi}(3 \cos^2 \theta - 1),$$
$$Y_{2,\pm 1} = \sqrt{15/8\pi} \cos \theta \sin \theta e^{\pm i\phi},$$
$$Y_{2,\pm 2} = \sqrt{15/32\pi} \sin^2 \theta e^{\pm 2i\phi}.$$

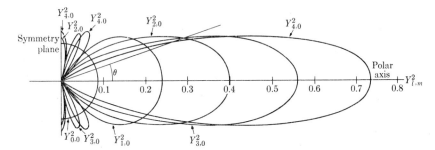

Fig. 7–2 Polar diagram of the functions $Y_{l,0}^2 (\theta)$.

Note that, because of the condition $|m| \leq l$, there are $2l + 1$ different spherical harmonic functions for each value of l. The functions listed in Eq. (7–29) are normalized as described further below.

Returning now to the radial part of the wave function, after equating the left-hand side of Eq. (7–16) with the separation constant $C = l(l + 1)$ and rearranging, we find

$$\frac{1}{r^2} \frac{d}{dr} \left(r^2 \frac{dR}{dr} \right) + \frac{2\mu}{\hbar^2} \left(E - V - \frac{l(l + 1)\hbar^2}{2\mu r^2} \right) R = 0. \qquad (7\text{–}30)$$

When the potential is a function of r only, this equation can, at least in principle, be solved. By moving the term with E over to the right-hand side, we see that this again is an eigenvalue equation. The eigenfunctions depend upon the parameter l, and to each eigenfunction corresponds an eigenvalue E. For the hydrogen problem, the potential V is the coulomb potential, given in Eq. (7–11). With a potential of this form, Eq. (7–30) as it stands proves to be the easiest to solve (see Section 7–4). For many other problems, however, the following substitution proves to be advantageous:

$$R(r) = u(r)/r. \qquad (7\text{–}31)$$

By inserting this in Eq. (7–30), we obtain

$$\frac{d^2u}{dr^2} + \frac{2m}{\hbar^2} \left[E - V - \frac{l(l + 1)\hbar^2}{2\mu r^2} \right] u = 0. \qquad (7\text{–}32)$$

Equations (7–30) and (7–32) are both called the *radial wave equation*. In the last form, it has a familiar look. Aside from the last term in parentheses, it is the one-dimensional wave equation. It will be shown in the next section that $l(l + 1)\hbar^2$ is the square of the angular momentum. Given this information, one can easily show (Problem 7–4) that the term in question is a potential-energy term associated with the centrifugal force. Equation (7–32) therefore is really a one-dimensional wave equation for the radial motion in a coordinate system rotating with the particle.

For each value of l, there presumably is a set of eigenvalues and eigenfunctions which we will identify with the index n. Then we can combine the solutions of the angular and radial wave equations in accordance with Eq. (7–16):

$$\psi_{n,l,m} = R_{n,l}(r)Y_{l,m}(\theta, \phi) = \frac{u_{n,l}(r)}{r} Y_{l,m}(\theta/\phi). \qquad (7\text{–}33)$$

These wave functions must satisfy the normalizing integral

$$\int_0^\infty dr \int_0^\pi r d\theta \int_0^{2\pi} r \sin \theta \, d\phi \, \psi^*\psi = 1. \qquad (7\text{–}34)$$

The size of the volume element in a spherical coordinate system is $d\tau = (dr)(rd\theta)(r \sin \theta \, d\phi)$, as indicated by the way the integral in Eq. (7–34) is written. Since the wave function ψ can be written as a product of three one-dimensional functions, the integration in principle is very simple. First, we integrate over the angles and we choose to make this part of the integral equal to unity:

$$\int_0^\pi d\theta \int_0^{2\pi} d\phi \sin \theta \, Y_{l,m}{}^*Y_{l,m} = 1. \qquad (7\text{–}35)$$

The spherical harmonic functions listed in Eq. (7–29) satisfy this equation, and we say that they are normalized over the angles. The radial part of the normalization integral then becomes

$$\int_0^\infty R_{n,l}^* R_{n,l} r^2 \, dr = 1. \qquad (7\text{–}36)$$

Or, by inserting Eq. (7–31),

$$\int_0^\infty u_{n,l}^* u_{n,l} \, dr = 1. \qquad (7\text{–}37)$$

These are the normalizing integrals for the radial wave functions. Note the factor r^2 in Eq. (7–36). This arises from the factor r^2 in the volume element in a spherical coordinate system.

7–3 ORBITAL ANGULAR MOMENTUM

It was demonstrated in the previous section that, if the potential energy depends only upon r, the wave equation can be separated, and the angular part can be solved once and for all. Some solutions are listed in Eqs. (7–29). In classical mechanics, we know that when the potential depends only upon r, the angular momentum of the particle is conserved because there is no torque acting on the particle (central force). In his theory of the hydrogen atom, Bohr assumed that the classical law of conservation of angular momentum could be retained, and he postulated that the angular momentum of the electron in the hydrogen atom is an integer times $\hbar$. In our new quantum-mechanical theory, we will not be surprised when we find that the orbital angular momentum for a particle in a central potential has a sharp value, an eigenvalue.

The construction of angular-momentum operators in a Cartesian coordinate system was described in Section 6–5. For instance, the operator for the z-component of angular momentum is

$$L_{zop} = \frac{\hbar}{i} \left(x \frac{\partial}{\partial y} - y \frac{\partial}{\partial x} \right). \tag{7–38}$$

To convert this expression into a spherical coordinate system, we use the substitutions given in Eq. (7–12) and find that the operator for the z-component can be written as

$$L_{zop} = \frac{\hbar}{i} \frac{\partial}{\partial \phi}. \tag{7–39}$$

The expressions for the x- and y-components in spherical coordinates are not quite so simple, but combining all three components to an operator for the square of the angular momentum, we obtain (Problem 7–6)

$$L_{op}^2 = L_{xop}^2 + L_{yop}^2 + L_{zop}^2 = -\hbar^2 \left[\frac{1}{\sin \theta} \frac{\partial}{\partial \theta} \left(\sin \theta \frac{\partial}{\partial \theta} \right) + \frac{1}{\sin^2 \theta} \frac{\partial^2}{\partial \phi^2} \right]. \tag{7–40}$$

Since this expression does not depend upon r, the value of the orbital angular momentum is clearly to be extracted from the angular part of the wave function. To ascertain whether or not the square of the angular momentum has a sharp value, we write

$$L_{op}^2 \psi_{n,lm} = -\hbar^2 R_{n,l} \left[\frac{1}{\sin \theta} \frac{\partial}{\partial \theta} \left(\sin \theta \frac{\partial Y_{l,m}}{\partial \theta} \right) + \frac{1}{\sin^2 \theta} \frac{\partial^2 Y_{l,m}}{\partial \phi^2} \right] = ?$$

The answer is found in Eq. (7–17). The spherical harmonic functions are solutions of this equation, and the value for C is $C = l(l + 1)$. Inserting this, we get

$$L_{op}^2 \psi_{n,l,m} = \hbar^2 l(l + 1) R_{n,l} Y_{l,m}, \tag{7–41}$$

which shows that the wave function $\psi_{n,l,m}$ is an eigenfunction of the operator for the square of the angular momentum and that the eigenvalue is $l(l + 1)\hbar^2$. The new wave mechanics therefore gives as a value for the numerical value of the angular momentum vector

$$L = \hbar \sqrt{l(l + 1)}, \tag{7–42}$$

in contrast to Bohr's equation, $L = n\hbar$.

The integers m and l characterizing the spherical harmonic functions are called *quantum numbers*. We have shown that there is a physical quantity associated with the quantum number l. Is there another physical quantity associated with the quantum number m? There is indeed; it is associated with the z-component of angular momentum. To show this, we apply the operator (7–39) to the wave function $\psi_{n,l,m}$:

$$L_{zop}\psi_{n,l,m} = R_{n,l}\Theta_{l,m}\left(\frac{h}{i}\frac{\partial\Phi_m}{\partial\phi}\right) = \hbar m R_{n,l}\Theta_{l,m}\Phi_m. \qquad (7\text{–}43)$$

We have here used Eq. (7–21). The result is that the z-component of the angular momentum has a sharp value,

$$L_z = m\hbar. \qquad (7\text{–}44)$$

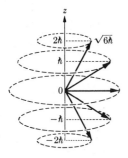

Fig. 7–3 Possible orientation of an orbital angular momentum L with quantum number $l = 2$.

A similar test for the x- and y-components of the angular momentum shows that the wave functions of the type we have discussed are *not* eigenfunctions for these operators. The expectation values can be calculated, and the results are zero in both cases. This situation is depicted in Fig. 7–3 for the example $l = 2$ and for the range of possible values of m from -2 to $+2$. The numerical value of the total angular momentum is sharp and is equal to $\sqrt{6}\hbar$. With the quantum number m specified, the component of the angular momentum in the z-direction is given, but the x- and y-components are undetermined. This means that the end point of the angular-momentum vector can be anywhere on the dashed circle in Fig. 7–3 when the particle is in a given state described by the type of wave function that we have discussed.

The question can be raised: What is so special about the z-direction? The answer is: Nothing fundamental. However, the z-direction is the axis relative to which the angular coordinates θ and ϕ are defined, so when a wave function is described in terms of spherical coordinates, it is natural that the z-direction should differ from the x- and y-directions. In a practical sense, for solving a given problem one chooses as the z-direction any direction in which a component of the angular momentum can be measured. Very often this will be the direction of a magnetic field. The advantage is that a given measurable quantum state can be expressed by one single wave function. If any direction other than the z-direction is chosen, it is necessary to construct wave functions that are linear combinations of functions of the type we have discussed.

In Section 6–12, we defined parity with reference to a one-dimensional wave function. For these three-dimensional wave functions, we write

$$\text{Positive parity:} \qquad \psi(-r) = \psi(r)$$

$$\text{Negative parity:} \qquad \psi(-r) = -\psi(r).$$

When ψ is written in terms of r, θ, and ϕ, one can check whether it has positive or negative parity by replacing θ and ϕ with $(\pi - \theta)$ and $(\pi + \phi)$, respectively. The coordinate r, which in spherical coordinates measures only the distance to the point from the origin, does not change. In other words, in spherical coordinates, the parity of a wave function is determined only by the angular part of the function. When this is a spherical harmonic function, it turns out that the value of l uniquely determines the parity as (see Problem 7–13)

$$\text{Parity} = (-1)^l. \tag{7-45}$$

7-4 THE HYDROGEN PROBLEM

Since the coulomb potential is a central (spherically symmetric) potential, $V = V(r)$, we can use the result of the previous sections for solving the hydrogen problem. We can immediately write the wave functions for a state of the hydrogen atom as Eq. (7–15). The angular part of this wave function is a spherical harmonic function of the type listed in Eq. (7–29) with the indices l and m specifying the orbital angular momentum and its z-component. What remains to be solved is the radial wave equation (7–30) with $V = -Ze^2/4\pi\varepsilon_0 r$, or

$$\frac{1}{r^2}\frac{d}{dr}\left(r^2\frac{dR}{dr}\right) + \frac{2\mu}{\hbar^2}\left(E + \frac{Ze^2}{4\pi\varepsilon_0 r} - \frac{l(l+1)\hbar^2}{2\mu r^2}\right)R = 0. \tag{7-46}$$

The method of solution of this equation is exactly the same as for the harmonic oscillator equation (Section 6–11), and we shall therefore only outline it here. We find an asymptotic solution of the form $\exp(-r/a_0)$ and a complete solution of the form

$$R(r) = G(r)\exp(-r/a_0), \tag{7-47}$$

in which a_0 is Bohr's first radius (Section 4–7),

$$a_0 = \frac{4\pi\varepsilon_0\hbar^2}{Z\mu e^2}. \tag{7-48}$$

The solution (7–47) diverges unless the power series $G(r)$ is truncated to a polynomial. This requires that the energy E be equal to

$$E_n = -\frac{\mu Z^2 e^4}{32\pi^2 \varepsilon_0^2 \hbar^2 n^2} ,\qquad (7\text{–}49)$$

where n is an integer larger than l:

$$n > l. \qquad (7\text{–}50)$$

Equation (7–49) is identical with Bohr's formula, Eq. (4–34), except that we have replaced the electron mass with the reduced mass of the system, μ. In a more rigorous development of Bohr's theory, the reduced mass also appears there. With numerical values inserted, Eq. (7–49) becomes

$$E_n = -\frac{13.6}{n^2} \text{ eV}. \qquad (7\text{–}49\text{a})$$

The radial wave functions corresponding to the energy eigenvalues (7–49) are given in Table 7–1 for $n = 1, 2,$ and 3. The same functions are plotted in Fig. 7–4. These wave functions must be combined with the angular part given by one of the Eqs. (7–29). The resulting total wave function is then specified by the quantum numbers n, l, and m with the physical connections being that n enters into the formula for the energy, l specifies the angular momentum, and m, the z-component of angular momentum. Note that in Fig. 7–4 all wave functions have a spike at the origin. This means that the second-order

Table 7–1 Several radial wave functions for hydrogenic atoms

$$R_{10}(r) = \left(\frac{Z}{a_0}\right)^{3/2} \cdot 2 \exp\left(-\frac{Zr}{a_0}\right)$$

$$R_{20}(r) = \left(\frac{Z}{2a_0}\right)^{3/2} \cdot 2 \left(1 - \frac{1}{2}\frac{Zr}{a_0}\right) \exp\left(-\frac{1}{2}\frac{Zr}{a_0}\right)$$

$$R_{21}(r) = \left(\frac{Z}{2a_0}\right)^{3/2} \cdot \frac{1}{\sqrt{3}}\frac{Zr}{a_0} \exp\left(-\frac{1}{2}\frac{Zr}{a_0}\right)$$

$$R_{30}(r) = \left(\frac{Z}{3a_0}\right)^{3/2} \cdot 2 \left[1 - \frac{2}{3}\frac{Zr}{a_0} + \frac{2}{27}\left(\frac{Zr}{a_0}\right)^2\right] \exp\left(-\frac{1}{3}\frac{Zr}{a_0}\right)$$

$$R_{31}(r) = \left(\frac{Z}{3a_0}\right)^{3/2} \cdot \frac{4\sqrt{2}}{3}\frac{Zr}{a_0}\left(1 - \frac{1}{6}\frac{Zr}{a_0}\right) \exp\left(-\frac{1}{3}\frac{Zr}{a_0}\right)$$

$$R_{32}(r) = \left(\frac{Z}{3a_0}\right)^{3/2} \cdot \frac{2\sqrt{2}}{27\sqrt{5}}\left(\frac{Zr}{a_0}\right)^2 \exp\left(-\frac{1}{3}\frac{Zr}{a_0}\right)$$

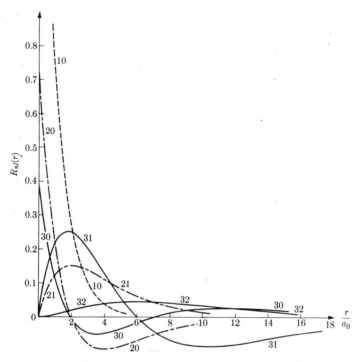

Fig. 7–4 The radial wave functions $R_{nl}(r)$ for hydrogenic atoms for $n = 1, 2, 3$. Each curve is labeled with two integers, representing the corresponding n and l values. Note the effect of the centrifugal force in "pushing out" the wave function from the center of the atom. Note also that the functions have $n - l - 1$ nodes.

derivative of the wave function is here infinite. Since the potential is also infinite for $r = 0$, Schrödinger's equation can still be satisfied.

Figure 7–5 is an energy-level diagram for the hydrogen atom. The levels are drawn so that all levels in one column have the same l-value, and the letter above that column is the spectroscopic notation that was mentioned in Chapter 4. After $l = 4$ (g-states), the letters simply follow the alphabet. In accordance with Eq. (7–50), only one l-value ($l = 0$) is allowed for $n = 1$, two l-values are allowed for $n = 2$, etc. Where several l-values are allowed for a given value of n, the corresponding s-, p-, and d-states, etc., are energy degenerate, clearly expressed by the fact that l does not enter into Eq. (7–49). This degeneracy or independence upon l is purely accidental. It happens only for the type of potential that varies with r as r^{-1}. A second degeneracy occurs because the energy is independent of the orientation of the angular-momentum vector, as specified by the quantum number m. This latter degeneracy occurs for a particle

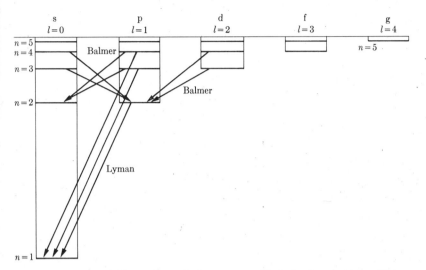

Fig. 7–5 Energy-level diagram for the hydrogen atom with the levels ordered according to *l*-value.

in any spherically symmetric potential (central force). In Fig. 7–5, each line represents $2l + 1$ states with different wave functions (different m's).

The transitions from state to state with emission or absorption of photons will be discussed in Chapter 8. We shall find that for these processes there are important restrictions called *selection rules*. For the most probable type of transition, the electric dipole transition, which can be compared with the radiation from an antenna, the most important selection rule is $\Delta l = \pm 1$. Examples of quantum jumps obeying this rule and yielding the Lyman and Balmer lines are indicated in Fig. 7–5.

7–5 MAGNETIC MOMENTS OF ATOMS

The strongest interaction in the hydrogen atom is the coulomb attraction between the nucleus and the electron. In many-electron atoms, the coulomb interaction is still the strongest force, although the situation is much more complex than in the hydrogen case. Magnetic effects are also present in atoms; these are internal magnetic forces as well as forces caused by external fields. The resulting physical effects are important and measurable, but because the energies involved are small, we do not need to solve Schrödinger's equation again with these interactions included. Rather, we regard these effects as small perturbations, as further discussed in Chapter 8. For the present, this simply means that we can add the energy found by simple calculations on the magnetic effects to the energy found by solving Schrödinger's equation without magnetic interactions.

The magnetic moment of a plane current loop is defined as

$$\boldsymbol{\mu} = i\boldsymbol{a}, \tag{7–51}$$

where $\boldsymbol{a}$ is the area vector, numerically equal to the area of the loop and with the direction of the normal to the plane. For a particle of charge q moving in a circular orbit with velocity v, the current is q times the frequency of circulation $v/2\pi r$, so that the magnetic moment is, numerically,

$$\mu = \frac{qv}{2\pi r}\,\pi r^2 = \frac{qvr}{2}\,.$$

In vector notation

$$\boldsymbol{\mu} = \frac{q}{2}\,\boldsymbol{r}\times\boldsymbol{v} = \frac{q}{2M}\,\boldsymbol{r}\times\boldsymbol{p} = \frac{q}{2M}\,\boldsymbol{L}, \tag{7–52}$$

where M is the mass of the particle. For a particle moving with constant angular momentum in a noncircular orbit, the result is the same although we shall not take time to prove it.

Equation (7–52) also holds for several identical particles of charge q, mass M, and total (sharp) angular momentum L, even if each individual particle does not have a sharp angular momentum*. The fraction of $\mu/L = q/2M$ is called the *gyromagnetic ratio*. For the electron, it is $-e/2m_e$.

Magnetic moments of atoms can be detected in several ways. In general, it is the component of the magnetic moment along the direction of a magnetic field B that is measured. According to Eq. (7–52), the ratio between any component of μ and the corresponding component of L is also the gyromagnetic ratio $-e/2m_e$. Specifically, for the z-component, we have $L_z = m\hbar$ (Section 7–3) and therefore

$$\mu_z = -\frac{e\hbar}{2m_e}\,m = -\mu_B m. \tag{7–53}$$

For the purpose of abbreviation, we have here introduced the *Bohr Magneton* for the electron

$$\mu_B = \frac{e\hbar}{2m_e}\,. \tag{7–54}$$

Clearly, a measurement of the z-component of the magnetic moment is a measurement of m, the magnetic quantum number.

---

*   It is implied that these are particles with no magnetic moment associated with an intrinsic spin; see next section.

The relationship (7–52) between the magnetic moment and the angular momentum holds also for more complex motion of charged matter about a center of mass, provided the charge density is everywhere proportional to the mass density. This condition is not necessarily always fulfilled, and to account for this fact, we introduce a correction factor called the *g-factor* into Eq. (7–53) changing it to

$$\mu_z = -g\mu_B m. \tag{7–55}$$

The *g*-factor for orbital motion of electrons is clearly $g = 1$.

From electricity and magnetism, we have the following relationships involving the magnetic moment:

Energy in magnetic field: $\quad E = -\boldsymbol{\mu} \cdot \boldsymbol{B}$ $\qquad$ (7–56)

Torque in magnetic field: $\quad \tau = \boldsymbol{\mu} \times \boldsymbol{B}$ $\qquad$ (7–57)

Force in inhomogeneous field: $F = \mu_z \dfrac{\partial B}{\partial z}$ $\qquad$ (7–58)

Equation (7–56) shows that the energy of an atom in an external magnetic field depends upon the orientation of $\boldsymbol{\mu}$ (i.e., $\boldsymbol{L}$) relative to the field. In general, the energy involved is small compared to the average separation of the atomic states, and the interaction can therefore be considered a small perturbation. The effect is observable and will be discussed further in Chapter 9 (Zeeman effect).

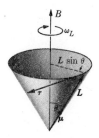

Fig. 7–6 Illustration of Larmor precession.

We shall here discuss atomic interactions involving Eqs. (7–57) and (7–58), starting with the torque. Figure 7–6 is a vector diagram showing the angular momentum vector $\boldsymbol{L}$ and the magnetic moment $\boldsymbol{\mu}$ at an angle θ from vector $\boldsymbol{B}$ (applied external magnetic field). The torque τ, given by Eq. (7–57) changes the angular momentum according to Newton's law:

$$\frac{d\boldsymbol{L}}{dt} = \tau = -\frac{eg}{2m_e} \boldsymbol{L} \times \boldsymbol{B}. \tag{7–59}$$

Since dL/dt is perpendicular to L, the angular momentum does not change in magnitude, only direction. The resulting motion is a precession of L about B. The numerical value of the angular frequency of precession is given by

$$\Omega_L = \frac{dL/dt}{L \sin \theta} = \frac{egBL \sin \theta}{2m_e L \sin \theta} = \frac{egB}{2m_e}. \qquad (7\text{–}60)$$

The process is called *Larmor precession* and Ω_L is the Larmor frequency. Transitions between m-states can be induced by an applied radio-frequency field when this field is in resonance with the Larmor precession.

7–6 EXPERIMENTAL TEST OF SPATIAL QUANTIZATION

A very surprising result of the analysis in Section 7–3 is that not only is the angular momentum itself quantized, but also a component thereof is quantized as well. This result was found experimentally by Stern and Gerlach* several years before the advent of wave mechanics. Stern and Gerlach demonstrated quantization of a component of the magnetic moment of atoms. This, as we have seen in the previous section, is equivalent to the detection of quantization of angular momentum.

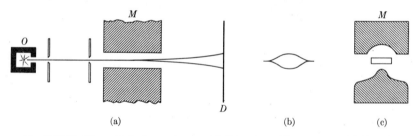

Fig. 7–7 The Stern-Gerlach experiment. (a) Side view. M = magnet. (b) Line shape on detector D. (c) End view of magnet pole pieces and beam.

Figure 7–7 is a schematic drawing of the Stern-Gerlach experiment. A highly collimated beam of neutral silver atoms is produced by evaporating silver in an oven and allowing some of the vapor to escape through a set of fine slits into an evacuated chamber. The beam passes between the pole pieces of a magnet that is shaped to produce an inhomogeneous field. After emerging from the magnetic field, the atoms impinge upon a detector (a photographic plate).

---

* O. Stern, *Z. Physik.* **7** (1921), p. 249, and W. Gerlach and O. Stern, *Z. Physik,* **8** (1922), p. 110.

If the atoms passing through the inhomogeneous field possess a magnetic moment, they will precess in accordance with the theory outlined in the previous section. They will also experience a net force in the vertical direction proportional to the z-component of the magnetic moment. This force is strong enough to cause a measurable deflection for silver atoms moving with velocities characteristic of a hot gas, assuming that the magnetic moment is of the order of one Bohr Magneton (Problem 7–15).

According to classical notions, the silver atoms should emerge from the oven with randomly oriented μ vectors, i.e., random distribution of the z-component between two extreme values $\pm \mu$. The precession in the magnetic field does not change the z-component since the precession takes place about the z-axis. The resultant mark of the beam on the detector should be a continuous smear. This mark would not have sharp vertical boundaries, since the atoms do not have the same velocity. However, knowing the temperature, dB/dz and the geometry of the system, we could calculate the distribution in the z-direction of atoms on the detector.

Stern and Gerlach found that the measured distribution was not consistent with the classical notion. They found two maxima in the distribution, almost describable as two sharp lines. This indicates that silver atoms in their natural (ground) state have a magnetic moment with two possible values of the z-component.

A Stern-Gerlach experiment was performed in 1927 by Phipps and Taylor[*] on atomic hydrogen. The result was again that the beam split in two, indicating two possible values of the z-component of μ.

Both results, from the experiments on silver and on hydrogen, are a puzzle. According to the theory of the hydrogen atom, the ground-state angular momentum should be zero with $m = 0$ the only possible value. For many-electron atoms, the theory of vector addition of angular momenta, which we are not going to discuss in any detail, predicts that the integer l-values for each electron must add up to a total integer L, with an *odd* number $(2L + 1)$ of possible orientations (m-values). Yet, the experimental result of Stern and Gerlach was *two* m-values. Something is missing in the total picture.

7–7 INTRINSIC SPIN OF THE ELECTRON

The energy-level diagram of the hydrogen atom shown in Fig. 7–4 had been constructed already on the basis of the old quantum theory in the extension of Bohr's work by Wilson and Sommerfeld. It was known that, except for the ground state, the levels were energy degenerate and the physical quantity that differed between the degenerate levels was the angular momentum, exactly as indicated in Fig. 7–4, except that zero angular momentum was not permitted

---

[*] T. E. Phipps and J. B. Taylor, *Phys. Rev.* **29** (1927), p. 309.

in the old theory. It was also known before the advent of wave mechanics that this diagram is too simple. The levels of the hydrogen atom, as well as of other atoms, were known to display a fine structure, not shown in Fig. 7–4. Specifically, for the hydrogen atom each level in all columns except the first are closely spaced doublets. This could be detected with optical spectrographs of very high resolving power as splitting of the emission lines.

In order to explain the fine structure in atomic transitions, the anomalous result of the Stern-Gerlach experiment, and the anomalous Zeeman effect, discussed further in Section 9–8, Uhlenbeck and Goudsmit* in 1925 suggested that the electron possesses an intrinsic spin, that is, an angular momentum of magnitude $\hbar/2$ about its own center of mass. P. A. M. Dirac† in 1928 developed a wave-mechanical theory which, contrary to Schrödinger's theory, is relativistically invariant; that is, the theory satisfies Einstein's principle that a physical law is the same no matter in what inertial coordinate system it is written. This principle does not hold for Schrödinger's wave mechanics since the latter is based on the nonrelativistic formula for kinetic energy.

Dirac's relativistic wave mechanics produces an electron which has an intrinsic angular momentum given by

$$L_s = \sqrt{s(s + 1)}\hbar, \qquad \text{with} \qquad s = 1/2, \tag{7–61}$$

and a z-component

$$L_{sz} = m_s\hbar, \qquad \text{with} \qquad m_s = \pm 1/2. \tag{7–62}$$

The magnetic moment associated with this intrinsic spin was predicted by Dirac to be given by a g-factor $g_s = 2$; that is, twice as large as the corresponding factor for orbital motion‡.

It is now easy to understand the result of the Stern-Gerlach experiments, both on silver and on hydrogen. The magnetic moment of hydrogen in its ground state is produced by the intrinsic spin of the single electron (disregarding a negligible contribution from the proton). The number of possible m_s states is two, as observed. For silver, the 46 electrons pair up such that their magnetic moments cancel, and the resulting total angular momentum is produced by the forty-seventh electron in an s-state.

We are not going to discuss Dirac's relativistic wave mechanics in this text. It therefore becomes necessary to include a description of the electron spin as

---

*   G. E. Uhlenbeck and S. Goudsmit, *Naturwiss.* **13** (1925) p. 593 and *Nature,* **117** (1926), p.264.

†   P. A. M. Dirac, *Proc. Roy, Soc.* **117**, 610, **118**, 351 (1928).

‡   Modern theories, which take into account some small perturbations caused by the electron's interaction with its surroundings, predict a g-factor for the electron $g_s = 2 \times 1.001159644$. Precise experiments agree with this value (see Section 7–10).

an addition to our Schrödinger-type wave function. We first proceed to define a *commutator*.*

We have pointed out (Section 6–9) that, when two operators commute, the eigenfunctions of one of the operators are simultaneously eigenfunctions of the other. Therefore both corresponding physical quantities are constants of the motion. We are here going to look at some operators that do *not* commute.

Consider two operators Q_1 and Q_2. We define a new operator, called the *commutator*, as

$$[Q_1, Q_2] \equiv Q_1 Q_2 - Q_2 Q_1. \tag{7–63}$$

The square bracket is used as a symbol for the commutator. It is clear from the discussion in Section 6–9 that when Q_1 and Q_2 have simultaneous eigenfunctions, then

$$[Q_1, Q_2] = 0. \tag{7–64}$$

As an example of commuting operators, let Q_1 be the operator for the square of the angular momentum (Eq. 7–40) and Q_2 be the operator for the z-component of angular momentum (Eq. 7–39). It is easy to show that Eq. (7–64) holds for this case (Problem 7–17).

Now let us look at the operators for the x- and y-components of angular momentum:

$$L_x = \frac{\hbar}{i} \left(y \frac{\partial}{\partial z} - z \frac{\partial}{\partial y} \right),$$
$$L_y = \frac{\hbar}{i} \left(z \frac{\partial}{\partial x} - x \frac{\partial}{\partial z} \right). \tag{7–65}$$

Forming the commutator bracket, we find

$$[L_x, L_y] \equiv (L_x L_y - L_y L_x) = \hbar^2 \left(x \frac{\partial}{\partial y} - y \frac{\partial}{\partial x} \right) = \hbar i L_z, \tag{7–66}$$

and similarly

$$[L_y, L_z] = \hbar i L_x, \tag{7–67}$$

$$[L_z, L_x] = \hbar i L_y. \tag{7–68}$$

These results show that no two components of angular momentum commute. Therefore, the spherical harmonic functions which are eigenfunctions of L_z are not eigenfunctions of L_x or L_y, except for the s-states for which all three components are zero.

The commutator rules (7–66) to (7–68) are the basis for an algebra of angular momentum, some of which is outlined in Appendix 5. We shall also

---

* It is possible to skip from here to the last paragraph of this section without loss of continuity.

have to require that our description of the electron spin be consistent with these rules.

The simplest mathematical representation that has been found to satisfy the commutator requirements (7–66) to (7–68) is a set of matrices, called *Pauli's spin matrices**, multiplied by $\hbar/2$. Pauli's spin matrices are

$$\sigma_x = \begin{pmatrix} 0 & 1 \\ 1 & 0 \end{pmatrix}, \qquad \sigma_y = \begin{pmatrix} 0 & -i \\ i & 0 \end{pmatrix}, \qquad \sigma_z = \begin{pmatrix} 1 & 0 \\ 0 & -1 \end{pmatrix}, \qquad (7\text{–}69)$$

and the corresponding spin operators are

$$S_x = \tfrac{1}{2}\hbar\sigma_x, \qquad S_y = \tfrac{1}{2}\hbar\sigma_y, \qquad S_z = \tfrac{1}{2}\hbar\sigma_z. \qquad (7\text{–}70)$$

We test one of the commutator equations (7–66):

$$\frac{\hbar^2}{4}(\sigma_x\sigma_y - \sigma_y\sigma_x) = \frac{\hbar^2}{4}\begin{pmatrix} 0 & 1 \\ 1 & 0 \end{pmatrix}\begin{pmatrix} 0 & -i \\ i & 0 \end{pmatrix} - \frac{\hbar^2}{4}\begin{pmatrix} 0 & -i \\ i & 0 \end{pmatrix}\begin{pmatrix} 0 & 1 \\ 1 & 0 \end{pmatrix}$$

$$= \frac{\hbar^2}{4}\begin{pmatrix} i & 0 \\ 0 & -i \end{pmatrix} - \frac{\hbar^2}{4}\begin{pmatrix} -i & 0 \\ 0 & i \end{pmatrix}$$

$$= \hbar i\,\frac{\hbar}{2}\begin{pmatrix} 1 & 0 \\ 0 & -1 \end{pmatrix} = \hbar i\,\frac{\hbar}{2}\,\sigma_z.$$

Testing the two other relationships is left to one of the problems (Problem 7–19).

The operator for the square of spin angular momentum is

$$S^2 = \frac{\hbar^2}{4}(\sigma_x^2 + \sigma_y^2 + \sigma_z^2) = 3\,\frac{\hbar^2}{4}\begin{pmatrix} 1 & 0 \\ 0 & 1 \end{pmatrix}. \qquad (7\text{–}71)$$

The spin wave function is a 2×1 column matrix

$$\chi = \begin{pmatrix} a \\ b \end{pmatrix}. \qquad (7\text{–}72)$$

The square of the upper entry, a^2, gives the probability for finding the electron with "spin up," i.e., with $m_s = +\tfrac{1}{2}$. Similarly, the square of the lower entry gives the probability for finding the electron with "spin down," i.e., with $m_s = -\tfrac{1}{2}$. The following two functions are eigenfunctions of S^2 and of S_z, but not of S_x and S_y:

$$\alpha \equiv \begin{pmatrix} 1 \\ 0 \end{pmatrix}, \qquad \beta \equiv \begin{pmatrix} 0 \\ 1 \end{pmatrix}. \qquad (7\text{–}73)$$

The first represents a "spin up" electron and the second a "spin down" electron. We write the eigenvalue equation for S^2 and α as

$$S_z\alpha = \frac{\hbar}{2}\begin{pmatrix} 1 & 0 \\ 0 & -1 \end{pmatrix}\begin{pmatrix} 1 \\ 0 \end{pmatrix} = \frac{\hbar}{2}\,\alpha,$$

---

* For the readers who are not familiar with simple matrix multiplication, a brief introduction is given in Appendix 4.

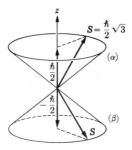

Fig. 7–8 The two-spin state of an electron, $\alpha =$ "spin up," and $\beta =$ "spin down."

showing that the z-component in the "spin up" state is $\hbar/2$, as required by Eq. (7–62).

Figure 7–8 is a vector diagram of the spin showing the two possible states α and β. In the rest of this book, we shall not use the spin algebra developed in this section, but we shall use the spin eigenfunctions α and β. If he desires, the reader can regard them as mere symbols indicating "spin up" and "spin down," respectively.

7–8 TOTAL ANGULAR MOMENTUM J

Angular-momentum coupling in the hydrogen atom is quite simple, since it involves only two angular momenta, i.e., that resulting from orbital motion and the spin angular momentum*. The two combine to a total angular momentum J with quantum number $j = l \pm \frac{1}{2}$ and with $2j + 1$ possible z-components $m_j\hbar$ with quantum number m_j, ranging from $m_j = j$ to $m_j = -j$.

We learned in Section 7–4 that the old spectroscopic notation s, p, d, f, g, etc. is associated with the orbital angular momenta $l = 0, 1, 2, 3, 4$, etc. A state was specified by the quantum numbers n, l, and m, which we now will call m_l. A notation was introduced to identify a particular state. It gave the principal quantum number n and the letter signifying the l-value; e.g., 1s, 2p, etc. We now add to this the j-value as a subscript. Thus

$3d_{5/2}$ is a state with $n = 3,$ $l = 2,$ and $j = 5/2;$

$2p_{1/2}$ is a state with $n = 2,$ $l = 1,$ and $j = 1/2.$

This coupling scheme and the quantum number j are appropriate only when the internal magnetic interaction between l and s (see the next Section) is stronger than the torques produced by an external magnetic field. Figure

---

* For the moment, we are disregarding the angular momentum of the nucleus. However, see Section 7–11.

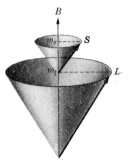

Fig. 7–9 Independent precession of the **L**- and **S**-vectors in a very strong magnetic field.

7–9 is a vector diagram appropriate for the case of a very strong external field. The spin vector and the orbital angular-momentum vector are precessing independently with different Larmor frequencies. The magnitude of the total angular momentum is clearly not constant.

Figure 7–10 is a vector diagram appropriate for the case of a very weak (or no) external field. The example is an electron in an f-state ($l = 3$) with a total j-value of $j = l - s = 5/2$ and a z-component with quantum number $m_j = 3/2$. The theory of angular-momentum coupling reveals that the magnetic quantum numbers m_l and m_s are not sharp. Rather, the wave function is a sum of two terms, one with $m_l = 3$, $m_s = -\frac{1}{2}$ and one with $m_l = 2$, $m_s = \frac{1}{2}$. According to Table A5–1 of Appendix 5, the probability amplitudes for the two possibilities are $-(2/7)^{1/2}$ and $(5/7)^{1/2}$. We write the total wave function for this state as

$$\psi = -(\tfrac{2}{7})^{1/2} \mid 3, \tfrac{1}{2}, 2, -\tfrac{1}{2}\rangle + (\tfrac{5}{7})^{1/2} \mid 3, \tfrac{1}{2}, 1, \tfrac{1}{2}\rangle \qquad (7\text{–}74)$$

where the symbols $\mid \rangle$ signify a wave function with angular-momentum quantum numbers as specified, with the sequence being l, s, m_l, m_s.

In the next section, we shall make a very simple calculation of the energy involved in the interaction between the intrinsic magnetic moment of the

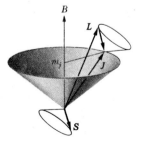

Fig. 7–10 Coupling of **L** and **S** to a total angular momentum **J** in a weak magnetic field. The **L**- and **S**-vectors precess in synchronism about the **J**-vector.

electron and the field resulting from the orbital motion. We shall not revert to the complex details of angular-momentum coupling nor to the notation of Eq. (7–74).

7-9 FINE STRUCTURE OF ATOMIC HYDROGEN

Long before the turn of the century, optical spectroscopy had already revealed that most emission and absorption "lines" are not single lines but display a fine structure. Very high resolution instruments are needed to show the fine structure of hydrogen lines, but such instruments have long been in existence. One of the most thoroughly studied lines is H_α in the Balmer series. This is the line with wavelength $\lambda = 6562.8$ Å in the transitions 3s to 2p, 3p to 2s, and 3d to 2p (Fig. 7–5). As discussed in Section 7–4 and further in Chapter 8, the atomic transitions are subject to selection rules. The rule $\Delta l = \pm 1$ is observed in the transitions shown in Fig. 7–5. There is another important selection rule requiring $\Delta j = \pm 1$ or 0. This means that the H_α-line consists of the following seven components:

$$
\begin{array}{lll}
1) & 3s_{1/2} & \text{to} \quad 2p_{1/2} \\
2) & 3s_{1/2} & \text{to} \quad 2p_{3/2} \\
3) & 3p_{1/2} & \text{to} \quad 2s_{1/2} \\
4) & 3p_{3/2} & \text{to} \quad 2s_{1/2} \\
5) & 3d_{3/2} & \text{to} \quad 2p_{1/2} \\
6) & 3d_{3/2} & \text{to} \quad 2p_{3/2} \\
7) & 3d_{5/2} & \text{to} \quad 2p_{3/2}
\end{array}
$$

None of these components coincide exactly. Partly this is so because of relativistic corrections to the basic energy formula, Eq. (7–49). However, the largest effect is a result of the magnetic interaction discussed below.

Figure 7–11(a) shows a microphotometer tracing across the H_α-line on a photographic plate exposed in a high-resolution spectrograph by R. C. Williams.* The line shows a definite structure, but the seven separate transitions are not resolved. The abscissa in the figure is the inverse wavelength λ^{-1} in cm^{-1}, as the convention is in optical spectroscopy. The mean value for the H_α-line is 15240 cm^{-1}.

The width of a peak in Fig. 7–11(a), as measured at half-maximum, is about $\Delta\lambda^{-1} \approx 0.17$ cm^{-1}. The resolving power is therefore

$$\text{Resolving power:} \quad \frac{\lambda^{-1}}{\Delta\lambda^{-1}} = 90{,}000.$$

This number is extremely difficult to improve upon for ordinary hydrogen because the major contribution to the peak width in Fig. 7–11(a) is Doppler

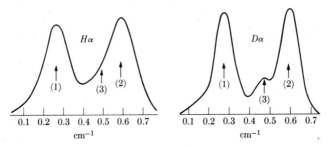

Fig. 7–11 Fine structure of the H_α line and the D_α line, as observed by R. C. Williams, *Phys. Rev.* **54** (1938), p. 558.

broadening that results from heat motion of the emitting hydrogen atoms. The radiation was produced in a specially cooled gas-discharge tube designed to minimize this effect. Figure 7–11(b) shows the D_α-line produced by utilizing deuterium gas instead of light hydrogen. At a given temperature, the rms velocity of deuterium atoms is $1/\sqrt{2}$ of that of light hydrogen atoms. Hence the Doppler broadening is only 71 percent of the broadening in Fig. 7–11(a).

We shall now proceed to develop a formula for the fine-structure splitting caused by the magnetic spin-orbit interaction. In calculating the interaction energy, we shall use the Bohr model. There really is no good justification for this, except that we are interested only in an order-of-magnitude calculation, and secondly, that this simple model again happens to lead to the same or very similar results as wave-mechanical calculations.

Consider an electron moving in the nth Bohr orbit. Define the z-axis to be the axis of rotation. Relative to this axis, the spin can have z-component $\pm\hbar/2$, and the associated component of the magnetic moment is $\pm\mu_B = \pm e\hbar/2m_e$ ($m_s = 1/2$ and $g = 2$). The orbital motion produces a magnetic field B at the site of the electron, and the interaction between this field and the magnetic moment will result in the small energy shift $\Delta E = \boldsymbol{\mu}\cdot\boldsymbol{B}$ (Eq. 7–56).

If v is the velocity of the electron, then the nucleus is moving with a velocity $-v$ in a coordinate system stationary with respect to the electron. From Biot-Savart's law, we find the magnetic field B at the site of the electron as

$$\boldsymbol{B} = \frac{\mu_0}{4\pi}\frac{i d\boldsymbol{l}\times\boldsymbol{r}}{r^3} = -\frac{1}{4\pi\varepsilon_0 c^2}\frac{Ze\boldsymbol{v}\times\boldsymbol{r}}{r^3} = \frac{Ze\boldsymbol{L}}{4\pi\varepsilon_0 c^2 m_e r^3}. \qquad (7\text{–}75)$$

The current element $i d\boldsymbol{l}$ has been replaced by $-Ze\boldsymbol{v}$, μ_0 has been replaced by $1/\varepsilon_0 c^2$, and we have introduced the orbital angular-momentum vector $\boldsymbol{L} = \boldsymbol{r}\times m_e\boldsymbol{v}$. The energy shift is

$$\Delta E = -\boldsymbol{\mu}\cdot\boldsymbol{B} = -\left(-\frac{e}{2m_e}g_s\boldsymbol{S}\right)\cdot\frac{Ze\boldsymbol{L}}{4\pi\varepsilon_0 c^2 m_e r^3} = \frac{Ze^2 g_s\hbar^2}{8\pi\varepsilon_0 c^2 m_e^2 r^3}\boldsymbol{l}\cdot\boldsymbol{s},$$
$$(7\text{–}76)$$

where $\boldsymbol{l}$ and $\boldsymbol{s}$ are $\boldsymbol{L}/\hbar$ and $\boldsymbol{S}/\hbar$, respectively.

In the Bohr model, r is, of course, the Bohr radius $n^2 a_0$. However, we shall here replace r^{-3} with the expectation value $\langle r^{-3} \rangle$. We then arrive at the formula that wave-mechanical calculations would have given us. Another modification that we shall make is to include a factor $\frac{1}{2}$, which arises from a relativistic effect called *Thomas precession* (see Appendix 6). The energy shift is then (with $g_s = 2$)

$$\Delta E = \frac{Ze^2 \hbar^2}{8\pi\varepsilon_0 c^2 m_e^2} \langle r^{-3} \rangle l \cdot s \qquad (7\text{-}77)$$

For the hydrogen ground state, the orbital angular momentum is zero, so $\Delta E = 0$. For the 2p-state it is easy to show that $\langle r^{-3} \rangle = Z^3/24a_0^3$, where $a_0 = 4\pi\varepsilon_0 \hbar^2/m_e e^2$. After inserting this and dividing Eq. (7-77) with the energy $E = Z^2 e^2/32\pi\varepsilon_0 a_0$ for the 2p-state, we get

$$\frac{\Delta E}{E} = \frac{1}{6}\left(\frac{e^2}{4\pi\varepsilon_0 \hbar c}\right)^2 Z^2 l \cdot s. \qquad (7\text{-}78)$$

We have kept the factor Z in these calculations to show its effect for electrons in other atoms but in hydrogenlike orbits.

The factor in parentheses in Eq. (7-78) is nondimensional and equal to

$$\alpha = \frac{e^2}{4\pi\varepsilon_0 \hbar c} = \frac{1}{137}. \qquad (7\text{-}79)$$

It is called the *fine-structure constant*. As indicated by Eq. (7-78) for the case of hydrogenlike orbits, the relative fine-structure splitting of atomic states is of the order of $\alpha^2 Z^2$. For the particular case of the hydrogen 2p-state we have the relative splitting between the $2p_{3/2}$ and the $2p_{1/2}$ component:

$$\frac{\Delta E_{LS}}{E} = \frac{1}{6}\alpha^2 [(l \cdot s)_{3/2} - (l \cdot s)_{1/2}].$$

In our vector model of angular-momentum coupling, the scalar products can be found by using the cosine rule on the triangle formed by j, l, and s (Fig. 7-12). Since the square of the lengths of these vectors is $j(j + 1)$, etc., we find

$$j(j + 1) = l(l + 1) + s(s + 1) - 2 l \cdot s.$$

From this, we find

$$(l \cdot s)_{3/2} - (l \cdot s)_{1/2} = \frac{1}{2}[\frac{3}{2}\cdot\frac{5}{2} - \frac{1}{2}\cdot\frac{3}{2}] = \frac{3}{2}.$$

The fine-structure splitting for the hydrogen 2p-state is therefore given by

$$\frac{\Delta E_{LS}}{E} = \frac{1}{6}\left(\frac{1}{137}\right)^2 \frac{3}{2} = 1.33 \times 10^{-5}.$$

With $E = 3.2$ eV, this gives $\Delta E_{LS} = 4.3 \times 10^{-5}$ eV, corresponding to $\Delta(\lambda^{-1}) = 0.35$ cm^{-1}. As mentioned above, this is the largest contribution to

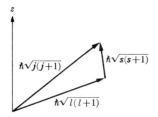

Fig. 7–12 Vector diagram used as an aid to find $l \cdot s$.

the separation of lines observed in Fig. 7–11. The fine-structure splitting of the 3d-state is smaller, in spite of the larger contribution from the $l \cdot s$ factor, because the factor $\langle r^{-3} \rangle$ is much smaller.

7–10 FURTHER REFINEMENTS OF THE THEORY OF HYDROGEN

As we have pointed out earlier, Schrödinger's wave mechanics is a nonrelativistic theory. The speed of the electron in the hydrogen atom is very low compared to the velocity of light; yet the experimental accuracies are so high that relativistic effects are detectable. Secondly, the intrinsic spin of the electron is, relatively speaking, so large that it definitely is in the relativistic range. Already before Schrödinger a relativistic theory of hydrogen was worked out by Sommerfeld (Section 4–8). In 1928, Dirac* formulated a relativistic quantum theory for the electron, in which the wave function is a 4-component column matrix. Dirac's theory has the electron spin built in and predicts a magnetic moment of the electron of one Bohr magneton.

Dirac's equations can be solved exactly for hydrogen. The results give a fine-structure splitting for the H_α-line which at first appeared to be in agreement with observations (Fig. 7–11). However, some observers, after very detailed analyses of the spectrograms, believed they had found discrepancies. They were proved correct.

In a very famous experiment, Lamb and Retherford† studied the relative positions of the $n = 2$ levels of hydrogen ($2s_{1/2}$, $2p_{3/2}$, and $2p_{1/2}$). Spontaneous transitions between these closely spaced states are not normally seen because the transition probability is proportional to the cube of the frequency and therefore exceedingly low. However, Lamb and Retherford, utilized microwave techniques to produce *stimulated* transitions between the states. A brief description of the experiment follows.

Hydrogen gas was heated in a tungsten oven (Fig. 7–13) to 2500°K, which temperature dissociates the molecules. The atoms were allowed to escape as a beam into an evacuated chamber and here bombarded crosswise with 10.8 eV

---

*   P. A. M. Dirac, *Proc. Roy. Soc.* **A117** (1928), p. 610.

†   W. E. Lamb and R. C. Retherford, *Phys. Rev.* **72** (1947), p. 241 and **79**, (1950), p. 549.

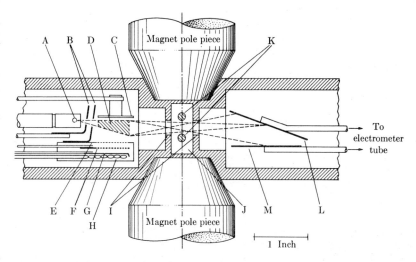

Fig. 7–13 Cross section of apparatus used by Lamb and Retherford. A. Tungsten oven of hydrogen dissociator. B. Shields. C. Anode of electron bombarder. D. Bombardment region. E. Accelerator grid of electron bombarder. F. Control grid. G. Cathode of electron bombarder. H. Heater for cathode. I. Slits. J. Wave guide. K. Quenching wires and transmission lines. L. Metastable detector target. M. Electron collector.

electrons. This excited some atoms to the $n = 2$ states. The $2p_{3/2}$ and $2p_{1/2}$-states rapidly decayed to the ground state, but the $2s_{1/2}$-state cannot decay by this route ($\Delta l = 0$). The beam passed through a region where the atoms could interact with a microwave field. It then fell upon a tungsten detector. Upon hitting the detector, the $2s_{1/2}$-atoms decayed to the ground state, releasing the energy to electrons in the metal, and some of these electrons were consequently ejected. The presence of (neutral) $2s_{1/2} =$ atoms in the beam was therefore detected as an electric current to the tungsten plate. A constant magnetic field could also be produced in the microwave interaction region by an external magnet.

When the frequency of the microwave field corresponded to the energy difference between one of the $2s_{1/2}$-substates and a 2p-substate, in the microwave interaction region, some of the atoms in the $2s_{1/2}$-state were transferred to this other state and then rapidly decayed to the ground state. Resonance was detected as a reduction in the current to the tungsten plate.

Figure 7–14(a) shows the relative positions of the three states in question and their Zeeman splitting as predicted by Dirac's theory. Note that the $2s_{1/2}$- and $2p_{1/2}$-levels coincide at zero field. Figure 7–14(b) shows the frequency of transitions expected from the Dirac theory from the $2s_{1/2}$-substate with $m_j = \frac{1}{2}$, marked α in Fig. 7–14(a). The corresponding experimental points are

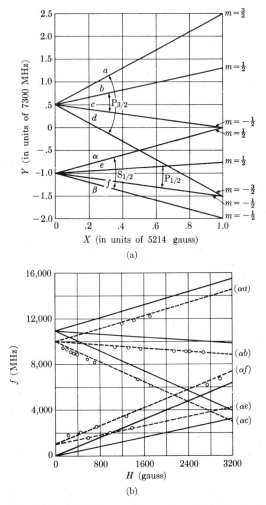

(a)

(b)

Fig. 7–14 a) Relative positions of n = 2 levels in hydrogen after Dirac's theory. b) Predicted and observed transitions between the states. After W. E. Lamb and R. C. Retherford, *Phys. Rev.* **78** (1947), p. 549.

shown as circles joined by dashed lines. An upward shift of the $2s_{1/2}$-level by about 1000 MHz is necessary to bring the theory into agreement with these data. This shift is called the *Lamb shift*.

The publication of the results of the Lamb-Retherford experiment spurred theorists to take a new look at quantum mechanics of the electron. Dirac's theory clearly did not have the whole picture. The difficulty seems to lie in the interaction of the electron and the electromagnetic field. The result of these theoretical studies is an improved theory called *quantum electrodynamics*. Dirac's theory is still the basis, but important perturbations have to be included.

In the new theory, the electric field is produced by emission from the source of *virtual photons*, i.e., photons that are emitted and reabsorbed again approximately over a lifetime Δt allowed by the uncertainty principle $h\nu(\Delta t) \approx \hbar$ (compare Section 12–4). In addition, electron-positron pairs with lifetimes of the order of $\hbar/2m_e c^2$ are continuously being produced and annihilated. The quantum field is thus a field with violent fluctuations over space and time, and the smaller the space-time volume of a sample taken, the larger the fluctuations.

One serious difficulty is that as a point particle the electron has an infinite energy in this quantum field. The difficulty is circumvented by subtracting from the integral expressions for the energy of the electron in, say, the $2s_{1/2}$-state of hydrogen, the integral expression for the energy of the "free" electron. This procedure is called *renormalization of mass*.

To make a long story short: Modern theories yield a theoretical Lamb shift of the $2s_{1/2}$-state in hydrogen relative to the $2p_{1/2}$-state of (1057.19 ± 0.16) MHz, whereas the best experimental value is (1057.77 ± 0.10) MHz.

The new theory predicts a value for the magnetic moment of the electron of 1.001159644 Bohr magnetons. The best experimental value* is (1.001159644 ± 0.000000007) Bohr magnetons, in perfect agreement.

7–11 HYPERFINE STRUCTURE IN HYDROGEN

With very high-resolution optical instruments, it is possible to resolve the transition lines of some elements into closely spaced *hyperfine* components. The true hyperfine structure is produced by an interaction between the magnetic dipole moments of the nucleus and unpaired electrons (Section 9–9). In the case of hydrogen in the ground state, the electron spin S and the proton spin I combine to a total angular momentum with quantum number F, which is 0 or 1.

Figure 7–15 shows the classical analogue with two parallel bar magnets moving about each other. The corresponding state is the $F = 0$ state (since μ and S are opposite in the electron). The classical interaction energy of the two bar magnets is

$$\Delta E = \frac{\mu_0}{4\pi}\left[\frac{\mu_n \cdot \mu_e}{r^3} - 3\frac{(\mu_e \cdot r)(\mu_n \cdot r)}{r^5}\right], \qquad (7\text{–}80)$$

where $\mu_0 = 4 \times 10^{-7}$ is the permeability of free space. This expression is positive or negative depending upon the angle between r and the two μ vectors. A perturbation calculation (Section 8–2) yields a negative net result for the

---

* J. C. Wesley and A. Rich, *Phys. Rev. Lett.* **24** (1970), p. 1320.

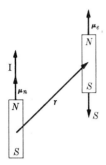

Fig. 7–15

$F = 0$ state and a positive result for the $F = 1$ state. The difference between the two states; i.e., the hyperfine splitting of the hydrogen ground state is

$$\Delta E_H = \frac{8\mu_0\mu_e\mu_n}{3\pi a_0^3}, \tag{7–81}$$

where μ_e and μ_n are in MKSA units and a_0 is the Bohr radius. By inserting numerical values (for μ_n, see Section 12–1), we find $\Delta E_H = 5.88 \times 10^{-6}$ eV, or more exactly in terms of frequency of transition we obtain

$$\nu = (\Delta E_H/h) = (1420.53 \pm 0.03) \text{ MHz.}$$

Spontaneous emission from the $F = 1$ to the $F = 0$ state has not been observed in the laboratory. However, induced transitions have been observed by an atomic-beam method similar to the one described in the previous section. The best experimental results combined give

$$\nu = (\Delta E_H/h) = (1420.405752) \text{ MHz.}$$

The discrepancy between the theoretical value given here and the experimental value is significant but has been removed by various small corrections to the theoretical formula.

As mentioned above, the spontaneous transition of the $F = 1$ to $F = 0$ state has not been observed *in the laboratory*. However, this is the source of the 1420 MHz ($\lambda = 21$ cm) radiation received from outer space. A whole new science, radioastronomy, has developed as a study largely of this line from our own galaxy and other galaxies.

The integrated intensity (number of photons in the 21-cm line) received in a given time interval from a given direction in space is a measure of the total amount of neutral hydrogen atoms within the cone of observation defined by the directional antenna. The receivers used have very narrow band widths, and a frequency profile of the line is always measured. Figure 7–16 shows such frequency profiles, i.e., intensities versus frequency measured at five-degree intervals in the galactic plane (Milky Way). The frequency variations are, of

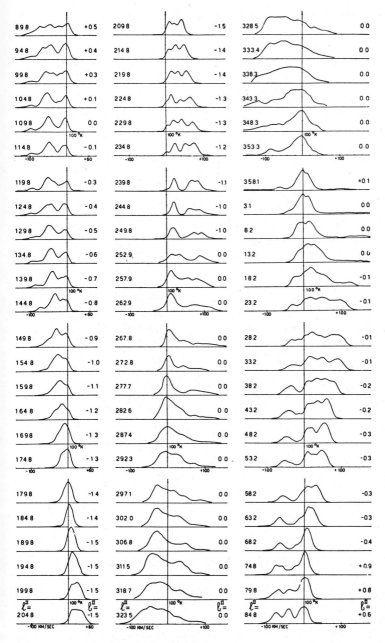

Fig. 7-16 Intensity of 21-cm radiation from our Galaxy measured at 5-degree intervals (longitude) in the galactic plane. The variation in frequency (horizontal axis) reflects variation in velocity relative to the earth by the Doppler shift. Reproduced by permission from F. J. Kerr and G. Westerhout, *Distribution of Interstellar Hydrogen in the Stars and Stellar System*, Vol. V, The University of Chicago (1965), p. 178.

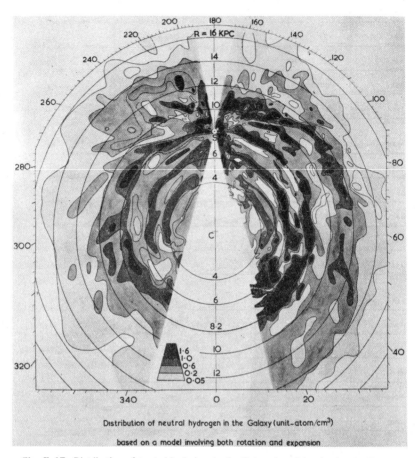

Distribution of neutral hydrogen in the Galaxy (unit-atom/cm³)

based on a model involving both rotation and expansion

Fig. 7–17 Distribution of neutral hydrogen in the Galaxy based on the data in Fig. 7–16 and a galactic model specifying the velocity distribution as a function of position. Distances in kilo-parseconds with 1 kpc = 3 × 10¹⁹ meters. F. J. Kerr and G. Westerhout, *loc. cit.*

course, caused by the Doppler shift. By assuming a given velocity distribution in the various parts of the galaxy (based on other information), it is now possible to construct a density-distribution map of the neutral (i.e., interstellar) hydrogen in the plane of our galaxy. Such a map is shown in Fig. 7–17.

The 21-cm radiation has also been observed from several other galaxies. This radiation is very weak, however, and because of the low directional resolution (about 0.5 degree) of the microwave antennas (compared to optical telescopes), very little spatial details have thus far been obtained from measurements on these distant sources.

PROBLEMS

7-1 Show that Eqs. (7–5) and (7–6) follow from Eq. (7–1) as indicated in the text.

7-2 Make the substitutions described in the text to prove Eq. (7–13).

7-3 Prove Eq. (7–27).

7-4 Show that the negative derivative of the last term in brackets of Eq. (7–32) gives a centrifugal force provided the constant $l(l + 1)\hbar^2$ is the square of angular momentum. Assume circular or quasicircular motion.

7-5 Show that the spherical harmonic function $Y_{2,1}(\theta, \phi)$ is normalized (Eq. 7–29).

7-6 Prove Eq. (7–40).

7-7 Show that when searching for spherically symmetric wave functions, we can reduce the Laplacian operator in Eq. (7–13) to

$$\nabla^2 = \frac{2}{r}\frac{\partial}{\partial r} + \frac{\partial^2}{\partial r^2}.$$

7-8 A particle of mass m moves under the influence of a spherically symmetric attractive force $F = -\beta r$, where β is a constant and r is the radial distance from the particle to the origin. Set up Schrödinger's equation for the motion and determine the energy of the ground state in terms of β, m, and fundamental constants. (*Hint:* The ground-state eigenfunction has the form Ae^{-ar^2}.)

7-9 A particle of mass M moves inside a spherical shell of radius a_0. The potential energy is $V = 0$ for $r < a_0$ and $V \to \infty$ for $r > a_0$. a) Write down the radial wave equation for $R(r)$ for the region $r < a_0$. Show that the functions

$$R_0(r) = \frac{A \sin kr}{kr}, \qquad\qquad l = 0,$$

$$R_1(r) = B\left[\frac{\sin kr}{(kr)^2} - \frac{\cos kr}{kr}\right], \qquad l = 1,$$

are solutions of this equation. b) Show that these functions are finite, even for $r = 0$. c) Find the energies of the ground state ($l = 0$) and first excited state ($l = 1$).

7-10 Assume that an electron is trapped inside a nucleus of radius $R = 5 \times 10^{-13}$ cm. Use the results of the previous problem to calculate the minimum kinetic energy of this electron. Estimate the same by using the uncertainty principle with $\Delta x = \Delta y = \Delta z \approx R$.

7-11 One of the excited states of the hydrogen atom has the wave function

$$\psi = Ar^2 e^{-r/3a_0} \sin \theta \cos \theta e^{i\phi}.$$

a) By using the operators for L^2 and L_z, find the quantum numbers l and m. b) What is the energy E of this state (use the radial wave equation to determine this)? c) Normalize ψ (find A).

7-12 A rod of length R and negligible mass has one end at origin and the other end is carrying a mass M. The rod can rotate freely about the origin both in the θ and ϕ directions. Apply the equation

$$-\frac{\hbar^2}{2M}\frac{1}{r^2}\frac{\partial}{\partial r}\left(r^2\frac{\partial}{\partial r}\right) + \frac{1}{r^2\sin\theta}\frac{\partial}{\partial\theta}\left(\sin\theta\frac{\partial}{\partial\theta}\right) + \frac{1}{r^2\sin^2\theta}\frac{\partial}{\partial\phi^2}\,\psi + V\psi = E\psi$$

to this problem. Making use of the fact that

$$-\frac{1}{\sin\theta}\frac{\partial}{\partial\theta}\left(\sin\theta\frac{\partial}{\partial\phi}\right) + \frac{1}{\sin^2\theta}\frac{\partial^2}{\partial\phi}\,\psi = l(l+1)\psi, \qquad l = 0, 1, 2, 3, \ldots,$$

for an acceptable wave function, show that the energy eigenvalues of this rotator are

$$E = \frac{\hbar^2(l+1)l}{2I},$$

where $I = MR^2$.

7-13 Show that Eq. (7-45) holds for the spherical harmonic function listed in Eqs. (7-29).

7-14 Show that for a rigid body spinning around an axis, the gyromagnetic ratio μ/L is equal to $q/2M$, provided that the charge q and the mass M are similarly distributed.

7-15 An atom with a magnetic moment (z-component) of one Bohr magneton moves with a velocity of $f_x = 100$ m s^{-1} in a magnetic field with a field gradient of 10^4 gauss cm$^{-1} = 10^2$ Wbm^{-3}. Find its vertical velocity v_z as it emerges and thereby the angle of deflection.

7-16 Can the Stern-Gerlach experiment be performed with ions rather than neutral atoms? Compare the transverse magnetic force with the force $F = \mu\,dB/dr$ for a single ionized ion with a magnetic moment equal to one Bohr magneton. Assume that

$$v = 100 \text{ m s}^{-1}, \qquad B = 1\,\frac{W}{m^2}, \qquad \frac{dB}{dr} = 100\,\frac{W}{m^3}.$$

7-17 Show that the operators L^2 and L_z commute.

7-18 Under what circumstances does the operator for linear momentum commute with the Hamiltonian?

7-19 Show that the operators given by Eqs. (7-70) satisfy the relationships (7-66) to (7-68).

7-20 Prove. Eq. (7-71).

7-21 Show that the spin function β is an eigenfunction of S^2 and of S_z.

7-22 In the emission spectrum of hydrogen there is a strong line at 4861.3 Å (Fig. 4-6). a) Between what states (n, l) does this transition occur? b) Draw an energy-level diagram showing the states involved in this transition. Include fine structure, and label each level with its term classifications (*example*: $3d_{5/2} - ?$, etc.).

7-23 Prove that the expectation value $\langle r^{-3}\rangle$ for the 2p-state of hydrogen has the value given in Section 7-9.

CHAPTER 8

Some Methods in Wave Mechanics*

8–1 EXPANSIONS; ORTHOGONALITY OF WAVE FUNCTIONS

The eigenfunctions of a particular operator, e.g., of a Hamiltonian, can be used in the form of a series to describe other functions of the same independent variables. For simplicity, let us go back to one-particle wave functions so that the variables are the position coordinates x, y, and z. Expressed mathematically, the statement made above is

$$\psi(x, y, z) = \sum_{n=1}^{\infty} a_n u_n(x, y, z). \tag{8–1}$$

The functions $u_1, u_2, \ldots, u_n, \ldots$ are a set of eigenfunctions of a particular Hamiltonian; thus

$$Hu_n = E_n u_n. \tag{8–2}$$

The function $\psi(x, y, z)$ can be any well-behaved function of x, y, and z. If the expansion (8–1) is possible, the set $u_1, u_2, \ldots, u_n, \ldots$ is called a *complete set*.

The expansion (8–1) is very similar to a Fourier expansion (Section 5–7). For the particle in an infinite square well, indeed, it is a Fourier expansion, since the wave functions are sine and cosine functions. The function to be expanded needs to be "well behaved," i.e., be finite and have a finite number of nonrepetitive discontinuities. Any wave function describing a possible physical situation is well behaved in this sense.

Some Hamiltonians produce an infinite set of wave functions with discrete eigenvalues (energies). Examples are the Hamiltonians representing the

---

* This chapter can be omitted in a first reading of the book without serious loss of continuity. For a more formal discussion of the material in this chapter, see any textbook on wave mechanics, e.g., R. H. Dicke and J. P. Wittke, *Introduction to Quantum Mechanics,* Reading, Massachusetts: Addison-Wesley (1960).

harmonic-oscillator potential and the infinite square well. Others produce a finite set of wave functions with discrete eigenvalues followed by an infinite set in which the eigenvalue is continuously variable. An example is the square well of finite depth (Section 6–8). For $E > 0$, the particle is not bound to the well, and the problem is similar to the barrier penetration problem (Section 6–11). Acceptable solutions exist for any value of $E > 0$. These solutions have to be included in the complete set for this particular Hamiltonian, and the expansion Eq. (8–1) has to include an integral over this continuous part of the set. In the following discussion, we shall use summation signs only for the expressions but shall assume that an integral is included if the Hamiltonian produces a continuum of eigenvalues.

In order for the coefficients a_n of Eq. (8–1) to be uniquely determinable, the set $u_1, u_2, \ldots, u_n, \ldots$ must be orthogonal. With this, we mean that any two functions of the set must satisfy the relationship

$$\int u_k^* u_n \, d\tau = 0 \qquad \text{for} \qquad k \neq n. \tag{8–3}$$

The integration is carried out over all space, which in practice means over the part of space in which at least one of the functions is nonzero.

It is simple to prove that eigenfunctions with different eigenvalues are orthogonal. We write the complex conjugate of Eq. (8–2) applied to another solution u_k with its eigenvalue E_k:

$$Hu_k^* = E_k u_k^*. \tag{8–4}$$

The Hamiltonian for a particle moving in a potential $V(r)$ is real, and so is the eigenvalue E_k. Both are therefore equal to their complex conjugates. We multiply Eq. (8–2) on the left-hand side with u_k^* and Eq. (8–4) with u_n and subtract. We get

$$u_k^* H u_n - u_n H u_k^* = (E_n - E_k) u_k^* u_n. \tag{8–5}$$

The two terms on the left-hand side immediately cancel each other for any part of the Hamiltonian not involving a differentiation, in other words, for the potential-energy part. We are left with

$$-\frac{\hbar^2}{2m} (u_k^* \nabla^2 u_n - u_n \nabla^2 u_k^*) = (E_n - E_k) u_k^* u_n. \tag{8–6}$$

For the rest of the proof, we assume a one-dimensional space only, leaving to a problem (Problem 8–1) the slightly more cumbersome work in three dimensions. We integrate Eq. (8–5) over x from $-\infty$ to $+\infty$:

$$-\frac{\hbar^2}{2m} \int_{-\infty}^{\infty} \left(u_k^* \frac{d^2 u_n}{dx^2} - u_n \frac{d^2 u_k^*}{dx^2} \right) dx = (E_n - E_k) \int_{-\infty}^{\infty} u_k^* u_n \, dx. \tag{8–7}$$

By partial integration, we get

$$-\frac{\hbar^2}{2m} \left[u_k^* \frac{du_n}{dx} - u_n \frac{du_k^*}{dx} \right]_{-\infty}^{\infty} = (E_n - E_k) \int_{-\infty}^{\infty} u_k^* u_n \, dx. \tag{8–8}$$

The two integrals left by the partial integration are identical and cancel.

We now assume that our eigenfunctions can be normalized and therefore vanish at $x = \pm\infty$. Equation (8–8) then gives

$$(E_n - E_k) \int_{-\infty}^{\infty} u_k^* u_n \, dx = 0. \tag{8–9}$$

We have therefore proved that, unless $E_n = E_k$, we must have

$$\int_{-\infty}^{\infty} u_k^* u_n \, dx = 0, \tag{8–10}$$

or, for the three-dimensional case

$$\int u_k^* u_n \, d\tau = 0. \tag{8–11}$$

When two eigenfunctions u_n and u_k are energy degenerate, that is, $E_n = E_k$, they may or may not be orthogonal. However, it can be shown that linear combinations of the two (or more) energy-degenerate functions can be formed that are orthogonal. We shall assume that all degenerate eigenfunctions we are dealing with here have been thus orthogonalized and also that they are normalized; i.e.,

$$\int u_n^* u_n \, d\tau = 1. \tag{8–12}$$

It is convenient to combine Eqs. (8–3) and (8–12) into a single equation:

$$\int u_k^* u_n \, d\tau = \delta_{kn}, \tag{8–13}$$

where δ_{kn} is the *Kronecker symbol*, defined as

$$\begin{aligned} \delta_{kn} &= 1, \qquad k = n; \\ \delta_{kn} &= 0, \qquad k \neq n. \end{aligned} \tag{8–14}$$

A set of functions satisfying Eq. (8–13) is said to be an *orthonormal set*.

8–2 TIME-INDEPENDENT PERTURBATION THEORY

There are very few problems in atomic physics for which Schrödinger's equation can be solved exactly and analytically. The techniques discussed in this section and in Section 8–4 deal with situations in which an exact solution, analytic or numeric, is difficult to obtain. Specifically, in this section, we want to study the effects of small changes in the Hamiltonian, e.g., in the potential. In other words, we want to know how the eigenfunctions and eigenvalues are changed by small perturbing forces. Similar methods have been used in classical mechanics since Newton.

As is well known, the planets move about the sun in approximately elliptical orbits; approximately, because the orbits are perturbed by the forces acting from the other planets. The method for studying the perturbations of planetary orbits is essentially as follows: First, we "turn off" the perturbing forces and place all the planets in elliptical orbits, starting with the observed positions of the planets at a given time. Then we calculate the resultant force as a function of time on a given planet from all other planets, assuming that they all continue to move in the elliptical orbits. From this, we can calculate the velocity and the displacement of the given planet from its elliptical orbit. This is first-order perturbation theory. If we desire to carry the calculations to a higher order of accuracy, we have to calculate the first-order perturbations of the orbits of all the planets, then recalculate the forces for the new orbits, and from this calculate the changes in the perturbations, i.e., the second-order effects. If the forces are small compared with the major interaction, in this case the pull of the sun, the terms describing the perturbation in displacement will represent a rapidly converging series.

In quantum mechanics we take essentially the same approach as in planetary perturbation. We shall not here consider anything beyond first-order perturbation theory. Let us assume that we have found an orthonormal set $u_1, u_2, \ldots,$ $u_n, \ldots$ that are eigenfunctions of the Hamiltonian H_0. The corresponding eigenvalues are $E_{01}, E_{02}, \ldots, E_{0n}, \ldots$. Thus

$$H_0 u_n = E_{0n} u_n. \tag{8-15}$$

The Hamiltonian H_0 can, for instance, be the Hamiltonian for the hydrogen problem (without spins) or for a more complex atom. We assume that we have found the solutions somehow, either analytically or by numerical integration of Schrödinger's equation.

Now assume that the Hamiltonian is changed slightly by addition of a small perturbing term H', for instance, a slight change in the potential function

$$H = H_0 + H'. \tag{8-16}$$

The problem is to find the new eigenfunctions and the new eigenvalues for the Hamiltonian, treating the addition H' as a small perturbation. We write Schrödinger's equation with this new Hamiltonian as

$$H\psi_k = E_k \psi_k, \tag{8-17}$$

where ψ_k is a wave function corresponding to the original u_k. In other words, we assume that there is a one-to-one correspondence between the old set of wave functions and the new set, that the functions are very similar to each other, and that their eigenvalues are close. Since the functions u_n form a complete orthonormal set, we can expand the new functions as

$$\psi_k = \sum_{n=1}^{\infty} a_{kn}u_n. \tag{8-18}$$

Inserted into Eq. (8-17), this becomes

$$(H_0 + H') \sum_{n=1}^{\infty} a_{kn}u_n = E_k \sum_{n=1}^{\infty} a_{kn}u_n. \tag{8-19}$$

By use of Eq. (8-15), we can rewrite this as

$$\sum_{n=1}^{\infty} a_{kn}H'u_n = \sum_{n=1}^{\infty} (E_k - E_{0n})a_{kn}u_n. \tag{8-20}$$

We now multiply from the left with the complex conjugate of another function of the original set u_m^* and integrate:

$$\sum_{n=1}^{\infty} a_{kn} \int u_m^*H'u_n \, d\tau = \sum_{n=1}^{\infty} (E_k - E_{0n})a_{kn} \int u_m^*u_n \, d\tau. \tag{8-21}$$

We introduce an abbreviation H'_{mn} called the *matrix element* of the perturbing Hamiltonian H' between states m and k. It is defined as

$$H'_{mn} \equiv \int u_m^*H'u_n \, d\tau. \tag{8-22}$$

By inserting this in Eq. (8-21) and by using the orthonormality property of the wave functions, we obtain

$$\sum_{n=1}^{\infty} a_{kn}H'_{mn} = (E_k - E_{0m})a_{km}. \tag{8-23}$$

On the right-hand side of the equation, all terms have vanished except the one for which $n = m$.

We set out to determine the new eigenvalues, e.g., E_k, and the new eigenfunctions, e.g., the expansion coefficients a_{kn}. We shall obtain this information from Eq. (8-23) by making some approximations. To understand the implications of the approximations made, consider Fig. 8-1. On the left is an unperturbed energy-level diagram, and next to it is shown the value of the expansion coefficients for a particular state ψ_k for the case of no perturbation. Clearly, $\psi_k = u_k$ and all coefficients a_{kn} are zero except a_{kk}. To the right is shown schematically what happens to the state ψ_k with the perturbation turned on. The energy has changed slightly, and the other expansion coefficients are generally not zero. However, if the perturbation is small, which we shall assume, then the value of a_{kk} is still approximately equal to 1, and all the other coefficients are small.

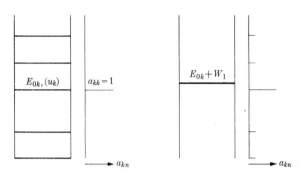

Fig. 8–1 (a) Unperturbed eigenstate with energy E_{0k} and eigenfunction u_k, i.e., amplitude $a_{kk} = 1$. (b) Perturbed eigenstate with shifted energy E_k and non-zero coupling amplitudes a_{kn}.

Equation (8–23) contains on the right-hand side an energy difference times one of the expansion coefficients a_{km}. On the left-hand side is the sum of a number of terms of which one, identified as $n = k$, is the dominant one. In first-order perturbation theory, we neglect all but the dominant term and we can therefore write

$$(E_k - E_{0m})a_{km} = H'_{mk}. \qquad (8\text{–}24)$$

For $m = k$, this equation gives the change in energy, i.e., the first-order perturbation energy for the kth state as

$$\Delta E_k = E_k - E_{0k} = H'_{kk}, \qquad (8\text{–}25)$$

where we again have used $a_{kk} \approx 1$.

The energy change of a given state k, i.e., the matrix element H'_{kk}, is simply the expectation value $\langle H' \rangle$ in state k, calculated with the unperturbed eigenfunction u_k. This simple result has already been used in the derivation of the formula for the fine-structure (spin orbit) energy (Eq. 7–77).

We find the expansion coefficients a_{km} for the state ψ_k also by using Eq. (8–24) but now with $m \neq k$. For convenience, we make the additional approximation $E_k \approx E_{0k}$ and obtain

$$a_{km} = \frac{H'_{mk}}{E_{0k} - E_{0m}} \qquad \text{for} \qquad m \neq k. \qquad (8\text{–}26)$$

It has been necessary to carry three indices k, m, and n in these calculations. Clearly, m can now be changed to n, if desired, in Eq. (8–26) to conform with the expansion Eq. (8–18).

8–3 EXAMPLES OF PERTURBATION CALCULATIONS

In atomic and nuclear physics, we are often mostly interested in the change in energy of a given state resulting from a perturbing interaction and less interested in the changes of the wave function. A case in point is the fine-structure energy mentioned above. In this section we shall work an example in which we calculate both the energy shift and the resulting change in wave function.

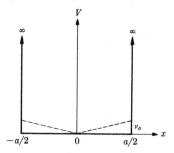

Fig. 8–2 Infinite square well and perturbing potential (dashed).

Figure 8–2 shows a square-well potential modified with the perturbation

$$H' = \frac{2v_0}{a} |x|. \tag{8-27}$$

The unperturbed wave functions and corresponding energies were worked out in Section 6–7. Using Eq. (8–25), we find the energy shift for the nth state,

$$\Delta E_n \begin{pmatrix} \text{odd } n \\ \text{even } n \end{pmatrix} = 2 \int_0^{a/2} \frac{2}{a} \frac{2v_0}{a} x \begin{pmatrix} \cos \\ \sin \end{pmatrix}^2 k_n x \, dx, \tag{8-28}$$

where the notation is meant to indicate that the cosine function applies to odd n values and the sine function to even n values. The wave number k_n is given by $k_n = n\pi/a$. Introducing $\alpha = k_n x = n\pi x/a$, we get

$$\Delta E_n \begin{pmatrix} \text{odd } n \\ \text{even } n \end{pmatrix} = \frac{8v_0}{a^2} \left(\frac{a}{n\pi}\right)^2 \int_0^{n\pi/2} \alpha \begin{pmatrix} \cos \\ \sin \end{pmatrix}^2 \alpha \, d\alpha \tag{8-29}$$

The integral is easily solved by introducing $\cos 2\alpha$ and using partial integration. The result is

$$\Delta E_n \begin{pmatrix} \text{odd } n \\ \text{even } n \end{pmatrix} = \frac{v_0}{2} \left(1 \mp \frac{4}{n^2 \pi^2}\right). \tag{8-30}$$

The new wave functions contain mixtures of other wave functions of the same parity.* We now proceed to calculate the mixing coefficients a_{nm}.

$$a_{nm} = \frac{2}{E_{0n} - E_{0m}} \int_0^{a/2} \frac{2}{a} \frac{2v_0}{a} x \begin{pmatrix} \cos \\ \sin \end{pmatrix} k_n x \begin{pmatrix} \cos \\ \sin \end{pmatrix} k_m x \, dx. \tag{8-31}$$

---

* Since H' is symmetric about the origin, it is clear from Eq. (8–22) that the integral vanishes when the product $u_m u/n^*$ is antisymmetric about the origin, i.e., when the states have opposite parity. Notice that a state with even parity has odd n, and conversely.

Table 8-1 Coefficients a_{nm} in units of v_0/E_{01}

n \ m	1	2	3	4	5	6	7	8	9	10
1	—	0	0.0254	0	0.0009	0	0.0005	0	0.0001	0
2	0	—	0	0.0150	0	0	0	0.0002	0	0
3	-0.0254	0	—	0	0.0127	0	0.0002	0	0.0003	0
4	0	-0.0150	0	—	0	0.0097	0	0	0	0.0000
5	-0.0009	0	-0.0127	0	—	0	0.0084	0	0.0001	0
6	0	0	0	-0.0097	0	—	0	0.0071	0	0
7	-0.0005	0	-0.0002	0	-0.0084	0	—	0	0.0063	0
8	0	-0.0002	0	0	0	-0.0071	0	—	0	0.0056
9	-0.0001	0	-0.0003	0	-0.0001	0	-0.0063	0	—	0
10	0	0	0	-0.0000	0	0	0	-0.0056	0	—

Introducing $n\alpha = k_n x = n\pi x/a$ and $m\alpha = k_m x = m\pi x/a$, we get

$$a_{nm} = \frac{8v_0}{(E_{0n} - E_{0m})a^2} \left(\frac{a}{\pi}\right)^2 \int_0^{\pi/2} \alpha \binom{\cos}{\sin} n\alpha \binom{\cos}{\sin} m\alpha \, d\alpha. \qquad (8\text{–}32)$$

The integral can be solved most easily by expressing the sine and cosine functions by complex exponentials. The result is

$$a_{nm}\binom{\text{odd-odd}}{\text{even-even}} = \frac{4}{\pi^2} \frac{v_0}{E_{01}} \frac{1}{n^2 - m^2} \left[\frac{(-1)^{(m-n)/2} - 1}{(m - n)^2} \pm \frac{(-1)^{(m+n)/2} - 1}{(m + n)^2} \right],$$

$$(8\text{–}33)$$

where the lowest state energy is $E_{01} = \pi^2\hbar^2/2Ma^2$, and we have used $E_{0n} = E_{01}n^2$, etc.

Table 8–1 gives the values of $a_{nm}E_{01}/v_0$, as calculated from Eq. (8–33), up to $n = m = 10$. The diagonal coefficients are not given in the table but are $a_{11} = a_{22} = \cdots \approx 1$. Since a first-order perturbation theory is used, the calculations are valid only when $v_0 \ll E_{01}$.

8–4 MATRIX DIAGONALIZATION

The first-order perturbation theory developed in Section 8–2 is very simple to use. The formulas are explicit, and it is, in principle, easy to calculate any matrix element and therefore any contribution to a state ψ_k from any of the eigenstates u_n. The method has the drawback that, unless the perturbing interaction is small, the results of first-order perturbation calculations are not very accurate. The method of matrix diagonalization to be developed in this section is more accurate; indeed, if an infinite set of eigenfunctions is used, the results are exact. However, the technique is much more cumbersome, and in all but very simple cases the solutions have to be worked out on electronic computers.

We assume that the Hamiltonian is given but that Schrödinger's equation is too difficult to solve directly. We are therefore seeking solutions ψ_k that can be expressed in the form of an expansion and also the corresponding eigenvalues E_k. For the moment, we shall drop the subscript k and write

$$\psi = \sum_{n=1}^{N} a_n u_n. \qquad (8\text{–}34)$$

We are seeking the coefficient a_n in this expansion. The functions u_n can be *any complete orthonormal set*, but, of course, a judicious choice of functions will make the series converge faster than otherwise. The summation over n in Eq. (8–34) is truncated at $n = N$ instead of being carried to infinity. In general, an exact description of ψ can be obtained only with $N \to \infty$, but for practical reasons, we must settle for something less perfect.

To find the coefficients a_n, we start by substituting Eq. (8–34) into Schrödinger's equation, thus

$$\sum_n a_n H u_n = E \sum_n a_n u_n. \tag{8–35}$$

We now use the standard trick of multiplying with the complex conjugate u_k^* of one of the functions from the orthonormal set and integrating over all coordinates. We then get

$$\sum_{n=1}^{N} a_n H_{kn} = E a_k, \tag{8–36}$$

with the matrix element H_{kn} defined as

$$H_{kn} \equiv \int u_k^* H u_n \, d\tau. \tag{8–37}$$

Of course, these matrix elements can be calculated when the set u_n is given and when H is known. By giving k all possible values from 1 to N, we get a series of N equations from Eq. (8–36). We can write them out as follows:

$$
\begin{aligned}
a_1(H_{11} - E) + a_2 H_{12} + a_3 H_{13} + \cdots + a_N H_{1N} &= 0, \\
a_1 H_{21} + a_2(H_{22} - E) + a_3 H_{23} + \cdots + a_N H_{2N} &= 0, \\
a_1 H_{31} + a_2 H_{32} + a_3(H_{33} - E) + \cdots + a_N H_{3N} &= 0, \\
\vdots \quad\quad\quad\quad & \\
a_1 H_{N1} + a_2 H_{N2} + a_3 H_{N3} + \cdots + a_N(H_{NN} - E) &= 0.
\end{aligned}
\tag{8–38}
$$

Equations (8–38) form a set of homogeneous first-order equations for the coefficients a_n. Our derivation is based on the assumption that the set is complete, which implies $N = \infty$. When, for practical reasons, we have to limit the number of terms N, it is not obvious that the coefficients a_n resulting from a solution of Eqs. (8–38) with finite N produces the best possible approximation for the wave function ψ (Eq. 8–34) that can be found with the set u_n. However, this turns out to be the case, although we shall not take space to prove it here.* It is well known that such a set of homogeneous equations only possesses nontrivial solutions for the unknowns when the determinant of the coefficients disappears. Therefore, we get

$$
\begin{vmatrix}
(H_{11} - E) & H_{12} & H_{13} & \ldots & H_{1N} \\
H_{21} & (H_{22} - E) & H_{23} & \ldots & H_{2N} \\
\vdots & & & & \\
H_{N1} & H_{N2} & H_{N3} & \ldots & (H_{NN} - E)
\end{vmatrix} = 0.
\tag{8–39}
$$

Since all the matrix elements H_{kn} are presumed known, this Nth-order equation in E can be solved. It is called the *secular equation* and gives N eigenvalues

---

* For proof see, for instance, J. C. Slater, *Quantum Theory of Atomic Structure*, Vol. 1, New York: McGraw-Hill (1960), p. 113 ff.

E for N approximate solutions of Schrödinger's equation. For a given eigen-value E, the set of N equations (8–38) gives the N coefficients a_n and thereby the eigenfunction ψ corresponding to that given E.

If the functions u_n happened to be eigenfunctions of the Hamiltonian H, all elements H_{kn} would be zero except those with $n = k$. The matrix formed by these elements would then have nonzero terms only on the diagonal. To find the eigenfunctions ψ_k of a given Hamiltonian is therefore equivalent to diagonalizing the matrix whose elements are of the form (8–37) with u replaced with ψ.

As an example of a diagonalization calculation, we show in Fig. 8–3 the approximate eigenvalues E of the s-states in hydrogen calculated by solving the secular equation for 15 separate cases with $N = 1$ to 15. The functions u_n

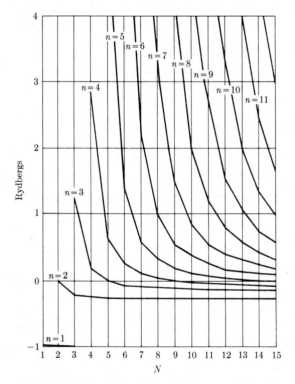

Fig. 8–3 Positions of the s-states of hydrogen calculated by diagonalizing matrices of dimension $N \times N$. Reprinted with permission from John C. Slater, *Quantum Theory of Atomic Structure*, Vol. 1, New York: McGraw-Hill © 1960, p. 118.

used were of the form $c_1 \exp(-ar)$, $c_2 \exp(-ar) + c_3 r \exp(-ar)$, etc. with one more term added for each new function up to the last, u_N, which had N terms. The coefficients c_1, etc. were chosen so as to make the functions orthonormal. The value for a was arbitrarily made equal to $\frac{27}{32}$ of the inverse Bohr radius. Figure 8–3 shows that with this set of functions a good value for the ground-state energy is obtained with $N \gtrsim 3$. A nearly correct value for the energy of the 2s-state is obtained with $N \gtrsim 5$, and for the 3s-state, $N = 10$ is required. The slow convergence indicates that the orthonormal set chosen is not very well suited for describing the higher s-states in hydrogen.

8–5 TIME-DEPENDENT PERTURBATION THEORY

Changes in the physical states of atoms, molecules, and nuclei are studied by use of time-dependent perturbation theory. An example is photon emission from an atom and an accompanying transition from one quantum state of the atom to a lower state. Other examples are beta, alpha, and gamma decay of nuclei, and atomic or nuclear collisions with accompanying changes of states of the colliding atoms or nuclei. To be specific, let us think of an atom in an excited state ψ_m of energy E_m. This quantum-mechanical system can change to a new state ψ_k, the full description of which has the atom in a state of lower energy and a photon moving in some direction away from the atom.

Another example is the Franck-Hertz experiment (Section 4–11). Before collision, the state ψ_m describes an atom in its ground state and an electron moving towards it with a specified momentum (plane wave). After the collision, the state ψ_k has the atom in an excited state, and the electron with reduced kinetic energy moving away from the atom in some direction.

In both examples, the states ψ_m and ψ_k are eigenstates of a Hamiltonian H_0 which clearly is more complex than just an atomic Hamiltonian, since a photon or an electron is also part of the system. A perturbing interaction H' brings about the change from ψ_m to ψ_k, as discussed formally below.

In these examples, as well as in any other example of atomic or nuclear decay, the number of states ψ_k that can be reached in the decay is very large, because the number of directions that the photon or electron can move in is very large (compare Section 3–9). However, if the wave functions of these particles are normalized in a box of finite volume, the number of particle states in a given energy interval is finite. An important question is then: Does *any* particle (electron or photon) state have the exact energy to match the difference between the initial state ψ_m and the final state of the atom? The answer is that it does not have to match a difference with infinite precision because of the uncertainty principle. At least one of the two atomic states involved is an excited state and therefore unstable with a finite lifetime. According to the uncertainty principle (Eq. 5–52), it then has a nonzero-energy uncertainty. Therefore, the energy of state ψ_m overlaps the energies of many states ψ_k.

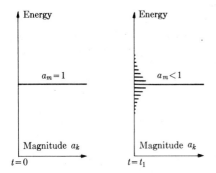

Fig. 8–4 Buildup of amplitudes in the states of system originally in state ψ_m.

The perturbation theory, being a wave theory, atuomatically takes this into account.

The objective of perturbation theory, specifically with reference to the two examples, is to determine transition rates, calculated as the buildup of probability amplitudes in the states ψ_k at the expense of probability in state ψ_m. We shall approach this problem in the following way. We shall assume that the system is known to be in state

$$\Psi = \psi_m e^{-E_m t/h} \tag{8–40}$$

at time $t \lesssim 0$. This is illustrated in Fig. 8–4(a). At time $t = 0$, the interaction that may bring about a change is "turned on." When this interaction, the perturbation H', has been working for some time, probability density has built up in other states, and the wave function can be expanded in the set ψ_n, as follows:

$$\Psi = \sum_{n=1}^{\infty} a_n(t)\psi_n e^{-iE_n t/\hbar}. \tag{8–41}$$

The individual functions ψ_n are orthonormal eigenfunctions of the Hamiltonian H_0. Thus

$$H_0\psi_n = E_n\psi_n. \tag{8–42}$$

The magnitude of the coefficients a_n is plotted (qualitatively) in Fig. 8–4(b). The vertical scale in this figure represents the mean energy of a state, whether it is sharp or not. The figure illustrates how a band (in practice, exceedingly narrow) of states can be reached by the decay or transformation of ψ_m.

The total wave function Ψ must satisfy Schrödinger's time-dependent equation

$$H\Psi = \hbar i \frac{\partial \Psi}{\partial t}, \tag{8–43}$$

where

$$H = H_0 + H'. \tag{8-44}$$

The total Hamiltonian includes the perturbing interaction H' which produces mixing of the states or, as expressed above, flow of probability from one state to another.

Inserting Eqs. (8–44) and (8–41) into (8–43) and with further use of (8–42), we obtain

$$\hbar i \sum_{n=1}^{\infty} \dot{a}_n \psi_n e^{-iE_n t/\hbar} = \sum_{n=1}^{\infty} H' a_n \psi_n e^{-iE_n t/\hbar}, \tag{8-45}$$

where the dot over a_n indicates differentiation with respect to time. We now multiply Eq. (8–45) from the left with ψ_k^*, one of the other eigenfunctions of H_0, and integrate over ψ space. We then get (remembering that the ψ_n's are orthonormal)

$$\dot{a}_k = \frac{1}{\hbar i} \sum_{n=1}^{\infty} a_n H'_{kn} e^{i\omega_{kn} t}, \tag{8-46}$$

where we have inserted the matrix element H'_{kn} as given by Eq. (8–22), and the angular frequency ω_{kn} defined by

$$\omega_{kn} \equiv \frac{E_k - E_n}{\hbar}. \tag{8-47}$$

We now assume that the perturbation is weak enough so that the buildup of probability in other than the initial state ψ_m is very small over the time considered. We can therefore in the *first-order perturbation theory* put $a_m = 1$ and all other a_m's equal to zero on the right-hand side of Eq. (8–46). We then obtain

$$a_k = \frac{1}{\hbar i} \int_0^t H'_{km} e^{i\omega_{km} t}\, dt. \tag{8-48}$$

The probability of finding the system in state ψ_k is then at any time given by $|a_k|^2$.

Experimentally, we cannot, in general, pinpoint the exact final state after the transition process. However, we can calculate the total transition rate by summing over all possible final states. We assume that a constant perturbation H' is turned on at time $t = 0$ and off again at $t = t_1$, a short time later. We calculate the total transition probability as the sum of all terms $|a_k|^2$ at time t_1 and find the transition rate by dividing by t_1.

For simplicity, we assume that in a small energy interval about E_m, the matrix element H'_{km} is a constant for all states considered; that is, for all states that can be reached in a given type of transition subject to, for instance, conservation of angular momentum. By integrating Eq. (8–48), we then get

$$a_k = \frac{H'_{km}}{\hbar} \frac{e^{i\omega_{km} t_1} - 1}{\omega_{km}} = \frac{H'_{km}}{\hbar} e^{i\omega_{km} t_1/2} \frac{2 \sin \omega_{km} t_1/2}{\omega_{km}} \tag{8-49}$$

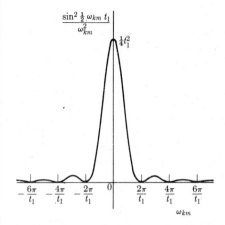

Fig. 8–5 A plot of the integrand of Eq. 8–52, assuming constant dN/dE.

The total transition rate from state ψ_m to all other states is given by

$$\lambda = \frac{1}{t_1} \sum_k |a_k|^2 = \frac{1}{t_1} \int_{-\infty}^{\infty} |a_k|^2 \frac{dN}{dE} \, dE_k, \qquad (8\text{–}50)$$

where dN/dE is the number of accessible final states per unit energy. We write $dE_k = \hbar \, d\omega_{km}$ (from Eq. 8–47) and get

$$\lambda = \frac{4}{\hbar t_1} |H'_{km}|^2 \int_{-\infty}^{\infty} \frac{\sin^2 \omega_{km} t_1/2}{\omega_{km}^2} \frac{dN}{dE} \, d\omega_{km}. \qquad (8\text{–}51)$$

Figure 8–5 shows that the most significant contribution to the integral comes from the region $-2\pi < \omega_{km} t_1 < 2\pi$. For any reasonable value of the observation time, this represents an extremely small energy interval $\Delta E_k = \hbar \, \Delta\omega_{km}$. In this interval we can assume, for practical applications, that dN/dE is a constant. Therefore, we can write, with $x = \omega_{km} t_1/2$,

$$\lambda = \frac{2}{\hbar} |H'_{km}|^2 \frac{dN}{dE} \int_{-\infty}^{\infty} \frac{\sin^2 x}{x^2} \, dx$$

$$= \frac{2\pi}{\hbar} |H'_{km}|^2 \frac{dN}{dE}. \qquad (8\text{–}52)$$

Equation (8–52) is the starting point for quantum-mechanical calculations of transition rates. It is sometimes called *the golden rule number two*.*

---

* Curiously, golden rule number one applies to second-order perturbations for which the direct matrix elements H_{km} vanish between states that can communicate without violating a conservation law.

8–6 ABSORPTION OF RADIATION

We learned in Chapter 7 how Schrödinger's wave mechanics can be used to calculate the energy levels of hydrogen without any further *ad hoc* assumptions.* We shall now show how wave mechanics can also predict transition rates and selection rules, a point where Bohr theory was at a complete loss. First, we shall calculate the probability for absorption of a photon with energy $\hbar\omega$ when a hydrogen atom is bathed in radiation of frequency ω. This probability can be found by use of time-dependent perturbation theory.

The wavelength of the first Lyman line of hydrogen, as an example, is about 1000 times the diameter of the atom. For all practical purposes we can assume that the electric field from radiation of this frequency has the same phase over the entire atom. We express this electric field as

$$\mathscr{E} = \mathscr{E}_1 \cos \omega t \qquad (8\text{–}53)$$

and assume that it is directed along the z-axis. The perturbing potential for the electron is therefore

$$H' = V = ez\mathscr{E}_1 \cos \omega t, \qquad (8\text{–}54)$$

where we have chosen to put $V = 0$ at $z = 0$. Because of this perturbing potential, the atom, originally in state ψ_j, will have a buildup of amplitudes in other states, specifically state ψ_k with amplitudes increasing as Eq. (8–46):

$$\dot{a}_k = \frac{1}{\hbar i} H'_{kj} e^{i\omega_{kj}t}. \qquad (8\text{–}55)$$

Here

$$\omega_{kj} = \frac{E_k - E_j}{\hbar}, \qquad (8\text{–}56)$$

and the matrix element H'_{kj} is given by

$$H'_{kj} = \int \psi_k^* ez\mathscr{E}_1 \cos \omega t \, \psi_j \, d\tau. \qquad (8\text{–}57)$$

We now introduce a new matrix element z_{kj}, defined by

$$z_{kn} \equiv \int \psi_k^* z \psi_j \, d\tau \qquad (8\text{–}58)$$

and write the cosine function as

$$\cos \omega t = \tfrac{1}{2}(e^{i\omega t} + e^{-i\omega t}). \qquad (8\text{–}59)$$

---

* We are for the moment not concerned with the fine details; they are mostly of a relativistic nature and are discussed in Section 7–10.

Substitution into Eq. (8–55) leads to

$$\dot{a}_k = \frac{e\mathscr{E}_1 z_{kj}}{2\hbar i} \left[e^{i(\omega_{kj} + \omega)t} + e^{i(\omega_{kj} - \omega)t} \right]. \tag{8–60}$$

Integration over time from 0 to t yields

$$a_k = -\frac{e\mathscr{E}_1 z_{kj}}{2\hbar} \left[\frac{e^{i(\omega_{kj} + \omega)t} - 1}{\omega_{kj} + \omega} + \frac{e^{i(\omega_{kj} - \omega)t} - 1}{\omega_{kj} - \omega} \right]. \tag{8–61}$$

Let us consider the last term first. When $\omega \approx \omega_{kj}$, the denominator is small, and this term produces a fast buildup rate of a_k, that is, a high transition probability. The condition is, of course (from Eq. 8–56),

$$\hbar\omega \approx E_k - E_j. \tag{8–62}$$

In this case, the final state ψ_k is higher than the initial state ψ_j, and therefore the process is absorption of a photon $\hbar\omega$.

Consider now the first term of Eq. (8–61). The buildup rate is high according to this term when

$$\hbar\omega = E_j - E_k. \tag{8–63}$$

In this case, the final state ψ_k is lower than the initial state ψ_j. Hence we have a release of energy, and this means that this term describes induced emission. We have therefore shown that, under otherwise similar circumstances, the probabilities for absorption and for induced emission of radiation are equal.

We shall now study the case of absorption of radiation in a radiation field, where the energy density in the frequency interval ω to $\omega + d\omega$ is $U(\omega)\,d\omega$ Jm^{-3}. We calculate the square of the numerical value of a_k from Eq. (8–61), retaining only the absorption term (compare Eq. 8–49).

$$|a_k|^2 = \frac{e^2 \mathscr{E}_1^2 |z_{kj}|^2}{\hbar^2} \frac{\sin^2 \frac{1}{2}(\omega_{kj} - \omega)t}{(\omega_{kj} - \omega)^2} \tag{8–64}$$

The energy density in the radiation field $\mathscr{E} = \mathscr{E}_1 \cos \omega t$ is*

$$U = \frac{\varepsilon_0 \mathscr{E}_1^2}{2}. \tag{8–65}$$

For the frequency interval ω to $\omega + d\omega$, we replace this with $U(\omega)\,d\omega$ and obtain

$$d|a_k|^2 = \frac{2e^2 U(\omega)|z_{kj}|^2}{\varepsilon_0 \hbar^2} \frac{\sin^2 \frac{1}{2}(\omega_{kj} - \omega)t}{(\omega_{kj} - \omega)^2}\,d\omega. \tag{8–66}$$

---

*   See any text on Electricity and Magnetism.

We assume that the energy density $U(\omega)$ is uniform over the frequency interval of interest and integrate (compare Eq. 8–52) to obtain

$$|a_k|^2 = \frac{\pi e^2 U(\omega)|z_{kj}|^2}{\varepsilon_0 \hbar^2} t. \tag{8–67}$$

The transition probability per unit time is therefore

$$\lambda_{j \to k} = \frac{\pi e^2 U(\omega)|z_{kj}|^2}{\varepsilon_0 \hbar^2}. \tag{8–68}$$

From the discussion above, it is clear that this formula can be used also for induced emission when $E_j > E_k$.

Equation (8–69) gives the transition probability per second for absorption of radiation for an atom bathed in radiation linearly polarized in the z-direction. Clearly, linear polarization in the x- or y-direction or circular polarization can give rise to absorption as well. We therefore introduce the quantities x_{kj} and y_{kj}, defined similarly as z_{kj}, and combine all three to get

$$r_{kj}^2 = x_{kj}^2 + y_{kj}^2 + z_{kj}^2. \tag{8–69}$$

The transition rate for absorption in an unpolarized field is then

$$\lambda_{j \to k} = \frac{e^2 U(\omega)|r_{kj}|^2}{3\varepsilon_0 \hbar^2}. \tag{8–70}$$

The selection rules discussed earlier can now be derived. Take first as an example the forbidden transition $1s_{1/2}$ to $2s_{1/2}$ in hydrogen. Why is it forbidden? A look at Eq. (8–58) reveals the answer. The wave functions ψ_k and ψ_j have even parity, while the function z has odd parity. The product function has therefore odd parity and hence integrates out to zero. Clearly, the elements x_{kj} and y_{kj} are also zero. In general, the two functions ψ_k and ψ_j must have opposite parity for r_{kj} to be nonzero.

In order to study what other restrictions there are on the relationship between ψ_k and ψ_j, we write the complete expression for z_{kj}, inserting hydrogen wave functions

$$z_{km} = \int R_k^* R_j r^3 \, dr \int\int Y_{l_k m_k}^* Y_{l_j m_j} \cos\theta \sin\theta \, d\theta \, d\phi. \tag{8–71}$$

The integral over ϕ is simply

$$\frac{1}{2\pi} \int e^{im_k\phi} e^{im_j\phi} \, d\phi = \begin{array}{ll} 1 & \text{for} \quad m_k = m_j, \\ 0 & \text{for} \quad m_k \neq m_s. \end{array} \tag{8–72}$$

This gives the transition rule $\Delta m = 0$ for radiation linearly polarized in the z-direction. The θ-integral is a bit more complicated, but yields 0, except when $\Delta l = \pm 1$.

For the elements x_{kj} and z_{kj}, the results are the same, except that we must have $\Delta m = \pm 1$. The final selection rules for absorption of electric dipole radiation in an unpolarized field are therefore

$$\Delta l = \pm 1, \qquad \Delta m = \pm 1 \text{ or } 0. \qquad (8\text{–}73)$$

The same selection rules clearly hold for induced emission. There are no perturbing forces influencing the spin direction, which consequently does not change.

When the electric dipole transition is forbidden, higher-order transitions can take place. Electric quadrupole interaction rests on the fact that the size of the atom is not entirely negligible compared to the wavelength as assumed above. Magnetic dipole interaction involves, of course, the magnetic fields of the atom. Both types of transitions are observed in atoms but not in competition with electric dipole transitions.

8–7 SPONTANEOUS EMISSION

For the proper treatment of spontaneous emission of radiation, one has to use quantum theory of the radiation field. We shall not go into this subject here but will derive the formula for the transition rate in a special case.

The case is one for which a large number of atoms have populations of states j and k in thermal equilibrium with the radiation field. The populations in the two states are N_j and N_k ,respectively. We can then write (Section 1–13):

$$N_k/N_j = e^{-\hbar\omega_{kj}/kT}. \qquad (8\text{–}74)$$

Since we have equilibrium, the number of transitions $j{\to}k$ must be equal to the number of transitions $k{\to}j$. We can write

$$N_j\lambda_{jk} = N_k(\lambda_{kj} + \lambda'_{kj}), \qquad (8\text{–}75)$$

where λ_{jk} is the absorption rate, λ_{kj} the rate of induced emission ($= \lambda_{jk}$), and λ'_{kj} is the rate of spontaneous emission. The latter is independent of the intensity U of the radiation field. By combining Eqs. (8–74) and (8–75) with $\lambda_{jk} = \lambda_{kj}$, we get

$$\lambda_{jk}(e^{\hbar\omega/kT} - 1) = \lambda'_{kj}. \qquad (8\text{–}76)$$

The frequency distribution of the radiation field is given by Planck's law. We rewrite Eq. (3–41) as

$$U(\omega) = \frac{\hbar\omega^3}{\pi^2 c^3(e^{\hbar\omega/kT} - 1)} . \qquad (8\text{–}77)$$

By introducing this into Eq. (8–70) and rearranging, we get

$$\lambda_{jk}(e^{\hbar\omega/kT} - 1) = \frac{e^2\omega^3}{3\pi\varepsilon_0 c^3\hbar} |r_{jk}|^2. \qquad (8\text{–}78)$$

We compare this with Eq. (8–76) and see that the transition rate for spontaneous emission of electric dipole radiation is

$$\lambda'_{jk} = \frac{e^2\omega^3}{3\pi\varepsilon_0 c^3\hbar}\,|r_{jk}|^2. \tag{8–79}$$

Clearly, the selection rules for absorption and induced emission apply also to spontaneous emission, since they depend upon the term $|r_{jk}|$.

We have derived Eq. (8–79) for a case of thermal equilibrium. The temperature T does not enter into the expression, and a more formal derivation reveals that the condition of thermal equilibrium is not necessary.

PROBLEMS

8–1 Carry out the proof of the orthogonality (Eqs. 8–4 to 8–10) in three dimensions.

8–2 Show that the wave functions for the two lowest states of the one-dimensional harmonic oscillator are orthogonal.

8–3 Show that any pair of the spherical harmonic functions $Y_{2,m}$, where $m = -2$ to $+2$, is orthogonal.

8–4 Consider the infinite square well problem discussed in Section 6–7. Introduce a rectangular perturbation potential at the center with height v_0 and width $a/2$, that is, cutoffs at $x = \pm a/4$. Compute the first-order energy shift of the three lowest states.

8–5 In the infinite square well, introduce a rectangular perturbation of height v_0 from $x = 0$ to $x = a/2$. Compute the first-order energy shift of the three lowest states. Show that the expansion coefficients a_{nm} in this asymmetric case are no longer zero, in general, for even-odd combinations (for $n + m =$ odd).

8–6 In the infinite square well, introduce at the center ($x = 0$) a very narrow but very tall potential peak (delta function). The area under the peak is $C = \Delta x v_0$, where the width $\Delta x \to 0$ and the height $v_0 \to \infty$. a) Show that this perturbation potential has no effect on the odd-parity states. b) For the even-parity states, develop a formula for the energy shift and for the mixing coefficients a_{nm}.

8–7 Given the square well with the perturbation potential described in Problem 8–5. a) Write the Hamiltonian, including perturbation potential, in two parts, that is, for $-a/2 < x < 0$ and for $0 < x < a/2$. b) Find the matrix elements H_{11}, H_{12}, H_{21}, and H_{22} using the two lowest unperturbed square-well wave functions. c) Diagonalize the resulting 2×2 matrix; that is, find the two new energies and the coefficients a_{11}, a_{12}, a_{21}, and a_{22}.

8–8 Go through the same steps as in Problem 8–7, but now using the two lowest even-parity wave functions and the perturbation potential of Problem 8–6.

8–9 Consider the infinite square well and the perturbation potential described in Problem 8–6 turned on at time $t = 0$. a) Calculate the matrix elements H'_{13}, H'_{15}, etc. b) Assuming that the particle is in the ground (lowest) state at time

$t = 0$ ($a_1 = 1$), calculate the buildup rate of probability in the other states (Eq. 8–46).

8–10 Consider two classical one-dimensional harmonic oscillators (masses m_1 and m_2 and springs) of natural frequencies ω_1 and ω_2 (rad s^{-1}). Assume that the two masses are connected with a weak spring such that a perturbing potential $H' = \frac{1}{2}\beta(x_2 - x_1)^2$ results. Using Table 6–1, write two unperturbed wave functions for this system as $\psi_n = \psi_0(x_1)\psi_2(x_2)$ and $\psi_k = \psi_2(x_1)\psi_0(x_2)$, where the indexes indicate the n values for the two unperturbed oscillators. a) Calculate the matrix elements H_{nk}^1 and H_{kn}^1. b) Using Eq. (8–46), find the initial buildup rate in state ψ_k when the system is in state ψ_n at time $t = 0$.

CHAPTER 9

Many-Electron Atoms

9–1 THE HELIUM PROBLEM

We learned in Chapter 7 how a two-body problem in wave mechanics can be reduced to a one-body problem and then solved analytically for the case where the potential is the Coulomb potential. Neutral helium has two electrons and a nucleus, so we are here faced with a three-body problem. If the two electrons did not interact and we could regard the nucleus as infinitely heavy compared to the electrons, the problem could be treated as two independent hydrogen-type problems. It is the mutual interaction between the two electrons that causes the difficulty.

In Bohr theory, also as modified by Wilson and Sommerfeld, there is no mechanism for dealing with the mutual interaction between the electrons. These theories were strictly one-electron theories. In wave mechanics, on the other hand, we have no difficulty in writing down Schrödinger's equation for 2, 3, or, in principle, even for 100 electrons. The problem is to solve the equation.

Let us pause for a moment and reflect over what we have retained of Bohr's theory and why we have abandoned that theory in favor of wave mechanics. A theory that is moderately successful in describing some physical phenomena is seldom completely abandoned, only modified. Bohr introduced the idea of energy levels, quantized angular momentum, and transitions with $\Delta E = h\nu$. All this was retained by Schrödinger, but otherwise we must admit that the modifications were major. Some crucial tests of wave mechanics have been mentioned already besides the test of the hydrogen spectrum. One is the Davisson-Germer experiment (Section 5–5); another is the explanation of alpha decay as a barrier-penetration process (Section 6–10). A third, and very important, test which we are now going to discuss is the applicability of the theory to many-electron atoms. The most convincing early work was the approximate solution of

Schrödinger's equation for helium by E. A. Hylleraas.* We are not going to discuss Hylleraas's approach to the problem here, only quote that he and others have been able to calculate helium energy levels, the separations of which agree with experimental spectroscopic data to within experimental errors. We shall here attempt to find qualitatively satisfactory, but much less exact, solutions of Schrödinger's equation for helium.

If we regard the nucleus as infinitely heavy relative to the electron, it can be regarded merely as a stationary source of an attractive potential. The time-independent equation for helium is then

$$[H_1 + H_2 + V_{12}] \psi = E\psi, \tag{9–1}$$

where H_1 and H_2 are the Hamiltonians appropriate for independent motion of electron 1 and electron 2 respectively, in the field of the nucleus, i.e., without the mutual interaction between the two:

$$H_1 = -\frac{\hbar^2}{2m_e} \nabla_1^2 + \frac{Ze^2}{4\pi\varepsilon_0 r_1}, \tag{9–2}$$

$$H_2 = -\frac{\hbar^2}{2m_e} \nabla_2^2 + \frac{Ze^2}{4\pi\varepsilon_0 r_2}. \tag{9–3}$$

The mutual interaction is

$$V_{12} = \frac{e^2}{4\pi\varepsilon_0 r_{12}}, \tag{9–4}$$

with

$$r_{12}^2 = (x_2 - x_1)^2 + (y_2 - y_1)^2 + (z_2 - z_1)^2. \tag{9–5}$$

The experimental data for helium available for checking the result of our calculation are represented by an energy-level diagram (Fig. 9–1) constructed from spectroscopic data. The terms *singlet* and *triplet* in Fig. 9–1 refer to the relative orientation of the spins of the two electrons and the associated fine-structure splitting. The spins add vectorially according to the rules of combination of angular momenta to a total spin vector S with quantum numbers $S = 0$ or $S = 1$. In the magnetic field associated with the orbital angular momentum, if any, three states are produced if the total spin quantum number is $S = 1$ (the triplet) and only one state if it is $S = 0$ (the singlet). If the orbital angular momentum of both electrons is zero, the three states of a triplet differing in the value of m_S are energy degenerate, but the degeneracy can be removed by an external magnetic field (Zeeman effect, see Section 9–8).

Since the most relevant data are given in the form of an energy-level diagram, we shall concentrate on a determination of the eigenvalues E of Eq.

---

* E. A. Hylleraas, *Z. Physik.* **54** (1929), p. 347.

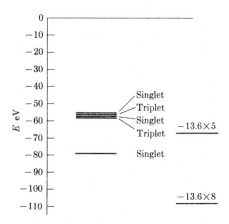

Fig. 9–1 Left column: Experimental data on states of He. Right column: Calculated levels with the mutual interaction between the two electrons ignored.

(9–1). The approach we shall take is a perturbation calculation with V_{12} being the perturbation interaction H'. Consequently, we must first solve the equation

$$(H_1 + H_2)\psi = E\psi. \tag{9–6}$$

We try to write the wave function as a product:

$$\psi = \psi_k(\mathbf{r}_1)\,\psi_n(\mathbf{r}_2). \tag{9–7}$$

Since the Laplacian operator, which is part of H_1, operates only on a function of $\mathbf{r}_1$ and the Laplacian in H_2 operates only on a function of $\mathbf{r}_2$, we can write

$$\psi_n(H_1\psi_k) + \psi_k(H_2\psi_n) = E\psi_k\psi_n. \tag{9–8}$$

This equation separates in the usual way to yield

$$H_1\psi_k = E_1\psi_k, \tag{9–9}$$

$$H_2\psi_n = E_2\psi_n,$$

where

$$E_1 + E_2 = E. \tag{9–10}$$

The two equations (9–9) are identical to Schrödinger's equation for a hydrogenlike atom. The solutions were worked out in Section 7–4. The unperturbed energy levels for helium are therefore given by

$$E = -54.4\left(\frac{1}{n_1^2} + \frac{1}{n_2^2}\right)\,\text{eV}, \tag{9–11}$$

where n_1 and n_2 are the principal quantum numbers for electron 1 and 2, respectively. Column 2 in Fig. 9–1 shows the levels for $n_1 = 1$ and $n_2 = 1$ or 2,

These levels correspond to the experimental levels shown, and the discrepancy in energy presumably arises from the fact that the term V_{12} so far has been neglected.

Looking further into the details of the states, we find that for the case where $n_1 = 1$ and $n_2 = 1$, (the level at -108.8 eV), there should be four states, one singlet, and one triplet. Experimentally, there is only one. "Parallel" spins ($S = 1$) are somehow forbidden in this case, but not when $n_1 = 1$ and $n_2 = 2$. This is an extremely important fact, unpredicted and unpredictable in terms of Schrödinger's wave mechanics. The discrepancy is discussed in the next section.

9-2 PAULI'S EXCLUSION PRINCIPLE; SYMMETRY

The absence of the ground-state triplet in helium is in agreement with a law of physics based purely on experimental observations and discovered by Pauli in 1925 before the publication of Schrödinger's wave mechanics. The law, called *Pauli's exclusion principle*, states that no two electrons can have the same set of quantum numbers, n, l, m_l, and m_s. In the case of the hypothetical ground-state triplet, the principal quantum numbers for the two electrons are both $n = 1$; both orbital angular momenta are $l = 0$ so that the m_l's also are zero; and, finally, the two electrons would have parallel spins, i.e., the same m_s values in the triplet state. The triplet is therefore excluded by Pauli's principle. Each one-electron state, as described earlier for hydrogen and further discussed in the previous section, can therefore contain only one electron. The buildup of more complex atoms follows the same pattern; the lowest single-particle states are filled first, and higher and higher principal quantum numbers n are needed to form the heavier atoms. This is discussed further in Sections 9-4 and 9-5.

Actually, by assigning quantum numbers n, l, m_l, and m_s to each individual electron, we are presuming that the electrons are moving independently of one another; or, put differently, they are in single-particle states. For instance, in the case of helium it is only by neglecting the term V_{12} that we can separate Schrödinger's equation and get hydrogenlike solutions. The field is then a central field and the orbital angular momentum, for example, is sharp; that is, l is a good quantum number. With the mutual interaction V_{12} reinstated, there is exchange of orbital angular momentum between the two electrons, and it is only the total angular momentum that is really conserved. To label the states with a given l_1 and a given l_2, as we have done in Fig. 9-1, is therefore an approximation. Perturbation theory would, of course, show us that higher single-particle states adding up to the same total angular momentum would mix with the states as labeled. However, so long as we clearly understand that the labeling refers only to the principal components of the wave function of a given state, no confusion arises. Pauli's exclusion principle can then be applied to that principal component.

Pauli's exclusion principle can be restated in a formally more acceptable way by use of the concept exchange symmetry or, for short, simply symmetry, which we shall now discuss in some detail.

The wave function ψ in Eq. (9–7) has electron number 1 in state ψ_k and electron number 2 in state ψ_n. From this we can presumably predict, for instance, the energies of electron number 1 and of electron number 2. We can check the predictions by experiment, except that experimentally we have no way of knowing which electron is number 1 and which is number 2. The particles are indistinguishable. Formally, we can take care of this by rewriting Eq. (9–7) in either of these two ways:

$$\psi_S = \frac{1}{\sqrt{2}} \left[\psi_k(r_1)\psi_n(r_2) + \psi_k(r_2)\psi_n(r_1) \right], \tag{9–12}$$

$$\psi_A = \frac{1}{\sqrt{2}} \left[\psi_k(r_1)\psi_n(r_2) - \psi_k(r_2)\psi_n(r_1) \right]. \tag{9–13}$$

The functions ψ_k and ψ_n are assumed to be orthonormal functions, and the factor $1/\sqrt{2}$ is then required to normalize the new function ψ_S and ψ_A. The function ψ_S has *positive exchange symmetry*, which means that it does not change sign when the two electrons change place (exchange of subscripts 1 and 2). The second function ψ_A, on the other hand, changes sign by an exchange of the two subscripts 1 and 2. It therefore has *negative exchange symmetry*. Both Eq. (9–12) and Eq. (9–13) have the property that the probability for finding particle 1 in state k and particle 2 in state n is equal to the probability of the reverse. Since Schrödinger's equation is a linear equation, a linear combination of solutions (with the same energy, E), such as given in Eq. (9–12) or (9–13), must also be a solution. But is it *necessary* to complicate things by replacing Eq. (9–7) with (9–12) or (9–13)? As we shall see, the answer, in the form of experimental evidence, is *Yes* for indistinguishable particles.

First we shall prove that the exchange symmetry of a wave function is conserved. We write Schrödinger's equation for any number of indistinguishable particles as

$$H\Psi = \hbar i \, (\partial \Psi / \partial t), \tag{9–14}$$

where H contains the kinetic-energy operators for all the particles, possibly potential-energy terms resulting from other sources (the nucleus), and then mutual interactions such as V_{12}. Since the particles are identical, their coordinates enter into the expression for H in identical ways. The Hamiltonian is therefore symmetric in the exchange of any two particles. If the wave function Ψ at a given time is symmetric in the exchange of two particles with given labels, say, number 5 and number 9, the left-hand side of Eq. (9–14) is symmetric, and therefore the *time derivative* of Ψ has a positive exchange symmetry for the pair 5 and 9. This symmetry therefore cannot change. Similarly, if Ψ at a given time is antisymmetric in the exchange of numbers 5 and 9, the time derivative according to Eq. (9–14) will be antisymmetric in the exchange of the two particles. Again, the initial symmetry will not change. Clearly, any mixture of symmetries, in the two-particle case a given linear combination of ψ_S and ψ_A, once started will also be conserved.

We still have not proved that it is necessary for the wave function for indistinguishable particles to have a definite exchange symmetry. The proof above that a given symmetry or mixture of symmetries is conserved does not forbid a constant arbitrary mixture of ψ_S and ψ_A—for instance, $(\psi_S + \psi_A)/\sqrt{2}$—and this brings us right back to Eq. (9–7). However, Pauli's exclusion principle, as stated above, is consistent with Eq. (9–13), because if ψ_k and ψ_n, including spin, are identical functions, the antisymmetric wave function (9–13) vanishes.

We now present a new postulate of quantum mechanics, which in its first part encompasses Pauli's exclusion principle:

1. Identical particles with *half-integral intrinsic spin* (fermions) are governed by a wave function that is antisymmetric under the exchange of any two particles.

2. Identical particles with *integral intrinsic spin* (bosons) are governed by a wave function that is symmetric under the exchange of any two particles.

This postulate does not require that the total wave function be written as a linear combination of products of single-particle wave functions. However, if this is possible, Eq. (9–12) is the proper wave function for two bosons (e.g., photons), and Eq. (9–13) is the proper wave function for two fermions (e.g., electrons). For more than two fermions, the product function is antisymmetrized by a simple technique, utilizing a *Slater determinant.**

9–3 THE HELIUM ATOM REVISITED

We are now ready to study the helium levels by use of perturbation theory. We will not actually carry out the detailed calculations, but will be able to make some important points by looking at the integral expressions. We write the total wave function for two particles as a product of a function of space coordinates and another function of spin coordinates. The total wave function

---

* See, for instance, J. C. Slater, *Quantum Theory of Atomic Structure,* Vol. I, New York: McGraw-Hill (1960), p. 288.

is properly antisymmetrized if the space wave function is symmetric and the spin wave function is antisymmetric, or conversely. The possibilities are then

Singlet, $k \neq n$, $S = 0$: $\psi = \frac{1}{2}(\psi_{kn} + \psi_{nk})(\alpha\beta - \beta\alpha)$, $m_S = 0$ (9–15a)

Singlet, $k = n$, $S = 0$: $\psi = \psi_{kk}(\alpha\beta - \beta\alpha)$ $m_S = 0$ (9–15b)

Triplet, $S = 1$: $\psi = \begin{cases} \dfrac{1}{\sqrt{2}}(\psi_{kn} - \psi_{nk})\alpha\alpha, & m_S = 1 \\[2mm] \frac{1}{2}(\psi_{kn} - \psi_{nk})(\alpha\beta + \beta\alpha), & m_S = 0 \\[2mm] \dfrac{1}{\sqrt{2}}(\psi_{kn} - \psi_{nk})\beta\beta, & m_S = -1. \end{cases}$ (9–16)

In these expressions, a short-hand notation has been used, as follows:

$$\psi_{kn} \equiv \psi_k(r_1)\psi_n(r_2) \qquad (9–17)$$

$$\alpha\beta \equiv \alpha(1)\beta(2) \qquad (9–18)$$

The spin wave functions α and β have been discussed in Section 7–7 and stand for spin up, that is, $m_s = \frac{1}{2}$, and spin down, that is, $m_s = -\frac{1}{2}$, respectively. The combination of the two spin-wave functions to a total spin-wave function with quantum numbers S and m_S is, of course, governed by the rules for combinations of angular momenta discussed in Appendix 5. An attempt to illustrate graphically how the two spin vectors combine to the three substates of a triplet and the single substate of a singlet is given in Fig. 9–2. Such graphical representations may be pedagogically useful but should not be taken too literally.

We can now, in principle, calculate the first-order perturbation energy as given by Eq. (8–25). The perturbing Hamiltonian is $H' = V_{12}$. We therefore get

$$\Delta E = \int \psi^* V_{12}\psi \, d\tau, \qquad (9–19)$$

where the function ψ is one or another of the five expressions in Eqs. (9–15a), (9–15b), and (9–16), and the integration is carried out over space and spin coordinates of particles 1 and 2. The perturbing interaction does not depend upon the spin coordinates and because they are orthonormal, integration over them produces unity. We therefore need to consider only the space coordinates.

We take first the case for the helium ground state, which is represented by Eq. (9–15b). Inserting this into Eq. (9–19), we obtain

$$\Delta E_0 = \int |\psi_{kk}|^2 \frac{e^2}{4\pi\varepsilon_0 r_{12}} \, d\tau_1 \, d\tau_2 = \frac{e^2}{4\pi\varepsilon_0} \langle r_{12}^{-1} \rangle = \langle V_{12} \rangle. \qquad (9–20)$$

As a rough estimate, we can put the expectation value of r_{12}^{-1} as the inverse of the Bohr radius. Equation (9–20) then gives for the energy shift 27 eV.

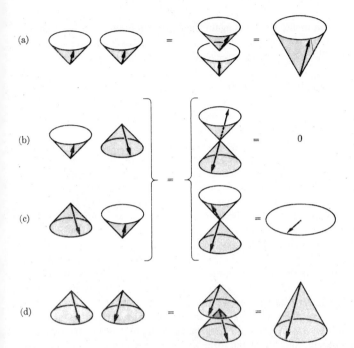

Fig. 9–2 Two spins $s = 1/2$ can combine in four different ways. Three of these yield triplet spin states, and one yields a singlet spin state.

Figure 9–1 shows that the difference between the experimentally observed energy level and the unperturbed state is about 30 eV.

To calculate the energy shift ΔE_1 for the states with $n_1 = 1$ and $n_2 = 2$, we write

$$\Delta E \begin{pmatrix} \text{singlet} \\ \text{triplet} \end{pmatrix} = \frac{e^2}{8\pi\varepsilon_0} \int (\psi_{kn}^* \pm \psi_{nk}^*)(\psi_{kn} \pm \psi_{nk}) r_{12}^{-1} \, d\tau_1 \, d\tau_2$$

$$= \frac{e^2}{8\pi\varepsilon_0} \int (|\psi_{kn}|^2 + |\psi_{nk}|^2) r_{12}^{-1} \, d\tau_1 \, d\tau_2$$

$$\pm \frac{e^2}{8\pi\varepsilon_0} \int (\psi_{kn}^* \psi_{nk} + \psi_{nk}^* \psi_{kn}) r_{12}^{-1} \, d\tau_1 \, d\tau_2. \tag{9–21}$$

The wave functions ψ_{kn} and ψ_{nk} differ only in the labeling of the electrons 1 and 2. Therefore in both integrals the two terms give identical contributions, and we can write

$$\Delta E \begin{pmatrix} \text{singlet} \\ \text{triplet} \end{pmatrix} = \frac{e^2}{4\pi\varepsilon_0} \int |\psi_{kn}|^2 r_{12}^{-1} \, d\tau_1 \, d\tau_2 \pm \frac{e^2}{4\pi\varepsilon_0} \int \psi_{kn}^* \psi_{nk} r_{12}^{-1} \, d\tau_1 \, d\tau_2$$

$$= \langle V_{12} \rangle \pm \Delta E_{\text{exch}}. \tag{9–22}$$

The first term in Eq. (9–22) is again the expectation value of the perturbation potential but now for another state, ψ_{kn}, (not antisymmetrized) and the second term, called the *exchange energy*, is given by the expression

$$\Delta E_{\text{exch}} = \pm \frac{e^2}{4\pi\varepsilon_0} \int \psi_k^*(r_1)\psi_n^*(r_2)\psi_k(r_2)\psi_n(r_1)r_{12}^{-1} \, d\tau_1 \, d\tau_2. \qquad (9\text{–}23)$$

The integral in this expression is positive, which can best be seen by the following argument. The factor r_{12}^{-1} is large when $r_1 \approx r_2$. When this is the case, we must be allowed to interchange r_1 and r_2 for two of the functions in Eq. (9–23), and the expression then becomes identical with the first term in Eq. (9–22), i.e., positive. At larger values of r_{12}, however, we do get negative contributions to the integral of the Eq. (9–23). The net result is that the integral is positive but much smaller than that in the first term of Eq. (9–22).

If we had reasoned completely along classical lines, we would clearly have found that, by turning on the mutual interaction between the two electrons, an energy shift in the positive direction, such as the one shown in Fig. 9–1 for the ground state, would result. However, the exchange energy is completely wave mechanical. It is a direct result of our insistence on writing the wave function as the sum of two terms, identical in every respect except for the exchange of the positions of particles 1 and 2. As we shall see in Section 11–2, the same kind of exchange energy plays a crucial role in the binding of atoms to molecules by the homopolar bond. Without this quirk of nature, chemistry would be quite a bit different, and life in the form we know it would certainly not exist.

Figure 9–3 shows schematically how the two terms in Eq. (9–22) add up to a total energy shift for each state. The first column shows the unperturbed energy levels, identified by the two principal quantum numbers n_1 and n_2. The second column shows the effect of the term $\langle V_{12} \rangle_{kn}$ for the three existing

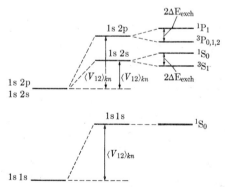

Fig. 9–3 The effect of the electrostatic interaction between the two electrons on the positions of the He levels. Fine structure further splits the ^{3}P-state into three closely spaced levels with $J = 0$, 1, and 2.

possibilities: the ground state, the (1s)(2s)-state, and the (1s)(2p)-state. Finally, the third column shows the effect of the exchange energy. As indicated by Eq. (9–22), the singlet state is higher than the triplet state by $2\Delta E_{exch}$.

The levels shown in the third column are the experimentally observed levels. Since we have used only first-order perturbation theory, the energy shift we would have found if we had actually carried out the calculations in detail would, of course, not have been exactly equal to the shift shown in Fig. 9–1. However, we have used the perturbation theory only to make qual-itative arguments, and this procedure is certainly justified.

The upper of the two triplet states in Fig. 9–3 is a genuine triplet in that the fine-structure splitting separates the levels by a small amount, too small to be shown on the diagram. The lower of the two triplet states shows no fine-structure splitting because both electrons are in s-states, so no internal magnetic field is produced by orbital motion. The convention in spectroscopy is, however, to use the terms singlet and triplet for the cases $S = 0$ and $S = 1$, respectively, whether or not an actual fine-structure splitting is produced.

It may be useful to ponder a bit on the exchange energy in terms of some general arguments about the relative motion of the two electrons. Figure 9–4 shows schematically the space wave function plotted as functions of the relative spacing r_{12} between two electrons.

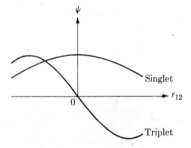

Fig. 9–4 Illustrating the symmetry of the He wave function in exchange of the two electrons. Schematic only.

The triplet wave function changes sign as r_{12} changes sign, and the singlet wave function does not, in accordance with Eqs. (9–15a and b) and (9–16). This means that the probability for the two electrons to be close to each other is small in the triplet state and large in the singlet state. The force between them is the same in both cases, so the difference is caused by the *dynamics* of the system; i.e., it is a result of wave mechanics including the symmetry require-ments. Because the electrons *stay away from each other* in the triplet state but not in the singlet state, the net increase in potential energy caused by V_{12} is smaller in the former case than in the latter.

9–4 MANY-ELECTRON ATOMS

In a many-electron atom, the interactions between one particular electron and all the others can no longer be regarded as a perturbation, especially if the electron is in one of the outermost orbits. The method that is usually employed in computing the energy-level diagram for complex atoms is *Hartree's method of the self-consistent field*. A given electron moves in the field of the nucleus, which is practically stationary, and in the rapidly changing field of the other electrons. The latter can be approximated with an average, spherically symmetric field.

We can describe the procedure used in the calculations by using element number 37, rubidium, as an example. In order to find the eigenfunction and energy for one of the electrons, we guess the density distribution for all the other 36 electrons. From this we can calculate the radial electric field (by Gauss's law) and thereby the potential. The potential of the nucleus with $Z = 37$ is added to this, and Schrödinger's equation is solved (numerically) for the one electron. The procedure is repeated for all 37 electrons, the charge distribution of the other 36 electrons being slightly different, depending on which electron (or state) we are doing the calculation for.

When all the wave functions have been calculated, a new set of density distributions has been obtained, and a second iteration can start. The process is carried on until the wave functions calculated are consistent with the charge distributions assumed. This is why the method is called the method of the *self-consistent field*. It is not extremely accurate, partly because the density distribution, in general, is not spherically symmetric, as assumed. However, the nonspherical part of the distribution and other effects (e.g., exchange symmetry) called the residual interactions can be treated as perturbations (see Section 9–6).

Figure 9–5 shows schematically the resulting energy-level diagram compared with the energy level of a hydrogenlike atom. The states that we are familiar with from the analysis of the hydrogen problem occur again but, for instance, the 2s- and the 2p-states are now separated, whereas in hydrogen they are energy degenerate. Indeed, the states with $n = 3$ are separated so much that the 3d-state falls between the 4s- and the 4p-states. The exact locations of these states depend upon the total number of electrons in the atom. In moving to heavier and heavier atoms, we find that the diagram stretches by approximately the factor Z^2, as indicated to the left in the figure. At the same time, more and more levels are filled with electrons, and the uppermost level filled is always minus a few electron volts for atoms in the ground state.

Figure 9–6 shows the total density distribution of the 36 electrons in Rb^+ and also the individual contributions from the electrons in the various states. As can be seen from the figure, the innermost electrons, the 1s electrons, spend most of the time inside all the other electrons. Therefore by Gauss's law, they experience practically nothing but the field from the nucleus. On the other hand, the 4p and 4s electrons spend nearly all the time outside a large number

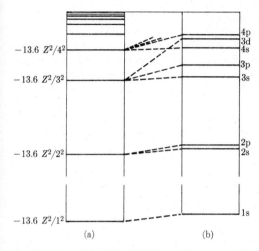

$-13.6\ Z^2/4^2$

$-13.6\ Z^2/3^2$

$-13.6\ Z^2/2^2$

$-13.6\ Z^2/1^2$

4p
3d
4s

3p

3s

2p
2s

1s

(a)   (b)

Fig. 9-5 Atomic levels in (a) hydrogenlike atom and (b) many-electron atom.

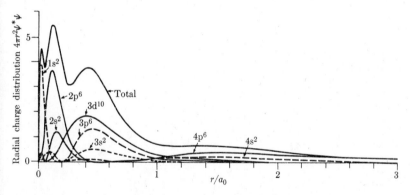

Radial charge distribution $4\pi r^2 \psi^* \psi$

$1s^2$

$2p^6$

Total

$2s^2$

$3d^{10}$

$3p^6$

$3s^2$

$4p^6$

$4s^2$

r/a_0

Fig. 9-6 Radial charge distribution of other electrons seen by the last electron in Rb. The unit for r is $a_0 = 0.529$ angstrom. Reproduced by permission from R. B. Leighton, *Principles of Modern Physics*, New York: McGraw-Hill © 1959.

of other electrons, and therefore they experience a much reduced field. The reduction of the field from the nucleus by inner electrons is called *screening*.

9-5 THE PERIODIC TABLE

Hydrogen in the ground state has its one electron in the 1s-state, and helium has both electrons in the 1s-state. Its *electronic configuration* is $(1s)^2$, where the superscript indicates the number of electrons in the given state. The helium configuration is allowed by the Pauli principle because the two electrons have different values of m_s. The ground-state configuration of the third element in the periodic table, lithium, is $(1s)^2(2s)$, and that of beryllium is $(1s)^2(2s)^2$. The number of electrons allowed by the Pauli principle in a state of given n and l is $2(2l + 1)$. In the configuration, 2p for instance, the quantum numbers that can vary are m_l with $(2l + 1) = 3$ values and m_s with two different values, spin up or spin down, giving six different substates. Table 9–1 gives the electronic configurations for the ground states of the first nineteen elements. A more complete table, for all elements, can be found in Appendix 2. As we see from Table 9–1, the electrons fill the available single-particle states in accordance with Fig. 9–5, completing a p-state at a noble-gas element.

Table 9–1

Element	Z	First ionization potential, V	Quantum number of last added electron		Electron configuration		Outer-most shell occupied
			n	l			
H	1	13.6	1	0	1s		K
He	2	24.6	1	0	$1s^2$		K
Li	3	5.39	2	0	Helium core, 2 electrons	2s	L
Be	4	9.32	2	0		$2s^2$	L
B	5	8.30	2	1		$2s^2\ 2p$	L
C	6	11.3	2	1		$2s^2\ 2p^2$	L
N	7	14.5	2	1		$2s^2\ 2p^3$	L
O	8	13.6	2	1		$2s^2\ 2p^4$	L
F	9	17.4	2	1		$2s^2\ 2p^5$	L
Ne	10	21.6	2	1		$2s^2\ 2p^6$	L
Na	11	5.14	3	0	Neon core 10 electrons	3s	M
Mg	12	7.64	3	0		$3s^2$	M
Al	13	5.98	3	1		$3s^2\ 3p$	M
Si	14	8.15	3	1		$3s^2\ 3p^2$	M
P	15	10.6	3	1		$3s^2\ 3p^3$	M
S	16	10.4	3	1		$3s^2\ 3p^4$	M
Cl	17	13.0	3	1		$3s^2\ 3p^5$	M
Ar	18	15.8	3	1		$3s^2\ 3p^6$	M
K	19	4.34	4	0	Argon core	4s	N

Another entry in Table 9–1 is the first ionization potential V for each element. Called the *binding energy*, this is the energy required to remove the most loosely bound electron from the atom. The ionization potential increases uniformly from lithium to neon, while the 2s- and 2p-states are being filled. The reason for this is that the energy-level diagram stretches by the factor Z^2 as we are increasing the number of electrons (Fig. 9–5). The eleventh electron, forming sodium, is forced into a substantially higher level and therefore the binding energy is again much smaller. The ionization potential increases again as we move through the 3s-3p shell and then drops from argon to potassium.

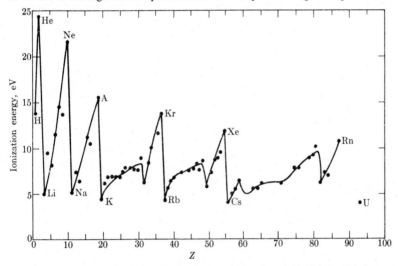

Fig. 9–7 Ionization energies. Reproduced by permission from R. M. Eisberg, *Fundamentals of Modern Physics,* New York: Wiley © 1961, p. 413.

Figure 9–7 shows the first ionization potential as a function of Z. In every instance there is a large drop following one of the noble gases, marking the closing of a p-shell. The inertness of the noble-gas atoms can be explained from the following two observations: (1) The binding energy of the last electron is large; therefore, the atom does not easily give up one electron. (2) Other atoms will readily accept the next electron to form a relatively tightly bound negative ion, but because of the large level spacing between shells, negative noble-gas ions are not bound at all.* These two facts imply that noble-gas atoms very reluctantly share electrons with other atoms to form neutral molecules. The alkaline metals represent another extreme in that they can very

---

* Negative helium ions can be formed in a state which is unstable, but with long enough lifetime for utilization in certain nuclear accelerators.

readily give up an electron since the binding energy of the last electron is very low.

The chemical properties of the elements are determined by the outermost electrons, the valence electrons. Elements belonging to the same column in the periodic table have similar configuration, e.g., fluorine $(2p)^5$, chlorine $(3p)^5$, bromine $(4p)^5$, iodine $(5p)^5$, and astatine $(6p)^5$. Some neighbor elements are very similar in chemical behavior because a given inner shell is being completed, while the electron population in the outermost shell is constant. The first example of this occurs for the metals between $Z = 20$ and $Z = 30$. Here the 3d subshell is being filled after two (or one) electrons have been placed in the outer subshell 4s (compare Fig. 9–4). Another example is provided by the rare-earth metals $Z = 57$ to $Z = 71$ (see Appendix 2).

9–6 *L-S* COUPLING

An atom in its ground state will always have all its electrons in the lowest possible shell. In any filled subshells (e.g., $2p^6$), the orbital angular momenta and spins of all electrons cancel. The total angular momentum for the ground state of an atom, in which a subshell is completely filled, is therefore equal to zero. If the last subshell is only partly filled, then there are certain rules that describe how these electrons combine their spins and orbital angular momenta in the lowest state, the ground state. These rules are outlined below.

In Chapter 7 we saw that the spin and orbital angular momentum of the electron in hydrogen combined to a total angular momentum j. For the electrons in a partly filled subshell, we can add the angular momenta in different ways. For instance, we can combine l and s for each individual electron to form a j for that electron and then combine all the j's. Or, we can combine all the spin angular momenta to a total angular momentum S, and all the orbital angular momenta to a total orbital angular momentum L, and finally combine L and S to a total angular momentum J for the atom. There are forces, direct or indirect, in an atom that depend upon the relative orientation of the angular momentum vectors. For instance, in heavy atoms coupling between the spin s and the orbital angular momentum l *for each individual electron* is strong, and the individual j's are conserved (see Section 7–9). A reasonable way to combining angular momenta is by the method first described. This is called *j-j* coupling, and the individual j's are called *good quantum numbers*.

In light atoms, it is best to describe the energy levels in terms of the *L-S* coupling, also called *Russell Sanders coupling*. The reason for the success of this scheme is the relatively strong indirect interactions between the individual spins. In the discussion of the helium energy levels, we saw that the triplet state always was lower than the singlet state, because the exchange energy was negative in one case and positive in the other. This applies also to the case of more than two electrons. The maximum antisymmetry in the space wave function occurs when the spin wave function has a maximum symmetry; that is, when all spins are aligned or as closely aligned as possible, subject to the limitations imposed by the Pauli exclusion principle. Subject to these restrictions, we find the following rules for the total angular momentum for the ground state of an atom with partly filled last subshell:

1. Hund's rule, which predicts that the lowest level will have the maximum possible value of the total spin S that can be obtained by combining the spins of all electrons in the partly filled subshell.

2. If there are several possible values of L that can be combined with the same maximum value of S without violating the exclusion principle, then the ground state will have the highest of these values of L. The reason for this is, again, that the residual electrostatic interaction will be a minimum in this case (minimum overlap of the wave functions).

3. With L and S given and both different from zero, one still can make a number of combinations for the final angular momentum J. The magnetic coupling between L and S (fine-structure splitting) results in a total angular momentum J for the ground state equal to $J = L - S$ if the subshell is less than half filled, and $J = L + S$ if the subshell is more than half filled.

As mentioned above, the situation is reversed somewhat for heavier elements. The magnetic interaction between the spin and orbital angular momentum of the individual electron is sufficiently strong so that these two quantum numbers tend to combine to a total angular momentum j for the individual electron. The j's of the electrons in a subshell will then combine to a total angular momentum J for the atom.

The L-S description is not perfect for light atoms, and the j-j description is not perfect for heavy atoms. Rather, each state of an atom can be thought of as a linear combination of states formed by these simple descriptions, and the number of terms needed to obtain an accurate description is smallest if we use L-S coupling for light elements and j-j coupling for heavy elements.

In L-S coupling, the notation used to describe a quantum state, also called a *spectroscopic term*, is $^{(2S+1)}L_J$; for example $^3D_3$, $^1S_0$, $^4P_{3/2}$, etc. The front superscript gives the S-value, or actually $2S + 1$. The body gives the L-value, and these two can combine to as many J-values (subscript) as the superscript denotes, except when $S > L$, in which case the number of states is $2L + 1$. For instance, the quadruplet D state has four members, $^4D_{1/2}$, $^4D_{3/2}$, $^4D_{5/2}$, and $^4D_{7/2}$, but the "quadruplet" P state really has only three members: $^4P_{1/2}$, $^4P_{3/2}$, and $^4P_{5/2}$. Note that atoms with even numbers of electrons have integral values of S and therefore form only singlets and triplets, etc., whereas atoms with odd numbers of electrons have half integral values of S and therefore form doublets, quadruplets, etc.

It may be instructive to see the operation of the Pauli exclusion principle in ruling out certain levels and in allowing others, in the case of partly filled shells. Take the example of nitrogen which has the configuration $(2p)^3$. The three spins can combine to a total spin of $\frac{1}{2}$ or $\frac{3}{2}$. The three orbital angular momenta $l_1 = l_2 = l_3 = 1$ can, in principle, combine to $L = 0, 1, 2,$ or 3. Without the Pauli exclusion principle, we could therefore get the following doublets and quadruplets: ^2S, ^4S, ^2P, ^4P, ^2D, ^4D, ^2F, and ^4F. The exclusion principle actually allows only the three terms ^2D, ^2P, and ^4S. To prove this, we should actually try to antisymmetrize the wave function, and we would find that it would be impossible to do so for the states that we have excluded. We shall take a simpler approach, using again the more visual *vector model of angular momentum*.

Table 9-2

m_l	m_s distribution in substates									
1	+	+	+	+	+			±	±	−
0	+	+	−	±		+	±	+		+
−1	+	−	+		±	±	+		+	+

In Table 9-2, we have ordered the three electrons in the 2p shell of nitrogen in boxes according to their m_l and m_s without violating Pauli's exclusion principle. An electron with $m_s = \frac{1}{2}$ is indicated in the table by a plus and $m_s = -\frac{1}{2}$ is indicated by a minus. Two electrons can have the same m_l value if they have opposite m_s. Therefore, a plus and a minus can appear in the same box. Each column in Table 9-2 represents a possible substate. It turns out that there are twenty different combinations, of which only ten are shown. The combinations shown all have a resulting positive m_s. The other combinations are found by changing all the plus signs to minus and all the minus signs to plus. The m_l's and m_s's of each state in Table 9-2 have been combined to give an m_L and an m_S. The number of states with a given set of m_L and m_S are shown in Table 9-3. All twenty substates are included. This way of combining the quantum numbers, of course, implies L-S coupling.

Table 9-3

m_L \ m_S	−3/2	−1/2	1/2	3/2
2		1	1	
1		2	2	
0	1	3	3	1
−1		2	2	
−2		1	1	

There is only one combination of final states (terms) that can have the sets of substates given in Table 9–3; these are ^2D, ^2P, and ^4S. Therefore, these are the only possible terms arising from the ground-state configuration $(2p)^3$ in nitrogen. Figure 9–8 shows an energy-level diagram of the closely spaced levels resulting from this configuration.

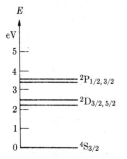

Fig. 9–8 Energies of the states of ^{14}N resulting from the configuration $(2p)^3$ relative to the ground state $^4S_{3/2}$. The fine-structure splittings are exaggerated.

9–7 ATOMIC SPECTROSCOPY

On several occasions in previous chapters, we have discussed the emission and absorption of photons in transitions between atomic states, particularly for hydrogen. In Sections 8–6 and 8–7 where we discussed the quantum theory of atomic transitions, we derived a set of selection rules that apply to atomic dipole radiation for one-electron atoms. The selection rules arise from the fact that the photon, when emitted in dipole radiation, carries with it an angular momentum of one unit with respect to the center of the atom and produces a parity change. Basically, the same rules apply to many-electron atoms, because it is found, theoretically and experimentally, that normally *only one electron makes a change of state*.

The transition between two states, for which one of the selection rules would be violated, can still take place by higher-order transitions, for instance, an electric quadrupole transition, or by collisions with other atoms or the wall of the container if the emitting atoms are in gaseous form. Since collisions are so frequent, spectral lines from higher-order optical transitions are usually very weak in atoms. However, such transitions do play an important role in de-excitation of nuclear excited states.

Since the perturbing forces or torques associated with the spin of the electron in the radiation field are very weak, the spin direction does not normally change in an electric dipole transition. We therefore can construct the following interaction rules for a many-electron atom in *L-S* coupling.

1. Dipole transitions take place between states in which one electron changes state, such that for that electron, $\Delta l = \pm 1$.

2. The quantum numbers for the atom are subject to the following selection rules:

   Parity changes

   $\Delta S = 0$ (not rigorous)

   $\Delta L = \pm 1 \ or \ 0$

   $\Delta J = \pm 1 \ or \ 0$ (but no 0→0 transition)

   $\Delta m_J = \pm 1 \ or \ 0$ (but $\Delta m_J = 0$ forbidden if $\Delta J = 0$)

The selection rules for an atom in *j-j* coupling are

1. Dipole transitions take place between states in which one electron changes state, such that for that electron, $\Delta l = \pm 1$. For the same electron $\Delta j = \pm 1$ or 0, and for all other electrons $\Delta j = 0$.

2. The quantum numbers for the *atom* are subject to the following selection rules:

   $\Delta J = \pm 1 \ or \ 0$,   but no 0-to-0 transition.

   $\Delta m_J = \pm 1 \ or \ 0$,   but $\Delta m_J = 0$ forbidden if $\Delta J = 0$.

The selection rules for m_J are meaningful only when the substates are separated by the action of an external magnetic field (Zeeman effect; see the next section).

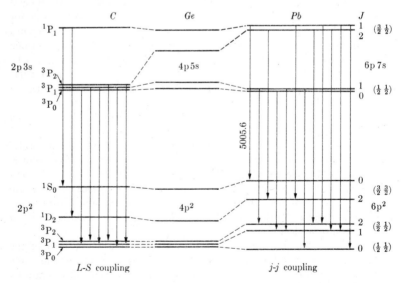

Fig. 9–9 Transition from *LS* coupling in carbon to *jj* coupling in lead. Reprinted with permission from Richtmyer, Kennard and Lauritsen, *Introduction to Modern Physics,* © 1955, p. 281.

Figure 9–9 shows as an example the transitions occurring in carbon between the configurations (2p)(3s), and $(2p)^2$, and the transitions occurring in lead between the configurations (6p)(7s), and $(6p)^2$. The L-S coupling scheme is most appropriate for carbon, whereas the j-j coupling scheme is most appropriate for lead. Germanium is somewhat intermediate between the two, as shown by the level diagram. The reader can easily verify that the transitions shown obey the selection rules given above for both cases.

In general, an excited state of an atom will undergo a dipole transition when there is a lower state that can be reached without violating the selection rules. The lifetime of the excited state is of the order of 10^{-8} s or less. If there are no lower states that can be reached by a dipole transition, de-excitation will take place by a higher order transition or by a collision. The $2s_{1/2}$-state in hydrogen (Section 7–10) is an example. In principle, a dipole transition could take place to the slightly lower $2p_{1/2}$-state, but the energy difference is so small that the lifetime (proportional to v^{-3}) is exceedingly long. Such a state is called a *metastable state*. Another example is the first excited state of helium (Section 9–3).

9–8 THE ZEEMAN EFFECT

In 1896, P. Zeeman* placed a sodium flame between the poles of a strong permanent magnet and studied the yellow D-lines with a spectrograph. He found the lines to be split into closely spaced components, and later also discovered that the light emitted was polarized. We can easily understand the Zeeman effect in terms of the simple semiclassical discussion of the magnetic moments of atoms in Section 7–5. The energy in the magnetic field, treated as a small perturbation, is given by Eq. (7–56), where the magnetic moment is the vector magnetic moment of the atom. Combining Eq. (7–55) with (7–56), we obtain

$$\Delta E = g\mu_B mB, \qquad (9\text{–}24)$$

where the magnitude of the Bohr magneton is given by Eq. (7–54).

In an atom in which the total angular momentum J results from orbital motion only, that is, $J = L$, the g-factor in Eq. (9–24) is 1. On the other hand, if $L = 0$ and $J = S$, the g-factor is 2. If neither L nor S is zero, the g-factor is somewhere between 1 and 2, and we can easily calculate it as follows.

Figure 9–10 is a vector diagram applying to L-S coupling in a weak magnetic field. In this diagram J and m_J remain constant, while the L-vector and the S-vector together precess about the J-vector. Rigorous quantum mechanical calculation of the sharp energy ΔE shows that it is equal to the *average* energy that we can calculate from this vector model. This is

$$\Delta E = (\langle \mu_{Lz} \rangle + \langle \mu_{Sz} \rangle)B. \qquad (9\text{–}25)$$

---

* P. Zeeman, *Phil. Mag.* **43** (1897), p. 226.

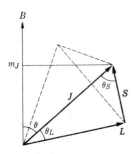

Fig. 9–10 Vector diagram used in the calculation of the Lande g-factor.

The average values of the two z-components of the magnetic moments are

$$\mu_{Lz} = \frac{e}{2m_e} \sqrt{L(L + 1)}\, \hbar \cos \theta_L \cos \theta, \qquad (9\text{–}26)$$

$$\mu_{Sz} = \frac{e}{m_e} \sqrt{S(S + 1)}\, \hbar \cos \theta_S \cos \theta. \qquad (9\text{–}27)$$

The cosines are given by

$$\cos \theta = \frac{m_J}{\sqrt{J(J + 1)}}, \qquad (9\text{–}28)$$

and the cosine rules,

$$S(S + 1) = J(J + 1) + L(L + 1) - 2\sqrt{J(J + 1)L(L + 1)}\, \cos \theta_S \qquad (9\text{–}29)$$

$$L(L + 1) = J(J + 1) + L(L + 1) - 2\sqrt{J(J + 1)S(S + 1)}\, \cos \theta_L \qquad (9\text{–}30)$$

By solving Eqs. (9–29) and (9–30) for the two cosines and inserting into Eqs. (9–26) and (9–27) and again into Eq. (9–25), we find

$$\Delta E = \frac{e\hbar}{2m_e}\, m_J B \left[1 + \frac{J(J + 1) + S(S + 1) - L(L + 1)}{2J(J + 1)} \right]. \qquad (9\text{–}31)$$

By comparison with Eq. (9–24), we find the new g-factor as

$$g = 1 + \frac{J(J + 1) + S(S + 1) - L(L + 1)}{2J(J + 1)}. \qquad (9\text{–}32)$$

This is called *Lande's g-factor*.

If S is equal to zero, the g-factor is 1. The energy splitting between the substates with different m_J values is then what could be calculated from the semi-classical formula before the intrinsic spin was discovered. In a transition between two singlet states ($S = 0$ for both) in a magnetic field, the spectral lines split into three components, corresponding to $\Delta m_J = -1$, 0, and $+1$.

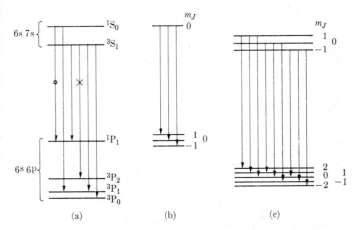

Fig. 9–11 Transitions between some excited states of mercury with electronic configuration $(6s)^1$ and $(7s)^1$ and $(6s)^1(6p)^1$. (a) With no external field. (Note: $^1S_0$ to $^3P_1$ violates the weak rule $\Delta S = 0$.) (b) The transition $^1S_0$ to $^1P_1$ in a magnetic field. (c) The transition $^3S_1$ to $^3P_2$ in a magnetic field.

Such a transition is said to display the *normal Zeeman effect*, normal because it could be understood at the time it was first observed.

When S is different from 0, and L changes in the transition in accordance with the selection rules of the previous section, the g-factor also changes, and a much more complex picture emerges. Such a transition is said to display an *anomalous Zeeman effect*. As an example, we shall look at the states found by the configuration $(6s)^1(7s)^1$ and $(6s)^1(6p)^1$ and the transitions between these states. Figure 9–11(a) shows the energy levels in no magnetic field and the electric dipole transitions between them. The transition marked with a circle displays the normal Zeeman effect, as shown in Fig. 9–11(b). In this particular case the upper level has $J = 0$ and is therefore not split at all. If it had been a $^1D_2$ state instead of a $^1S_0$ state, the splitting between substates would have been the same as for the lower ($^1P_1$) state, and therefore lines of only three different frequencies would be seen because of the m_J selection rule ($\Delta m_J = \pm 1$ or 0).

The transition marked with a cross in Fig. 9–11(a) displays an anomalous Zeeman effect, as shown in detail in Fig. 9–11(c). The g-factor for the upper level is 2 and for the lower level it is $g = 1.5$. Because of this, none of the nine lines shown in the figure correspond to exactly the same energy jump. Therefore this transition splits into nine separate spectroscopic lines in a magnetic field.

The Zeeman splitting shown in Fig. 9–11 is greatly exaggerated. A high-resolution spectrograph is required for these effects to be detectable.

In a very strong field, the coupling between the L-vector and the S-vector becomes disjointed, and the two vectors precess independently about the B-axis (see Fig. 9–12). This is called the *Paschen-Back effect*. A transition in

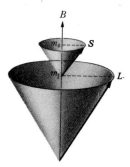

Fig. 9–12 The Paschen-Back effect.

this case involves only changes in L and m_L; in fact, we can completely neglect the spin. The splitting in a very strong field therefore displays a normal Zeeman pattern with energy differences calculated from Eq. (9–31) with $g = 1$.

9–9 HYPERFINE STRUCTURE

Optical spectroscopy was developed to an extremely exact science in the latter part of the last century. Very high resolving powers were obtained with interferometers, and with such an instrument Michelson in 1891 discovered a new effect, a fine structure which could be seen only with the ultimate of resolutions. When it was discovered later that the elements may have nuclei of different masses, the ultrafine splitting of the lines was thought to be related to this fact, an interpretation that appears to be correct in some cases. However, it was soon revealed that some of the elements displaying this ultrafine structure are monoisotopic, and a different explanation had to be sought. In 1924 Pauli correctly contended that the nucleus might possess an angular momentum and an associated magnetic dipole moment, which, through a coupling with the magnetic field produced by the electrons, gives rise to a very fine splitting of the levels. It has been found that part of the effect is sometimes caused by an electric quadrupole moment of the nucleus interacting with an electric field gradient.

The splitting of the atomic levels resulting from the fact that the various isotopes have different masses is now called the *isotope effect*, and the splitting caused by the magnetic moment and electric quadrupole moment of the nucleus is called *hyperfine structure*. Figure 9–13 shows two exposures taken with an interferometer called the *Fabry-Perot etalon*. Figure 9–13(a) shows the splitting of a line in the element tungsten which has five stable isotopes, the three at mass numbers 182, 184, and 186 being more abundant than the others. The three lines in Fig. 9–13(a) are believed to be caused by atoms having these three isotopes as nuclei. The shifts in energy are caused not only by the

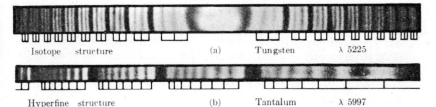

Isotope structure   (a)   Tungsten   λ 5225

Hyperfine structure   (b)   Tantalum   λ 5997

Fig. 9–13 High-resolution optical spectra taken with a Fabry-Perot etalon: (a) isotope effect in tungsten, (b) hyperfine structure of a tantalum line. Adapted from H. E. White, *Introduction to Atomic Spectra*, New York: McGraw-Hill © 1934. Reproduced by permission.

differences in mass of the nuclei, but also by differences in nuclear size and charge distribution which produce minute changes in the electron wave functions at the position of the nucleus. The repetition of the pattern of the three lines in Fig. 9–13(a) results from higher-order reflections in the interferometer.

The photograph in Fig. 9–13(b) shows the hyperfine splitting of a certain line in the tantalum spectrum into eight components. Tantalum is virtually monoisotopic, and the splitting is caused by a coupling between the magnetic moment of the tantalum nucleus and the magnetic field produced at the nucleus by the electrons.

Angular momenta of electrons in atoms and angular momenta of nuclei are of the same order of magnitude (multiples of $\hbar/2$). The total angular momentum for the atom results from a vector addition of the nuclear angular momentum I with numerical value $\sqrt{I(I + 1)}\,\hbar$ and the electronic angular momentum J with numerical value $\sqrt{J(J + 1)}\,\hbar$. The same rules apply for this coupling as for the coupling between L and S to J; indeed, they apply for the coupling of any two quantum-mechanical angular momenta. Figure 9–14 illustrates this vectorial coupling of I and J to a grand total angular momentum F with

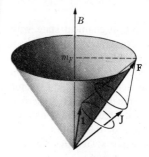

Fig. 9–14 Vector diagram illustrating the coupling of the nuclear angular momentum I and the electronic angular momentum J to a total angular momentum F with quantized z-component m_F.

quantum number F and numerical value $\sqrt{F(F + 1)}\,\hbar$. If I and J are both integral or both half-integral, F can take on any integral value between $|J - I|$ and $J + I$. If one of the two numbers if half-integral, then F takes on half-integral values only, but the same rules for maximum and minimum apply. When J and I are given, the number of different values of F, that is, the number of hyperfine levels is $2I + 1$ or $2J + 1$, whichever is smaller. This fact can be used to determine I when $I < J$.

The mutual torque between the nuclear magnetic moment μ_I and the atomic magnetic moment μ_j causes a slow precession of I and J about the vector F, as indicated in Fig. 9–14. If, in addition, an external torque is provided, for instance by a magnetic field in the z-direction, a precession of F about the z-axis results. The part of the hyperfine structure that concerns us at the moment is a result of the coupling between the two magnetic dipoles μ_I and μ_J. Classically, the energy of the coupling is given by Eq. 7–80. The quantum-mechanical calculation of the hyperfine splitting is quite complex, and the reader is referred to other texts.* For a hydrogenlike (single-electron) atom of nuclear charge Z, the coupling energy is

$$E_{\mathrm{H}} = \frac{\mu_0}{4\pi}\mu_I\mu_{\mathrm{B}} \frac{Z^3}{n^3 a_0^3} \frac{F(F + 1) - I(I + 1) - J(J + 1)}{IJ(J + 1)(L + \tfrac{1}{2})}, \qquad (9\text{–}33)$$

where μ_I is the magnetic moment of the nucleus in MKSA-units, μ_{B} is the Bohr magneton, n is the principal quantum number of the atom, a_0 is the first Bohr radius, and L is the orbital angular momentum of the electron.

Another contribution affecting the magnitude of the hyperfine-structure splitting arises from the coupling between the electric quadrupole moment (Section 12–1) of the nucleus and the gradient of the electric field produced by the electrons. In atoms, the effect of the electric quadrupole moment on the hyperfine structure is usually smaller than the effect of the magnetic dipole moment. In molecules, where a magnetic field from the electrons is frequently absent and the field produced by rotation of the molecule may be very weak, the situation is often reversed.

A given hyperfine level, as defined by a quantum-mechanical state with angular-momentum parameters I, J, and F, has a degeneracy $2F + 1$, which is the number of possible orientations of the F-vector relative to a given direction in space. When the direction is defined by a magnetic field, the interaction between this field and the magnetic dipole moment associated with the F-vector will remove the degeneracy, and $2F + 1$ levels emerge from each hyperfine level. When the field is very weak, the F-vector will precess about an axis in the field direction and the I- and J-vectors, because of their mutual inter-action, will precess about F (Fig. 9–14). When the external field is increased

---

*   For example, J. C. Slater, *Quantum Theory of Atomic Structure,* Vol. II, New York: McGraw-Hill (1960), p. 266.

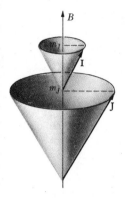

Fig. 9-15 Breakup of the coupling between *I* and *J* (μ_I and μ_J) by a stronger external field (compare with Fig. 9-12).

beyond typically 100 gauss, a decoupling of the *I*- and *J*-vectors takes place, *F* loses its identity, and the two vectors *I* and *J* will precess independently about the field direction (Fig. 9-15).

Consider as an example one of the alkali atoms, Li, Na, K, Rb, or Cs, in its atomic ground state, a $^2S_{1/2}$ state. The magnetic field produced at the position of the nucleus by the magnetic moment of the electron will fluctuate wildly in magnitude and direction, depending on the position of the electron and the orientation of its spin vector. The average value of this field can be computed, and the result is:

$$B \approx \frac{\mu_0}{2} \frac{\mu_B}{a_0^3} \approx 15 \text{ Wb m}^{-2} = 150,000 \text{ gauss.}$$

On the other hand, the field from the nucleus at the position of the electron is about a factor of 1000 smaller than this because the magnetic moments of these nuclei are only of the order of magnitude of $10^{-3} \mu_B$ Section 12-1). When the external field at the position of the electron is larger than the average field produced by the nucleus, the electron will start precessing about an axis parallel to the external field. This in turn will align the average field produced by the electron at the position of the nucleus in the same direction, and therefore the nucleus will also precess about the external field axis. The action of the external field on the nucleus is mostly an indirect one in that it aligns the usually much stronger field produced by the electron.

Figure 9-16 illustrates on an energy scale the hyperfine splitting of a $^2S_{1/2}$ state ($L = 0$, $S = \frac{1}{2}$, $J = \frac{1}{2}$) with nuclear angular momentum $I = 1$ and the further splitting of the magnetic substates in an external field. At very weak fields, i.e., below 100 gauss, the appropriate designation of the states and substates is given in terms of the quantum numbers F and m_F. At weak fields,

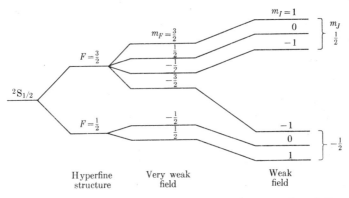

Fig. 9–16 Schematic drawing of the splitting of a $^2S_{1/2}$ state ($L = 0$, $S = \frac{1}{2}$, $J = \frac{1}{2}$) with nuclear angular momentum $I = 1$ caused by internal fields (hyperfine structure) and a weak external field.

i.e., à few hundred gauss, the appropriate designation of the states is in terms of the electron angular momentum J and its z-component m_J and the nuclear momentum I and its z-component m_I. For an atomic S-state, which is what we are dealing with now, this designation is still the appropriate one at high field strengths. However, for other atomic states at very high field strengths, the quantum number J will also be broken up into its components S and L (Paschen-Back effect).

In the weak-field region, the orders of the substates m_I are opposite in the two branches and the separations of the substates within a branch are virtually independent of B. This illustrates again the fact that the field produced at the position of the nucleus by the electron is much stronger than the external field, the magnitude is independent of B, and the direction is determined by m_J. Another interesting observation is that the number of hyperfine levels in each branch is $2I + 1$. This fact, which applies also to atomic levels with higher J-values, can be used for determining I.

9–10 NONRESONANT ABSORPTION

In Section 8–6, we discussed the absorption of energy by an atom bathed in electromagnetic radiation with a continuous energy spectrum (white light). We showed that absorption took place when the photon energy was close to the difference between the energy levels. The calculations we made were based on first-order perturbation theory. There is a very weak second-order effect, called the *Raman effect*, which allows a transition of absorption when the photon energy *exceeds* the required energy for the quantum jump. The excess energy is then released in the form of a reduced-energy photon, pretty much as in the Compton effect. The energy balance is simply

$$hv_1 = \Delta E_{atom} + hv_2, \qquad (9\text{--}34)$$

where hv_1 is the energy of the original photon and hv_2 is the energy of the residual photon.

A different absorption process is of much greater practical importance. This is the process called *fluorescence*. So far we have discussed atoms and atomic spectra only. When the atoms are bound in molecules and solids, the spectra are no longer simple line spectra (Chapter 11). In particular, a solid absorbs and emits radiation with a continuous spectrum. This is utilized in the fluorescent lamps and for modern lighting. It works as follows. The electric discharge within the fluorescent lamp is through mercury vapor. The spectrum of mercury has some lines in the visible region, but most of the emitted radiation is concentrated in a line in the ultraviolet. If the tube were made of quartz, which can transmit ultraviolet light, this radiation would be able to get out of the tube, where it could be used for air sterilization or to produce "sunburn." But a clear tube is a poor source of visible light. Therefore the inside of a fluorescent lamp is coated with a material which absorbs the invisible ultraviolet light. Thus the atoms of this fluorescent material become excited. If the excited electrons fell back to their normal state in one step, they would re-emit the ultraviolet light, which would still be invisible. But the excited electrons return to their normal state in more than one step. Each step produces radiation of less energy than the original excitation, so that the energy of the ultraviolet light is converted into visible light. The various tints that different lamps have are controlled by the nature of the fluorescent material used.

In some materials, the atoms may be left in a metastable state after receiving the incoming radiation. Such materials have a persistent light, called *phosphorescence*, which may last several hours after all external excitation is removed. These materials are sometimes used on the screens of cathode-ray tubes, and they are sometimes used to make light switches glow, so that they may be found in the dark. Most fluorescent tubes have some phosphorescence. It may be observed in a dark room a few minutes after the light is turned off.

PROBLEMS

9–1 The first ionization potential of helium is 24.6 V. a) How much energy in eV and in J must be supplied to ionize it? b) To what temperature would an atmosphere of helium have to be heated so that an atom (if moving with the most probable speed in a Maxwellian distribution) would have just enough kinetic energy of translation to ionize another helium atom by collision?

9–2 Draw energy-level diagrams for helium similar to Fig. 9–3 unperturbed and perturbed (qualitatively), but with $n_1 = 1$ and $n_2 = 3$.

9–3 Using Table 7–1 and Eqs. (7–29), write down one of the unperturbed, anti-symmetrized wave functions for helium with one electron in the 1s-state and the other in the 2p-state. The resulting state should have $S = 1$ and $m_S = 1$.

9–4 Consider the case of the helium atom when the electron configuration is (1s)(2p). Show in a series of parallel diagrams the energy levels to be expected when a) all interactions except nuclear attraction on the electrons are neglected. b) The mutual electrostatic interaction between the electrons is taken into account. c) Both the internal electrostatic and magnetic interactions are considered. d) Same as c) with the addition of an external magnetic field. Label the states by their term classification.

9–5 Calculate the perturbation energy $\langle V_{12} \rangle$ for the helium ground state using the following oversimplified picture. Since an electron is *on the average* at $r = 0$, assume that one is always there. For electron 2, use the ground-state wave function given by Table 7–1 and Eqs. (7–29). Explain why the result is a much too large value for $\langle V_{12} \rangle$.

9–6 Two electrons are confined to the interior of a spherical shell of radius a_0. In the approximation in which the electrostatic repulsion of the electrons is ignored, the ground state of each electron is described by a wave function of the form

$$\psi(i) = A \frac{1}{r_i} \sin(\pi r_i / a_0),$$

where i denotes the number of the electron involved. Using these wave functions and spin functions $\alpha(i)$ and $\beta(i)$, write down the complete wave function (or functions) that describes the state in which the electron spins are antiparallel. Make allowance for the fact that the electrons are indistinguishable particles.

9–7 a) Show that the maximum number of electrons that can be accommodated in a shell specified by the quantum number n is $2n^2$. b) How many elements would there be if the electronic shells through $n = 7$ were completely occupied?

9–8 Two angular momenta with quantum numbers $J_1 = 2$ and $J_2 = 3$ combine. a) What are the number of possible values of the total angular momentum (quantum number)? b) For one of these possibilities, namely $J = 2$, list all the values of m and the possible combinations of m_1 and m_2 giving each of these values.

9–9 Two angular momenta with quantum numbers $j_1 = \frac{3}{2}$ and $j_2 = 2$ combine to states with quantum numbers j and m. a) How many such states are there (how many different sets of j and m)? b) Draw vector diagrams showing the four different ways in which the state with $j = \frac{3}{2}$ and $m = \frac{1}{2}$ can be found by different combinations of m_1 and m_2. The true quantum-mechanical state is a linear combination of these four cases.

9–10 Show by use of the vector model, as in Section 9–6, that the configuration $(2p)^2$ in carbon can produce the following states: $^1S_0$, $^3P_{0,1,2}$, and $^1D_2$. Draw an energy-level diagram for these states, using the rules given in Section 9–6.

9–11 The atomic number of beryllium is 4. a) What is the electronic configuration of Be in its ground state? b) What spectral terms arise from this configuration (e.g., $^2P_{1/2}$, etc)? c) What is the electronic configuration of Be in its first excited state? d) What terms arise from this configuration? e) How many spectrum lines can be emitted in the transitions between the states formed by these two configurations in the absence of an external magnetic field? f) How many spectrum lines can be emitted in the transitions between the states formed by these two configurations in the presence of an external magnetic field? [In e) and f), show the transitions in energy-level diagrams.]

9–12 The atomic number of aluminum is 13. a) What type of spectral series (i.e., singlets, doublets, etc.) would you expect from neutral aluminum? b) What type of spectral series (i.e., singlets, doublets, etc.) would you expect from singly ionized aluminum? c) What is the electronic configuration $(1s)^2 (2s)^2 \ldots$, etc. of the aluminum atom in its ground state? d) What is the term classification for this state (e.g., $^4S_{3/2}$)?

9–13 a) Give the term classifications (including J-values) of the states which would arise from the L-S coupling of three nonequivalent p-electrons (that is, electrons with different principal quantum numbers $n_1 \neq n_2 \neq n_3$). How many distinct energy levels would there be in the presence of a magnetic field? b) Repeat the work of part a) for three equivalent p-electrons ($n_1 = n_2 = n_3$). c) Indicate the ground-state term in part a) and in part b).

9–14 The atomic number of sodium is 11. a) What is the electronic configuration of the ground state of Na? b) Into how many components would a beam of Na atoms (all in the ground state) split when passed through an inhomogeneous magnetic field?

9–15 Sodium is a "hydrogenlike" atom with one electron outside closed shells. Show in a diagram the energy levels involved and the allowed transitions when the outer electron jumps from the 3d- to the 3p-shell. Write beside each level of the diagram its corresponding term classification, including the total angular momentum quantum number J.

9–16 Aluminum 27 has a nuclear angular momentum of $\frac{5}{2}^+$. How many hyperfine compounds are in the ground-state term of the aluminum atoms? How many levels do they split into in an external magnetic field?

X-rays and Crystallography

10–1 DISCOVERY

In Chapter 2 we reported how the study of electric discharges through gases at low pressure led Thomson to the discovery of the electron and of isotopes. Let us now consider an earlier discovery made in 1895 in connection with electric discharges: Roentgen's discovery of x-rays. We quote a translation of Roentgen's words:*

"If the discharge of a fairly large induction-coil be made to pass through a Hittorf vacuum-tube, or through a Lenard tube, a Crookes tube, or other similar apparatus which has been sufficiently exhausted, the tube being covered with thin, black card-board which fits it with tolerable closeness, and if the whole apparatus be placed in a completely darkened room, there is observed at each discharge a bright illumination of a paper screen covered with barium planto-cyanide, placed in the vicinity of the induction-coil, the fluorescence thus produced being entirely independent of the fact whether the coated or the plain surface is turned towards the discharge-tube . . .

"The most striking feature of this phenomenon is the fact that an active agent here passes through a black card-board envelope which is opaque to the visible and the ultra-violet rays of the sun or of the electric arc; an agent, too, which has the power of producing active fluorescence . . .

"We soon discover that all bodies are transparent to this agent, though in very different degrees. I proceed to give a few examples: Paper is very transparent; behind a bound book of about one thousand pages I saw the fluorescent screen light up brightly, the printers' ink offering scarcely a noticeable hindrance. In the same way the fluorescence appeared behind a double pack of cards; a single card held between the apparatus and the screen being almost unnoticeable to the eye. A single sheet of tin-foil is also scarcely perceptible;

---

* Reprinted by permission of the publishers from William Francis Magie, *Source Book in Physics*. Cambridge, Mass.: Harvard University Press, 1935.

it is only after several layers have been placed over one another that their shadow is distinctly seen on the screen. Thick blocks of wood are also transparent, pine boards two or three centimeters thick absorbing only slightly. A plate of aluminum about fifteen millimeters thick, though it enfeebled the action seriously, did not cause the fluorescence to disappear entirely."

The history of science has many instances of "accidental" discovery and of these the discovery of x-rays is a prime example. Columbus' discovery of America was another instance where a man looking for one thing found another. Although accidents can happen to anyone, "accidental" discovery of truth seems to be reserved to those observers who have earned the right to be lucky. Such luck falls on the deserving few whose courage, patience, insight, and objectivity enable them to take advantage of the "breaks of the game." There is a word for this process that is better than the word "accident." It is "serendipity"—the process or art of taking advantage of the unexpected.

Of all the discoveries made by man, there is probably none that attracted public attention more quickly than the discovery of x-rays. The fact that the rays permitted one to "see" through opaque objects was sensational "tabloid material" and there was great consternation lest, by their use, fully dressed people might be made to appear unclothed. When such speculation died down, however, there was wide appreciation of the value of x-rays in setting broken bones, and the rays were quickly put to this use.

10–2 PRODUCTION OF X-RAYS

As Roentgen said in his paper, the observed x-rays came from low-pressure gas discharge tubes like those already described in our discussion of cathode rays. We quote further from Roentgen's original paper published in 1895.* "According to experiments especially designed to test the question, it is certain that the spot on the wall of the discharge-tube which fluoresces the strongest is to be considered as the main centre from which the x-rays radiate in all directions. The x-rays proceed from that spot where, according to the data obtained by different investigators, the cathode rays strike the glass wall. If the cathode rays within the discharge-apparatus are deflected by means of a magnet, it is observed that the x-rays proceed from another spot—namely, from that which is the new terminus of the cathode rays."

Modern x-ray tubes still produce x-rays by causing cathode rays to strike a solid target, but the techniques have been greatly refined. In a modern Coolidge tube, the source of the cathode-ray electrons is a heated filament. There is no need for a residual gas to be ionized, and so modern tubes are evacuated to a high degree. The target of modern tubes is a metal having a high melting point and a high atomic number. In the production of x-rays, a

---

*   Magie, *op. cit.*

large amount of heat is generated in the target and so it is usually made hollow to permit cooling water or oil to be circulated through it. In addition to the tube itself, the other major part of the apparatus is a source of high potential to accelerate the cathode-ray electrons. Originally, this was provided by an induction coil (spark coil), but the common technique today is to use step-up transformers which operate at power-line frequency alternating current. If a.c. is applied to the tube, cathode rays and, consequently, x-rays are produced during only one-half of the cycle and the potential across the tube is constantly changing. Most x-ray machines rectify and filter the high alternating potential so that there is a steady high voltage across the tube. The potential used depends on the ultimate use of the x-rays, but it usually ranges between ten thousand and a million volts. A schematic diagram of the essential features of an x-ray machine is shown in Fig. 10–1.

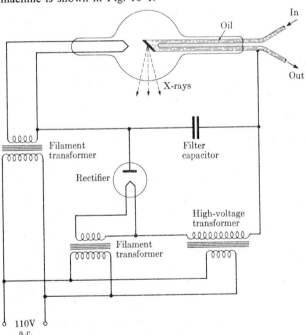

Fig. 10–1 X-ray apparatus: Coolidge tube.

10–3 THE NATURE OF X-RAYS; X-RAY DIFFRACTION IN CRYSTALS

Roentgen failed to determine the nature of x-rays. He eliminated some possibilities and he suggested what they might be, but his own uncertainty is shown by the fact that he chose the name x-rays.

Upon finding that x-rays are not deflected by electric or magnetic fields on the one hand or perceptibly refracted or diffracted on the other, Roentgen concluded that the rays were neither charged particles nor light of any ordinary sort. Tongue-in-cheek, he proposed that x-rays might be the "longitudinal component" of light, in analogy with the fact that acoustic vibrations in solids have both a longitudinal and a transverse part. There is some appeal in the idea that light might have a component which, being longitudinal, might be "slimmer" than the transverse part and therefore penetrate solids more easily than the "fatter" transverse waves. But Maxwell's wave theory of light, which was then at its height, accounted for light being a transverse wave motion, and an effort was made to identify x-rays with this more familiar phenomenon.

In 1912, Max von Laue conceived of a way of testing the idea that x-rays might be light of very short wavelength. Recall the diffraction grating formula,

$$n\lambda = d \sin \theta, \tag{10-1}$$

where n is the spectrum order $(1, 2, 3, \ldots)$, λ is the wavelength, d is the grating space, and θ is the angle of diffraction. We can see that if λ is very small compared with d, the diffraction angle must be very small unless the order n is large. Since the intensity in high orders is very weak, we can see that assuming λ to be very small can account for the observed failure of gratings to produce measurable diffraction for x-rays.

The obvious remedy is to make gratings with much finer rulings, although we shall see in Section 10–9 that there is another remedy. But the art of making gratings was already in a high state of mechanical perfection. To improve gratings by reducing their grating space by a few orders of magnitude would have required better materials for both the ruling machine and the grating material itself. However, the basic granularity of matter imposes limitations. This dilemma led Laue to the idea of taking advantage of the very granularity that stood in his way. It was felt that the regular shapes of crystals, with their plane cleavage surfaces and well-defined edges, must mean that the atoms are regularly arranged throughout their structure. Laue thought that the atoms of a single crystal might provide the grating needed for the diffraction of x-rays. At Laue's suggestion, Friedrich and Knipping directed a narrow beam (pencil) of x-rays at a crystal and set a photographic plate beyond it. The result was a picture like that shown in Fig. 10–2. (Most of the x-rays go directly through the crystal and strike the plate at its center. To prevent gross overexposure at this point it is usual to fasten a disk of lead over the center of the plate. When the photograph shown in Fig. 10–2 was taken, a lead disk masked the center for all but the last second of a 40-min exposure.) Laue knew he had met with success when he observed the complicated but symmetrical pattern on the plate. These spots could only be due to diffraction from the atoms of the crystal. [Strictly, the structural units of such crystals as NaCl and KCl are ions, not neutral atoms. These are called *ionic crystals* because they are held together

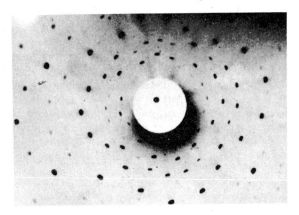

Fig. 10–2 Laue diffraction of NaCl taken with radiation from a tungsten-target tube operated at 60 kV. The dark patch below the center disk was caused by scattered x-rays.

by strong electrostatic forces acting between charged particles, e.g., $(Na^+)(Cl^-)$ and $(K^+)(Cl^-)$.]

This diffraction pattern is hardly like that produced by a man-made grating. In optical spectroscopy, the grating consists of parallel lines in a plane. You can appreciate that its diffraction would become more complex if a grating were turned ninety degrees and then ruled again with a second set of lines perpendicular to the first. If many such gratings made of glass were stacked behind one another, the diffraction pattern would be further complicated. Since a crystal consists of a regular array of atoms in three-dimensional space, it produces an intricate pattern.

Later we shall discuss qualitatively why a Laue pattern looks as it does. Our immediate point, however, is that by diffracting x-rays Laue demonstrated that x-rays can be combined destructively—the sole, unique experimental criterion for wave motion. At the same time, Laue patterns established that x-rays have very short wavelengths, and confirmed the supposition that crystals have their atoms arranged in a regular structure.

Late in 1912, shortly after the Laue experiment, William L. Bragg devised another technique for diffracting x-rays. Instead of observing the effect created by passing the rays through a crystal, Bragg considered how x-rays are scattered by the atoms in the crystal lattice. Consider an x-ray wave front incident on a surface row of atoms in a crystal plane, as shown in Fig. 10–3. Each atom becomes a source of scattered x-radiation. In general, the scattered x-rays from all the atoms in the crystal combine destructively as they fall on top of one another in a random manner. If certain conditions are met, however, constructive interference will occur at a few places. One of the relations which must be satisfied for reinforcement can be derived with the aid of Fig. 10–3. In this

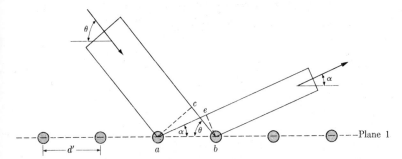

Fig. 10–3 Path difference construction for waves scattered from a single plane of atoms in a crystal.

figure d' is the distance between adjacent atoms, θ is the angle* between the incident rays and a row of atoms in the surface plane, and α is the angle between scattered rays and the surface plane. To obtain the path difference between rays from adjacent atoms, we construct the lines $\overline{ac}$ and $\overline{be}$ perpendicular to the incident and scattered rays, respectively. This path difference is obviously $\overline{ae} - \overline{cb}$, and, for reinforcement, this difference must equal some integral multiple of the x-ray wavelength, or $m\lambda$. Therefore, we have $\overline{ae} - \overline{cb} = m\lambda$, which can be written as

$$d' \cos \alpha - d' \cos \theta = m\lambda. \tag{10–2}$$

The other relation which must be satisfied for maximum reinforcement is that the scattered rays from successive planes of atoms meet in phase. Referring to Fig. 10–4, in which d is the distance between successive planes, we note that rays scattered from the second plane travel a greater distance than those from the first plane. In order that the rays from successive planes reinforce one another, it is necessary that these additional distances shall be some integral multiple of the wavelength, $n\lambda$. If we draw the line $\overline{ea}$ normal to the incident rays and the line $\overline{ec}$ normal to the scattered rays, we see that the length of the path for a ray from the second plane exceeds that for a ray from the first plane by the sum of the distances $\overline{ab}$ and $\overline{bc}$. Therefore the rays from the two planes will interfere constructively when $\overline{ab} + \overline{bc} = n\lambda$, which is equivalent to

$$d \sin \theta + d \sin \alpha = n\lambda. \tag{10–3}$$

In general, the conditions imposed by Eqs. (6–2) and (6–3) cannot be satisfied simultaneously without considering the scattered wavelets from atoms which

---

* Note that whereas in optics it is usual to measure angles of incidence and reflection between the rays and the normal to the surface, the Bragg angle is measured between the ray and a crystal plane.

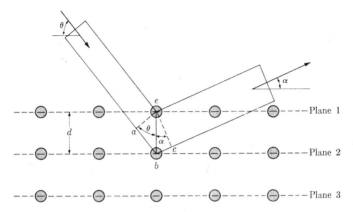

Fig. 10–4 Path difference construction for waves scattered by successive planes of atoms in a crystal.

are in the various layers but not in the plane of incidence. Both conditions are met, however, in the special case where $\theta = \alpha$. Then Eq. (10–2) reduces to zero and Eq. (10–3) becomes

$$n\lambda = 2d \sin \theta, \qquad (10\text{–}4)$$

where n is the order of the spectrum. When $\theta = \alpha$, we have precisely the condition of regular optical reflection. Because of this, Bragg scattering is usually called Bragg "reflection." This is actually a *misnomer*, but we shall follow common usage. The planes of atoms in the crystal which are responsible for Bragg reflection are called *Bragg planes*. Let us now summarize the conditions for constructive interference of x-rays scattered from Bragg planes. The *first condition* is that the angle the incident beam makes with the planes must equal that made by the reflected beam; and the *second condition* is that the reflections from the several Bragg planes must meet in phase, that is, must satisfy the relation, $n\lambda = 2d \sin \theta$.

The Bragg technique of using crystals as diffraction gratings for an x-ray spectrometer is shown in Fig. 10–5. The x-rays coming from the tube at the left are restricted to a narrow beam or collimated by a lead sheet which absorbs all rays except those which pass through a small slit. These rays fall on a crystal which can be rotated about an axis parallel to the slit and perpendicular to the plane of the figure. The angle θ between the crystal planes and the original x-ray direction can be measured. Bragg reflection can take place only in the direction 2θ from the original x-ray direction. Whether or not the rays actually reinforce one another in this direction depends on whether the second Bragg condition is fulfilled. Since d is a fixed crystal property, the measurements of those angles for which reflections do occur provide a measure of the

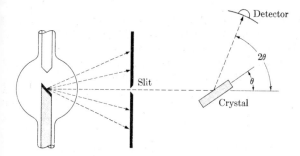

Fig. 10–5 Crystal spectrometer.

x-ray wavelengths that are present. In order that spectra measured in this way may be quantitative, the crystal spacing d must be known. How this quantity is determined is discussed in Sections 10–9 and 10–11.

10–4 MECHANISM OF X-RAY PRODUCTION

Roentgen reported in his original paper that x-rays are produced where cathode rays strike some material object. Since we now know that cathode rays are high-velocity electrons, we can restate Roentgen's observation by saying that x-rays are produced when high-velocity electrons hit something. To explore the mechanism of x-ray production, let us ask what happens when electrons strike solid matter.

Many of the electrons that strike matter do nothing spectacular at all. Most of them undergo glancing collisions with the particles of the matter, and in the course of these collisions, the electrons lose their energy a little at a time and thus merely increase the average kinetic energy of the particles in the material. The result is that the temperature of the target material is increased. It is found that most of the energy of the electron beam goes into heating the target.

Some of the bombarding electrons make solid hits and lose most or all of their energy in just one collision. These electrons are rapidly decelerated. We have pointed out that radiation results when a charged body is accelerated. Therefore when an electron loses a large amount of energy by being decelerated, an energetic pulse of electromagnetic radiation is produced. This is an *inverse photoelectric effect* in which an electron produces a photon. In Chapter 3 we found that photons of a given energy produce photoelectrons with a certain maximum energy. Here we find that electrons of a given energy produce x-ray photons with a certain maximum energy. Both effects confirm the quantum view of radiation. According to classical electromagnetic theory, there is no lower limit to the wavelength of the radiation that a moving electron can produce when it is stopped suddenly. But there is a quantum limit. Given that an electron has been accelerated through a difference of potential of V volts, we can use Eq. (3–47), which Duane and Hunt showed was valid for x-rays, to compute the wavelength of the resulting radiation in angstroms if the electron loses all its energy in a single encounter. In this case the energy loss of the electron in eV is *numerically* equal to the accelerating potential in volts. Therefore we have

$$\lambda_{min} (\text{Å}) = \frac{12400}{V}. \qquad (10\text{–}5)$$

This expression gives the minimum wavelength, since no electron can lose more energy than it has, and there will be a continuous distribution of radiation toward longer wavelengths because there are all sorts of collisions, from direct hits to glancing ones. Thus glancing collisions account for the *continuous spectrum* of x-rays from any target material and also for the inefficiency of the conversion of electron energy into x-ray energy. The Germans named this continuous radiation *bremsstrahlung*, meaning literally "braking radiation." This is a highly descriptive term, since it refers to the radiation that results from the braking or stopping of charged particles. Some continuous spectra are shown in Fig. 10–6.

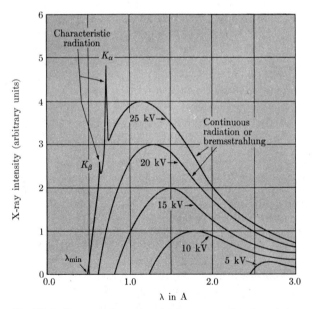

Fig. 10–6 X-ray spectrum of molybdenum as a function of the applied voltage. Line widths are not to scale. The K-series excitation potential of this element is 20.1 kV. The shortest L-series wavelength is 4.9 Å.

Looking at the collision process more closely, however, we find there is another very important kind of collision energy exchange. The bombarding electron may also give energy to electrons bound to the target atoms. If these atomic electrons are freed from their home atoms, ions are produced. Since x-ray producing electrons have energies of the order of many thousands of electron volts, it is very easy for them to produce ions by removing outer electrons. X-ray producing electrons may also have enough energy to produce ions by removing inner electrons from the atom, even down to the innermost or K-shell. Such an ion has a low-energy hole in its electronic structure, and this vacancy is promptly filled when one of its electrons in a higher energy state falls to this low-energy level. Although the energy required to ionize an atom by removing an outer electron is much less than 100 eV, the energy required to ionize by removing an inner electron may be as high as 120,000 eV. When an outer electron falls into such a vacancy, it will radiate a photon of this energy. Such photons are in the x-ray region and have wavelengths which are fractions of angstroms. This mechanism, which accounts for a significant part of x-ray production, produces x-rays having particular wavelengths which are *characteristic* of the target material.

10–5 THE CHARACTERISTIC X-RADIATION

When a K electron is removed from an atom, as described above, that atom is excited. We can illustrate this in an energy-level diagram, as shown in Fig. 10–7 for tungsten. The *ground state*, by definition, is the neutral atom with all electrons in the lowest possible states. The K level shown is at a position that represents the energy needed to remove a K electron to infinity. Because a K electron experiences very little screening (Section 9–4) of the electrons, we can calculate its approximate energy by using the Bohr formula for $n = 1$:

$$E_K \approx -13.6\,Z^2 \text{ eV}. \tag{10–6}$$

It is customary to account for the screening by rewriting Eq. (10–6) as

$$E_K = -13.6\,(Z - \sigma)^2 \text{ eV}, \tag{10–7}$$

where $\sigma \approx 1$ for the K-shell.

The K level shown in Fig. 10–7 represents a missing electron in the K-shell. Correspondingly, the L levels shown represent a missing electron in one of the states in the L-shell. The corresponding electronic configurations are

$$K: (1s)^1(2s)^2(2p)^6(3s)^2, \quad j = 1/2.$$
$$L_I: (1s)^2(2s)^1(2p)^6(3s)^2, \quad j = 1/2.$$
$$L_{II}: (1s)^2(2s)^2(2p)^5(3s)^2, \quad j = 1/2.$$
$$L_{III}: (1s)^2(2s)^2(2p)^5(3s)^2, \quad j = 3/2.$$

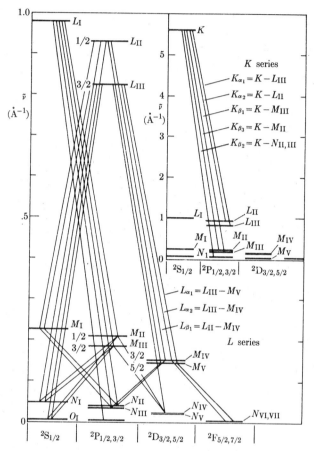

Fig. 10–7 X-ray term diagram for tungsten. Reproduced by permission from R. B. Leighton, *Principles of Modern Physics*. New York: McGraw-Hill © 1959.

Note that we pay no attention to the outer electron and to the total angular momentum of the atom. Relative to the binding energy of a K electron, the interaction energy involving the spin of the remaining K electron and the angular momenta of the outer electrons is exceedingly small. Consequently, we neglect this effect.

The energy-level diagram, Fig. 10–7, can best be thought of as an electron hole diagram. The K level, for instance, represents a missing electron in the 1s-state. The L_{III} level represents a missing electron, or hole, in the 2p-state, in this case one of the four electrons that in j-j coupling have angular momentum $j = \frac{3}{2}$.

When a hole has been created in the 1s-state, for instance, an electron from another state will drop down and fill the hole. The transitions are subject to the usual rules for the jumping electron in *j-j* coupling,

$$\Delta l = \pm 1,$$

$$\Delta j = \pm 1 \text{ or } 0.$$

Figure 10–7 shows the transitions that involve the *K*-state. They are labeled K_α for transitions to the *L* levels, K_β for transitions to the *M* levels, and K_γ for transitions to the *N* levels. As shown in the figure, all *K* lines are doublets because of the spin-orbit splitting of the p-states involved.

It is clear that, in order to excite, for instance, one of the K_α lines, the energy required is the energy of the *K* level and not only the amount of energy released in the K_α transition. For example, for tungsten this *K* excitation energy, also called the *K* absorption limit, is 69.55 keV. The energy of a $K_{\alpha 1}$ photon is 59.34 keV. For molybdenum, the *K* excitation energy is 20.1 keV. Therefore, 20-keV electrons in the x-ray tube do not have sufficient energy to excite the *K* lines when the anode is molybdenum. This is clearly demonstrated in Fig. 10–6.

When a hole is created in the *L*-shell by K_α radiation, an electron from the *M*-, *N*-, or *O*-shells etc. will make a transition to fill the hole. The resulting characteristic *L* radiation has much lower energy than the *K* radiation. There are also more *L* lines, since transitions from the p-state holes can go both to s- and d-state holes. Characteristic *L* radiation can, of course, also be excited by removal of an *L* electron directly by the electron beam in the tube. In the case of tungsten this requires a minimum of 10.21 keV.

The picture that we have now drawn of characteristic x-radiation is that one electron hole, originally in the *K*-shell, for instance, may produce a cascade of x-rays with rapidly decreasing quantum energies. In competition with this series of events is another interesting process called the *Auger effect*. In this process, the available energy released in the *K* to *L* transition is used not to emit a photon but to eject another *L* electron. Hence two holes appear in the *L*-shell. More Auger electrons and/or *L* radiation etc. follow.

10–6 X-RAY SPECTRA OF THE ELEMENTS; ATOMIC NUMBER

In 1913, Moseley* used a large number of elements as x-ray tube targets and found that the K_α radiation of each element was distinct from that of any other element. This result not only provides a unique way of identifying the various elements, but also is of theoretical significance. Specifically, Moseley's law states that the frequencies of corresponding x-ray spectral lines, such as

---

* H. G. J. Moseley, *Phil. Mag.* **26** (1913), p. 1024; **27** (1914), p. 703.

K_α's, as we go from element to element, may be represented by an equation of the form

$$\sqrt{f} = a(Z - b),\qquad\qquad (10\text{–}8)$$

where a and b depend on the particular line and Z is the atomic number of the element.

Moseley was a contemporary of Niels Bohr. Both were working in Rutherford's laboratory in Manchester, England. By extending Bohr's theory of the hydrogen atom to heavier elements, Moseley could account for his observations as resulting from a transition from $n = 2$ to $n = 1$, as explained above for K_α radiation. (Compare Eqs. 10–7 and 10–8.)

The original ordering of the elements in the periodic table was on the basis of their atomic weights. Initially, atomic numbers were mere ordinal numbers specifying where the element lay in a list based on these weights. These atomic numbers had no more physical significance than the house numbers that identify the houses on a given street. Moseley found that if he arranged the wavelengths of the K_α lines in the order of atomic weights, these wavelengths formed a remarkably regular progression. The sequence was not perfect, however, since he found both gaps and wavelengths out of order. He attributed the gaps in the series to undiscovered elements and proposed that there should be a unique correlation between the wavelength series and atomic number. His words were, "We have here a proof that there is in the atom a fundamental quantity, which increases by regular steps as we pass from one element to the next. This quantity can only be the charge on the central positive nucleus." In Moseley's day, nickel with an atomic weight of 58.69 was listed ahead of cobalt with an atomic weight of 58.94. There was some chemical evidence that the order of these two elements in the periodic table should be reversed, and Moseley demonstrated this by showing that the atomic number of cobalt is 27 and that of nickel is 28.

The missing elements according to Moseley were numbers 43, 61, 72, and 75. Element 72, hafnium, was discovered in 1923, and element 75, rhenium, was discovered in 1925. The two final elements, numbers 43 and 61, have no stable isotopes, but were produced artificially, technetium (43) in 1937, and promethium (61) in 1947. The former has an isotope ($A = 97$) with a half-life of 2.6×10^6 years, and the latter has an isotope ($A = 145$) with an 18-year half-life.

10–7 X-RAY ABSORPTION

The most spectacular property of x-rays is their ability to penetrate materials that are opaque to less energetic radiation. The basic mechanism of absorption of ultraviolet, visible, and infrared radiation is the transfer of photon energy to the electronic, vibrational, and rotational energy states of the material doing the absorbing. For an x-ray photon, whose energy is orders of magnitude greater than visible radiation, these mechanisms are trivial because a high-energy photon has a small probability of interacting in a comparatively low-energy process. These relatively high-energy x-ray photons are more likely to interact with electrons in the K- or L-shells. Since the probability of an x-ray interacting with the many loosely bound electrons in an absorber is small and since there are relatively few tightly bound electrons, high-energy (short-wavelength or hard) x-rays have remarkable penetrating ability.

Roentgen first detected x-rays by the fluorescence they produce in certain materials. This effect can be used for quantitative intensity measurements if it is coupled with an objective measurement of the fluorescent light produced. Roentgen also observed that x-rays blacken a photographic plate, and this may be used to measure the intensity if a densitometer is used to measure the blackening. A third method was suggested by Roentgen's experiments on the conductivity of air caused by x-rays. The x-rays ionize the air, and this effect can be measured quantitatively with an ionization chamber. There are many forms of ionization chambers. One of these is shown schematically in Fig. 10–8. The chamber itself is a metallic box into which an electrode is inserted through an insulating plug. This electrode is usually maintained at a positive potential, so that any free electrons within the chamber will be attracted to it. The potential difference is chosen low enough so that the dielectric strength of the air prevents a discharge, and high enough so that the charges are collected before the electrons recombine with positive ions. When x-rays enter the chamber and produce ions, the collected charges constitute a small current which is very nearly proportional to the intensity of the x-rays. This current is in modern instruments amplified electrically and displayed by a microammeter.

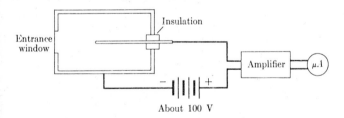

Fig. 10–8 Ionization chamber used to determine x-ray intensities.

An ionization chamber can be used to study the penetrating ability of x-rays with apparatus like that shown in Fig. 10–9. X-rays are collimated by slits, rendered monochromatic by a Bragg reflection, and passed through a material under study; then their intensity is measured by the ionization chamber. If we vary the thickness of the absorbing material, a plot of transmitted intensity against thickness looks like that in Fig. 10–10. This is an exponential decay

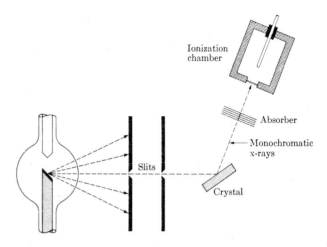

Ionization chamber

Absorber

Monochromatic x-rays

Slits

Crystal

Fig. 10–9 Schematic diagram of the apparatus for x-ray absorption experiments.

curve which can be derived by assuming that a small thickness of absorber, dx, reduces the intensity of the beam by an amount $-dI$ proportional to both the intensity I and the thickness dx. This assumption leads to the differential equation

$$dI = -\mu I \, dx, \tag{10–9}$$

where μ is a constant of proportionality. If the intensity of the beam which is incident on a layer of material of thickness x is I_0, then I, the intensity of the *transmitted* beam, can be found by integrating Eq. (10–9). The result is

$$I = I_0 e^{-\mu x}. \tag{10–10}$$

This is the equation of the curve in Fig. 10–10.

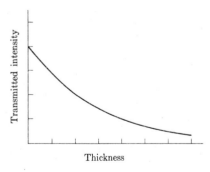

Thickness

Fig. 10–10 Graph of x-ray transmission through a material.

The quantity μ is usually called the *linear absorption coefficient*, although *macroscopic absorption coefficient* and *linear attenuation coefficient* are also used. When Eq. (10–9) is solved for μ, we see that the linear absorption coefficient is equal to the fractional decrease in intensity of the radiation per unit thickness of the absorber. Thus it has the dimensions of reciprocal length. The linear absorption coefficient μ measures the decrease in full-energy x-rays in a pencil beam. Since some of the photons are scattered out of the beam by the Compton effect but still continue in the forward direction, μ does *not* correctly represent the decay of intensity through a shielding wall subjected to large-area radiation. A correction factor, called the *build-up factor*, must then be applied.

Three effects contribute to x-ray absorption, the photoelectric effect, the Compton effect, and above 1.02 MeV, pair production.

We discussed the photoelectric effect and Einstein's explanation of the process in Chapter 3. The experiments discussed concerned knockout of electrons from a solid by photons of a few electron-volts energy. In the present discussion we are concerned with photons of energies 10 keV and up. The process is basically the same, but for the higher energies the probability for ejecting a low-orbit electron is much higher than it is for a loosely bound electron.

Figure 10–11 shows schematically how the absorption coefficient varies with x-ray wavelength. At energies above or wavelengths below the K absorption edge, a very large percentage of the events are ejections of K electrons in spite of the fact that they are definitely in the minority. For lead the K absorption edge is at $h\nu = 88.10$ keV or $\lambda = 0.141$ Å. Somewhat below this wavelength the curve in Fig. 10–11 has been discontinued. Up to this point in energy, at least for heavy elements, the photoelectric process is entirely dominant. At higher energies, Compton scattering and pair production become important, relatively speaking. Compton scattering was discussed in Section 5–1. The pair production process is discussed below.

The shifting of x-ray spectra with atomic number provides an important technique for obtaining essentially monochromatic x-rays. Suppose we have an x-ray tube with a copper target. The K-series of the copper consists of an intense K_α line, and weak K_β and K_γ radiations, listed in the order of decreasing wavelength and of increasing energy. Nickel is a metal whose atomic number is one less than that of copper. Its energy levels are less negative than those of copper, and its emission lines and absorption edges are at slightly longer wavelengths than those of copper. The K_γ wavelength of nickel is almost identical with its λ_K absorption edge, and it falls between the strong K_α and the weaker K_β and K_γ emission lines of copper. Figure 10–12 shows the K-series emission spectrum of copper and the linear absorption coefficient of nickel as a function of wavelength. Since the minimum of the absorption curve is at a slightly shorter wavelength than one of the K lines but at a longer wavelength than the others,

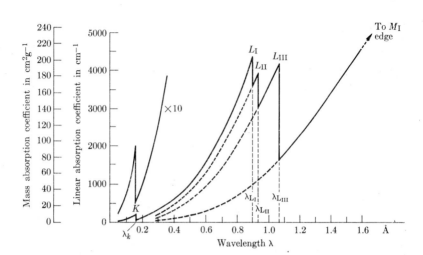

Fig. 10–11 X-ray absorption spectrum for platinum.

nickel filters out most of the radiation from the copper except its strong K_α line. There are several sets of elements such that by using one as a filter for the emission of the other, nearly monochromatic x-rays are obtained.

The absorption coefficient depends strongly on the density of the absorbing material which, of course, changes greatly if the material goes from gaseous to solid states.

We can write

$$\mu x = \frac{\mu}{\rho}\, x\rho, \qquad (10\text{–}11)$$

where ρ is the mass density of the material. The quantity μ/ρ is called the *mass absorption coefficient*, μ_m. Its units are of the form of area divided by mass. Dimensional analysis shows that $(x\rho)$ is a mass per unit area, m_a. It is the mass of a sheet or slab of the absorber which has the thickness x and a unit of surface area normal to the incident x-ray beam. In these terms, the exponent of Eq. (10–10) becomes $-\mu_m m_a$ and we have

$$I = I_0 e^{-\mu_m m_a}. \qquad (10\text{–}12)$$

Although the mass absorption coefficient varies from material to material far less than the linear coefficient does, it is still far from constant. Materials with large atomic numbers absorb x-rays more readily than the lighter elements,

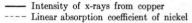

—— Intensity of x-rays from copper
---- Linear absorption coefficient of nickel

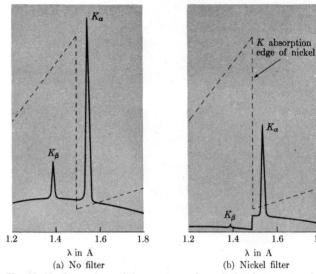

(a) No filter

(b) Nickel filter

Fig. 10–12 Comparison of the spectrum of x-radiation from copper (a) before and (b) after passing through a nickel filter.

so that a certain mass per unit area of lead is more effective than the same mass per unit area of, say, carbon. This is particularly true for low-energy x-rays, but not so pronounced in the 2- to 10-MeV range.

10–8 PAIR PRODUCTION

Certainly one of the most dramatic instances of the relativistic change of energy from one form to another is in the phenomenon known as pair production. *Pair production* is the process in which a photon becomes an electron and a new positive particle. This new particle was anticipated by Dirac in 1928 from his relativistic wave-mechanics theory of the energy of an electron, and was experimentally observed by Anderson in 1932.

The discovery was made in the course of cosmic-ray research with a cloud chamber. This is a device in which the ions formed by a charged particle moving through a gas act as condensation nuclei for droplets of alcohol, for instance, mixed with the gas and supercooled. These droplets then produce a visible trail of the particle. Figure 10–13 is Anderson's most famous cloud-chamber photograph. It shows the path of a charged particle curved by a magnetic field directed into the paper. The particle is seen to traverse a sheet of lead

Fig. 10–13 Cloud-chamber track of a positive electron (positron) in a magnetic field (Courtesy of C. D. Anderson, California Institute of Technology).

6 mm thick in the middle of the chamber. From the beady nature of the track it was established that the particle was electronlike. Since the lead sheet could have only slowed the particle, its direction of motion must have been from the region of low curvature to the region of high curvature. From the observed direction of curvature and the known direction of the motion and of the magnetic field, it was concluded that the charge of the particle was positive. On the basis of this picture and others similar to it, Anderson announced the discovery of a new particle that he called the *positron* or positive electron.* The positron is just like the electron except for the sign of its electric charge.

Figure 10–14 shows a cloud-chamber picture of charged particles originating in a lead sheet bombarded from above by high-energy photons. The curvature of the paths is due to a magnetic field normal to the plane of the paper. Since the tracks of the particles of the pair are oppositely curved, the particles must have opposite charge. In each case one particle is a positron and the other an ordinary electron. A quantum of radiant energy coming from above the lead sheet has changed into matter forming a *pair* consisting of a positron and an electron. In the process of *pair production*, we have the *materialization* of energy.

---

* At this time, it was proposed that the electron be called the *negatron* or negative electron. These names have never come into general use.

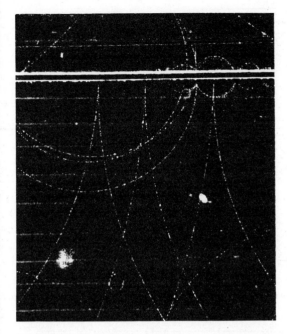

Fig. 10–14 Cloud-chamber tracks of three electron-positron pairs in a magnetic field. Three gamma-ray photons entering at the top materialize into pairs within a lead sheet. The coiled tracks are due to low-energy photoelectrons ejected from the lead. (Courtesy of Radiation Laboratory, University of California.)

Since the rest energy of an electron is 0.51 MeV, a photon must have energy of at least 1.02 MeV to create a pair. A photon could never convert into just one electron or positron, since this would violate the law of conservation of electric charge, among others. Each of the photons which produced the pairs shown in Fig. 10–14 must have had much more than 1.02 MeV of energy, since these pairs were not only created but also given considerable kinetic energy.

A photon cannot produce a pair just anywhere. The process must take place in an intense electric field such as that close to the nucleus of an atom. The nucleus also absorbs the excess momentum of the photon. It can be shown (Problem 10–14) that the momentum of a given energy photon (zero rest mass) is always larger than the momentum of an assembly of material particles with the same total energy.

The three mechanisms of x-ray absorption are summarized in Fig. 10–15. The contribution of each of these to the mass absorption coefficient in lead for photons of different energies is shown in Fig. 10–16. The slope of the photoelectric variation in Fig. 10–11 is positive because the abscissa is the wavelength.

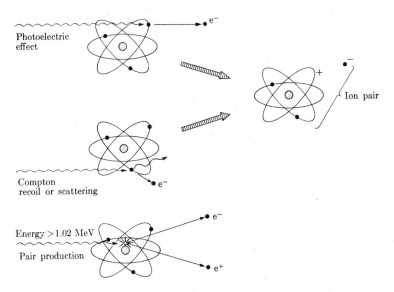

Fig. 10–15 Summary of x-ray and gamma-ray interactions with matter.

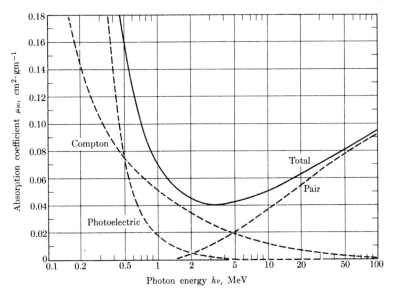

Fig. 10–16 Total mass-absorption coefficients for gamma rays in lead and the contributions from the photoelectric effect, the Compton effect, and pair production.

In Fig. 10–16 the abscissa is energy and thus this slope is negative. The discontinuities of Fig. 10–11 do not show on Fig. 10–16 because the scales are very different.

10–9 DIFFRACTION WITH RULED GRATINGS

X-rays were first diffracted with crystals but eventually a method was also devised for diffracting them with man-made gratings. This method is an interesting and important example of how physical research often builds crosslinks that reinforce the entire structure of our ideas.

We stated earlier that x-rays were not diffracted by man-made gratings because the wavelength of x-rays is much less than the separation of the closest lines man can rule with the granular materials at his disposal. Compton found a way around this difficulty which was certainly ingenious. He used a grating in an unusual way. The index of refraction of glass for x-rays is slightly *less* than one. Thus when x-rays go from air or vacuum into glass, they are passing from an *optically* dense medium into one less dense, and the rays are refracted away from the normal. Recall that whenever light goes from a more dense to a less dense medium, there is a critical angle, and that if the rays approaching the interface make an angle greater than the critical angle, total reflection results. X-rays striking glass at "grazing incidence" will not enter the glass at all, but will be totally reflected. If, now, the glass surface is a ruled grating, these rulings will appear closer together from a grazing angle than when viewed from a point normal to the grating surface. Thus the very geometrical situation which makes the bands between the rulings of the grating capable of reflecting also makes the apparent grating space much less. Compton found that with his ingenious arrangement he could diffract x-rays by measurable amounts.

The important result of this work was that Compton could measure x-ray wavelengths absolutely. The grating space was determined by a screw whose pitch could be measured by counting the threads in a length measured by an ordinary length standard. Therefore, the grating space was known from very direct elementary measurement. All prior x-ray wavelength measurements had been made in terms of calculated crystal spacing which depended on the Avogadro constant, and the Avogadro constant depended in turn upon the charge of the electron. When high precision measurements were made, it was found that the wavelengths measured by a grating differed from those measured by crystal diffraction by about 0.3%. Since this was an absolute measurement, it was concluded that the crystal spacings that had been used formerly were in error. Shiba, a Japanese physicist, traced this back through the Avogadro constant to the charge of the electron and concluded that Millikan's value was in error. Shiba pointed out that the error lay in the viscosity of air used in the calculations in the oil-drop method. Once the new value of the charge was accepted, all physical constants based on that charge were revised. It is interesting that an experiment in x-ray spectroscopy should provide a technique for measuring the basic unit of electrical charge.

10–10 RADIATION UNITS

Some of the energy absorbed from ionizing radiation which passes through matter damages the medium by causing molecular changes or by altering the crystalline form. The amount of damage produced depends upon the nature of the absorbing material, the energy of the photon, and the intensity of the radiation. The effects are large in complex organic molecules and so x-rays are injurious to living tissue. To study this quantitatively, it is necessary to define a unit for the amount of radiation absorbed.

One of the units of the amount of x-radiation is the *roentgen*, R. The roentgen is the amount of x- or gamma radiation that produces in 1 cm³ of *air* under standard conditions ions carrying $1/(3 \times 10^9)$ coulomb of charge of either positive or negative sign.* Air was chosen for the ionized medium because its mass absorption coefficient is nearly the same as that of water and of body tissue over a considerable range of wavelengths. The *milliroentgen*, mR, is a thousandth of a roentgen. In radiobiology these units are usually called the *exposure* units for radiation delivered to a specified area or volume of the body. Note that the units of amount of radiation do not depend upon time, and they are not a measure of the energy flux in a beam of radiation.

The *exposure rate* is measured by the quantity of radiation delivered per unit time. Some of the units are the *roentgen per hour*, R h^{-1}, the *milliroentgen per hour*, mR h^{-1}, and so on.

Absorbed radiation frees photoelectrons and Compton recoil electrons. These secondary particles or corpuscles will also ionize the air as they move toward the collecting electrodes in an ionization chamber. The charges carried by these ion pairs produced by the secondaries must be counted as a part of the quantity of charge to be measured. [An *ion pair*, is composed of the positive ion and the negative ion (initially an electron) produced when a neutral particle is ionized. The magnitude of the charge on each member of the pair is necessarily the same. Each ion of an ion pair produced in air is singly charged.] Although all the secondary particles originate in 1 cm³ of air where the absorption occurred, the measured charge comes from the whole volume through which these secondaries range.

---

* The definition adopted by the International Commission on Radiological Units and Measurements is as follows: "The roentgen is that quantity of x- or gamma-radiation such that the associated corpuscular emission per 0.001293 g of dry air produces, in air, ions carrying 1 esu of quantity of electricity of either sign." This mass of air has a volume of 1 cm³ at 0°C and a pressure of 760 mm of mercury, and 1 esu of charge is equal to $1/(3 \times 10^9)$ C.

When a large number of ions are formed in air, it is found that the *average* energy required to produce an ion pair is 33.7 eV. This is much greater than the minimum energy needed to ionize either oxygen or nitrogen. The value is larger because some photons eject inner electrons whose binding energies are much greater than the minimum ionization energy. If we take the product of the number of ion pairs in air corresponding to a roentgen and the average energy required to produce such a pair, we find that the roentgen is equivalent to 0.112 ergs of energy absorbed per cubic centimeter of standard air or 86.9 ergs per gram of air. When a beam of x-rays enters another medium where the atoms have different atomic numbers, the absorption of energy changes. Thus it was found that exposure to a dose of 1R of x-rays results in the absorption of *about* 97 ergs per gram of soft body tissue. The *Rep* (roentgen equivalent physical) is that dose of ionizing radiation which results in the absorption of 97 ergs per gram of body tissue. This unit is *not* very *definite* because of the variations in the composition of the body. However, a definite unit is the *rad* (radiation absorbed dose), which is 100 ergs (10^{-5} J) of *absorbed* energy per gram of *any* absorbing material. The *millirad*, mrad, is a thousandth of a rad.

Radiation damage to the human body depends upon the absorbed dose, the exposure rate, and the part of the body exposed. The safe limit for those exposed to radiation over the *whole* body during their working day is now set at 100 mR per week. This is an exposure rate of 2.5 mR h^{-1} based on a 40-hour week. Up to a few years ago, the safe tolerance level was thought to be twice this amount. It is likely that it will be lowered again soon. Although the absorbed dose from long exposure to low-level radiation is large, the resulting direct damage is negligible because the body has time to repair the injury. The effects of acute radiation exposure over the *whole* body are about as follows: 20–50 R, some blood changes; 100–250 R, severe illness but recovery within 6 months; 400 R, fatal to 50% of the persons affected (this is called the median lethal dose, MLD or LD-50); and 600 R, fatal to all.

The mechanism of tissue destruction is not completely understood. When radiation is absorbed by the various complex organic molecules in the body, an electron is either raised to a higher energy level within the molecule or removed altogether. One might expect that after the electron returns, all would be normal again, as in the case of hydrogen and other single atoms. However, during the time the molecule is in the excited state, its constituent atoms sometimes rearrange themselves. Then, although the system is again neutral after the electron's return, it is no longer the same molecule. A reaction which occurs in some cases is that two hydroxyl radicals, OH, combine to form hydrogen peroxide, H_2O_2. The molecular situation is somewhat analogous to a high tower which a child builds with small wooden blocks. If we "ionize" the tower by pulling out a block near the base, it is evident that the tower will not rebuild itself when we return the "electron" to the heap. It is unlikely that any substantial change would have occurred if only the topmost block had been removed and then returned. Destruction of a body cell depends upon which electron in the molecular structure absorbs the radiation energy.

In the human body, the hands and feet can receive a much larger dose of radiation without permanent injury than any other part. However, the genes in the cells of the body are readily damaged. Injury to those in the reproductive cells is particularly serious because it gives rise to mutations in the generations which follow. These mutations are almost always adverse and the process is irreversible. There is no safe lower limit of radiation when considering the inheritance of genetic damage. It has been said that "a little radiation is a little bad, and a lot is a lot bad." This means that the probability of absorption by any one gene or group of genes is less for a small dose than for a large one. However, the damage per quantum of radiation absorbed is the same in both cases. It is estimated that the rate of mutation will show significant increase if the exposure is more than 10 R during their reproductive lifetime—a period of about 30 years. During that length of time, one will receive about 4 R from cosmic rays and from the radioactive materials which are found in low concentrations everywhere. Any exposure to x-rays adds to the accumulated dose. Remember that the damage discussed here is transmitted to the generations to come. A whole body exposure of 10 R over a period of three decades would not harm the parent.

The things considered in this section lie in the field of radiological physics. As we advance into the nuclear age, the solution of an increasing number of problems of public health will become the responsibility of persons trained in this area of science.

10–11 X-RAY CRYSTALLOGRAPHY

X-ray diffraction in crystals has become a powerful, indeed the most powerful, method for studying the structure of crystals. We shall discuss some of these techniques very briefly here.

The regular arrangement of the space positions of the atoms in a crystal is called a *lattice array*. The basic interplanar distance or *principal grating space*, d, is shown for the cubic crystal KCl in Fig. 10–17. Note that d is the distance between *adjacent* atoms. The *unit cell* of a lattice is the smallest block or geometric figure of a crystal which is repeated again and again to form the lattice structure. The length of the side of a unit cell is the distance between atoms of the *same* kind. This is equal to 2d for the cubic crystal in Fig. 10–17. The length of the side of the unit cell is equal to the basic distance d only in the case of a simple cubic structure in which all of the atoms are of the same kind. Some pure metals form crystals of this type. These basic interatomic distances can be computed from knowledge of the molecular weight of the crystalline compound, Avogadro's number, the density of the material, and its

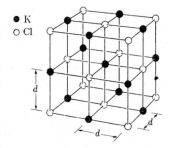

Fig. 10–17 Cubic lattice of sylvite, KC1.

crystalline form. For the cubic type, in particular, the procedure is simple, as illustrated in the example that follows.

Example. KCl (sylvite) is a cubic crystal having a density of 1.98 g·cm^{-3}. (a) Find the distance between adjacent atoms in this crystal, and (b) find the distance from one atom to the next one of the same kind.
Solution.

a) Molecular weight of KClM $= 39.10 + 35.45 = 74.55$ amw. We therefore get

$$\frac{N_A \rho}{M} d^3 = \frac{1}{2},$$

with $N_A = 6.02 \times 10^{23}$ molecules/mole. This gives

$$d = \left(\frac{74.55}{2 \times 6.02 \times 10^{23} \times 1.98}\right),$$

$$= 3.14 \times 10^{-8} \text{ cm},$$

$$= 3.14 \text{ Å} = 3140 \, XU^*.$$

This is the principal grating space, or basic interplanar distance, of KCl.

b) The distance between two atoms of the same kind is twice the above value, or 6.28 Å. This is the length of the side of a unit cell of KCl.

The calculation of the grating space is simple only for a cubic crystal, and the distance thus computed is only the *basic* or *principal* interplanar distance.

---

* X-ray wavelengths are commonly less than an angstrom, 10^{-10} m, and are often expressed in X-units, abbreviated XU. The XU is about 10^{-13} m. Its true definition is not based on the meter but on the interatomic distance or lattice constant of rock salt, NaCl. When the XU was first used, the lattice constant of rock salt was taken to be 2.8140 Å or 2814.0 XU. High-precision measurements have revised the rock salt lattice constant so that we now have 1000.00 XU = 1.00202 Å.

Within a crystal there are many crystal planes from which Bragg reflection can result. Consider the many possibilities presented by the two-dimensional situation of a marching band on a football field, Fig. 10–18. The basic distance between any adjacent members of the band might be 5 ft. But as the band marches past, it is evident that there are many lines through the band which resemble a three-dimensional array of parallel planes. These sets of parallel lines or planes are separated from one another by different amounts which can be computed from the basic interatomic distance. Reflections from some sets of planes are more intense than those from some other sets. Intensity variations are introduced by the differences in the nature of the planes in crystals composed of more than one type of atom. Elements with high atomic numbers scatter radiation more effectively than those with low atomic numbers. If the x-marked band members in Fig. 10–18 represent one kind of atom and the dot-marked ones another kind, we note that some planes contain only x-marked scatterers, some only the dot-marked type, and some have a mixed population. (It should be kept in mind that the lines in Fig. 10–18 are actually analogous only to the traces of the crystal planes in the plane of the paper. These planes of the crystal are not necessarily normal to the paper. It is evident from a study of Fig. 10–17, for example, that a plane containing only potassium atoms is not perpendicular to any of the faces of the cube.)

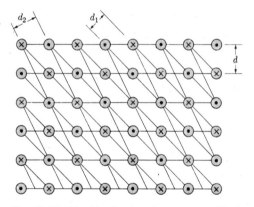

Fig. 10–18 Marching band analogy to a crystal lattice.

We are now in a position to appreciate both why the Bragg method of x-ray spectroscopy is simple and why Laue pictures are complex. In the Bragg method, the crystal can be set so that one set of populated planes is reflecting a beam of x-rays, and the three-dimensional crystal is used in a two-dimensional manner. In the Laue method, a pencil of x-rays is made to pierce the crystal perpendicular to a set of planes of the crystal. Most of the spots are due to diffraction from sparsely populated planes that happen to be situated so that both of the Bragg conditions for reflection are satisfied. The Bragg method is better for the study of the wavelengths of x-rays, but the Laue technique is very useful for the study of crystals. It is a tedious but rewarding task to start with a Laue pattern and work back to the geometry of the array of atoms that must have produced it. An ingenious type of microscope employing both x-rays and visible light has been devised for crystal study. With its aid an enormous, useful magnification can be obtained, so that one can "look" into the lattice structure, as shown in Fig. 10–19.

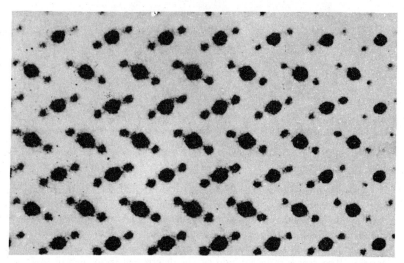

Fig. 10–19 Atoms in marcasite FeS_2, looking along the crystallographic c-axis magnified 4.5 million times. The larger spots are iron atoms with 26 electrons each; the smaller dots are sulfur atoms with 16 electrons each. The regular array of the atoms in the crystal is quite evident. This remarkable photograph was taken with a two-wavelength microscope (Courtesy of M. J. Burger, Massachusetts Institute of Technology.)

There is another x-ray crystallographic technique we must mention in passing. The Bragg and Laue methods require single crystals large enough for study. Many materials that are basically crystalline cannot be obtained as large single crystals, but these materials may be studied by means of the powder technique. One form of this technique, the Debye-Scherrer method, requires that the substance be ground and powdered, so that it can be assumed that all the tiny crystals have random orientation. When a pencil of x-rays is passed through this powder, a series of rings is formed on a photographic film. Each ring is the intersection of the film plane and a cone of rays. Each cone is the locus of rays for which some set of crystal planes is so oriented that both

Bragg conditions of reflection are fulfilled. The formation of a powder diffraction pattern is shown schematically in Fig. 10–20, and Fig. 10–21 is the pattern for NaCl made with the x-radiation from copper.

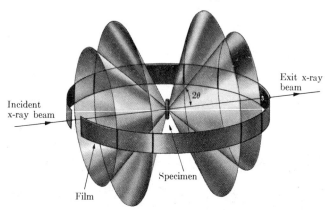

Fig. 10–20 Relation of film to specimen and incident beam in the Debye-Scherrer powder diffraction method. X-rays forming the cone having a half-angle of 2θ were reflected from the same kinds of planes, all oriented at an angle θ to the incident beam. Other cones are formed in a similar way.

Another form of powder technique is used to study the orientation of crystals in an extruded or drawn material such as a wire. If the crystallites in the wire actually are random in their orientation, a true powder pattern of circles results. But if the crystallites are somewhat oriented, then each circle has nonuniform intensity and the pattern on the film tends toward a Laue pattern. The degree of orientation can be determined from such pictures.

Laue patterns of metals or other materials rather opaque to x-rays are sometimes obtained by studying the x-rays scattered back from the side of the material nearer the x-ray source. This technique is used, for example, to study the crystalline structure of steel.

X-rays of a single wavelength are often useful. One way of obtaining such monochromatic rays is to use x-rays that have undergone a single-crystal Bragg reflection before they are used for powder studies. Another way is by the use of filters, as discussed in Section 10–7.

Since a single crystal is used for Laue patterns, there are only a very small number of planes that fulfill the Bragg conditions for constructive interference for any one x-ray wavelength. Therefore, obtaining many Laue spots requires the use of an incident beam containing many wavelengths. On the other hand, the minute crystals in a powder have random orientations, so that many planes are available for the production of interference maxima even when monochromatic x-rays are used.

Fig. 10–21 Powder diffraction pattern of NaCl made with the K_α and K_β wavelengths of copper. During exposure, the left portion of the film was covered with nickel foil. This filtered out the K_β line.

10–12 MILLER INDICES

The orientations of the various lattice planes in a crystal are usually specified by a system that was first used in 1839 by W. H. Miller, an English mineralogist, to describe the faces of a crystal. In the general case, a face or an internal plane will be inclined to all of the crystallographic axes. These axes are a convenient coordinate frame that can be used to determine the orientation of a plane by giving the distances from the origin to its points of intersection with the three axes. All the series of planes which are parallel to this plane will have intercepts whose ratios to the axial lengths of the *unit* cell, *a*, *b*, and *c*, are independent of the particular axial lengths involved in the given lattice. Since we are concerned only with the orientation of a plane and not its absolute position, these ratios could serve to specify the plane. But these ratios cause difficulty when the plane is parallel to a crystallographic axis as in Fig. 10–22(a). In this case, the planes do not intersect two of the axes at all; that is, their intercepts are said to be at infinity. To avoid the introduction of infinity into the specification of the orientation of a plane, the reciprocal of the fractional intercept is used. Thus the reciprocal will be zero when the plane and axis are parallel. This leads to the system of determining the orientation of a plane in a crystal lattice by the *Miller indices,* which are defined as *a set of integers in the ratio of the reciprocals of the fractional intercepts which the plane makes with the crystallographic axes.* It is customary to designate the Miller indices of a plane as $(h\,k\,l)$, which means that the plane has fractional intercepts of $1/h$, $1/k$, and $1/l$ with the axes and that the actual intercepts are a/h, b/k, and c/l. It is evident that the intercepts in Fig. 10–22(a) are 1, ∞, ∞. The reciprocals of these are 1, 0, 0, and therefore the Miller indices are (100). (This is read "one-zero-zero" or "one-aught-aught," not "one hundred.") These (100) planes are parallel to the *BC*-plane. A similar group of planes could be drawn parallel to the *AC*-plane and might be designated the (010) planes; and a set parallel to the *AB*-plane might be called the (001) planes. It is evident, however,

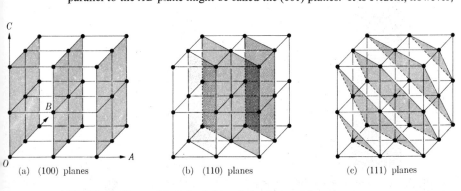

(a) (100) planes   (b) (110) planes   (c) (111) planes

Fig. 10–22 Some of the sets of planes in a cubic crystal.

that these three sets of planes in a cubic crystal are equivalent. Whether a set be called (100), (010), or (001) planes depends entirely upon the selection of axes in the crystal, and hence all three of these sets of planes are named the (100) planes. The indices given for the series of planes in Figs. 10–22(b) and (c) are self-evident. This is not always so. For example, let the intercepts of plane be 1, 2, and 3 units on the three axes, respectively. The indices of this plane are therefore in the ratio 1/1, 1/2, and 1/3. When these fractions are multiplied by their lowest common denominator, 6, we obtain (632), the Miller indices of the plane.

The distance d between successive members of a series of parallel planes involves a, b, and c, the axial lengths of the unit cell, and $(h\,k\,l)$, the Miller indices of the planes. We shall derive an expression for the interplanar distance d for the relatively simple case of an orthorhombic crystal. The three axes of such a crystal are mutually perpendicular. In Fig. 10–23, ABC is one of a series of parallel planes which has intercepts $OA = a/h$, $OB = b/h$, and $OC = c/l$. The origin of coordinates O is in the next plane of the set parallel to ABC. Therefore, ON, the length of the normal from the origin to the plane, is equal to d. Let θ_a, θ_b, and θ_c be the angles ON makes with the three crystallographic axes, respectively. Then the direction cosines of ON are $\cos\theta_a = ON/OA$, $\cos\theta_b = ON/OB$, and $\cos\theta_c = ON/OC$. Since the sum of the squares of the direction cosines of a line equals unity, upon squaring the cosine expressions and substituting for the intercepts OA, OB, and OC, one gets

$$\left(\frac{d}{a/h}\right)^2 + \left(\frac{d}{b/k}\right)^2 + \left(\frac{d}{c/l}\right)^2 = 1,$$

or, upon rearranging, this becomes

$$d = \frac{1}{(h^2/a^2 + k^2/b^2 + l^2/c^2)^{1/2}}.$$

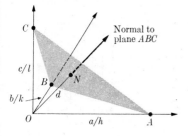

Fig. 10–23 A lattice plane in an orthorhombic crystal.

If the orthorhombic crystal is cubic, the basic interplanar distances are equal. In a simple cube, these distances are the lengths of the sides of a unit cell. Then $a = b = c$, and the preceding equation reduces to

$$d = \frac{a}{(h^2 + k^2 + l^2)^{1/2}}. \tag{10–13}$$

When this relation is substituted into Eq. (10–4), we find that the *first-order* diffraction maxima in Bragg reflections are given by

$$\lambda = \frac{2a}{(h^2 + k^2 + l^2)^{1/2}} \sin \theta. \tag{10–14}$$

This equation can be used to calculate the axial length of a side of a *cubic* crystal, and the Miller indices of the set of planes involved in giving a particular maximum if the wavelength λ of the radiation and the Bragg angle θ are known. The value of λ can be found in tables of the characteristic radiation for the various x-ray tube-target materials. Referring to Fig. 10–20, it is seen that the data for finding θ can be obtained by measuring the distance along the film from the exit beam to a diffracted line and the distance halfway around the film in its circular mounting from the exit beam to the entrance of the incident beam.

To find ($h\,k\,l$), let us first rearrange Eq. (10–14) so that we have

$$\frac{\lambda^2}{4a^2} = \frac{\sin^2 \theta}{h^2 + k^2 + l^2}.$$

The sum of the squares of the Miller indices is always integral, and the left-hand side of the last equation is constant for any given diffraction pattern. Therefore, having determined θ for each line in a pattern, one can now find the Miller indices of the planes associated with each line by choosing integers h, k, and l for each line, so that the ratio $[\sin^2 \theta/(h^2 + k^2 + l^2)]$ has the same value for every line.

Three types of lattice with cubic symmetry are shown in Fig. 10–24. In (a) the diffracting centers are at the corners of a simple cube; in (b) a body-centered cube, an additional lattice point is located at the center of the cube; and in (c)

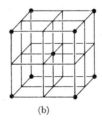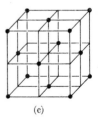

(a)   (b)   (c)

Fig. 10–24 The three types of crystal lattice with cubic symmetry (a) simple, (b) body-centered, (c) face centered.

a face-centered cube, an additional lattice point is located at the center of each face of the cube. Both NaCl and KCl crystals have the face-centered cubic configuration. The reader should consult a book on crystallography for descriptions of configurations of crystals that are not cubic.

PROBLEMS

10-1 Potassium iodide, KI, is a cubic crystal which has a density of 3.13 g cm^{-3}. Find a) the basic interplanar distance, and b) the length of a side of the unit cell.

10-2 The spacing between the principal planes in a crystal of NaCl is 2.820 Å. It is found that a first-order Bragg reflection of a monochromatic beam of x-rays occurs at an angle of 10°. a) What is the wavelength of the x-rays in Å and in XU, and b) at what angle would a second-order reflection occur?

10-3 What is the shortest wavelength that can be emitted by the sudden stopping of an electron when it strikes a) the screen of a television tube operating at 10,000 V and b) the plate of a high-power radio transmitter tube operating at 30,000 V?

10-4 a) At what potential difference must an x-ray tube operate to produce x-rays with a minimum wavelength of 1 Å? of 0.01Å? b) What is the maximum frequency of the x-rays produced in a tube operating at 20 kV? at 60 kV?

10-5 The electronic configuration of zinc in its ground state is

$$(1s)^2(2s)^2(2p)^6(3s)^2(3p)^6(4s)^2(3d)^{10}.$$

a) The x-ray line of the longest wavelength in the K-series is called $K\alpha_1$. What is the electronic configuration of zinc immediately *before* and immediately *after* the emission of a $K\alpha_1$ line? b) What is the term classification (e.g., $^4P_{3/2}$, etc.) of each of the two states mentioned? c) What is the bombarding energy of the electrons needed to excite the $K\alpha_1$ line in zinc?

10-6 X-rays from a certain cobalt target tube are composed of the strong K-series of cobalt and weak K lines caused by impurities. The wavelengths of the K_α lines are 1.785 Å for cobalt and 2.285 Å and 1.537 Å for the impurities. Using Moseley's law, calculate the atomic number of each of the two impurities. b) What elements are they? (For the K-series, $b = 1$ in Moseley's law.)

10-7 The K absorption edge of tungsten is 0.178 Å and the average wavelengths of the K-series lines are $K_\alpha = 0.210$ Å, $K_\beta = 0.184$ Å, and $K_\gamma = 0.179$ Å. a) Construct the x-ray energy-level diagram of tungsten. b) What is the least energy required to excite the L-series? c) What is the wavelength of the L_α line? d) If a 100-keV electron struck the tungsten target in a tube, what is the shortest x-ray wavelength it could produce, and e) what is the shortest wavelength characteristic of tungsten that could be emitted?

10-8 A thin sheet of nickel is placed successively in a beam of x-rays from cobalt, then in one from copper, and finally in one from zinc. Discuss the effect of each of these beams on the nickel atoms and show that the filtered radiation from copper is essentially monochromatic. X-ray data for these elements are given in the accompanying table. Consider only K-shell absorption.

Element	Emission wavelengths, Å		
	K_α	K_β	K_{absorb}
Co	1.79	1.62	1.61
Ni	1.66	1.49	1.48
Cu	1.54	1.39	1.38
Zn	1.43	1.29	1.28

10–9   For 0.2 Å x-rays, the mass absorption coefficients in $cm^2 \, g^{-1}$ for several metals are as follows: aluminum, 0.270; copper, 1.55; and lead, 4.90. a) What is the half-value thickness of each for a narrow beam of x-rays? b) What thickness of each is required to reduce the intensity of the transmitted beam to $\frac{1}{32}$ of its incident value? c) If the "buildup" from scattering and other processes for a broad beam of radiation is equivalent to making the incident beam 1.5 times its actual intensity, what thickness of each material is then needed to obtain an intensity reduction to $\frac{1}{32}$?

10–10   Observations made from very high altitude balloons and from rockets that go to the "top" of the earth's atmosphere show that the sun and certain stars emit x-rays (x-ray astronomy). Why does visible light from these sources reach the surface of the earth whereas the x-rays do not?

10–11   Three quanta, each having 2 MeV of energy, are absorbed in a material. One of the quanta is absorbed by the photoelectric process, another is involved in a Compton scattering, and the third is involved in pair production. a) Discuss the possible methods by which the scattered photon and each of the charged particles produced can be involved in energy interchanges until all the original photon energy is reduced to thermal energy. b) Will all this final thermal energy be freed at the point where absorption occurred originally?

10–12   A photon of wavelength λ undergoes Compton scattering from a free electron as shown in Fig. 5–3. Prove that, regardless of the energy of the in-coming photon, the scattered photon cannot undergo pair production if α is greater than 60°.

10–13   A photon of energy 1.92 MeV undergoes pair production in the vicinity of a lead nucleus. The created particles have the same speed, and both travel in the direction of the original photon. Calculate the recoil momentum of the lead nucleus.

10–14   Use the conservation laws to show that it is impossible for pair production to take place in free space. Assume that the velocity v of each of the particles of the pair is parallel to the direction of motion of the incident photon.

10–15   A common form of exposure meter or dosimeter is a cylindrical capacitor filled with a gas. One model worn by personnel working in the vicinity of x-ray equipment has an absorption equivalent of 6 cm^3 of standard air. a) If the electrodes are charged to a difference of potential of 400 V, what must be the resistance of the electrode insulation so that the charge leakage in 8 hours shall not exceed 10 percent of an assumed safe tolerance level of 20 mR per 8-hour day? (Assume that the voltage remains constant.) b) What would be the effect on the accuracy of the dosimeter if (1) there are finger streaks on the insulator, and (2) the relative humidity is high?

10–16 The principal lines in the K x-ray spectrum of nickel have the following wavelengths: 1.656 Å, 1.497 Å, and 1.485 Å. Determine the Bragg angles at which these lines are reflected in the third order from the (111) planes in a simple cubic crystal for which the unit axial length is 6 Å.

10–17 Referring to Fig. 10–20, one finds that in a particular experiment the distance halfway around the circular film mounting was 22.53 cm, and the distance along the film from the exit beam to one of the lines was 6.34 cm, and to another one, 11.03 cm. What was the Bragg angle for each line?

10–18 When K_α radiation from copper ($\lambda = 1.54$ Å) is used to obtain a powder diffraction pattern of KCl, a face-centered cubic crystal, first-order maxima occurs at $\theta = 25.3$, 29.6, 44.1, 54.5, and 58.4°. a) Calculate the interplanar distance d associated with each of these Bragg angles. b) Find the Miller indices for the set of planes for each value of d. c) Calculate the basic interplanar distance from the data for each case. d) What is the length of a side of a unit cube of this face-centered cubic crystal? e) Draw three face-centered cubic crystals and sketch in the (100) planes in one, the (110) planes in another, and the (111) planes in the third. [*Hint:* In part b), the sum of the squares of the Miller indices can easily be found by the use of the C- and D-scales of a slide rule. These make possible the simultaneous division of one set of numbers by another set if the quotient is constant. The values of $\sin^2 \theta$ are marked on the D-scale with a pencil, and then the C-scale is moved until integers on it are directly above or nearly above all of the pencil marks. These integers are the sums of the squares sought.]

CHAPTER 11

Molecules, Liquids, and Solids

11–1 MOLECULES; POLAR AND HOMOPOLAR BONDS

In the previous chapters, we have seen that the forces that bind atoms together are basically electrostatic forces, governed by the simple Coulomb force law, but that the dynamics of the motion of the electrons about the nucleus is very complex. The binding of two or more atoms together to form a molecule is equally complex, but again the principal forces involved are electrostatic forces. When the atoms and molecules are condensed to liquids and solids, the same holds true. Coulomb's law and wave mechanics can, in principle, explain all observed atomic and molecular processes except the minor perturbations that are of magnetic origin. In the first three sections of this chapter, we are going to discuss the binding and the spectroscopy of simple molecules. The rest of the chapter treats the physics of solids and, to a lesser extent, liquids. The discussion of these subjects in the present volume must necessarily be short, and, for further details, the reader is referred to more specialized texts.

The binding of the atoms in a molecule is classified as ionic or covalent. The ionic bond, in principle, is very simple, and we shall describe it here. The covalent bond, responsible for the binding of such molecules as H_2, N_2, O_2, etc., is discussed in the next section. Usually most molecules classified as ionic are also bound partly by the covalent bond. However, for simplicity, we shall here disregard that fact, and in particular for the example discussed, NaCl, the ionic binding is exceedingly strong.

In Section 9–5, we described how the binding energy of the last electron (ionization potential) increases while a shell is being filled; for instance, in the L-shell this binding energy increases substantially from lithium to neon. The first element in the next shell, sodium, has a binding energy of the last electron of 5.138 eV. Element 17, chlorine, has the relatively large binding energy of 13.01 eV for the last electron. Chlorine is one number removed from a closed shell with 18 electrons (argon). It can therefore very easily form a negative ion, and, indeed, the binding energy for an extra electron is 3.79 eV. When a sodium atom and a chlorine atom get close to each other, an electron can be transferred from sodium to chlorine. This requires an expenditure of energy of $5.138 - 3.79 = 1.348$ eV. In the process, however, sodium becomes a positive ion and chlorine becomes a negative ion. The two ions attract each other, and therefore they have a potential-energy curve, as shown schematically in Fig. 11–1. This potential is deep enough so that the 1.348 eV needed to transfer the electron from sodium to chlorine is more than made up for by the decrease in electrostatic potential energy when the two atoms are at the equilibrium distance. The net result is therefore that NaCl is bound by 3.58 eV.

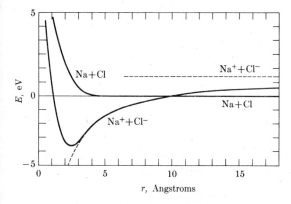

Fig. 11–1 Potential-energy curves for the ionic molecule NaCl.

The resulting NaCl molecule is, of course, an electric dipole, and there are several chemical and physical effects that result from this large dipole moment. One of the effects is the strong optical transition probability for rotational transitions described in Section 11–3.

11–2 THE H₂ PROBLEM

We have discussed earlier some of the great successes of wave mechanics in explaining observed phenomena in atomic and nuclear physics. The first was the explanation of the alpha-decay process by using barrier-penetration calculations; the second was the explanation of the level scheme and optical transitions in the hydrogen atom, including the selection rules; and the third was the accurate description of the helium spectrum. We are now going to discuss another landmark in atomic physics: the explanation of the binding of the H_2 molecule by Heitler and London in 1927.*

---

* W. Heitler and F. London, *Z. Physik* **44** (1927), p. 455.

One of the unsolved puzzles of atomic physics before wave mechanics was the homopolar chemical bond, as exemplified in particular by the binding of two identical atoms to form a gas molecule: H_2, N_2, O_2, etc. Our treatment of this problem by the Heitler-London method is similar to the discussion carried out in Section 9–2 on the helium atom. We shall use perturbation theory and, just as in the case of the helium atom, it will be necessary to use antisymmetrized wave functions. Figure 11–2 defines the coordinates used. The two nuclei a and b are origins of two coordinate systems. The radius vectors r_{1a}, etc. to the two electrons 1 and 2 from both origins are shown in the figure. The nuclear separation r_{ab} is considered a constant, although we shall discuss later how the total energy of the system depends upon this parameter.

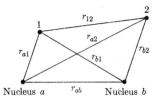

Fig. 11–2 Definition of distance parameters used in the theory of the hydrogen molecule.

When the two atoms are far away from each other, their position wave functions are those appropriate for the hydrogen ground state:

$$\psi_a(1) = (\pi a_0^3)^{-1/2} e^{-r_{1a}/a_0}, \tag{11-1}$$

$$\psi_b(2) = (\pi a_0^3)^{-1/2} e^{-r_{2b}/a_0}. \tag{11-2}$$

Here a_0 is Bohr's radius. Note that the first function is expressed in coordinate system a, and the second in coordinate system b. We want to use perturbation theory to calculate the shift in energy when the two wave functions have a nonnegligible overlap, as they do in the H_2 molecule. Heitler and London expressed the position part of the unperturbed antisymmetrized wave functions for a singlet and triplet as

$$\psi \begin{pmatrix} \text{singlet} \\ \text{triplet} \end{pmatrix} = B[\psi_a(1)\psi_b(2) \pm \psi_b(1)\psi_a(2)], \tag{11-3}$$

where $\psi_a(2)$ is constructed simply by replacing the numeral 1 with the numeral 2 in Eq. (11–1), etc.

We shall first normalize these wave functions. It may appear as if the normalizing constant B should be the familiar factor $1/\sqrt{2}$. This is not the case, however, because the two wave functions ψ_a and ψ_b are not orthogonal. They are identical in form, but are defined in two different coordinate systems. If the two nuclei are infinitely far apart, there is no overlap between them and they are orthogonal. When they overlap partly, however, the normalizing procedure yields for the singlet/triplet

$$\int \psi^* \psi \, d\tau = B^2 \int \psi_a^2(1) \, d\tau_1 \int \psi_b^2(2) \, d\tau_2 + B^2 \int \psi_b^2(1) \, d\tau_1 \int \psi_a^2(2) \, d\tau_2$$

$$\pm 2B^2 \int \psi_a(1)\psi_b(1)\psi_a(2)\psi_b(2) \, d\tau_1 \, d\tau_2$$

$$= (2 \pm 2S)B^2 = 1, \tag{11-4}$$

where S is given by

$$S = \int \psi_a(1)\psi_b(1)\psi_a(2)\psi_b(2) \, d\tau_1 \, d\tau_2. \tag{11-5}$$

Equation (11-4) gives

$$B \begin{pmatrix} \text{singlet} \\ \text{triplet} \end{pmatrix} = (2 \pm 2S)^{-1/2}. \tag{11-6}$$

The term S can be regarded as a small correction. It is zero for infinite separation of the nuclei and small ($S \ll 1$) for separations considered here. We shall return to this point.

The total Hamiltonian for the H_2 molecule, constructed on the assumption that the two nuclei are at rest, is

$$H = -\frac{\hbar^2}{2m}(\nabla_1^2 + \nabla_2^2) + \frac{e^2}{4\pi\varepsilon_0}\left(\frac{1}{r_{ab}} + \frac{1}{r_{12}} - \frac{1}{r_{a1}} - \frac{1}{r_{b1}} - \frac{1}{r_{a2}} - \frac{1}{r_{b2}}\right). \tag{11-7}$$

The kinetic-energy terms and two of the potential-energy terms have been used to construct the unperturbed wave functions (Eq. 11-3). The perturbing Hamiltonian is therefore

$$H' = \frac{e^2}{4\pi\varepsilon_0}\left(\frac{1}{r_{ab}} + \frac{1}{r_{12}} - \frac{1}{r_{1b}} - \frac{1}{r_{2a}}\right) \tag{11-8}$$

for the first part of the wave function (Eq. 11-3), and

$$H' = \frac{e^2}{4\pi\varepsilon_0}\left(\frac{1}{r_{ab}} + \frac{1}{r_{12}} - \frac{1}{r_{1a}} - \frac{1}{r_{2b}}\right) \tag{11-9}$$

for the second part. In other words, the perturbing Hamiltonian is given by Eq. (11-8) when electron 1 is in state ψ_a and electron 2 is in state ψ_b, and Eq. (11-9) is used when the two electrons are exchanged.

We can now write the perturbation energy as

$$\Delta E = \int \psi^* H' \psi \, d\tau, \tag{11-10}$$

where the integral is taken over the six-dimensional space defined by the position vectors for the two electrons. We get

$$\int \psi^* H' \psi \, d\tau = B^2 \int H' \psi_a^2(1)\psi_b^2(2) \, d\tau_1 \, d\tau_2 + B^2 \int H' \psi_a^2(2)\psi_b^2(1) \, d\tau_1 \, d\tau_2$$

$$\pm \, 2B^2 \int H' \psi_a(1)\psi_b(2)\psi_a(2)\psi_b(1) \, d\tau_1 \, d\tau_2. \tag{11–11}$$

The two first terms are identical, except for the interchange of labels 1 and 2. In the last term, there may be some question about whether Eq. (11–8) or Eq. (11–9) should be used for H'. As can be easily seen, it makes no difference. Inserting B^2 from Eq. (11–6), we can therefore write

$$\Delta E = \frac{C \pm A}{1 \pm S}. \tag{11–12}$$

Here C and A are given by

$$C = \frac{e^2}{4\pi\varepsilon_0} \int \left(\frac{1}{r_{ab}} + \frac{1}{r_{12}} - \frac{1}{r_{1b}} - \frac{1}{r_{2a}} \right) \psi_a^2(1)\psi_b^2(2) \, d\tau_1 \, d\tau_2, \tag{11–13}$$

$$A = \frac{e^2}{4\pi\varepsilon_0} \int \left(\frac{1}{r_{ab}} + \frac{1}{r_{12}} - \frac{1}{r_{1b}} - \frac{1}{r_{2a}} \right) \psi_a(1)\psi_b(1)\psi_a(2)\psi_b(2) \, d\tau_1 \, d\tau_2. \tag{11–14}$$

In the final expression for the perturbation energy (Eq. 11–12), the two terms A and S would not have occurred if we had written the wave function ψ as a simple product function $\psi_a(1)\psi_b(2)$. The perturbation energy would then have been simply $\Delta E = C$, which is equal to the simple classical expression for the electrostatic interaction between the two atoms when the wave-mechanical probability densities of the two electrons are regarded as continuously distributed charge clouds. As we shall see, this classical part produces weak binding, since $C < 0$ for moderate separation. However, the dominating term in the expression is the *exchange* interaction A.

In order to get a qualitative feeling for how the integral C varies with the nuclear separation r_{ab}, we refer to Fig. 11–3. This represents schematically the two atoms with their nuclei and electronic clouds surrounding the nuclei. For simplicity, we consider the electronic clouds as having sharp cutoff radii,

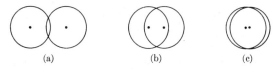

(a)   (b)   (c)

Fig. 11–3 Schematic representation of the overlapping of two atoms. The points represent the nuclei, the circles the regions occupied most densely by negative electronic charge distributions.

beyond which the charge density is zero. We recall from electrostatics that the force between a point charge q_1 and a spherically symmetric charge distribution q_2 or between two spherically symmetric charge distributions q_1 and q_2 is equal to the force between two point charges q_1 and q_2, provided there is no overlap between q_1 and q_2. At distances where there is no overlap, there is then no force acting between the two neutral atoms (Fig. 11–3a). In Fig. 11–3(b), the two electronic clouds partly overlap. The repulsive force between the two nuclei is, of course, in the same form as before, so that the first term in Eq. (11–13) is unchanged. The second term is reduced because of the overlap, since the electric field inside the spherically distributed charge is smaller than it would have been if all the charge had been concentrated at the center. The two last terms in Eq. (11–8) are increased because of the fact that some of the charge from atom A has penetrated beyond some of the electronic shielding surrounding nucleus B and conversely. The net result is that, at moderate distances, C is negative. At smaller distances, when the nucleus from one atom penetrates into the shielding cloud of the other atom, the nuclear repulsion becomes dominant, and the integral C goes positive. Figure 11–4 shows how the term C varies with the nuclear separation r_{ab}.

In order to study the significance of the integral A (Eq. 11–14), we introduce a new concept called the *exchange charge*, defined by

$$\rho_1 \equiv \psi_a(1)\psi_b(1),$$
$$\rho_2 \equiv \psi_a(2)\psi_b(2). \tag{11–15}$$

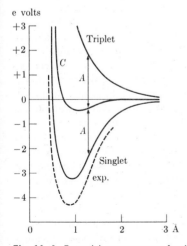

Fig. 11–4 Potential-energy curves for the H₂ molecule in the singlet and triplet states.

The integral of the exchange charge over all space is

$$\alpha \equiv \int \psi_a(1)\psi_b(1) \, d\tau_1 = \int \psi_a(2)\psi_b(2) \, d\tau_2. \qquad (11\text{-}16)$$

Since the two wave functions ψ_a and ψ_b are identical, except that they are written with respect to two different coordinate systems, the integral α is equal to 1 when those coordinate systems coincide ($r_{ab} = 0$). For increasing r_{ab}, the integral α is rapidly decreasing. The term S, defined by Eq. (11–5), can be written as a product of two integrals of the form Eq. (11–16). This gives $S = \alpha^2$ and

$$\Delta E \begin{pmatrix} \text{singlet} \\ \text{triplet} \end{pmatrix} = \frac{C \pm A}{1 \pm \alpha^2}. \qquad (11\text{-}17)$$

Exchange charge is a mathematical concept without any real physical meaning. With the aid of this new concept, we rewrite Eq. (11–14) as

$$A = \frac{e^2}{4\pi\varepsilon_0} \left[\frac{\alpha^2}{r_{ab}} + \int \frac{\rho_1 \rho_2}{r_{12}} \, d\tau_1 \, d\tau_2 - \alpha \int \frac{\rho_1}{r_{1b}} \, d\tau_2 - \alpha \int \frac{\rho_2}{r_{2a}} \, d\tau_2 \right]. \qquad (11\text{-}18)$$

Figure 11–5(a) shows qualitatively the density of the exchange charge for the H_2 molecule, and Fig. 11–5(b) is a plot of the magnitude of the exchange charge along a line through the two nuclei. Because ψ_a is a decaying exponential and ψ_b is an increasing exponential between the two nuclei, the product of the two is a constant. However, to the left of nucleus A and to the right of nucleus B, both exponentials are decaying, and the product is decaying faster.

Returning now to Eq. (11–18), we see that the first term is equal to the potential energy that one would get with a charge αe at each nuclei. This is the smaller of the terms at moderate separations. The second term is the interaction of exchange charge 1 with exchange charge 2, and, since they are equally distributed in space, it is equal to twice the self-energy, that is, the energy it takes to assemble a charge cloud identical with the exchange charge. The third term is equal to the potential energy resulting from a point charge αe at nucleus b interacting with the exchange charge ρ_1. Similarly, the fourth term is equal to the potential energy resulting from a point charge αe at nucleus a interacting with the exchange charge ρ_2. When r_{ab} is large compared to the Bohr radius, as in Fig. 11–5, the averages of the distances involved in the three last integrals are of the order of magnitude of $r_{ab}/2$. Therefore the three last integrals are numerically of the same order of magnitude, while the first integral is smaller. The net result is that the term A is negative for distances down to approximately the Bohr radius and numerically larger than the numerical value of C. In this range of r_{ab}, we have $\alpha^2 \ll 1$. Therefore, the energy ΔE, which is the potential energy of a system of two neutral hydrogen atoms approaching each other from infinity, is negative in the singlet state and positive in the triplet state.

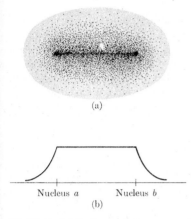

(a)

(b)

Nucleus *a*   Nucleus *b*

Fig. 11–5 (a) Exchange charge $\rho = \psi_a$ (1) ψ_b (1) in H_2. An abstract concept. (b) Plot of the magnitude of the exchange charge in H_2 along a line connecting the two nuclei.

Figure 11-4 shows the magnitudes of the terms C and A and the calculated total energy ΔE in the singlet and triplet states. Also shown is the experimental potential-energy curve for the singlet case. The experimental parameters used to deduce the shape of this curve are measurements of the dissociation (binding) energy, the size of the molecule, and the spectrum of vibrational energies (see the next section). The vibrational spectrum determines the width of the potential well as a function of the vertical distance (energy increment) from the bottom. The discrepancy between the theoretical and experimental curve arises from the fact that we again have used first-order perturbation theory in a case where the perturbing interaction is not small.

We have seen how exchange symmetry is a physical concept of utmost importance. We found it necessary to introduce it in order to explain the helium spectrum. More important, the observed strength and spin-dependence of the covalent bond can be explained only by the use of this concept.

11–3 MOLECULAR SPECTROSCOPY

When we discussed atomic-emission spectroscopy in previous chapters, we assumed that the source was a gas discharge tube in which the molecules had been dissociated into charged or neutral atoms. In a less violent discharge the molecules may not be dissociated, but excited such that a molecular-emission spectrum is produced, usually superimposed upon atomic spectra. A simpler method for studying important features of molecules is to pass white light through a cold molecular gas and measure the absorption lines. The initial states in a transition can then only be the lowest state (ground state) or an excited state within a few kT (0.025 eV) of the ground state.

Three major types of molecular excitation are observed in such studies. First, it is obvious that the orbital states of the electrons can change in the individual atoms.   This kind of excitation is called *electronic excitation* in molecular spectroscopy.   Second, the individual atoms vibrate with respect to the center of mass in a *vibrational excitation*.   Third, the molecule rotates about the center of mass in a *rotational excitation*.   The minimum excitation energy of the third form is so low that a molecule at room temperature may be "highly excited," relatively speaking.

The electronic type of excitation will, of course, be influenced by the presence of other atoms, and therefore the spectral lines seen do not have the exact same wavelengths as for the case of the free atom.   However, the process is basically the same and well understood in terms of the description in Sections 8–7 and 9–7.   We shall therefore proceed to a discussion of the theory of vibrational and rotational excitations.

Let us assume that the molecule is diatomic and has zero total angular momentum in its ground state.   We write the Hamiltonian for the motion of the two nuclei of the molecule as

$$H = - \frac{\hbar^2}{2M_1} \nabla_1^2 - \frac{\hbar^2}{2M_2} \nabla_2^2 + V(r_{12}). \tag{11–19}$$

Here ∇_1^2 and ∇_2^2 are derivatives with respect to the position coordinates of nucleus 1 and nucleus 2, respectively.   For heavy atoms in particular, the inner electrons will follow the nucleus to which they are bound when it is moving relative to the other nucleus, while the valence electrons, in general, move less.   The two masses M_1 and M_2 are therefore intermediate between the respective atomic and nuclear masses.

Section 7–1 discussed the reduction of a wave-mechanical two-body problem to a one-body problem by introduction of the reduced mass

$$\mu = \frac{M_1 M_2}{M_1 + M_2} \tag{11–20}$$

and the separation vector $\mathbf{r} \equiv \mathbf{r}_{12}$ between the two particles. With these modifications, Schrödinger's equation with the Hamiltonian (11–19) is a one-body equation with spherically symmetric potential.   The solutions are therefore spherical harmonic functions times a solution of the radial wave equation (Eq. 7–30), rewritten here as

$$\frac{1}{r^2} \frac{d}{dr} \left(r^2 \frac{dR}{dr} \right) + \frac{2\mu}{\hbar^2} \left(E - V - \frac{J(J+1)\hbar^2}{2\mu r^2} \right) R = 0. \tag{11–21}$$

The total wave function is

$$\psi = R(r) Y_{J,m}(\theta, \phi). \tag{11–22}$$

The angular part, $Y_{J,m}(\theta,\phi)$, describes a rotational motion about the center of mass with angular momentum quantum numbers J and m. The radial part, which contains the information about changes in the distance r between the two nuclei, depends, of course, upon the shape of the potential $V(r)$. Qualitatively, this shape is as shown in Fig. 11–4 for all diatomic molecules. Near the minimum of this curve, it can be approximated by a parabola. Except at very large angular momenta, the centrifugal potential $J(J + 1)\hbar^2/2\mu r^2$ is only a minor perturbation on this potential. The solutions of Eq. (11–21) are therefore to a good approximation harmonic-oscillator wave functions describing a vibrational motion by the two nuclei relative to each other. The energy eigenvalues combining rotational and vibrational motion will be approximately

$$E = (v + \tfrac{1}{2})\hbar\omega + \frac{J(J + 1)\hbar^2}{2\mu r_0^2}, \qquad (11\text{–}23)$$

where r_0 is the average or equilibrium nuclear separation (compare Eq. 6–106). In Eq. (11–23), v is the *vibrational quantum number*; $v = 0, 1, 2, 3$, etc., and J is the *rotational quantum number*, $J = 0, 1, 2, 3$, etc.

A vibration-rotation energy-level diagram is shown in Fig. 11–6. The spacing between the rotational levels is, in general, much smaller than the spacing between the vibrational levels, so that, for each quantum number v, corresponds a family of rotational levels. Also shown in Fig. 11–6 are some absorption lines between two neighboring vibrational states. The selection rule for this type of transition is $\Delta J = \pm 1$.

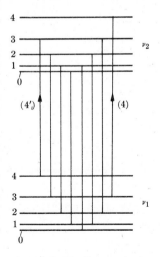

Fig. 11–6 Vibration-rotation energy levels for two arbitrary values of v and for $J = 0, 1, 2, 3, 4$. Transitions of absorption are shown. *Note:* $\Delta J = \pm 1$.

As an example of a vibration-rotation spectrum, consider the absorption lines at about $\lambda = 3.5$ microns (μ) in HCl gas. Figure 11–7 shows a potential-energy diagram for the HCl molecule. The dissociation energy is 4.430 eV, and the equilibrium separation is 1.275 Å. The parabola, drawn as a dashed line, follows the equation $\Delta E = 15(r - r_0)^2$. The "spring constant" is therefore $\beta = 30$ eV/Å$^{-2} = 480$ J/m^{-2}. According to Eq. (11–20), the reduced mass for HCl^{37} is

$$\mu = \frac{1.67 \times 10^{-27}}{1 + 1/37} = 1.63 \times 10^{-27} \text{ kgm.}$$

With this we get a vibrational frequency

$$\omega = \sqrt{\beta/\mu} = 5.42 \times 10^{14} \text{ s}^{-1}.$$

This corresponds to a wavelength

$$\lambda = 2\pi c/\omega = 3.48 \times 10^{-6} \text{ m} = 3.48 \ \mu.$$

The quantum energy of a vibrational transition is $\Delta E = \hbar\omega = 5.72 \times 10^{-20}$ J $= 0.357$ eV. The zero-point energy, i.e., the kinetic energy of the ground state of the harmonic oscillator, is $\hbar\omega/2 = 0.178$ eV ($v = 0$ and $J = 0$ in Eq. 11–23). The dissociation energy is the difference between this state and the state of infinite separation.

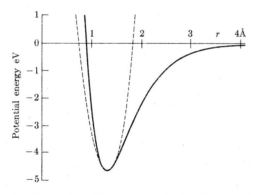

Fig. 11–7 Potential-energy curve for HCl. The dashed curve is a parabola approximating the real curve at the minimum.

The rotational energy is given by the second part of Eq. (11–23) and is

$$E_{\text{rot}} = CJ(J + 1),$$

with the constant C given by

$$C = \hbar^2/2\mu r_0^2 = 2.10 \times 10^{-22} \text{ J} = 1.31 \times 10^{-3} \text{ eV.}$$

The change in rotational energy in a transition from J_1 to J_2 is

$$\Delta E_{rot} = C[J_2(J_2 + 1) - J_1(J_1 + 1)].$$

Inserting $J_2 = J_1 \pm 1$, we get

$$\Delta E_{rot} = \pm 2CJ_>, \tag{11–24}$$

where $J_>$ is the larger of the two J values J_1 and J_2.

The rotational energy for moderate values of J is so small that it can clearly be excited by collisions at room temperature. The transition $v = 0$ to 1 therefore can be associated with a rotational change in which J decreases or increases. The energy change in such a transition is then

$$\Delta E = \hbar\omega \pm 2CJ_> = (0.357 \pm 0.00262\, J_>)\, \text{eV},$$

where $J_> = 1, 2, 3, \ldots$ (not 0).

The observed absorption spectrum of HCl in the region around 3.5 μ is shown in Fig. 11–8. The numbers given under each peak are the upper rotational quantum numbers $J_>$. The unprimed numbers are for rotational transitions up; that is, $J_2 > J_1$, and the primed numbers are for rotational transitions down.

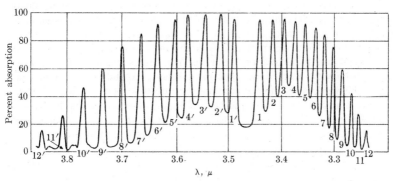

Fig. 11–8 The absorption spectrum of HCl vapor in the near infrared. [After Imes, *Astrophys. J.* **50**, 251 (1919).]

We started the discussion of the HCl spectrum by presenting the potential-energy diagram, Fig. 11–7, implying that this was known. Actually, the best experimental information available for constructing such a diagram comes from the kind of spectroscopy we have discussed.

11–4 SOLIDS AND LIQUIDS

Everybody who has studied a little bit of chemistry knows that the interatomic forces binding the atoms together to form a molecule are saturable. This means that when a bond between two hydrogen atoms, for instance, has been formed, a third, fourth and fifth are not added to form a larger hydrogen molecule. As we have stated before, the basic forces involved are electrostatic forces obeying Coulomb's law. However, wave mechanics and Pauli's exclusion principle juggle the positions of the particles in such a way that, as an average, no strong electric field appears on the outside of a saturated molecule to attract further atoms. The field is not zero, however. Take the example of the NaCl molecule, a strong dipole. Clearly, it has an electric field outside it, and this field gives rise to weaker forces called *intermolecular forces*. As we shall see, there are also intermolecular forces between H_2 molecules and between helium or neon atoms. These weak forces are responsible for the formation of liquids and solids.

When the substance under discussion is in gas form, the intermolecular forces are not strong enough to hold the molecules tightly together. However, the forces are responsible for known deviations in a real gas from the ideal gas law $pV = RT$. They are often called *van der Waals' forces* because they are the source of one of the correction terms in van der Waals' equation for a real gas.

In a solid or a liquid the molecules are packed such that the potential energy from the intermolecular forces is a minimum. The magnitude of this potential energy per molecule can easily be estimated as follows. The heat of vaporization per mole of a substance divided by Avogadro's number is the energy needed to release one molecule from a liquid and bring it over into the gaseous state. This is not exactly the quantity we are seeking, because the heat of vaporization also includes the work done when the substance expands from a liquid to a gas. This work is per mole at constant pressure $W = p(V_{gas} - V_{liq}) \approx RT$.

An empirical law* gives the heat of vaporization as approximately $H = 10.5\, RT_B$ per mole, where T_B is the absolute temperature at the boiling point. Therefore, the potential-energy minimum per molecule is approximately

$$V_{min} \approx \frac{(10.5 - 1)RT}{N_A} = 9.5\, kT_B, \qquad (11\text{–}25)$$

where k is Boltzmann's constant which, in convenient units, is $k = 8.64 \times 10^{-5}\, \text{eV} \cdot {}^\circ\text{K}^{-1}$. This formula gives for a substance with a boiling point of $T_B = 400\,{}^\circ\text{K}$, $\Delta E = 9.5\, kT_B = 0.328$ eV. This is about an order of magnitude smaller than the potential energy binding the atoms together in a molecule.

For molecules bound by the ionic bond, the origin of van der Waals' force is basically the dipole moment of the molecule. Two molecules approaching each other will attract or repel each other, depending upon the orientation of the dipole moments relative to the line connecting their centers. However, the field of one molecule will exert forces on the other, polarizing it, that is, orienting

---

*   Prouton's rule; for instance, see G. W. Castellan, *Physical Chemistry*, Reading, Mass.: Addison-Wesley (1964), p. 154.

it in such a way that the net force between the two is attractive. A simple calculation shows that, at large distances, a net force proportional to r^{-6} results. This force law clearly must break down, at short distances, when the two electronic clouds start to overlap each other substantially. Since we are presumably dealing with saturated molecules, these other forces are repulsive and they vary more rapidly with r than the van der Waals' force. Figure 11–9 shows a potential of the form $V = -c_1 r^{-6} + c_2 r^{-12}$, which is a fair representation of the van der Waals' force.

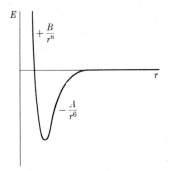

Fig. 11–9 van der Waals' potential. A/r^6 modified with a repulsive potential B/r^n with $n = 12$.

The molecules that are bound with the covalent bond do not have a static dipole moment. The same is true, of course, for single atoms, as for instance the helium atom. However, both atoms and covalent molecules have rapidly fluctuating dipole moments because of the motion of the electrons about the nucleus or nuclei. Two helium atoms, for instance, attract each other very weakly because they mutually polarize each other in a dynamic sense. The best way to describe this perhaps is to say that to a small extent the electrons of the two helium atoms oscillate in synchronism. The result is a potential which, at large distances, obeys the r^{-6} law. For helium, these forces are extremely weak, as manifested by the fact that helium liquifies at 4.2 °K. However, many molecules bound by the covalent bond have attractive intermolecular forces (heat of vaporization) comparable to typical ionic molecules. Generally speaking, the heavier a molecule is, the larger will be the heat of vaporization of that substance. This is because the polarizability is higher the more electrons that are involved, and the larger the distances within the molecule that a given electron can be displaced.

At sufficiently low temperatures, most substances are crystalline solids. A closely packed regular array of the molecules then gives the lowest potential energy of the system. When the temperature is raised to a given point, the melting point, this regularity is broken because of the heat motion of the molecules or atoms. The molecules are still closely packed on a microscopic scale, but there are several voids that allow an easy slippage of layers of molecules past one another. Therefore the liquid flows, although it exhibits a certain resistance to the flow (viscosity). The presence of the voids and irregularities is the reason why a liquid normally occupies a larger volume than a solid.

An amorphous material is technically a liquid with a very high viscosity. Glass, for instance, does not crystallize when cooled. For decreasing temperature, the viscosity increases to the point where the material does not flow, but breaks when strong forces are applied. The arrangement of the molecules in such a solid has the disorder of a liquid.

The physics of a gas is basically the physics of individual molecules. This we have learned to understand or to describe in detail, albeit with some difficulty, by use of wave mechanics. The physics of a solid is more complex, but certain general features can be understood because of the regularity of the crystalline structure. Of the three phases, gas, liquid, and solid, the liquid phase is hardest to understand or describe because liquids do not have the simplicity of a single particle or the regularity of a crystal. We shall not discuss the liquid state further in this book.

11–5 CLASSICAL THEORY OF ELECTRON GAS IN SOLIDS

The *classical* theory of insulators is that in these materials the electrons are bound to their molecules, which are in turn tied to fixed locations in the solid. Conductors, on the other hand, are assumed to have atoms whose outer electrons are free to migrate from atom to atom throughout the solid crystalline structure. Copper, for instance, has one such free electron per atom. These electrons are assumed to behave within a conductor like an ideal gas. This assumption leads to the conclusion that the number of degrees of freedom in a conductor should be nine: three for the kinetic energy of the atoms, three for the elastic potential energy of the atoms, and three for the kinetic energy of the electrons. We shall explain the inconsistency between the nine degrees of freedom that every conductor should have classically and the experimentally verified six degrees of freedom of the law of Dulong and Petit after seeing where we are led by the "electron gas" theory as it applies to conduction.

In order to calculate the resistivity of the metal, we assume that the electron gas is thermally agitated and has a root-mean-square velocity which may be obtained by solving Eq. (1–18) for v. We get

$$v_{\text{rms}} = \sqrt{\frac{3kT}{m_e}}. \qquad (11\text{–}26)$$

If the electrons have a mean free path L, then the average time $\bar{t}$ between collisions is

$$\bar{t} = \frac{L}{v_{\text{rms}}} = L\sqrt{\frac{m_e}{3kT}}. \qquad (11\text{–}27)$$

Suppose that the electrons are in a bar of cross-sectional area A and length l, across which there is a potential difference V. This potential difference causes an average electric field V/l which exerts a force on each electron. The force on the electron is

$$F = eE = \frac{eV}{l}.$$ (11–28)

This force accelerates the electrons an amount

$$a = \frac{e}{m_e} \frac{V}{l}.$$ (11–29)

They accelerate for an average time $\bar{t}$ and acquire an average drift velocity $\overline{v_d}$ given by

$$\overline{v_d} = \frac{eV}{2m_e l} L \sqrt{\frac{m_e}{3kT}}.$$ (11–30)

This drift velocity is along the bar and is very small compared with the random v_{rms}. Indeed, $\overline{v_d}$ is so small that each interval between thermal collisions begins a new acceleration "from rest" and the transport of electrons proceeds at an average velocity of $\overline{v_d}$.

If the concentration of free valence electrons is n per unit volume, then the number which pass across a plane perpendicular to the axis of the bar per unit time is $nA\overline{v_d}$, and the electrons constitute a current given by

$$I = enA\overline{v_d} = \frac{e^2 nLA}{2m_e l} \sqrt{\frac{m_e}{3kT}} V.$$ (11–31)

Comparison with Ohm's law shows that this development gives the resistance of the bar as

$$R = \frac{2l}{e^2 nLA} \sqrt{3kTm_e}.$$ (11–32)

Since in terms of the specific resistance we may write $R = \rho(l/A)$, we see that

$$\rho = \frac{2\sqrt{3kTm_e}}{e^2 nL},$$ (11–33)

and the electrical conductivity is

$$\sigma = \frac{1}{\rho} = \frac{e^2 nL}{2\sqrt{3kTm_e}}.$$ (11–34)

It is interesting to find that for some pure metals, assuming that n is the number of valence electrons per unit volume and that L is the interatomic distance, the prediction of this formula is quite good at room temperature. Unfortunately for this theory, it is well known that the resistivity of most metals over a wide range is closer to being proportional to the absolute temperature than to its square root. Therefore this agreement is largely coincidental. Still worse, we have already pointed out that this theory would assign a molar heat capacity of $3R/2$ to the electron gas, while in fact the molar heat capacity of metals is quite readily explainable on the basis of translational and vibrational energy of the molecules alone.

Good conductors of heat are also good conductors of electricity. The proportionality of these two kinds of conduction is called the *Wiedemann-Franz* relationship, and it strongly implies that the two types of conduction have the same mechanism. If the motion of electron gas accounts for electrical conductivity and therefore thermal conductivity, it is paradoxical that the thermal motions of the electrons do not contribute to the specific heat of the material.

11–6 WAVE MECHANICAL THEORY OF ELECTRON GAS IN SOLIDS

In Sections 11–1 and 11–2, we described how the outermost electrons in the atoms of a molecule are exchanged and shared by the atoms. In a solid, the atoms are so tightly packed that the attractive potential experienced by the outermost electrons permeates the whole sample. This applies to an insulator as well as to a conductor, and the difference between the two is a bit more subtle than implied by the opening sentence in the previous section. (See the next section.)

Figure 11–10 shows qualitatively the potential in the regular array of a crystal. At the site of the nucleus, the potential well is much deeper than indicated. However, this is a forbidden region for the outer electrons, by the Pauli principle.

For simplicity, we shall disregard the oscillations of the potential and assume that the electrons are enclosed in a box with a constant potential inside and with impenetrable walls. We want to calculate the energy distribution of these electrons, keeping in mind that their distributions over the available quantum states are determined by Pauli's exclusion principle. The problem is very similar to the one we tackled when we derived Planck's law for black-body radiation (Sections 3–9 and 3–10).

Schrödinger's equation for an electron in a constant potential ($V = 0$) is

$$-\frac{\hbar^2}{2m_e} \nabla^2 \psi = E\psi, \tag{11–35}$$

and the solutions satisfying the boundary conditions at the "impenetrable" walls of the box can be written as

$$\psi = A \sin k_x x \sin k_y y \sin k_z z. \tag{11–36}$$

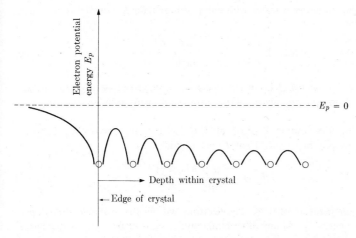

Fig. 11–10 Schematic diagram of the variation of the electron potential energy along a row of atoms within a crystal and the potential barrier at the edge.

The origin is assumed to be at one corner of the box, and the boundary condition at $x = L$, $y = L$, and $z = L$ is

$$k_x L = n_x \pi,$$

$$k_y L = n_y \pi, \qquad \qquad (11\text{--}37)$$

$$k_z L = n_z \pi.$$

By inserting this solution into Eq. (11–35), we obtain

$$E = \frac{\hbar^2}{2m_e} (k_x^2 + k_y^2 + k_z^2) = \frac{\pi^2 \hbar^2}{2m_e L} (n_x^2 + n_y^2 + n_z^2). \qquad (11\text{--}38)$$

To each allowed state corresponds a set of integers n_x, n_y, and n_z. Exactly as in Section 3–9, the energy of a state is proportional to the square of the magnitude of a vector $\boldsymbol{n}$ with components n_x, n_y, and n_z, as plotted in Fig. 3–8. The maximum value of n is given by Eq. (11–38) as

$$n_{\max} = \frac{L}{\pi \hbar} (2m_e E)^{1/2}. \qquad (11\text{--}39)$$

The number of electron states with energy lower than E is therefore (compare Section 3–9):

$$N = 2 \frac{1}{8} \frac{4}{3} \pi n_{max}^3 = \frac{L^3}{3\pi^2\hbar^3} (2m_eE)^{3/2}. \qquad (11\text{–}40)$$

The factor 2 is included because in each state described by a given position wave function, we can place two electrons, one with spin up and one with spin down.

Inserting the volume $V = L^3$ into Eq. (11–40), and solving for E, which we will now call the *Fermi energy* E_f, we obtain

$$E_f = \frac{3^{2/3}\pi^{4/3}\hbar^2}{2m_e} \left(\frac{N}{V}\right)^{2/3} \qquad (11\text{–}41)$$

At a temperature of 0 °K, the electrons will fill the available states up to the Fermi energy E_f. At any other temperature, some of the states with energies above the Fermi level will be occupied and some of the lower ones unoccupied. We shall discuss this further below, but first, as an illustration, let us calculate the Fermi energy for copper. Assuming that copper has one free electron per atom, we find

$$\frac{N}{V} = \frac{6.02 \times 10^{23} \times 8.9 \times 10^6}{63.5} = 8.43 \times 10^{28} \text{ electrons} \cdot \text{m}^{-3}.$$

By inserting this into Eq. (11–41), we obtain for the Fermi energy

$$E_f = \frac{3^{2/3}\pi^{4/3} \times 1.054^2 \times 10^{-68} \times 84.3^{2/3} \times 10^{18}}{2 \times 9.11 \times 10^{-31} \times 1.60 \times 10^{-19}} = 7.05 \text{ eV}.$$

Figure 11–11 shows an approximate potential-energy diagram for copper with the position of the Fermi level drawn in at about 7 eV from the average bottom of the potential. The Fermi level is approximately 4.5 eV below the potential outside the metal. This energy drop is, of course, the work function, which is a difficult quantity to calculate with any accuracy (see Problem 11–10). The work function is determined experimentally by measurements on the photoelectric effect and on thermionic emission (see Sections 3–11 and 3–14).

Figure 11–11 also shows the distribution of electrons versus energy. For a temperature of 0 °K, this distribution can be found from Eq. (11–40), which gives the total number of electron states with kinetic energies from 0 to E. Regarding E as a variable, we find the number of states dN in the interval E to $E + dE$ by differentiation

$$N(E, 0)\, dE \equiv dN = \frac{m_e^{3/2}V}{2^{1/2}\pi^2\hbar^3} E^{1/2}\, dE. \qquad (11\text{–}42)$$

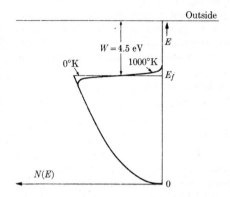

Fig. 11-11 Fermi distribution of the "free" electrons in Cu. The work function W is the energy required to move an electron from the top of the distribution to outside the metal.

At any temperature above 0 °K, this distribution is modified, as mentioned above. The changes take place mostly within an energy of $\pm kT$ from the Fermi level. At room temperature, we have $kT = 0.025$ eV; hence, one may think that the changes are of little significance. However, as we shall see in the following section, the temperature effect is of major significance for many electronic devices.

The correction to Eq. (11–37) for higher temperatures is called the *Fermi probability distribution*, and it has the form

$$F(E, T) = \frac{1}{1 + e^{(E - E_0)/kT}} \, . \qquad (11\text{--}43)$$

The derivation of this formula is somewhat difficult and similar to the derivation of Boltzmann's distribution formula (Section 1–13). The total distribution now becomes

$$N(E, T) \, dE = \frac{m_e^{3/2} V E^{1/2}}{2^{1/2} \pi^2 \hbar^3} \, F(E, T) \, dE. \qquad (11\text{--}44)$$

The constant E_0 in Eq. (11–43) is determined by integrating Eq. (11–44) and setting the result equal to the total number of electrons N. Although E_0 varies slightly with temperature, for practical purposes, we can regard it as a constant and equal to the Fermi energy E_f. The total distribution (Eq. 11–44) is plotted in Fig. 11–11 for $T = 1000$ °K.

We can now get a better understanding of the thermionic-emission process, described briefly in Section 3-14. At elevated temperatures, the upper tail of the distribution function will contain a significant number of electrons with energies greater than $E_f + W$. These electrons have enough energy to escape. A continuous stream of them is directed toward the surface of the metal. The probability for escape is of course not unity, but can easily be calculated, as outlined in Section 6-10. A formula for the emission current per unit area as a function of temperature can thus be derived (Richardson's formula).

11-7 ENERGY BANDS IN SOLIDS

In Section 11-2, we discussed two states of the hydrogen molecule, one binding and one nonbinding. In the bound state, the total spin-wave function is antisymmetric (singlet) and the position wave function symmetric. In the unbound state (triplet), it is the other way around. The important point, for the present discussion, is that there is a splitting of the states, a splitting that increases as the atoms approach each other from an infinite separation (Fig. 11-4).

Similarly, if we bring more than two similar atoms of any kind close together, the states occupied by the outer electrons will overlap and an energy splitting will result. Figure 11-12 shows schematically what happens to the energy levels of carbon when N carbon atoms are brought together. There are two electrons in the 2p-shell in carbon. For decreasing separation r between neighbor atoms, the 2p-states start to overlap, and the result is an *energy band* with a total of $6N$ states, of which $2N$ are occupied. The wave functions of all

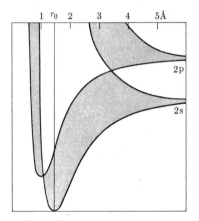

Fig. 11-12 Energy bands in diamond. At distances below 3Å, two of the p-states join with the s-states to form a lower fully occupied band. At the equilibrium distance r_0, the gap to the next (unoccupied) band is very large. Reproduced by permission from J. C. Slater, *Quantum Theory of Matter.* New York: McGraw-Hill © 1951.

$6N$ states permeate the whole sample. Some change sign rapidly from atom to atom. Others have approximately the same phase in a large number of neighboring atoms. For the former, the energy will be higher than the free-atom wave functions. For the latter, the energy is lower. The $2N$ electrons occupy the lowest one-third of the band at 0 °K. At a higher temperature, the occupation is determined by the Fermi probability distribution.

The lower atomic states are similarly split into bands. The splitting of the 2s-state in the case of carbon is shown in Fig. 11–12. The total number of levels found in a sample of N atoms is $2N$, accommodating all $2N$ 2s electrons. For a completely filled band, the number of electrons moving through the solid in one direction is exactly equal to the number moving in the other direction. In a partly occupied band, this is also true so long as no perturbing forces (an electric field) upset the balance. The properties of solids are largely determined by the highest occupied band, as discussed in detail below.

If the highest occupied band is only partly occupied, as in Fig. 11–13(a), the electrons in this band may be excited from a lower to a higher energy level within the band. The separation of the levels within the band is so slight that

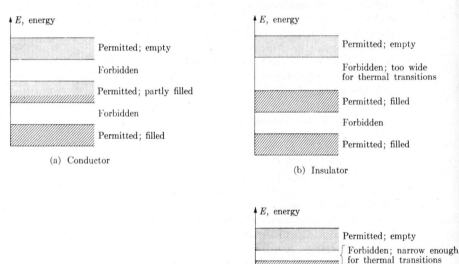

Fig. 11–13 Schematic energy bands (a) of a conductor, (b) of an insulator, and (c) of a pure intrinsic semiconductor at absolute zero.

the electrons are readily able to be accelerated to higher energies by weak electric fields. A material with such an electronic band structure is a conductor. All metals fall into this class.

Most nonmetals are insulators. For insulators, the highest occupied band is always completely filled. Although one might suppose that this case should be rare, it is actually the most common. Not only is the higher occupied band filled, as shown in Fig. 11–13(b), but also the energy gap to the next empty band is wide on the energy scale. Since thermal agitation at normal temperatures is unable to lift electrons from the filled band to the next higher permitted band, the electrons cannot absorb small amounts of energy due to electric fields or thermal agitation. Therefore, these electrons are "fixed," and the material must be both a thermal and electrical insulator. In an intense electric field, of course, some electrons may be pulled into the higher permitted band, where they may migrate conductively. This is dielectric breakdown.

Semiconductors comprise a third class of materials. The difference between semiconductors and insulators is that the gap between the band which is filled at absolute zero, called the *valence band*, and the higher permitted band is narrow in a semiconductor, as shown in Fig. 11–13(c). In this case thermal energy at room temperature is sufficient to raise some electrons from the valence band to the higher permitted band, called the *conduction band*. Electrons in the conduction band are free to transport electrical charge. Their number per unit volume is the n in Eqs. (11–31) through (11–34). For a semiconductor, n increases exponentially with temperature. It is easy to see that if n increases with temperature faster than L decreases, the electrical conductivity of a semiconductor will increase with temperature instead of decreasing as it does for conductors, since the population in the conduction band is determined by the tail on the Fermi distribution.

When electrons are transferred to the conduction band from the valence band, the valence band is no longer filled, and there are then energy states within the valence band available to the valence electrons. Valence electrons can then move successively, like automobiles in a traffic jam. When an opening appears, one car moves to fill it, leaving an opening behind. This is repeated over and over, so that the net effect is that the physical motion of the cars is forward while the gap between them moves backward. In the electrical case, the vacancy created by the removal of an electron is a small positively charged region called a *hole*. When a nearby electron moves into a positive hole, it leaves another positive hole at its original location, and so on. Thus there is a net transport of positive charge which is called *hole migration*. Holes are less mobile than electrons, and therefore hole currents are usually less than electron currents. Collectively, electrons and holes are called *carriers*. There is a dynamic equilibrium between mutual cancellation and thermal creation of conduction electrons and holes.

While amorphous materials have no proper place in our discussion, there is nevertheless an interesting demonstration that may be performed with a glass rod to illustrate the possibility of an insulator becoming a conductor at a high temperature. If two leads are connected to the ends of a thick glass rod, with suitable resistance in series with the rod, and connection is made to an ordinary 110-V line, only an extremely feeble current will flow. But application of a Bunsen burner flame to the rod will soon heat the glass to the point where it becomes conducting. If the burner is then shut off, the I^2R heating alone will sustain the temperature of the glass, so that it finally glows brightly and begins to melt.

In actual insulators, there are usually sufficient imperfections and chemical impurities in the lattice so that additional intermediate conducting levels exist. One would certainly expect, then, that such an irregularly arranged solid as glass would possess a large proportion of such localized conducting regions and hence exhibit the behavior described above.

Detailed examination of the known crystalline structure of various solids, plus study of the electronic structure of individual atoms in the solid, have made it possible to predict fairly well what the band structures of various materials should be, and hence which particular arrangements should be conductors, insulators, or semiconductors.

It is now easier to understand why electrons in a solid take such a minor part in the absorption of heat energy (specific heat). In an insulator, the electrons are not allowed to absorb small increments of energy at all. In a conductor, only a relatively few electrons at the top of the distribution near the Fermi level can and do absorb energy. These do indeed contribute to the specific heat of the solid, but because they are so few, only to a minor extent.

We can also now make a more nearly correct interpretation of the formula for electrical resistivity, Eq. (11–33), derived by classical calculations. The formula is basically correct, except that we have to modify the meaning of the parameters n, T, and L. The electrons that can change state, and thereby upset the balance of currents flowing in two opposite directions, are only the electrons at the top of the distribution near the Fermi level. Therefore, n is much smaller than previously assumed. These electrons move with velocities practically independent of the temperature (kinetic energy ≈ 7 eV). Therefore T in Eq. (11–33) is a high and constant artificial "temperature." Finally, the scattering centers for these electrons are not each atom, but irregularities in the atomic structure, mostly heat vibrations. The number of such irregularities increases with the temperature, such that in metals L is roughly inversely proportional to the real absolute temperature T. With these modifications, Eq. (11–33) is in agreement with the observed facts.

We conclude this portion of our discussion with a summary of the differences between conductors, insulators, and semiconductors. A *conductor* is a solid with a large number of current carriers, a number independent of temperature. An *insulator* contains very few carriers at ordinary temperatures. A *semiconductor* contains relatively few carriers at low temperatures but a rather large number at higher temperatures. For semiconductors the actual dependence of resistance upon temperature is a result of two opposite effects. First, the increase in scattering of the electron wave with temperature tends to diminish the conductivity. This tends to cancel the second effect, which is due to increase in the number of carriers. At room temperature semiconductors may have either positive or negative resistance-temperature slopes.

11–8 IMPURITY SEMICONDUCTORS

The characteristics of *pure* semiconductors, called *intrinsic* semiconductors, can be changed in very important ways by the introduction of trace amounts of impurities. Intrinsic semiconductors to which impurities have been added are said to be *doped*. Consider the intrinsic semiconductor, germanium, doped with antimony. Each germanium atom has four valence electrons, and therefore each atom has four neighboring atoms bonded to it. Atoms of antimony will fit into this structure, but they have five valence electrons of which four participate in bonding to neighbor atoms. The fifth electron is superfluous to the structure and is therefore loosely bound to the antimony atom. Since thermal energy is sufficient to cause some of the germanium electrons to leave their valence bonds and jump to the conduction band, it is easy to see that the fifth antimony electron is even more easily excited into this conduction band. Thus practically every antimony atom introduced into the germanium lattice contributes a conduction electron without creating a positive hole. Of course, each antimony atom has become a positive ion, but this ion is tied into the lattice structure so that it cannot contribute to conduction. Thus in addition to the electrons and holes intrinsically available in germanium, the addition of antimony greatly increases the number of conduction electrons. In this case antimony is called a *donor* impurity and it makes the germanium an *n-type* (*n* is for negative) semiconductor.

Gallium, on the other hand, has three valence electrons. If it is introduced into germanium, it can supply only three of the four electrons necessary to fit into the germanium lattice. Since thermal energy is sufficient to excite some bonded germanium electrons into the conduction band, it is easy to see that thermal excitation is sufficient to cause germanium valence electrons to complete the lattice structure by attaching themselves to the gallium without leaving the valence band. This causes the gallium to become a fixed negative ion and it leaves an electron hole in the valence band. Thus gallium is an *acceptor* which, at room temperature, causes as many positive holes as there are gallium impurity atoms. The acceptor, gallium, makes germanium a *p-type* (*p* for positive) semiconductor.

The Fermi level for an intrinsic semiconductor is approximately in the middle of the energy gap between the valence and conduction bands. Figure 11–14(a) shows schematically the distribution of electrons in the conduction band and holes in the valence band. Figure 11–14(b) shows the Fermi function and the resulting distribution of *electrons* in the two bands, assuming that the distribution of electron *states* is uniform in both.

Figure 11–15(a) illustrates the population of electrons and holes in an *n*-type semiconductor. Since the number of electrons is larger than the number of holes, the Fermi level is higher than the middle of the gap (Fig. 11–14(b) shifted upwards). Note that in this diagram only the mobile charge carriers are represented. The fact that the negative carriers outnumber the positive ones does not mean that the semiconductor has a net negative charge. The donor atoms are positive but immobile. The total positive charge of the donors normally just cancels the net negative charge of the carriers.

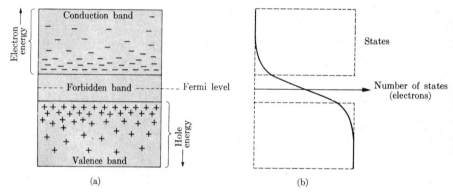

Fig. 11–14 Schematic energy-level diagram of an intrinsic semiconductor at room temperature.

Figure 11–15(b) shows the situation in a *p*-type semiconductor, and Fig. 11–15(c) shows a junction between an *n*-type and a *p*-type. Such a junction can be made by starting with a *p*-type and letting donor atoms diffuse from the left into the crystal.

When the two ends of the crystal are not connected to any external source of electricity, the Fermi levels of the two parts will coincide. This is easy to understand if the crystal is at 0 °K. The electrons at the Fermi level are mobile, and if this level is higher in one part than in the other, some electrons will move to the lower states in the other half. The slight displacement of charge will bring the energies at the Fermi levels to equilibrium. At a higher temperature, the two Fermi distribution curves will match each other, so here again the above statement holds true. If the crystal is in a circuit, so that one

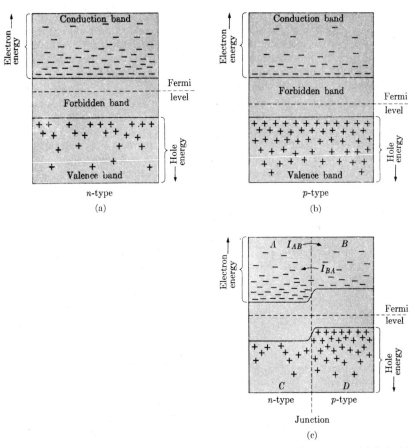

Fig. 11-15 Schematic energy-level diagrams of impurity semiconductors: (a) isolated *n*-type, (b) isolated *p*-type, and (c) *n-p* junction.

type is held at a different potential than the other, then there is a discontinuity in their Fermi levels equal to this potential difference. These facts will help us explain semiconductor rectifiers and transistors.

11-9 SEMICONDUCTOR DIODES

Diodes are electrical components that have the property of passing an electric current in one direction much more easily than in the other. They are useful for the conversion of alternating currents into direct currents and other electronic purposes. We propose to show why the junction between n- and p-type semiconductors has rectifying properties.

The principal mechanism of conduction within a semiconductor is diffusion. The diffusion current is proportional to the change in concentration per unit distance, or the *concentration gradient*. The diffusion current across any layer is equal to a constant times the concentration gradient, and this proportionality constant is called the *diffusion coefficient*.

Both the electrons and the holes in semiconductors move about because of thermal diffusion, but we shall fix our attention on the electrons, which are more mobile than the holes. If we refer to Fig. 11–15(c), we see that there are two electron currents between regions A and B. The one to the right, I_{AB}, results from the fact that region A is n-type whereas region B is p-type. The concentration of conduction electrons is far greater in A and they extend to higher energies in spite of the fact that the bottom of the conduction band in B is higher than that in A. The magnitude of this current is sensitive to the relative concentrations of electrons at the top of the conduction bands. The current to the left, I_{BA}, is due to electrons near the junction and at the bottom of the B conduction band "falling over" the potential "hill" into region A. This current is called a *saturation current* because its magnitude depends on the concentration of conduction electrons in region B and on *the slow rate at which they can diffuse toward the junction*. The saturation current is very small because the concentration of electrons in B, the p-type region, is small. *The saturation current does not depend on the height of the potential "hill."* In the situation pictured, these two opposing electron currents are both small and equal, since the saturation current *must* be small and since the two currents are in equilibrium. The exchange of positive holes has a similar explanation.

The equilibrium situation just described is upset if electrodes are connected to the right and left sides of the crystal and if these electrodes are maintained at different potentials. Figure 11–16(a) depicts the situation when the n-type end is made negative and the p-type end is made positive. This is called biasing in the forward direction. This bias increases the band height and consequently the energy of the electrons in A relative to those in B. The saturation electron current, I_{BA}, has the same magnitude as before, but now the more energetic electrons in A can surmount the junction barrier far more easily and the net electron current is overwhelmingly to the right. Of course, the transport of electrons to the right and holes to the left constitutes a conventional current to the left.

If the forward bias situation has been understood, there is hardly need to describe the reverse bias situation depicted in Fig. 11–16(b). The fact that the back current is small and independent of the backward potential is clear, since it consists only of the saturation current. The characteristics of two different n-p rectifier junctions are shown in Fig. 11–17.

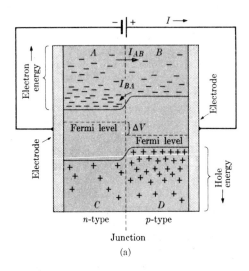

(a)

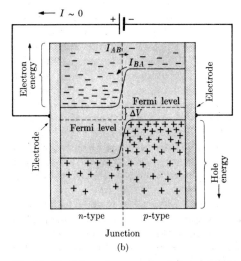

(b)

Fig. 11-16 Schematic energy-level diagrams of biased semiconductor junctions with (a) forward bias ΔV, and (b) reverse bias, ΔV.

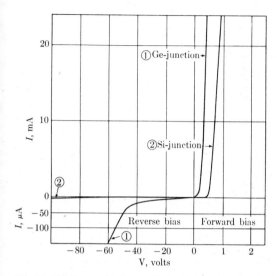

Fig. 11–17 *I* versus *V* characteristics of typical diodes. (Note scale change for forward and reverse currents and voltages.)

11–10 SEMICONDUCTOR RADIATION DETECTORS

We have indicated that the energy to create conduction electrons and holes can be supplied from thermal energy. Another way to supply this energy is from ionizing radiation such as x-rays or charged particles. An electron released within the solid becomes a conduction electron, and a conduction hole is left at the source atom. If the semiconductor is in an electric field, the electrons and holes can migrate and constitute a measurable current. This behavior of the semiconductor material is in close analogy with the gas in an ionization chamber. But, since the concentration of atoms in a solid semiconductor radiation detector is much greater than in a gas, the semiconductor detector can be much smaller than an ionization chamber.

In order to minimize the current flowing in the detector when no radiation is striking it, a reverse-biased diode is always used. A schematic drawing of a *pn*-junction used as a particle detector is shown in Fig. 11–18. The basic material of the conductor is *p*-type silicon; that is, silicon with an acceptor-type impurity which produces positive charge carriers. From the surface of the *p*-type silicon, an *n*-type (donor type) impurity is diffused into the material, producing *n*-type silicon in a thin layer at the surface. Contact is made with this layer by a thin evaporated film of gold, through which the particles to be detected can pass. A positive (reverse) bias applied to the gold film will push all the positive-charge carriers away from the junction and produce a *depletion*

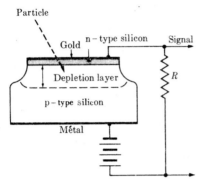

Fig. 11–18 A *pn*-junction detector. The operation is similar to the gas-ionization chamber.

layer, indicated in the figure. The negative space charge of the depletion layer produces an electric field and an accompanying potential drop corresponding to the bias voltage. The higher the bias voltage, the deeper the depletion layer will be, and the limit is set by electrical breakdown in the semiconductor. An ionizing particle passing through the gold foil and into the depletion layer will produce both negative and positive charge carriers that are swept away by the applied field and registered as a voltage pulse over the resistor R.

The number of charge-carrier pairs produced in a semiconductor material is approximately 10 times as large as the number of ion pairs produced in a gas ion chamber; i.e., the energy expended per pair is about 3 eV instead of 30. The voltage pulse will therefore be about 10 times larger, assuming that the circuits have approximately the same capacitances. The greatest significance of this factor 10 in the number of pairs N lies in the fact that the relative statistical fluctuations in the voltage pulses produced is $\sqrt{N}/N$ and therefore down by about a factor of $\sqrt{10}$ for the solid-state counter. Hence the inherent resolving power of a solid-state counter used as a spectrometer to determine particle energy is about three times better than that for an ion chamber.

When used as a particle spectrometer, the solid-state detector must have a depletion layer deep enough and/or wide enough so that the particle can come to rest inside this layer. This initially limited the use of the solid-state spectrometer to applications involving alpha particles or low-energy protons or deuterons. The techniques for producing larger and larger depletion volumes are, however, being improved at a rapid rate. The solid-state spectrometer has already been used quite extensively for longer range particles as, for instance, electrons in the MeV range and, as described below, also for gamma rays or x-rays.

In solid-state detectors for charged particles, silicon has been used most because of its low intrinsic conductivity. This means that the detector can be operated at room temperature without excessive leakage current. The silicon detector has not been found to be very suitable as a gamma-ray detector, since its relatively small volume and low Z give a very low counting efficiency. Germanium is much better in this respect because of its higher element number; on the other hand, germanium has a smaller gap between the valence band and the conduction band, and therefore its intrinsic conductivity is higher. This prevents the establishment of a thick depletion layer if the detector is kept at room temperature. However, by cooling the germanium to liquid-nitrogen temperatures, this problem can be alleviated. Methods have also been developed to reduce the conductivity produced by impurities, thus making feasible depletion layers of 1 cm thickness.

11–11 TRANSISTORS

In Section 11–9 we discussed the diode rectifier rather fully because all of the ideas will be useful in describing another important device, the *transistor*. A transistor can transform a small electrical current into a larger electrical current, that is, amplify. We shall consider the case of a junction transistor that is used so that a small amount of power can control a relatively large amount of power.

A schematic energy-level diagram of an isolated *n-p-n* junction transistor is shown in Fig. 11–19. A comparison with earlier figures shows that it may be regarded as two rectifiers back-to-back. An *n-p-n* junction transistor can be used as an amplifier when it is biased as shown in Fig. 11–20, where the left-hand *n*-type region, called the *emitter*, is heavily doped, so that it has a large electron conductivity. The central *p*-type region is called the *base*, and the junction between these regions, J_e, has a small forward bias of a few tenths of a volt. Considering this junction as a rectifier leads to the conclusion that the emitter-to-base resistance is small and the electron current is large.

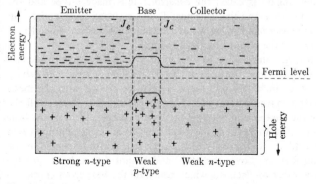

Fig. 11–19 Schematic energy-level diagram of an isolated *n-p-n* transistor.

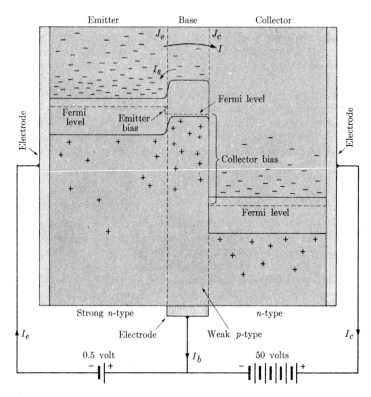

Fig. 11–20 Schematic energy-level diagram of a biased *n-p-n* transistor. (Arrows indicate the direction of electron flow.)

The right-hand region is called the *collector*. It is made *n*-type and the junction between the base and the collector, J_c, has a strong reverse bias—up to 50 V. Considered as a rectifier, we would conclude that the base-to-collector resistance is large and the electron current is small.

The next considerations lead us to alter what we can predict from rectifier behavior. The essential new fact is that the base region is *very thin*—about one-thousandth of an inch. This distance is small compared with the mean distance an electron moves before recombining with a hole. Almost all the electrons leaving the emitter and entering the base pass right through the base into the collector. The thinness of the base leads to an artificially increased "saturation current," I, to the collector. After the electrons penetrate the collector junction they are "over the wall" and cannot diffuse back into the base. Since the number of electrons which penetrate the base from emitter to collector includes almost all of the electrons in the large emitter current I_e, the current I to the collector is large also. In fact, the collector current is less than the emitter current by only the amount of the very small base current. Since this result is very different from what we would conclude from considering the transistor as two back-to-back rectifiers, we now review what happens in more detail.

The applied bias potentials appear mainly at the junctions, since each region of the transistor is a rather good conductor. Away from the junctions, the more important forces on electrons and holes are due to thermal agitation. When electrons pass into the emitter from the electrode an excess of electrons is produced at the left side of this region. This concentration of electrons has two effects. First, it upsets the equilibrium between electrons and holes, which are constantly recombining because of electrostatic attraction and re-forming because of thermal agitation. The excess electrons promote the recombination process, which tends to reduce the number of useful carriers in the emitter region. This effect is small, however, because this region is a heavily doped n-type material and there never were many positive holes anyway. The second effect of the added electrons is the establishment of an electron concentration gradient. This gradient causes electrons to diffuse toward the base.

When these electrons reach the emitter junction they are "emitted" into the base. We have already seen that electrons in n-type material have an energy distribution high enough to enable them to surmount an n-p junction barrier that is somewhat reduced, in this case by the small emitter bias. If the base were thick, most of these electrons would either migrate to the base electrode or combine with holes in the p-type base region. Such undesirable behavior is minimized in two ways. First, the base is a weak p-type material, so that the number of positive holes is not large. Second, the base is made very thin, so that the probability of an electron from the emitter encountering a hole in the base is very small. Once these electrons have been "collected" into the collector they suffer collisions that reduce the kinetic energy of most of them below the relatively high collector bias potential barrier, so that very few of them can diffuse back into the emitter. Thus the current to the electrode of the thin, weak, p-type base is kept small. This second discussion of transistor behavior leads to the same conclusion: almost all the current entering the transistor in the low-resistance emitter region finally emerges from the high-resistance collector region with only a small loss to the base electrode.

The transistor is basically a current amplifier. A small change in the current to the base produces a much larger change in the current to the emitter. Figure 11-21 shows a circuit for an ac amplifier with grounded emitter utilizing an npn transistor. A pnp transistor would have the power source reversed. A small ac power source connected to the input produces changes in the base current. This produces much larger changes in the collector current I_c. Part of this ac current goes through the capacitor C_c to the output load. Another fraction of it flows through R_c. Depending upon the combined impedance of

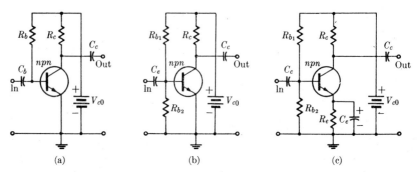

Fig. 11–21 Transistor amplifiers. Various methods for producing emmiter-base bias are shown. (a) Series resistor, (b) voltage divider, (c) stabilized bias circuit.

R_c and the output load, large voltage swings may also be produced at the output. Hence the transistor operates here both as a current and a voltage amplifier. As in a vacuum tube, voltage amplification is possible because the collector current does not depend strongly upon the collector voltage.

Transistors can be wired as oscillators, switches, memory units, and otherwise perform most functions that vacuum tubes earlier handled. The main advantages of transistor circuits compared to vacuum-tube circuits are compactness, reliability, including ruggedness and "infinite" lifetimes, and low power consumption. They have caused a major revolution in computers and electronic control circuits.

11–12 OTHER PROPERTIES OF SOLIDS

Optical Properties. It is interesting to note that the same quantum-mechanical explanation of the electrical properties of solids can be used to gain an understanding of their optical properties. In particular, when a beam of light containing photons of low energy strikes a metal in which there are many electrons in the conduction band with empty energy levels above them, the light will be absorbed. Thus a good conductor should be expected to have the opacity to visible light which experimentally it proves to have. On the other hand, since these low-energy photons cannot excite the electrons in the filled bands of an insulator to the next higher unfilled band, the light must pass through unabsorbed. Thus, in general, good insulators are also transparent to visible light. Experimentally, we know that as the wavelength of the electromagnetic radiation shortens toward the ultraviolet, these transparent solids become strongly absorbing. This is what one would expect for those insulators in which the energy gap in the forbidden region is just that corresponding to energies of ultraviolet photons. Because semiconductors have very narrow forbidden zones at room temperature, they are opaque to visible light but transparent in the far infrared.

Dislocations. While it is possible by the above methods to reach a good understanding of the thermal, electrical, and optical properties of solids, we must at the same time be aware of the fact that actual solids cannot truly be perfectly regular in atomic arrangement. Even the most carefully grown crystal has some imperfections in its structure. It has become increasingly evident over the past few years that imperfections play a vital role in the behavior of solids. In particular, it had long been known that the theoretical breaking strength of a solid is about 1000 times the actual maximum breaking strength attainable. Similarly, design engineers have been aware of the tendency of matter under continued stress to deform plastically, that is, to flow, even though the total stress was maintained well below the elastic limit. This *creep*, as it is called, can now be understood on the basis of a new theory of solids dealing with the imperfections alone. A complete comprehension of the mechanical properties of solids has by no means been reached, and such problems as the fatigue of metals under continued cyclic stressing have come increasingly to the fore in modern aircraft design.

11–13 MASERS AND LASERS

Masers and Lasers. We now have the background to understand a whole group of new devices called *masers* [*m*olecular (formerly microwave) *a*mplification by *s*timulated *e*mission of *r*adiation]. We shall discuss the underlying principle of these devices and then consider their functional and practical differences.

In general, a gas at room temperature has all or practically all atoms in the lowest state, the ground state. For instance, if we assume that we have monatomic hydrogen gas at room temperature (chemically impossible), then it is easy to calculate the relative numbers of atoms in higher energy states. Thermal collisions will raise some atoms to higher energy states. In Chapter 1 we derived the law of atmospheres, Eq. (1–42), which we generalized to the Boltzmann distribution law, Eq. (1–44). To compare the numbers of atoms at two different energies in thermal equilibrium we write this distribution law as

$$n_2/n_1 = \exp\left[-(E_2 - E_1)/kT\right]. \qquad (11\text{--}45)$$

For hydrogen at room temperature $T = 293°K$ this becomes (with $E_2 - E_1 = 10.2$ eV)

$$\frac{n_2}{n_1} = \exp\left[-\left(\frac{10.2 \times 1.60 \times 10^{-19}}{1.38 \times 10^{-23} \times 293}\right)\right] = e^{-404} = 11^{-176},$$

which is incredibly small. Note that if the temperature had been much higher (as in the atmosphere of the sun, $6000°K$) the proportion of atoms in the excited state would then have been significant, $n_2/n_1 = 10^{-8.6}$. Note too that the fraction of excited atoms would have been great, even at room temperature, if the separation of the energy levels had been much less. Note especially that

e^0 equals 1 so that no matter how small the energy level difference or how high the temperature, the number of atoms in the higher state cannot exceed, on the average, the number in the lower state (this whole discussion assumes the hydrogen to be in thermal equilibrium).

As discussed in Section 8–6, stimulated emission and absorption of radiation are equally probable processes *under otherwise identical circumstances.* The circumstances, however, are not normally identical. At room temperature the populations of states in hydrogen that can emit, respectively, absorb 10.2 eV photons are vastly different; therefore absorption is overwhelmingly predominant compared to stimulated emission. If we could invent a way to establish a condition in which more atoms were in the higher state, then stimulated emission would exceed absorption. We would get out more than we "put in,' and amplification would result.

Several ingenious ways of accomplishing this have been found. In 1955 Gordon, Zeiger, and Townes operated the first maser. They used ammonia molecules instead of the hydrogen we have been discussing. The ammonia molecule (NH_3) has an excited state at a mere 10^{-4} eV and thus at 20°C we have

$$\frac{n_2}{n_1} = \exp\left(-\frac{10^{-4} \times 1.60 \times 10^{-19}}{1.38 \times 10^{-23} \times 293}\right) = \exp\left(-\frac{1}{252}\right) \approx 1.$$

In thermal equilibrium the relative fraction of excited atoms is nearly unity. There are "naturally" almost as many molecules excited as unexcited. The remarkable achievement of Townes and his associates was their invention of a molecule sorter. They passed ammonia through a jet into a vacuum. The stream of molecules passed through an electrode structure where, because of their differing electrical properties, excited molecules were deflected one way and unexcited molecules were deflected the other. The excited molecules were allowed to pass on into a chamber. Now, the energy of the excited state is 10^{-4} eV which corresponds to a wavelength of 1.24 cm and a frequency of 23,870 MHz. This is in the microwave region. By making the chamber of proper size it became a resonant cavity for the radiation produced. If one molecule went from its excited state to its ground state, it was likely to stimulate another, and since initially all atoms were excited, this process could quickly build up to significant proportions. As excited molecules were converted to absorbing molecules, new excited molecules were introduced to sustain the production of photons. Thus the cavity "sang" with microwave radiation like a sounding organ pipe. It was an oscillator.

The maser just described has many remarkable properties. One of these is its stability. The frequency of the oscillations is determined by the nature of the ammonia molecule itself. One excited ammonia molecule is indistinguishable from another. They all cause radiation of the same frequency. By electronic techniques, this oscillator can be made to govern the frequency of slower oscillators. A succession of such frequency reductions provides a

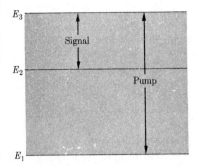

Fig. 11–22 Basic energy-level diagram for a ruby maser.

low-frequency oscillator which ticks like a clock but which has all the stability built into ammonia molecules. Such a clock is called an *atomic clock* and its precision is such that it will neither gain nor lose more than one second in 1000 years Whereas this gas maser is superb as a stable oscillator, another type, the *solid-state maser*, makes a better amplifier.

The most common solid-state maser is made from ruby. A ruby is basically clear alumina made red by a small concentration of chromium. It is the chromium "impurity" that is the active atom of the maser. When the ruby is in a steady magnetic field, the chromium acquires energy states, three of which are represented schematically in Fig. 11–22. In thermal equilibrium the number of atoms in the three states obeys Boltzmann's law, as shown graphically in Fig. 11–23(a). The ruby material is irradiated with photons from an external

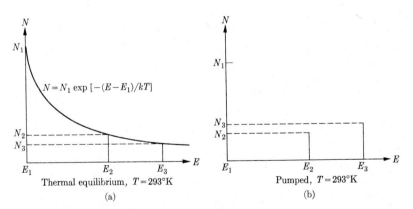

Fig. 11–23 (a) Normal population of energy levels. (b) Population inversion between E_2 and E_3 resulting from pumping from E_1 to E_3.

source whose frequency (energy) corresponds to the energy difference, $E_3 - E_1$. This causes absorption transitions from E_1 to the *metastable* state E_3 and stimulated transitions from E_3 to E_1. Although these latter transitions are stimulated, they themselves do not account for the maser action. The effect of these transitions is, as we have seen, to make the concentration of chromium atoms in states E_1 and E_3 tend to become equal. The concentration of atoms in E_2 remains substantially unchanged, as shown in Fig. 11–23(b). This *optical pumping* of atoms from E_1 to E_3 causes a population inversion between states E_2 and E_3, which is enhanced because E_3 is a metastable state of chromium. If the ruby material is now exposed to photons whose energy is $E_3 - E_2$, transitions will occur both up and down between these two levels. The significant fact is that with this inverted population of these states, there are more stimulated emissions than there are absorptions. Amplification results.

It is true that signal frequency photons (with power in the microwatt range) tend to make the populations of states 2 and 3 become equal, but the over-whelming pumping between states 1 and 3 (milliwatts) keeps state 3 more populated than state 2.

Spontaneous transitions from state 3 to state 2 also do occur. Photons thus produced are random in origin and constitute the ultimate defect of all amplifiers, noise. But these random transitions are so remarkably rare that this amplifier has less noise and can amplify weaker signals than amplifiers of any other type. One application of maser amplifiers is in detecting and measuring extremely weak microwave signals from outer space.

The frequency of microwaves that this maser can amplify is determined by the energy difference $E_3 - E_2$. This difference can be varied by changing the magnetic field in which the ruby material is placed. Thus, unlike the frequency stability of the ammonia maser, the solid-state maser has versatility as an amplifier.

Ruby masers are always operated at low temperatures—frequently at the temperature of liquid helium, 4.2°K. Comparing Fig. 11–24(a) and (b) to the earlier figures shows how chilling enhances the inversion between states 2 and 3.

Lasers (*L*ight *a*mplification by *s*timulated *e*mission of *r*adiation) are, in principle, no different from the maser just described. A material is used which has an energy diagram like that shown in Fig. 11–22, except that the energy differences are much greater, and thus the wavelengths are in the visible region instead of in the microwave region. The pumping is done with light and the laser produces light. Of course the pumping light must be "bluer" than the laser light. Like the ammonia maser, lasers are usually used as oscillators, light sources. The laser crystal is a cylinder with optically parallel ends, one of which is fully silvered and the other is partly silvered. The pumping light is admitted through the sides, and the laser light emerges from the partly transmitting end. Laser light traveling off axis is quickly lost by absorption at the sides, but the beam along the axis builds up to a high intensity as portions

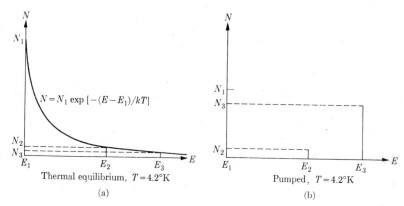

Fig. 11-24 Effect of temperature on population inversion. Compare with Fig. 11-23 (a) Schematic energy-level diagram of an intrinsic semiconductor. (b) The same with a Fermi curve showing the electron population in the two bands.

of the beam go back and forth between the reflecting surfaces insuring encounter with as many excited atoms as possible. We mentioned near the beginning of this discussion that stimulated radiation is in phase with stimulating photons. As photons stimulate more and more photons, there results a cascade of photons, all of which are in phase (coherent) and almost all of which move parallel to the crystal axis. As a consequence, laser light forms a beam with almost no "spread," If a laser produces a spot of light one centimeter in diameter on a nearby wall, the spot will be very little larger on a distant building. Recently, space scientists have succeeded in detecting laser light aimed from earth to the moon and reflected back by a mirror system placed on the moon by the Apollo 11 crew.

PROBLEMS

11-1 a) Plot the values of the two wave functions (11-1) and (11-2) along an axis through the two nuclei. Assume that the distance between the nuclei is one Bohr radius a_0. b) Plot the value of the exchange charge ρ_1 (Eq. 11-15) along the axis. c) Estimate the value of α by integrating ρ_1 along the axis (Eq. 11-16) and assuming that it has a constant value along a line perpendicular to the axis out to a radius $r = a_0$ and is zero for $r > a_0$.

11-2 Using Fig. 11-1 as an aid, estimate the "spring constant" of NaCl, calculate the vibrational frequency for this molecule and the energy $h\nu$ in electron volts.

11-3 Calculate the moment of inertia of the NaCl molecule and use it to calculate the rotational energy spectrum in electron volts.

11-4 a) Calculate the "zero point" energy $\frac{1}{2}\hbar\omega$ (in electron volts) for the hydrogen molecule by using the experimental information that the transition from the $n = 1$ to the $n = 2$ vibrational levels absorbs infrared light of wavelength 22,750 Å.

11-5 Verify the statement that at room temperature the order of magnitude of the electrical conductivity of copper is given by Eq. (11-34). The interatomic spacing for copper is 3.6 Å.

11-6 The photoelectric threshold for tungsten is 2900 Å. a) Calculate the work function W_o (Section 3-11) and use this to determine the Fermi factor (Eq. 11-43) for those electrons that can barely escape at T = 1000°K, 2000°K, and 3000°K. b) Find the Fermi energy for tungsten (atomic mass 183.9, density 19.3 g · cm^{-3}) assuming one free electron per atom.

11-7 a) How could one determine experimentally whether electrical conduction is by holes or by electrons? (*Hint:* Consider the effect of a transverse magnetic field on an electric current.) b) The ratio of the electric field per unit current density per unit magnetic induction, where all three are mutually perpendicular, is known as the Hall coefficient. Show that the Hall coefficient should be a sensitive measure of the number of conducting holes or electrons per unit volume. c) Show that this coefficient has opposite signs for conduction by electrons and by holes.

11-8 The "mobility," μ, of an electric charge is defined as the velocity increment per unit accelerating electric field. If n is the number of conducting electrons or holes per unit volume of a solid, show that the electrical conductivity is given by

$$\sigma = ne\mu.$$

11-9 Estimate the Fermi energy E_f in MeV for protons in a nucleus. The average nuclear radius is $R = 1.2\ A^{1/3} \times 10^{-15}$ m, where A is the nucleon number, approximately 2 times the proton number Z.

11-10 Assume that an electron is 1 Å from a perfectly plane conducting surface. (Clearly, on this scale, such a thing does not exist.) Calculate, by using the idea of a mirror charge, the energy required to move this electron away to infinity. You will find that this is of the order of magnitude of the work functions for metals.

11-11 a) Referring to Eq. (11-14b) and using Eqs. (11-41), (11-43), and (11-44), calculate the fraction of the electrons that are excited to the conduction band of a semiconductor at $T = 300°K$. The gap spacing is $E_k = 1.6$ eV. Assume $\exp(E_k/kT) \gg 1$ and use $E \approx E_f$ in Eq. (11-44). b) Double E_k and compare the results.

11-12 A donor impurity level is 0.02 eV below the conduction band. a) What is the fraction of the donor atoms that is ionized at 300°K? b) at 100°K?

11–13 A semiconductor radiation detector and the input lead to the associated electronics have a total capacitance of 20 pF. An alpha particle deposits 10 MeV in the depletion layer of the detector. What is the magnitude of the resulting voltage pulse?

CHAPTER 12

The Atomic Nucleus*

12-1 GENERAL PROPERTIES OF NUCLEI

Introduction

In Section 4-3 we discussed Rutherford's theory of the nuclear atom, and in Section 4-4 we mentioned that the data indicated a deviation from the pure electrostatic field for distances smaller than about 5×10^{-13} cm. Rutherford interpreted this as an indication of the size of the nucleus. Hence the discovery of the nucleus immediately gave a fairly good estimate of its size. This was in 1912.

From alpha-decay studies, it was known that heavy nuclei can, to some extent, break up into smaller and identical constituents. Clearly, it is therefore built up of more elementary particles. However, it was not known before 1932 exactly what these particles were. In that year Chadwick discovered the neutron, and, since that discovery, it has been generally accepted that the nucleus is built up of neutrons and protons. In beta decay and induced reactions at high energies, other particles may emerge from the nucleus. However, we now believe that these particles are created in the nucleus at the moment of emission and are therefore not to be considered as constituents of the nucleus.

Nomenclature

Two nuclei with identical numbers of protons, Z, and identical numbers of neutrons, N, belong to the same nuclear species. A nuclear species is called a *nuclide*. It is identified by its chemical symbol and a superscript indicating the total number of nucleons, $A = Z + N$. Sometimes the number of protons

---

* This chapter is made up mostly of excerpts from *Introduction to Nuclear Physics*. Reading, Mass.: Addison-Wesley (1966).

(implied by the chemical symbol) is given as a subscript in front of the symbol. Examples are given in Table 12–1. Nuclides with identical Z are called *isotopes*,

Table 12–1

Symbol	Element	Z	N	A
^{12}C or $^{12}_{6}$C	Carbon	6	6	12
^{13}C or $^{13}_{6}$C	Carbon	6	7	13
^{86}Kr or $^{86}_{36}$Kr	Krypton	36	50	86
^{192}Hg or $^{192}_{80}$Hg	Mercury	80	112	192

a term which is often incorrectly used instead of "nuclide." For instance, ^{192}Hg is often called a "radioactive isotope." It is a radioactive nuclide. Nuclides with identical A are called *isobars*; those with identical N are called *isotones*. Finally, an excited state of a given nuclide may be relatively long-lived, so that its decay time is directly observable. Such an excited state is called an *isomeric* (or metastable) state, and thus two nuclei of the same species but in different energy states, of which at least one is metastable, are called *isomers*.

Size

Nuclear sizes have in recent years been measured more accurately by scattering high-energy electrons off various target elements throughout the periodic table. Most of this work has been done at Stanford University by R. Hofstadter and coworkers.* What is measured is the angular distribution of the scattered electrons (similar to Rutherford's experiment). Figure 12–1 shows an example of such an angular distribution, and Fig. 12–2(a) gives the result of a wave-mechanical analysis of the data. The responsible interaction is Coulomb attraction between the electron and the proton in the nucleus, so the result is given in the form of a charge density. By assuming equal distribution of protons and nucleons, we can compute a mass distribution, or nucleon distribution (Fig. 12–2b). A result of the analyses of such data is that the *mean electromagnetic radius* of the nucleus defined as the radius to the 50-percent point in the density distribution (Fig. 12–2) is given by

$$R_e = (1.07 \pm 0.02) \, A^{1/3} \times 10^{-15} \, \text{m} = 1.07 \, A^{1/3} \, F, \qquad (12\text{–}1)$$

where 1 fermi (F) = 10^{-15} m. Another result is that the surface thickness, defined as the distance between the 10-percent and 90-percent points in the density distribution is the same for all nuclei and is given by

$$t = (2.4 \pm 0.3) \times 10^{-15} \, \text{m}.$$

---

* For instance, see a series of papers in *Revs. Mod. Phys.* **30** (1958), p. 142–584.

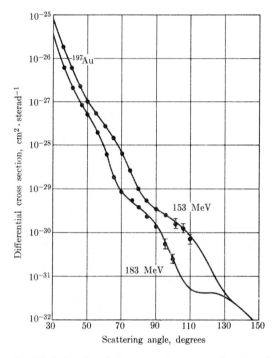

Fig. 12-1 Results of electron-scattering experiments performed on gold. From B. D. Hahn, D. G. Ravenhall, and R. Hofstadter, *Phys. Rev.* **101** (1956), p. 1131.

Various other methods for measuring the nuclear radius R yield slightly varying values for the constant in front of $A^{1/3}$. However, the dependency upon A is the cube root, which reflects the fact that the density of nucleons is approximately the same in the center of all nuclei (Fig. 12-2).

Mass and Binding Energy

The nucleus contains about 99.975% of the mass of an atom. A table of nuclear masses can be made from an atomic-mass table by subtracting the electron masses (with due consideration of the mass reduction associated with the atomic binding energies when accuracy warrants this). However, except for the nuclear "particles," which are ionized hydrogen, helium, or heavier atoms, *atomic*, rather than nuclear masses, are almost always used in nuclear physics. Often it makes no difference which of the two is used, because the number of electrons cancels out in most equations involving masses (e.g., nuclear-reaction energies). In many cases, the presence of the atomic electrons should not be neglected, because they directly take part in the nuclear processes considered

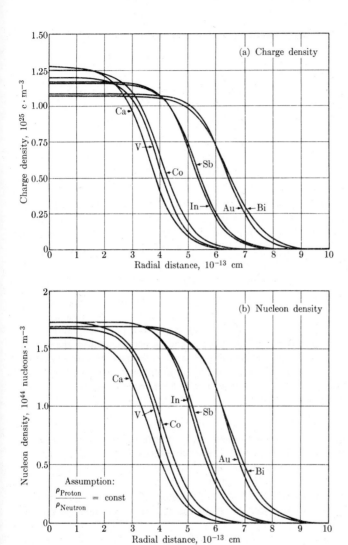

Fig. 12–2 Charge density and nucleon density as determined by high-energy electron scattering. (From B. Hahn *et al., op., cit.*)

(e.g., electron capture, internal conversion). The measurement of atomic masses is discussed in Section 2–7.

The rest mass and energy equivalent of the particles (ions) encountered in low-energy nuclear physics are listed in Table 12–2. The rest masses for some

Table 12–2   Mass and energy equivalent of nuclear particles

	u	m_0c^2, MeV
Electron	5.48597×10^{-4}	0.511007
Neutron	1.008665	939.551
Proton	1.007277	938.258
Deuteron	2.013554	1875.585
Triton	3.015501	2808.879
$(He^3)^{++}$	3.014933	2808.350
Alpha particle	4.001506	3727.323

examples of atomic species are listed in Table 12–3. This table also lists the binding energies of the nuclei, that is, the energy that is released when the appropriate numbers of protons and neutrons are combined to form the nucleus. The binding energy (BE) can be calculated as the reduction in mass times the square of the velocity of light,

$$BE = [Zm_p + (A - Z)m_n - _zm^A]c^2, \qquad (12-2)$$

where Z is the number of protons, $A - Z$ is the number of neutrons, and m_p, m_n, and $_zm^A$ are the rest masses of the proton, neutron, and the final nucleus, respectively. Note that the binding energy is a positive quantity.

Table 12–3 also gives the total *atomic* binding energy, that is, the energy that is released when the nucleus combines with Z electrons to form a neutral atom. Clearly, the atomic binding energy is quite small compared with the nuclear binding energy. We can therefore, without appreciable error, compute the nuclear binding energy as

$$BE = [ZM_H + (A - Z)M_n - _zM^A]c^2, \qquad (12-3)$$

where the M's represent *atomic* masses. For the neutron, of course, the mass is the same as above. What Eq. (12–3) actually expresses is the energy that will have to be removed when Z hydrogen atoms and $A - Z$ neutrons form the neutral atom $_zM^A$ in its nuclear and atomic ground state. Since the electron rest masses cancel in Eq. (12–3) and since the atomic binding energies are very small, Eq. (12–3) can be used instead of Eq. (12–2) to compute the nuclear binding energies.

Spin Magnetic Moment

As already discussed in earlier chapters, the nucleons have intrinsic spins with quantum number $s = \frac{1}{2}$. The total angular momentum of the nucleus is quantized in the same way as for an atom with a total angular momentum quantum number I, which is half-integral for odd nucleon number A and integral for even A. The parity of the nucleus is, by convention, given as a superscript on the I value. Table 12–3 shows some examples.

Table 12–3 Examples of atomic masses, binding energies, nuclear angular momenta and parities, magnetic dipole moments, and electric quadrupole moments

Nuclide	Atomic mass, u	Nuclear binding energy MeV	Atomic binding energy, MeV	Nuclear angular momentum and parity	Nuclear magnetic moment nm	Nuclear electric quadrupole, moment, 10^{-24} cm^2	$\Delta R/R$
$^1_1$H	1.007825	—	0.000014	$\frac{1}{2}+$	+2.79275	—	—
$^2_1$H	2.014102	2.225	0.000014	$1+$	+0.85735	+0.00282	0.04*
$^4_2$He	4.002603	28.295	0.000079	$0+$	0	0	0
$^7_3$Li	7.016004	39.244	0.00019	$\frac{3}{2}-$	+3.2564	−0.04	?
$^{16}_8$O	15.994916	127.617	0.0020	$0+$	0	0	0
$^{35}_{17}$Cl	34.968851	298.20	0.012	$\frac{3}{2}+$	+0.8218	−0.0790	−0.032
$^{57}_{26}$Fe	56.935398	499.90	0.034	$\frac{1}{2}-$	0.05	0	0
$^{176}_{71}$Lu	175.942660	1417.97	0.37	$7-$	+3.180	+8.0	0.26
$^{235}_{92}$U	235.043915	1783.17	0.69	$\frac{7}{2}-$	−0.35	±4.1	±0.083

*   For the deuteron, a radius $R = 2.4$ F has been used. Equation (1–2) yields 1.35 F, but this formula is not applicable for a two-nucleon system.

Both the proton and the neutron have magnetic moments associated with their intrinsic spins. The values are

$$\text{Proton} = 2.79275 \text{ nuclear magnetons,}$$

$$\text{Neutron} = -1.9135 \text{ nuclear magneton,}$$

with

$$1 \text{ nuclear magneton (nm)} \frac{e\hbar}{2m_p} = 5.0505 \times 10^{-27} \text{ J-m}^2 \cdot \text{Wb}^{-1}.$$

Orbital motion of the proton in the nucleus produces another contribution to a total magnetic dipole moment of the nucleus. Some examples are listed in Table 12–3.

Electric Quadrupole Moment

The nucleus, as well as the atom, does not possess a static electric dipole moment. However, it does, in general, have an electric quadrupole moment that is actually a measure of the eccentricity of the ellipsoidal nuclear surface. The quadrupole moment is defined as

$$Q = \left(\frac{1}{e}\right) \int (3z^2 - r^2)\rho \, d\tau, \tag{12–4}$$

where ρ is the charge density in the nucleus. The quadrupole moment is measured and calculated for the state in which the I-vector is as parallel to the z-axis as possible; that is, $m_I = I$. Some examples of measured quadrupole moments and corresponding deviation ΔR of the radius from the mean nuclear radius R are given in Table 12–3.

12–2 THE DEUTERON

In Chapter 7 we discussed the simplest atomic system, the hydrogen atom, by use of wave mechanics. In this case, the basic force between the two particles is the Coulomb force, well known from macroscopic measurements. In nuclear physics, the situation is somewhat different in that the nuclear forces are inaccessible to direct macroscopic observations. However, wave mechanics has been applied with some success, at least in some areas of nuclear physics. We may therefore try to use the principles of wave mechanics on nuclear problems and then, by comparison with experimental data, hope to find a consistent description of the nuclear forces acting between two or more bodies in terms of relative separations, spin orientations, and so forth. The simplest system to analyze, obviously, is the system consisting of only two nucleons.

Two different types of experimental data exist for two-nucleon systems. One set consists of the result of a study of the only existing bound nuclear two-body system, the deuteron. In atomic physics, the success of wave mechanics or any other theory is measured in terms of the ability of the theory to produce exactly the energies of the observed excited states. Unfortunately, the deuteron possesses only one single bound level, the ground state. The experimentally determined static properties of the deuteron that can be used for testing theories are therefore essentially only the energy of the ground state, its angular momentum, parity, electric quadrupole moment, and magnetic dipole moment, and also some measurements on the size of the deuteron by high-energy electron scattering.

Another type of experimental data on the two-nucleon system arises from studies of the scattering of one nucleon by another. In practice, this means that a beam of nucleons hits a target of nucleons, and collision probabilities, angular distributions, etc., are measured. Since it is not practical to make a neutron target, the experiments are limited to so-called neutron-proton scattering and proton-proton scattering. Two-nucleon scattering is discussed in Section 12–3.

We shall now try to apply the methods of quantum mechanics in an effort to obtain a theoretical description of the deuteron. The objective is to learn something about the nuclear forces by requiring that theoretically predicted quantities agree with experimentally observed ones. In the center-of-mass system, the Schrödinger equation for the two-body problem is

$$-\frac{\hbar^2}{2\mu}\nabla^2\psi + V\psi = E\psi, \tag{12–5}$$

where m is the reduced mass

$$\mu = \frac{m_1 m_2}{m_1 + m_2}, \tag{12–6}$$

V is the potential describing the forces acting between the two bodies, and E is the total energy of the system. For the ground state of the deuteron, the energy is

$$E = -E_B = -2.225 \text{ MeV}.$$

The potential V is an unknown function of the separation between the two particles and possibly also of other variables. It is our aim with these calculations to throw some light on this function. For simplicity, let us start by assuming that the potential is a function only of the separation between the two particles, $V = V(r)$. When the potential is spherically symmetric, we know that the wave equation can be separated and that the solutions can be written in the following way:

$$\psi = (u_l/r)Y_{lm}(\theta, \phi). \tag{12–7}$$

Here, $Y_{lm}(\theta, \phi)$ is a spherical harmonic function, and u_l is the solution of the radial wave equation

$$\frac{d^2 u_l}{dr^2} + \frac{2\mu}{\hbar^2}\left[E - V - \frac{l(l+1)\hbar^2}{2mr^2}\right]u_l = 0. \tag{12–8}$$

The last term in the brackets is the familiar centrifugal potential. To achieve binding, we need an attractive, or negative, potential V that will more than compensate for the repulsive centrifugal potential, at least over a certain range of the particle separation r. Clearly, this is most easily accomplished in the $l = 0$ state. For any two-body system with a spherically symmetric potential, the lowest quantum-mechanical state is therefore always an $l = 0$ state (an S-state).

The potential function that gives the simplest solution of Schrödinger's equation is the square well (Fig. 12–3). The "hard core" (infinitely high) potential for $r < c$ effectively prevents the particles from getting closer to each other than the distance c. From scattering studies and from the study of nuclear structure, we have reasons to believe that the neutron-proton potential actually contains such a hard core. We have no reason to believe that the attractive part of the actual potential is of the square-well type; the only justification for trying the square-well potential here is its simplicity. In the following, the core radius c, the width b, and the depth V_0 of the well will be treated as adjustable parameters.

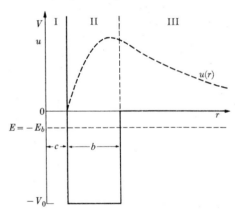

Fig. 12–3 Simplified neutron-proton potential and deuteron radial wave function.

Since the wave function must be zero in region I (Fig. 12–3), it suffices to solve the radial wave equation in regions II and III. In region II, we can write the equation (for $l = 0$), dropping the subscript on u:

$$\frac{d^2u}{dr^2} + \frac{2m}{\hbar^2}[V_0 - E_B]u = 0, \tag{12-9}$$

where V_0 and E_B are positive numbers. The solution of this equation satisfying the boundary condition $u = 0$ at $r = c$ is

$$u_{\text{II}} = A \sin K(r - c), \tag{12-10}$$

where A is a normalization constant and

$$K = (1/\hbar)\sqrt{2m(V_0 - E_B)}. \tag{12–11}$$

In region III the radial equation takes the form

$$\frac{d^2u}{dr^2} - \frac{2m}{\hbar^2} E_B u = 0. \tag{12–12}$$

The solution of this equation that satisfies the boundary condition $u = 0$ at $r = \infty$ is

$$u_{\text{III}} = Be^{-\kappa r}, \tag{12–13}$$

where B is a normalization constant and

$$\kappa = (1/\hbar)\sqrt{2mE_B}. \tag{12–14}$$

The complete wave functions in region II and III are given by Eq. (12–7) with the spherical harmonic for $l = 0$ being $Y_{0,0} = (4\pi)^{-1/2}$ and with u_0 equal to u_{II} or u_{III}, respectively. In the following we will work with the radial wave functions only. By matching u_{II} with u_{III} at the boundary between the two regions, we obviously also match the total wave functions ψ_{II} and ψ_{III}.

Equations (12–10) and (12–13) now have to be matched at the boundary $r = c + b$ in such a way that both the function u itself and its first derivative are continuous across the boundary. This is the only way in which Schrödinger's equation (12–9) can also be satisfied at that point. These boundary requirements (with $r = c + b$) yield

$$AK \cos Kb = -\kappa Be^{-\kappa(c+b)},$$
$$A \sin Kb = Be^{-\kappa(c+b)}. \tag{12–15}$$

Since at the moment we are not interested in the normalization constants A and B, we divide the two equations by each other and obtain

$$K \cot Kb = -\kappa. \tag{12–16}$$

Equation (12–16) implicitly relates the binding energy E_B of the two-nucleon system to the width b and depth V_0 of the assumed square-well potential. The core radius c does not enter into the equation. Since E_B has been measured, Eq. (12–16) gives one relationship between the two unknown parameters V_0 and b. Therefore, to determine these parameters we must find another equation connecting them; that is, we have to make use of another pertinent experimental result.

Obviously, we can choose any positive wave number K or well depth V_0 and then solve Eq. (12–16) for b. A curve showing this functional relationship between V_0 and b is plotted in Fig. 12–4 (curve a). As indicated by this curve,

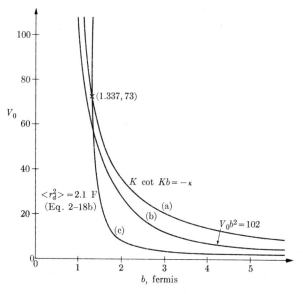

Fig. 12–4 Potential-well depth versus well width(a) which gives correct binding energy for the deuteron, (b) which barely binds a neutron to a proton, and (c) which gives correct size of deuteron.

a square well of any width can be adjusted in depth so that it gives the correct binding energy for the deuteron.

The experimental angular momentum of the deuteron is $I = 1$, which indicates parallel spins ($S = 1$, triplet). Curve (a) in Fig. 12–4 therefore applies to the triplet force. Also shown in the figure is the well depth V_0 versus the width b for the case $E_B \approx 0$ as calculated from Eq. (12–16) (curve b). The singlet state $^1S_0$ (opposite spins) is not bound, and from this we conclude that, in the singlet state, the well parameters are represented by a point below curve b.

Equation (12–16) and the known binding energy for the deuteron give one relationship between the parameters V_0 and b in the triplet state. High-energy scattering gives some indications that a repulsive-core parameter of about $c = 0.4$ F is reasonable. We then need one more relationship between V_0, b, and c to determine all of them. This is provided by the root-mean-square radius $\langle r_d^2 \rangle^{1/2} = 2.1$ F measured by electron-scattering experiments (Section 12–1). Using the radial wave function u (Eqs. 12–10 and 12–13 normalized together), we can write

$$\langle r_d^2 \rangle = \tfrac{1}{4} \int_0^\infty r^2 u^2 \, dr + \langle r_p^2 \rangle. \qquad (12\text{–}17)$$

The factor $\frac{1}{4}$ arises from the fact that $r/2$ is the distance from the center of mass of the deuteron to the center of the proton. The first term in Eq. (12–17) would be the expectation value of the square of the electromagnetic radius for the deuteron if the proton were a point particle. It can easily be shown that, since it is not, the square of the proton radius must be added.

By calculating the value of the integral and inserting $\langle r_d^2 \rangle^{1/2} = 2.1$ F, $\langle r_p^2 \rangle^{1/2} = 0.8$ F, and $c = 0.4$ F, we find another relationship between V and b. This is plotted in Fig. 12–4, curve (c). The curves (a) and (c) cross at $b = 1.337$ F and $V_0 = 73$ MeV, indicating that these values are consistent with the experimental data.

It should be emphasized again at this point that the square-well potential is unrealistic and was chosen because of the simplicity of the ensuing analysis. However, we can make a similar analysis for any other reasonable potential shape, and we will then find a relationship similar to Eq. (12–16) between a characteristic width parameter and a characteristic depth parameter for this type of well.

Two experimental data are slightly at odds with the above theory. One is the measured magnetic dipole moment, and the other is the electric quadrupole moment. According to the theory, the magnetic dipole moment should be the algebraic sum of the dipole moments of the two nucleons. The measured value is off by 2.5 percent. Of course an s-state is spherically symmetric, so the quadrupole moment should be zero. It is not. Both facts can be explained by assuming that the neutron-proton force depends upon the relative orientation of the spin vector s and the separation vector r (tensor force).

12–3 NUCLEON-NUCLEON SCATTERING

In the study of nucleon-nucleon scattering, as well as of other subjects in nuclear physics, we continuously compare theoretical and experimental results. For nucleon-nucleon scattering a convenient meeting ground for theory and experiment is the scattering cross section. The concept of a scattering cross section was introduced in Section 1–10, and differential cross sections were discussed in Section 4–3. We are here going to quote some experimental and theoretical cross sections for low-energy nucleon-nucleon collisions in which a target of nucleons is bombarded with nucleons. At a bombarding energy $E \leq 10$ MeV, it turns out that one needs to consider only a relative s-state ($l = 0$) for the two particles. We cannot go into a detailed explanation of this, except to say that the range of the nuclear forces is so short that one must have a practically head-on collision to see an effect. This means in quantum terms zero relative angular momentum.

According to our classical notions, the spins of two colliding nucleons should tend to be antiparallel in half of the events and parallel in the other half. The quantum-mechanical prediction for the neutron-proton system is as follows. The total spin vector **S** of the system is quantized in the same fashion as in the stationary state (the deuteron). The total spin quantum number is $S = 0$ in the singlet state and $S = 1$ in the triplet state. The triplet state, as indicated by the notation, has therefore three substates with different spatial orientations of the spin vector, whereas the singlet state has only one substate. The occurrence of each substate is equally probable so that the average total $l = 0$ cross section is

$$\sigma_0 = \tfrac{3}{4}\sigma_{t,0} + \tfrac{1}{4}\sigma_{s,0}. \tag{12–18}$$

The subscript t stands for triplet, and s for singlet. (Compare Fig. 9–2.)

For proton-proton scattering at low energies, the triplet state is forbidden by Pauli's exclusion principle. Hence the active potential is the singlet potential plus the Coulomb potential.

The wave-mechanical theory of nucleon-nucleon scattering at low energies (below ≈ 20 MeV) is quite straightforward, but we cannot take space for it here. The scattering cross section critically depends, of course, upon the nucleon-nucleon potential. However, it turns out that at low energies, the cross sections are not sensitive to the *shape* of the potential. As we shall see, the square well is again adequate. This is because, in any experiment involving waves, it is difficult to discern details that are much smaller than the wavelength.

Neutron-proton scattering cross sections are most easily measured by measuring the attenuation of a neutron beam in passing through a given sample of hydrogen. Figure 12–5 shows the results of many such measurements

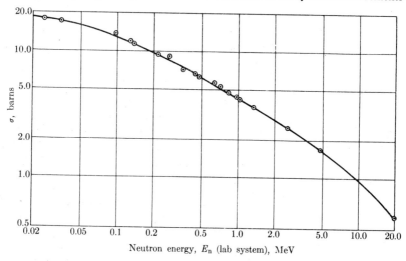

Fig. 12–5 Total cross section for *n-p* scattering. Theoretical curve based on $a_t = 5.38$ F, $a_s = 23.7$ F, $r_{0t} = 1.70$ F, $r_{0s} = 2.40$ F. Experimental points from a review paper by R. K. Adair, *Rev. Mod. Phys.* **22**, (1950) p. 249.

at several laboratories for the energy range 0.02 to 20 MeV. Not shown is a series of measurements at lower energy giving an extrapolated value of the cross section at $E \approx 0$ as 20.36 barns. (1 barn = 10^{-24} cm^2.)

The curve in Fig. 12–5 represents theoretically calculated cross sections with square-well potentials for the singlet as well as the triplet force. For the triplet force, we have used the well that fits the deuteron data. For the singlet force, the well parameters are

$$\text{Singlet potential} \begin{cases} c = 0.4\,\text{F}, \\ b = 1.45\,\text{F}, \\ V = 39\,\text{MeV}. \end{cases}$$

These well parameters were determined by fitting the total cross section at $E \approx 0$ and at $E_n = 1.315$ MeV. As can be seen from Fig. 12–5, the fit is very good over the whole energy range. The experimental uncertainties are of the order of the radii of the circles shown.

Even more impressive than the fit in Fig. 12–5 is the agreement between experimental and theoretical results for low-energy proton-proton scattering. Figure 12–6 shows measured differential cross sections and corresponding theoretical curves. The theoretical cross sections have been calculated by using the Coulomb force and a *singlet potential of strength given above for the proton-neutron case.* Aside from the consequences of the Pauli exclusion principle, the implication is that the nucleon-nucleon force is *charge independent,* i.e., the same for a neutron-proton pair as for a proton-proton pair and, by extrapolation, a neutron-neutron pair.

Except for the very beautiful fit, the most interesting feature of Fig. 12–6 is the slight dip in the cross section at about 50 degrees. This is a result of destructive interference between a part of the wave scattered by the nuclear potential and another part scattered by the Coulomb potential. It would be hard to produce such a result with anything but a wave theory.

12–4 NUCLEAR FORCES

The exercises of the last two sections have taught us that wave mechanics is a powerful theoretical tool in a new area, nuclear physics. We have learned something about the strength of nuclear forces, but not much detail about the shape of the potential. More details can be learned by higher energy studies. However, instead of describing such experiments here, we shall look at advances that have been made in theoretical derivations of the nucleon-nucleon potential.

It is now generally accepted that the nuclear forces are produced by a meson field which is similar in origin to electromagnetic fields but is of much shorter range. Yukawa* pointed out that the short range is consistent with a

---

* H. Yukawa, *Proc. Phys. Math. Soc. Japan* **17** (1935), p. 48.

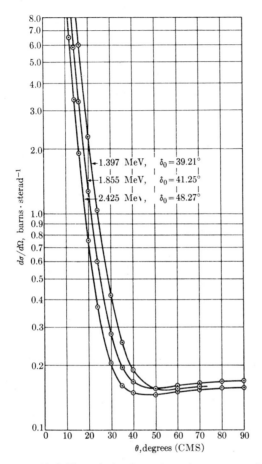

Fig. 12–6 Theoretical and experimental *p-p* cross sections at three energies. From data given by D. J. Knecht, S. Messelt, E. D. Berners, and L. C. Northcliffe, *Phys. Rev.* **114** (1959), p. 550.

field carried by field quanta with a rest mass different from zero, contrary to the electromagnetic field which is carried by photons of zero rest mass. Yukawa's arguments, greatly simplified, are approximately as follows.

Electromagnetic fields obey a wave equation that can be derived from Maxwell's equations. For instance, the scalar electric potential U in free space obeys the well-known wave equation

$$\left(\nabla^2 - \frac{1}{c^2}\frac{\partial^2}{\partial t^2}\right) U = 0. \tag{12–19}$$

For a static field, we have $\nabla^2 U = 0$ (Laplace's equation) in free space or $\nabla^2 U = -\rho/\varepsilon_0$ (Poisson's equation) in the presence of charges. By integrating these equations we find the familiar static solution $U = q/4\pi\varepsilon_0 r$ for the scalar potential at a distance r from a point charge q.

According to modern theories, the electromagnetic field is carried by virtual photons which are continuously emitted and absorbed by the charged particles. In accordance with this view, we can regard Eq. (12–19) for the scalar potential and the equivalent equation for the electromagnetic vector potential as quantum-mechanical wave equations for the photon fields. In complete analogy with Schrödinger's equation, the electromagnetic wave equations of the form (12–19) can be derived by substituting the operator for momentum square, $-\hbar^2 \nabla^2$, and the energy operator, $-\hbar i \, \partial/\partial t$, into the equation

$$-p^2 + \frac{1}{c^2} E^2 = 0. \tag{12–20}$$

This equation, of course, is the correct relationship between momentum and energy for a particle of zero rest mass. The corresponding equation for a particle with rest mass m different from zero is (see Appendix 3)

$$-p^2 - m^2 c^2 + \frac{1}{c^2} E^2 = 0. \tag{12–21}$$

If we make the same substitution as above, we obtain

$$\left(\nabla^2 - \frac{m^2 c^2}{\hbar^2} - \frac{1}{c^2} \frac{\partial^2}{\partial t^2} \right) \Phi = 0. \tag{12–22}$$

Equation (12–22), which is the correct wave equation for a spinless relativistic particle, is regarded as the equation for a scalar meson field Φ. We separate out time exactly as we do for Schrödinger's equation, and we obtain a time-independent wave equation for the meson field for total energy $E = 0$ (binding energy equals rest energy),

$$(\nabla^2 - \mu^2)\phi = 0, \tag{12–23}$$

where

$$\mu = mc/\hbar. \tag{12–24}$$

An acceptable spherically symmetric solution of Eq. (12–23) is

$$\phi = g \frac{e^{-\mu r}}{r}, \tag{12–25}$$

where g is an undetermined constant which plays the same role as the charge q in the electrostatic case, i.e., it depends on a "source" at the origin.

In the electrostatic case, the mechanical potential resulting from the interaction between two charges q is $qU = q^2/4\pi\varepsilon_0 r$. This interaction results from the continuous transmission of virtual photons between the two charges. By analogy, for nuclear forces, the mechanical potential resulting from the interaction between two nucleons of strength g is

$$V = -g^2 \frac{e^{-\mu r}}{r}, \tag{12–26}$$

arising from the continuous transfer of virtual mesons of rest mass m between the two nucleons. The term "virtual" implies that the meson cannot be released from the nucleons unless an energy of at least mc^2 is supplied. The order of magnitude of the duration of an excursion of the meson Δt is given by the uncertainty relationship $\Delta t\, \Delta E \approx \hbar$, where $\Delta E = mc^2$. This gives, for the range of the force, $\Delta r \approx \Delta tc \approx \hbar/mc$, in agreement with Eqs. (12–24) and (12–25).

From the observed range of nuclear forces, we can estimate by Eqs. (12–25) and (12–24) that the mass of the field-carrying mesons must be of the order of 300 electron rest masses. The class of mesons that comes closest to this is the pi mesons or *pions*, of which there are three kinds: positive, negative, and neutral, all with intrinsic spin $s = 0$. The mass, about 270 rest masses, inserted into Eq. (12–24) yields $\mu = 0.70$ F^{-1}. The force field between two protons or between two neutrons can be carried only by a neutral pi meson, but the force between a proton and a neutron can also be carried by a charged pi meson. In the latter case, the charge will be transferred from one nucleon to the other, so that the neutron changes into a proton, and vice versa.

Another kind of particle, the *muon*, discovered before the pion, was originally thought to be Yukawa's particle. However, the muon or muons ($+$ or $-$) interact very weakly with nuclear matter and do not have a neutral member in the family. Furthermore, they are spin $\frac{1}{2}$ particles that cannot be transferred from any system without changing the angular momentum of the system.

In this brief outline of the meson theory of nuclear forces, we have not discussed several important factors. First, it has been observed that the pion has negative intrinsic parity; therefore it cannot be transferred from a neutron to a proton in an $l = 0$ state and still conserve parity. To conserve both angular momentum and parity, the only possible state for the pion is the $l = 1$ state. When it is created and transferred, the spin of the parent nucleon flips over so that the resulting spin is still $\frac{1}{2}$. If this is taken into account, it turns out that the force field between two nucleons in the triplet state is not spherically symmetric, as suggested by Eq. (12–26), but has an additional term which is just the tensor force mentioned in Section 12–2.

The one-pion exchange potential (OPEP) discussed above is based on the transfer of a single meson from one nucleon to another. In an important extension of this theory, one also considers the *simultaneous* transfer of *two* pions. The mathematically complicated term describing the two-pion exchange potential (TPEP) has the general character of an exponential of the form $e^{-2\mu r}$. The factor 2 causes the TPEP to decrease much more rapidly for increasing distance than the OPEP so that the term is unimportant beyond about 2 F.

Figure 12–7 shows as an example the singlet nucleon-nucleon potential for even relative orbital momenta ($l = 0, 2, 4$, etc.) plotted beyond $r = 0.7$ F. At smaller distances, the interactions are very strong (attractive or repulsive), and not much has been learned about them to date, experimentally or theoretically. At such small distances, it is presumably possible to have multi-pion exchanges as well as exchanges of heavier mesons.

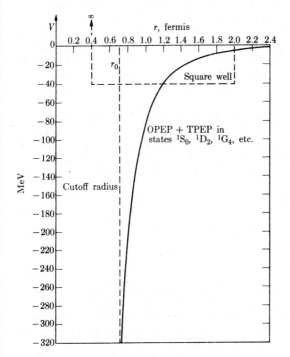

Fig. 12–7 Pion-exchange potential for singlet even l-states. A square well that fits low-energy singlet scattering data is shown for comparison (Courtesy of E. Lomon).

In conclusion, we can say that the laws governing the nuclear forces, also called the *strong interaction*, are very complex indeed. We may never learn to express these laws in an exact mathematical form as we can with the electro-magnetic interaction.

12–5 THE NUCLEAR SHELL MODEL

The shell model of the atom, as described in Section 9-4, essentially pictures the electrons as moving in practically independent orbits in an average field of the nucleus and the other electrons. The gross level scheme computed on the basis of this picture is modified by the perturbations caused by the electron spin and accompanying magnetic moment. Since the early days of nuclear physics several workers have tried the same approach in attempting to find a model for the nucleus. However, these attempts were not very successful until 1949 when, independently, M. G. Mayer* and Haxel, Jensen, and Suess† postulated a strong coupling between the spin and orbital angular momentum of each nucleon. This produced qualitative agreement between theory and certain experimental observations, discussed further below.

In the nucleus there is no central attractive potential such as the one acting on the electrons in the atom. Rather, the individual nucleons attract one another by the strong interaction discussed in the previous section. We shall assume that they can move in individual orbits and that the sum of all forces acting on a given nucleon can be represented by a spherically symmetric potential, for simplicity, a square well.

Here, we shall first treat the manageable problem of calculating the position of the various energy levels in an infinitely deep square well of radius r_0, realizing, of course, that the nuclear well actually has a finite depth. For simplicity, assume that the potential is zero inside the well and infinite outside. The solution of the one-particle Schrödinger equation in a spherically symmetric potential is, in general,

$$\psi = R_l(r)Y_{l,m}(\theta, \phi), \tag{12–27}$$

where the radial wave function $R_l(r)$ is a solution of

$$\frac{1}{r^2}\frac{d}{dr}\left(r^2\frac{dR_l}{dr}\right) + \frac{2m}{\hbar^2}\left[E - \frac{l(l+1)\hbar^2}{2mr^2}\right]R_l = 0. \tag{12–28}$$

Here, E is the part of the total energy which is due to the motion of the nucleon studied and m is the reduced mass, which, in a heavy nucleus, is practically equal to the nucleon mass. We require that the wave function be finite for all values of r. The solutions of Eq. (12–28) that satisfy this requirement are the spherical Bessel functions

$$R_l(r) = j_l(kr) = \left(-\frac{r}{k}\right)^l\left(\frac{1}{r}\frac{d}{dr}\right)^l\left(\frac{\sin kr}{kr}\right), \tag{12–29}$$

where

$$k = \frac{1}{\hbar}\sqrt{2mE}. \tag{12–30}$$

---

*   M. G. Mayer, *Phys. Rev.* **75** (1949), p. 1969.

†   O. Haxel, J. H. Jensen, and H. E. Suess, *Phys. Rev.* **75** (1949), p. 1766.

The three lowest-order spherical Bessel functions ($l = 0$ to 2) are plotted in Fig. 12–8. Also shown are spherical Neumann functions $n_l(kr)$ which have the same mathematical form as $j_l(kr)$ except that $-\cos kr$ is substituted for $\sin kr$ in Eq. (12–29). The Neumann functions satisfy Eq. (12–28) but are irregular at $r = 0$.

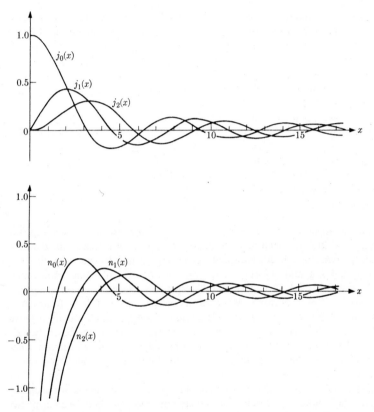

Fig. 12–8 Spherical Bessel and Neumann functions for $l = 0, 1, 2$.   From R. H. Dicke and J. P. Wittke, *Introduction to Quantum Mechanics*, Reading, Mass.: Addison-Wesley, 1960.

For our particular problem there is an additional boundary condition, namely, that the wave function (12–27) should be zero for all values of θ and ϕ at $r = r_0$. We call any value of the argument kr that makes a spherical Bessel function equal to zero a "zero" for the function and denote it by η. Each l-value has a set of zeros, and to each of them corresponds, for our particular problem, a value of k, given by $kr_0 = \eta$. From Eq. (12–30), we then get for the energy of a given level, described by a radial wave function terminating at the zero η,

$$E = \frac{\hbar^2 k^2}{2m} = \frac{\hbar^2 \eta^2}{2mr_0^2} .$$

(12-31)

The zeros η can be taken from Fig. 12–8 or they can be found in a table of functions. Table 12–4 gives the squares of the zeros or, according to Eq. (12–31), the energy levels of the infinite square well in units of $\hbar^2/2mr_0^2$.

Table 12–4 Energy levels in infinite square well

State	1s	1p	1d	2s	1f	2p	1g	2d
η^2	9.87	20.14	33.21	39.48	48.83	59.68	66.96	82.72

State	1h	3s	2f	1i	3p	1j	2g	
η^2	87.53	88.83	108.51	110.52	118.90	135.86	137.01	

The notation for nuclear levels is the same as for atomic levels, except for the principal quantum number. To discern between, for instance, the d-states, we label them 1d, 2d, 3d, etc., and 1d simply means the first d-level. The letters s, p, d, f, g, and so forth, stand for levels with orbital angular-momentum quantum number $l = 0, 1, 2, 3,$ and 4, respectively, just as in atomic physics. Each shell-model level, for instance 2d, actually consists of $2l + 1$ substates, each with a different angular wave function $Y_{l,m}(\theta, \phi)$. Because of the two different possible orientations of the nucleon spin, a level can accommodate $2(2l + 1)$ protons. In addition, it can accommodate $2(2l + 1)$ neutrons, since the two particles are different and they do not therefore mutually exclude each other.

Figure 12–9 shows in the second column the relative positions of the energy levels of the infinite square well. The first column shows the levels of a harmonic-oscillator well adjusted to match the 1s- and 4s-levels with those of the square well. The drawing is only schematic.

The infinite square-well potential as a model for the nucleus is, of course, unrealistic, and a much more realistic potential is a well with finite depth V_0. The depth and also the radius r_0 can be determined for a given nucleus by imposing the requirement that the well produce a theoretical nucleus which has the observed radius and total binding energy. The calculation proceeds as above, except that the wave function does not go to zero at r_0 but penetrates into the region with negative kinetic energy. In this region, that is, for $r > r_0$, the radial wave function is a solution of Eq. (12–28) with negative energy E.

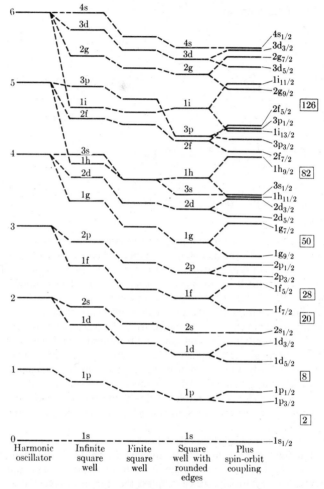

Fig. 12–9 Order of energy levels according to the independent-particle model with various assumptions for the shape of the nuclear potential. From B. T. Feld, *Ann. Rev. Nucl. Sci.* **2** (1953), p. 249. Reproduced by permission.

The solutions that satisfy boundary conditions at $r \to \infty$ are spherical Hankel functions

$$h_l(kr) = j_l(kr) + in_0(kr), \qquad (12\text{–}32)$$

with complex argument

$$k = i\kappa = (2mE)^{1/2}/\hbar; \qquad \text{that is,} \qquad \kappa = (-2mE)^{1/2}/\hbar. \qquad (12\text{–}33)$$

The first few of these functions are:

$$h_0(i\kappa r) = -\frac{1}{\kappa r} e^{-\kappa r}, \qquad\qquad \text{for } l = 0;$$

$$h_1(i\kappa r) = i\left(\frac{1}{\kappa r} + \frac{1}{(\kappa r)^2}\right) e^{-\kappa r}, \qquad\qquad \text{for } l = 1;$$

$$h_2(i\kappa r) = \left(\frac{1}{\kappa r} + \frac{3}{(\kappa r)^2} + \frac{3}{(\kappa r)^3}\right) e^{-\kappa r}, \qquad\qquad \text{for } l = 2;$$

$$h_3(i\kappa r) = -i\left(\frac{1}{\kappa r} + \frac{1}{(\kappa r)^2} + \frac{15}{(\kappa r)^3} + \frac{15}{(\kappa r)^4}\right) e^{-\kappa r}, \qquad\qquad \text{for } l = 3;$$

$$h_4(i\kappa r) = -\left(\frac{1}{\kappa r} + \frac{10}{(\kappa r)^2} + \frac{45}{(\kappa r)^3} + \frac{105}{(\kappa r)^4} + \frac{105}{(\kappa r)^5}\right) e^{-\kappa r}, \qquad \text{for } l = 4.$$

$$(12\text{–}34)$$

The solutions outside and inside the well have to be matched at the boundary $r = r_0$. If V_0 and r_0 are given, the matching equation can be used to determine the energy E. The results of these calculations are that the levels are depressed slightly as compared with the levels for the infinite square well. This is shown, again only schematically, in Fig. 12–9 (finite square well).

Finally, the square well does not give a self-consistent image of the nucleus. The particle density in the nucleus, as computed from the wave functions discussed above, will be approximately constant in the central region but will taper off toward and through the boundary. This has also been experimentally observed (Fig. 12–2). Clearly, since the potential is produced by the interaction between the particles, the potential must also taper off in similar fashion. Column four of Fig. 12–9 shows the results of modifying the square well by tapering and rounding the corners. This gives a self-consistent density distribution of the nucleons.

The final modification made in these calculations is to introduce a spin-orbit coupling for each individual nucleon. This is similar in form to the magnetic coupling producing the fine structure in atoms, only of opposite sign and relatively stronger. Mathematically, we can express the spin-orbit potential as

$$V_{SL} = a_{S0}^2 \frac{1}{r} \frac{\partial V}{\partial r} \, l \cdot s, \qquad (12\text{–}35)$$

where V is the main central potential. Equation (12–35) is empirical, and the parameter a_{S0} regulating the strength is adjusted to give a level spacing (last column, Fig. 12–9) approximately as observed.

Each shell-model energy level, as shown in Fig. 12–9, can have $2j + 1$ nucleons of each kind. For instance, the $1f_{5/2}$ level has six protons with different

m_j values and six neutrons. As an example, $^{27}_{13}\text{Al}$ has the following configuration in the ground state:

Protons: $(1s_{1/2})^2(1p_{3/2})^4(1p_{1/2})^2(1d_{5/2})^5$

Neutrons: $(1s_{1/2})^2(1p_{3/2})^4(1p_{1/2})^2(1d_{5/2})^6$

The nucleon states differing only in m_j value (e.g., the four $1p_{3/2}$ states) are often collectively called a *subshell*.

Between some of the levels shown in Fig. 12–9, there are relatively large energy gaps. The gaps occur at nucleon numbers 2, 8, 20, 28, 50, 82, and 126. These numbers play somewhat the same roles in nuclear physics as the atomic numbers of the noble gases do in atomic physics. Before the spin-orbit model was advanced, they were called *magic numbers*. We also say that $Z = 50$, for instance, represents a closed proton shell.

The residual interaction between protons or between neutrons in a partly filled subshell is almost always such as to pair all like nucleons, except the last if the number is odd. These pairs have resulting angular momentum zero. Therefore, an odd nucleus in the ground state has the angular momentum of the odd nucleon, in the case of ^{27}Al, $J = 5/2$. An even-even nucleus has always $J = 0$ in the ground state.

The shell model has been extremely successful in describing nuclear phenomena, in particular for nuclei close to filled shells. Between shells the nuclei tend to deviate from spherical symmetry (quadrupole moment $Q \neq 0$). A more sophisticated model, formed by adding shell-model wave functions, has had a considerable success in these regions.

12–6 RADIOACTIVITY

Natural radioactivity was discovered quite accidentally by Henri Becquerel in 1896. Becquerel had left a substance containing uranium on a photographic plate which was wrapped in black paper. After it was developed, the plate showed images of the crystals of uranium compounds. Intensive research by Becquerel, Madame Curie, Rutherford, and others led to the discovery of several other radionuclides (radioactive elements). Three different kinds of radiations were found, alpha, beta, and gamma, and subsequently it was shown that the alpha particle is identical to the helium nucleus, that beta radiation consists of electrons, and that gamma radiation is electromagnetic waves, as are also, for instance, x-rays. Much later (see Section 12–10), it was found that an elusive particle, the *antineutrino*, is always emitted simultaneously with the electron in beta decay. The three kinds of radiation are discussed in Sections 12–8, 12–9, and 12–10. In particular, it is shown in Section 12–9 why an alpha particle, which consists of two neutrons and two protons, is emitted rather than a neutron or a proton. In Section 12–10, it is shown that of two neighbor isobars, the one with the greater atomic mass is always unstable, and will decay by a beta process into the other. In natural radionuclides, alpha processes and beta processes very often compete; that is, they may both be energetically possible. Whether or not a given nuclide is observed to be simultaneously an alpha emitter and a beta emitter depends on whether the probabilities of occurrence of the two processes are sufficiently close in order of magnitude.

In alpha emission the nucleon number A changes by four units; in beta emission the nucleon number A does not change, but Z and N change by one unit in opposite directions. In gamma emission neither Z nor N changes. There is, then, what we may call beta-decay correspondence between all members of a chain of nuclides with the same nucleon number A, and alpha-decay correspondence between this chain and the chain in which the nucleon number is $A - 4$. There are thus four families of natural radioactive nuclides, one with $A = 4n$, where n is an integer, and others with $A = 4n + 1, 4n + 2$, and $4n + 3$. Figure 12–10 shows as an example the uranium-radium $4n + 2$ series marked out on a part of the chart of the nuclides, with arrows indicating directions of decays. Figure 12–10 shows only the branches of the chain that have been observed in natural radioactivity. Many radioactive isotopes with $A = 4n + 2$ have been artificially produced on both sides of this chain, and they are found to be linked to it as side branches.

Table 12–5 is a list of the members of the uranium-radium series, their types of disintegration, and half-lives. The parent nuclide (origin) of this

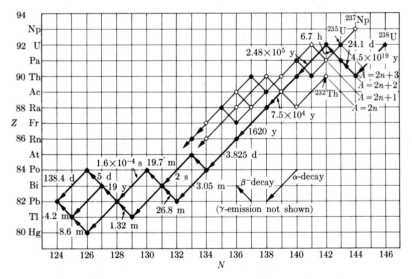

Fig. 12–10 The $A = 4n + 2$ radioactive series and the first few links of the other three series. Where branching occurs, the half-life is written beside the main branch.

series is ^{238}U, with a half-life of 4.5×10^9 y. Since the elements in our solar system are presumed to have been formed about 4×10^9 years ago, ^{238}U is sufficiently long-lived so that a large fraction of what was originally formed has survived up to the present. The end product of the uranium-radium series is ^{206}Pb, which is stable. The nuclide ^{234}Pa is listed twice in Table 12–5; one faction, UX$_2$, is an excited state of ^{234}Pa, an isomeric state with a half-life of 1.18 m. Both factions are formed by beta decay of ^{234}Th. An excited state will, in general, decay by gamma emission to the ground state much faster than it can decay by beta or alpha emission; however, in the case of UX$_2$, the difference in angular momentum between the excited state and the ground state is so large that the gamma lifetime, relatively speaking, is very large. A large fraction of the ^{234}Pa nuclei formed in the isomeric state, therefore, decays by beta emission to ^{234}U.

Radioactive nuclei that are found in nature either have long half-lives or else they are members of a radioactive chain of which the first member, the

Table 12–5 The uranium-radium ($4n + 2$) series, with type of disintegration and half-life

Old name	Old symbol	Atomic number	New symbol	Half-life	Main type of decay	Alternate branch Decay	Alternate branch Fraction
Uranium I	UI	92	^{238}U	4.50×10^9 y	α		
Uranium X$_1$	UX$_1$	90	^{234}Th	24.1 d	β^-		
Uranium X$_2$	UX$_2$	91	^{234m}Pa	1.18 m	β^-	γ	0.005
Uranium Z	UZ	91	^{234}Pa	6.7 h	β^-		
Uranium II	UII	92	^{234}U	2.48×10^5 y	α		
Ionium	Io	90	^{230}Th	7.5×10^4 y	α		
Radium	Ra	88	^{226}Ra	1620 y	α		
Radon	Rn	86	^{222}Rn	3.825 d	α		
Radium A	RaA	84	^{218}Po	3.05 m	α	β^-	2×10^{-4}
		85	^{218}At	2 s (1.3)	α		
Radium B	RaB	82	^{214}Pb	26.8 m	β^-		
Radium C	RaC	83	^{214}Bi	19.7 m	β^-	α	4×10^{-4}
Radium C′	RaC′	84	^{214}Po	1.6×10^{-4} s	α		
Radium C″	RaC″	81	^{210}Tl	1.32 m	β^-		
Radium D	RaD	82	^{210}Pb	19 y	β^-	α	1.8×10^{-8}
Radium E	RaE	83	^{210m}Bi	5.0 d	β^-	α	5×10^{-7}
Polonium	Po	84	^{210}Po	138.4 d	α		
		80	^{206}Hg	8.6 m	β^-		
	RaE″	81	^{206}Tl	4.2 m	β^-		
Radium G	RaG	82	^{206}Pb		Stable		

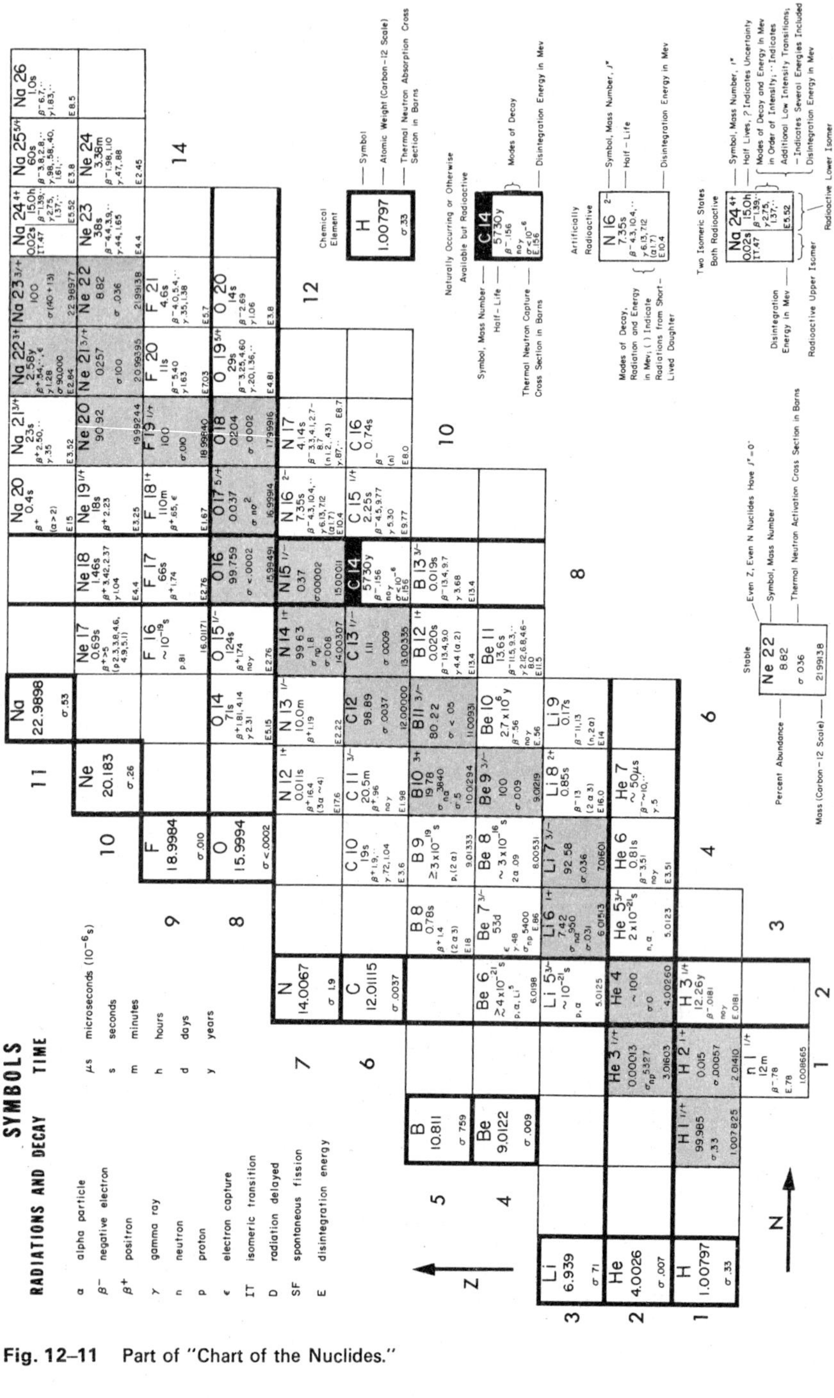

Fig. 12-11 Part of "Chart of the Nuclides."

parent nucleus, has a lifetime of the order of 10^9 years or longer.* The parent thus has been able to survive since the formation of the solar system.

In the laboratory, man has been able to produce more than 1000 other radioactive nuclides with half-lives down to a small fraction of a second. The properties of all known nuclides are displayed in a graph, the Chart of the Nuclides, kept up to date by the Knolls Atomic Power Laboratory†. Figure 12–11 shows a small section of the Chart of the Nuclides, and Fig. 12–12 shows the general layout of the complete chart without any details. Two solid lines in the figure give the boundaries of what can rightfully be called nuclides. Over and below this area an assembly of nucleons is either proton unstable or neutron unstable. In either case, it will decay by proton or neutron emission within about 10^{-20} s.

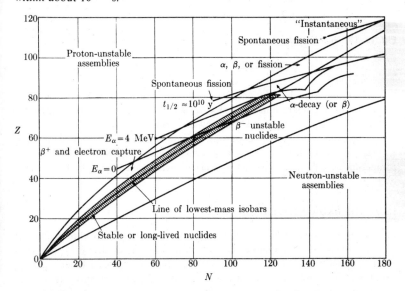

Fig. 12–12 General arrangement of the Chart of Nuclides with lines of stability against various break-up modes.

Figure 12–13 illustrates the various kinds of breakup or disintegration processes that radioactive (unstable) nuclei may undergo. The nucleus is represented as an assembly of protons and neutrons, a proton being indicated

---

* A notable exception is ^{14}C with a half-life of 5730 years. This is continuously being formed in the atmosphere by cosmic-ray neutrons in the reaction ^{14}N + $n \rightarrow$ ^{14}C + p.

† Operated by the General Electric Company for the United States Atomic Energy Commission.

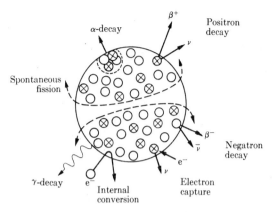

Fig. 12–13 Nuclear decay modes.

by a cross, and a neutron by an open circle. In addition to the processes mentioned above, the figure illustrates *positron decay*, in which a proton changes to a neutron while emitting a positron and a *neutrino*, and *spontaneous fission*, in which the nucleus breaks into two, sometimes three, large fragments. Competing with the positron-decay process is *electron capture* (see Section 12–10), and competing with gamma emission is *internal conversion* (Section 12–8).

12–7 THE RADIOACTIVE DECAY LAW

Let us consider a sample containing a very large number of radionuclides, all of the same kind and assume that all of these nuclides decay by the same process, either by the emission of an alpha particle, a beta particle, or a gamma quantum. The process is a statistical one-shot process, meaning that when one particular nucleus has decayed, it cannot repeat the process again. As long as the nucleus has not decayed, the probability for its so doing during the next second remains a constant. In other words, the nucleus does not age as does a biological system. The probability for it to decay between now and a second from now may be, for instance, one percent; and, if it happens to survive for an hour, the probability for it to decay during a given second is still one percent. Assume that in a given sample at time t there are N nuclei that have not decayed. The number that decays during the time interval from t to $t + dt$ must be proportional to N and also proportional to dt. This can be written as

$$-dN = \lambda N \, dt, \qquad (12\text{–}36)$$

where the proportionality coefficient λ is called the *decay constant*. We rewrite Eq. (12–36) as

$$\lambda = -\frac{1}{N}\frac{dN}{dt},$$

and see that the decay constant is equal to the fraction of nuclei in a given sample that decays per unit time, or, for a single nucleus, it is the probability for decay per unit time. We integrate Eq. (12–36) and find that

$$N = N_0 e^{-\lambda t}, \tag{12–37}$$

where N_0 is the total number of radioactive nuclei at time $t = 0$. The exponential decay of the number N of nuclei left, as expressed by Eq. (12–37), is usually observed by measuring the *counting rate*, $-dN/dt$, as a function of the time. By taking the derivative of Eq. (12–37), we find

$$-\frac{dN}{dt} = \lambda N = \lambda N_0 e^{-\lambda t} = \left(-\frac{dN}{dt}\right)_0 e^{-\lambda t}. \tag{12–38}$$

As expressed by Eq. (12–38), the counting rate shows the same exponential behavior as the number of undecayed nuclei. Taking the logarithm of base 10 of Eq. (12–38), we find

$$\log_{10}\left(-\frac{dN}{dt}\right) = \log_{10}\left(-\frac{dN}{dt}\right)_0 - \lambda t \log_{10} e.$$

This shows that, when the counting rate is plotted on a semilogarithmic paper, as a function of time, the resulting plot should be a straight line with slope $-\lambda \log e$. Figure 12–14(a) shows an example of counting-rate data plotted on a linear scale, and Fig. 12–14(b) gives the same data on a semilogarithmic scale.

The half-life of a radioactive nucleus is defined as the time $t_{1/2}$ during which the number of nuclei reduces to one-half the original value. Using Eq. (12–37), we get $\frac{1}{2} = e^{-\lambda t_{1/2}}$, which gives

$$t_{1/2} = \ln 2/\lambda = 0.693/\lambda. \tag{12–39}$$

The mean life, or average life, of the radioactive nuclei is given by

$$\tau = \frac{1}{N_0}\int_0^\infty t(-dN) = \int_0^\infty t\lambda e^{-\lambda t}\,dt = \frac{1}{\lambda}, \tag{12–40}$$

where we have used Eq. (12–38). From Eqs. (12–39) and (12–40) we see that the mean life and half-life differ by a factor $\ln 2 = 0.693$.

The decay constant λ, together with the type of decay and the energy of decay, characterizes a given radioactive nucleus and can be regarded as its signature.

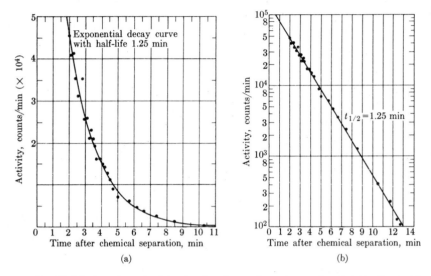

Fig. 12–14 Counting-rate data showing the positron decay of metastable (isomeric) ^{82}Rb, (a) plotted on a linear scale and (b) plotted on a logarithmic scale. The experimental points are taken from L. M. Litz, S. A. Ring, and W. R. Balkwell, *Phys. Rev.* **92** (1953), p. 288.

12–8 GAMMA TRANSITIONS

Nuclei in highly excited states most often de-excite themselves by the emission of a heavy particle, whenever this is energetically possible. Below the dissociation energy, i.e., the binding energy of the last neutron, proton, or alpha particle, whichever is smallest, the de-excitation can only take place by electromagnetic interaction (and sometimes by beta decay, which ordinarily is a slower process). In the electromagnetic de-excitation process the nucleus drops to a lower excited state or to the ground state, in exact analogy with the emission of light from excited atoms. However, the energies of the electromagnetic quanta emitted by nuclei are mostly in the range 10^4 to 10^6 times the energy of a photon in the visible spectrum. The wavelength is therefore smaller than the optical wavelength by the same factor. The relationship between the energy and the wavelength of an electromagnetic quantum is, in general:

$$E_\gamma = h\nu = hc/\lambda = 1239.8/\lambda \text{ MeV}, \tag{12–41}$$

with λ in fermis. This formula shows that a 1-MeV gamma ray has a wavelength which is of the order of magnitude of 100 nuclear diameters.

In atomic physics (optics and x-rays) photon energies are determined almost exclusively by means of wavelength measurements. Since the energy ranges of gamma rays and of characteristic x-rays overlap, it is possible to some extent to employ the same techniques for wavelength measurements in the two areas of physics. The physical process utilized is, of course, the coherent scattering of the electromagnetic radiation by a crystal lattice. By converting the gamma energy to electron energy (via the photoelectric effect in a thin nickel foil), one can also use magnetic spectrographs for gamma-ray studies. More recently, the semiconductor radiation detector (Section 11–10) has all but taken over the field of gamma-ray spectroscopy.

Radioactive nuclides, natural or artificially produced, are one source of material for gamma-ray studies. Most often the gamma radiation is emitted following a beta or alpha decay. Figure 12–15 shows a simple example of a decay scheme in which beta decay of ^{187}W produces ^{187}Re in excited states that subsequently decay to the ground state. Note that the observed energies of the gamma rays alone do not provide enough information to design this energy-level diagram. There is no way of telling what the sequence is of the three gamma rays emitted in cascade. When the energy levels are measured by alpha decay (Section 12–9) or by a nuclear reaction (Section 12–12), there is no such ambiguity.

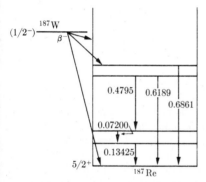

Fig. 12–15 Decay scheme for ^{187}W with gamma transitions in ^{187}Re measured with the bent-crystal spectrometer.

The theory of photon (gamma) emission in nuclear physics is essentially the same as that of photon emission in atomic physics. There is one important difference. In atomic physics, practically nothing but electric dipole radiation is observed, because the transition probabilities for magnetic dipole or higher-order electric multipole radiations are so low that de-excitation by collision takes place first. Nuclei do not collide in the normal states of a radioactive material. Gamma transitions are therefore often the only way of de-excitation, and lifetimes of millions of years are possible.

We shall not discuss the theory of gamma emission here, but will confine ourselves to an explanation of the terminology. An electric dipole radiation ($E1$) has as a classical analogue the radiation from a dipole antenna. Electric quadrupole radiation ($E2$) corresponds classically to the radiation from an object with four electrical poles, alternating pluses and minuses with the charges oscillating between these poles. Correspondingly, magnetic dipole $M1$ is classically an object with two magnetic poles, oscillating between north and south pole, etc. Selection rules for these various types of radiation (multipolarities) are given in Table 12–6.

Table 12–6   Selection rules for gamma-ray transitions

Type	Symbol	Angular momentum change, l	Parity change
Electric dipole	$E1$	1	Yes
Magnetic dipole	$M1$	1	No
Electric quadrupole	$E2$	2	No
Magnetic quadrupole	$M2$	2	Yes
Electric octupole	$E3$	3	Yes
Magnetic octupole	$M3$	3	No
Electric 16-pole	$E4$	4	No
Magnetic 16-pole	$M4$	4	Yes

Two examples.   The first excited state of ^{29}Si is a $3/2^+$ state at 1.273 MeV. It decays to the ground state $(1/2^+)$ via an $M1$ transition or by a combination of $M1$ and $E2$. The electric quadrupole transition ($E2$) is possible because the *vector* difference between the initial and final angular momenta can be as large as $[l(l + 1)^{1/2}\hbar]$ with $l = 2$. In general, $l_{\max} = J_1 + J_2$, and $l_{\min} = |J_1 - J_2|$.

The first excited state of ^{45}Sc is a $3/2^+$ state at 12.4 keV. It decays to the ground state $(7/2^-)$ via an $M2$ transition with a 0.30-s half-life. $E3$ and $M4$ transitions are also theoretically possible. Most often, however, the transition with the lowest l-value is faster than the others by several orders of magnitude. The combination $M1 - E2$, as mentioned in the first example, is an exception to this rule.

Internal conversion competes with gamma emission, and the ratio of the probabilities of the two processes depends strongly upon the multipolarity ($E1$, $M3$, etc.). Figure 12–16 shows an example of an energy-level diagram that has been studied by measuring alpha energies (Section 12–9). The multipolarities indicated for the gamma lines have been determined by measuring for each line the internal conversion coefficient

$$\alpha = N_c/N_\gamma. \tag{12–42}$$

Here N_c and N_γ are numbers of conversion electrons and gamma rays emitted for a given de-excitation step in a large sample of nuclei over a given time.

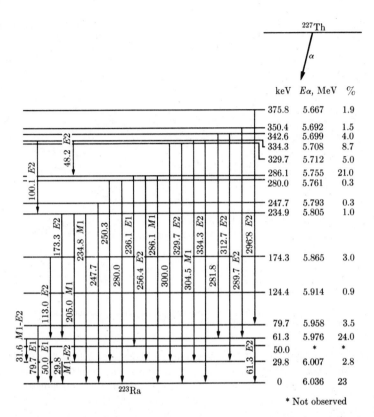

Fig. 12–16 Energy-level diagram of ^{223}Ra derived from the alpha-particle spectrum of ^{227}Th shown in Fig. 12–19. Also shown are observed electromagnetic transitions. From F. S. Stephens in *Nuclear Spectroscopy*, Part A, Ed. Fay Ajzenberg-Selove. New York: Academic Press, (1960), p. 202. Reproduced by permission.

12–9 ALPHA DECAY

In Section 6–10 we discussed briefly the mechanism of alpha decay by barrier penetration. We now raise the question: Why are four nucleons emitted together in the form of an alpha particle, rather than one proton or one neutron at a time? In this section, we shall answer that question.

In Section 12–1, we discussed the binding energy of the nucleons in the nucleus. Because of the Coulomb effect, the binding energy per new added particle decreases slightly with increasing A for heavy nuclei. This is illustrated in Fig. 12–17, which shows the range of the binding energy of the last nucleon

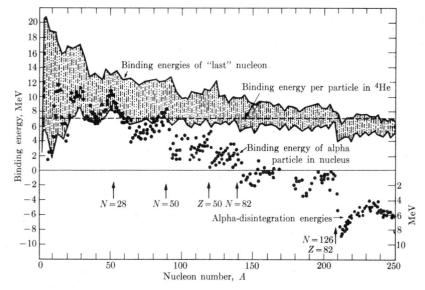

Fig. 12–17 Minimum and maximum binding energy for "last" nucleon and binding energies of "last" alpha particle for beta-stable nuclei.

added for beta-stable nuclei. The binding energy of the last nucleon fluctuates rapidly with A, and only the limits on this fluctuation are shown in the figure. For no nuclide found in nature is the binding energy of the last nucleon anywhere close to zero. They are, therefore, all stable against nucleon breakup.

The reason that many of these heavy nuclei are unstable for alpha-particle breakup is the following. The total binding energy of the alpha particle is 28.3 MeV (Table 12–3). If in a heavy nucleus the binding energy of the last four nucleons (the last two protons and the last two neutrons) averages about 7 MeV, then it will require 28 MeV to remove them from the nucleus. If these four nucleons afterward combine to form an alpha particle, the binding energy of the alpha particle (28.3 MeV) is released. In the complete process, then, the total expenditure of energy is less than the gain. Alpha decay is therefore energetically possible. We have to think of the process as one in which four nucleons combine at the surface of the nucleus to form an alpha particle which then escapes from the nucleus.

In general, we may say that the binding energy of an alpha particle in a nucleus is 28.3 MeV less than the sum of the binding energies of the two last protons and the two last neutrons. In Fig. 12–17 the range of the binding energy of an alpha particle is shown as a function of A for beta-stable nuclides. At about $A = 140$ the points fall below zero, and the indication is that most of the heavier nuclei are alpha unstable. Why, then, are not practically all nuclei above $A = 140$ observed to be radioactive; indeed, why do we find these nuclides in nature at all? The answer is that in order to reach the state of increased entropy, the higher disorder toward which nature moves, the alpha particle has to pass a hurdle—the Coulomb barrier. Unless the energy available is sufficiently high, the lifetime of the unstable state will be longer than the age of the universe; in many cases, so long that it becomes impossible or impractical to observe the radioactivity.

Figure 12–18 shows an energy-level diagram with the ground state of ^{232}U and other states involving the same number of nucleons. Clearly, the nuclide ^{232}U is stable against proton breakup and against neutron breakup. It is also beta stable. However, it can release about 5.42 MeV in kinetic energy by alpha breakup. In Fig. 12–18, A is the nucleon number of the daughter nucleus, that is, the nucleus that is left after a particle has been removed. For beta decay, of course, A does not change; hence, beta decay is indicated by a vertical line when the energy levels are arranged as they are in this figure. All the nuclei involved in the diagram have low-lying excited states, but only the ground states are indicated in this figure.

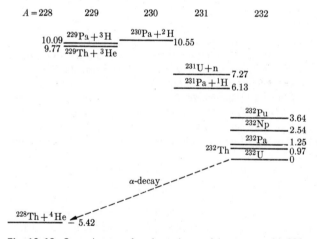

Fig. 12–18 Ground states of nucleus-plus-particle systems with 232 nucleons.

The study of energy spectra of alpha particles has yielded important information about the energy levels of the daughter nucleus. Figure 12–19 shows number of alpha particles versus energy from ^{227}Th measured with a magnetic spectrograph. The resulting energy-level diagram of the daughter nucleus ^{223}Ra was shown in Fig. 12–16.

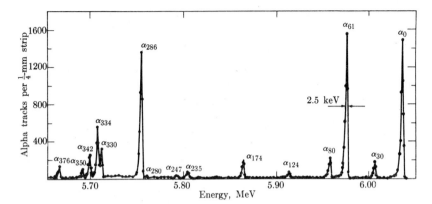

Fig. 12–19 Alpha-particle spectrum of ^{227}Th taken by Pilger *et al.*   R. C. Pilger, Ph.D. thesis, University of California Radiation Laboratory Report UCRL-3877 (1957).   The subscripts on the alpha peaks indicate the excitation energies of the corresponding levels in the daughter nucleus ^{223}Ra.

12–10   BETA DECAY

A perusal of the Chart of the Nuclides or a table of nuclides reveals that among the nuclear species that are found in nature, there are very many with identical nucleon numbers A, that is, for a given A there may be several stable isobars. However, there are very few cases of naturally occurring *neighbor* isobars, or pairs of the type $^{115}_{50}$Sn and $^{115}_{49}$In, where Z differs by one unit only.   There are good reasons to believe that in every case where such pairs exist, one member is actually unstable, but may have an exceedingly long lifetime.   In the case mentioned, $^{115}_{49}$In is known to decay with a half-life of 6×10^{14} years into $^{115}_{50}$Sn.

In contrast to the situation for neighbor isobars, there is an abundance of cases of apparently stable isobars separated by two units of Z (and N). The observations are that between two neighbor isobars the one with the larger *atomic* mass will decay by a beta process to the lighter one, but that apparently there is no process which, with sufficient speed, can change the nuclear charge by two units.

We may think of the Chart of the Nuclides as a three-dimensional plot with mass being the quantity plotted in the third dimension.   The stable nuclei will then represent the bottom of a valley.   All neutron-rich nuclides will decay by β^- emission along its isobar line toward the bottom of the valley, and all proton-rich nuclides will decay similarly with β^+ emission or electron capture. A cross section of the valley, along an isobar line, may exhibit local minima (Fig. 12–20).   The naturally occurring isobars are located at the minima.

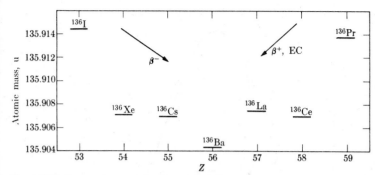

Fig. 12–20 Cross section of the valley of nuclides at isobar line, $A = 136$.

In the beta-decay process a positive or negative electron is emitted from the nucleus, or an orbital electron is captured by the nucleus. In all cases, a neutrino or an antineutrino is simultaneously emitted.

The electron and positron are antiparticles, i.e., they can annihilate each other when brought in close contact. Correspondingly, there are two kinds of neutrinos involved in beta decay, the neutrino emitted in β^+ (positron) decay and the antineutrino emitted in β^- (negatron) decay. All four belong to a class of particles called leptons, which, according to observations, are always created or annihilated in pairs. For instance, the creation of an electron in β^- decay is always accompanied by the creation of an antineutrino, and in β^+ decay a positron and a neutrino are created. These observations can be formulated into a physical law expressing conservation of lepton number. (Compare with conservation of charge.) That is, we give the electron and the neutrino lepton number 1 and the positron and antineutrino lepton number -1. The sum of these numbers is then always constant in any reaction (beta decay, pair production, etc.).

The neutrino and the antineutrino were postulated by Pauli in 1931 to explain an otherwise unaccountable loss of energy and angular momentum in the β-decay process. Consider a simple example, the decay of a free neutron:

$$n \rightarrow p + \beta^- + \bar{\nu}.$$

The neutron has half-integer spin quantum number and so has the proton as well as the electron. Without the antineutrino on the right-hand side of the equation, angular momentum cannot be conserved, since a possible *orbital* angular momentum of the electron relative to the proton must have integer quantum number. The other argument in favor of a two-particle emission stems from the fact that the energy of the emitted electron displays a broad continuous spectrum with a maximum energy that corresponds to the neutron-proton mass difference (Fig. 12–21). Clearly, this agrees with the view that the energy is shared in a random fashion between two particles.

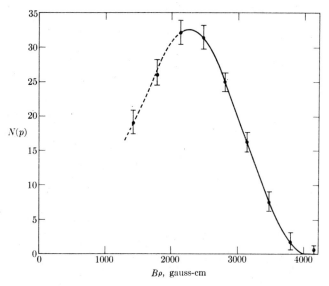

Fig. 12–21 Beta-minus spectrum from the decay of free neutrons. From J. M. Robson, *Phys. Rev.* **83** (1951), p. 349.

For a beta process to take place there must be energy available for the creation of the leptons. The basic processes are

$$n \rightarrow p + \beta^- + \bar{\nu}, \qquad \beta^- \text{ decay};$$ (12–43)

$$p \rightarrow n + \beta^+ + \nu, \qquad \beta^+ \text{ decay};$$ (12–44)

$$p + e^- \rightarrow n + \nu, \qquad \text{Electron capture (EC).}$$ (12–45)

Clearly, in these processes, both charge and lepton number are conserved. The symbol ν indicates the neutrino, and the symbol $\bar{\nu}$, the antineutrino. The symbol β^- is used to represent an electron created in a β-decay process, and the symbol e^- is used for an atomic (orbital) electron. They are, of course, identical particles. Process (12–43) is energetically possible for a free neutron which has a 0.78-MeV 12-m (half-life) decay. The processes (12–44) and (12–45) are then, of course, not possible without an extra supply of energy which may be present in the field of other nucleons inside the nucleus.

The maximum kinetic energy available for the decay products in a beta process can be found from the following balance sheet between the *atomic* rest energies of two members of an isobaric pair.

Process	Before	After
β^-	$_z^A M c^2$	$_{z+1}^A M^+ c^2$ (positive ion) $+ m_0 c^2 + Q_{\beta-}$
β^+	$_{z+1}^A M c^2$	$_z^A M^- c^2$ (negative ion) $+ m_0 c^2 + Q_{\beta+}$
EC	$_{z+1}^A M c^2$	$_z^A M^* c^2$ (neutral but excited) $+ Q_{EC}$

The energy Q released in the process in the form of kinetic energy of the decay products must, of course, be equal to the reduction in rest energy. This is essentially what the balance sheet expresses.

The β^- process increases the nuclear charge by one unit but leaves the number of atomic electrons unchanged. Since the energy of the neutral daughter atom is

$$_{z+1}^A M c^2 = _{z+1}^{A+} M c^2 + m_0 c^2 - I,$$

where I is the binding energy of the last atomic electron, we get

$$Q_{\beta-} = _z^A M c^2 - _{z+1}^A M c^2 - I. \tag{12–46}$$

The binding energy I (ionization energy) is so small that it is usually neglected.

The β^+ process decreases the nuclear charge by one unit and hence leaves a negative ion. The rest energy of this negative ion can be written:

$$_z^A M^- c^2 = _z^A M c^2 + m_0 c^2 - I.$$

From the balance sheet, we then get

$$Q_{\beta+} = _{z+1}^A M c^2 - _z^A M c^2 - 2m_0 c^2 + I. \tag{12–47}$$

The electron-capture process reduces the number of elementary charges by one unit, and at the same time removes one electron from one of the atomic shells. Most often this is one of the innermost shells, for instance, the K-shell. The process therefore leaves the atom excited, and a cascade of photons will, in general, follow the capture. The rearrangement energy is equal to the binding energy, E_B, of the captured electron minus the binding energy, I, of an electron in the lowest orbit that is not occupied when the daughter atom is in its ground state.

From the balance sheet, we get

$$Q_{EC} = _{z+1}^A M c^2 - _z^A M c^2 - E_B + I. \tag{12–48}$$

The binding energy for a K-electron in heavy elements is over 100 keV, but the L- and M-electrons are bound by only about 20 and 5 keV, respectively. If $_{z+1}^A M$ is larger than $_z^A M$, electron capture is therefore, in practice, possible. Equations (12–46) and (12–48) show that between two neighbor isobars, in practice, one has enough energy to decay into the other. This explains the observations made in the first paragraph of this section about neighbor isobars. For β^+ decay, Eq. (12–43) shows that an excess energy of $2m_0 c^2 = 1.022$ MeV must be available for the process to go.

The masses entering into Eqs. (12–46) and (12–48) are atomic masses for the neutral species with both the nuclei and the atoms in the ground states. Very often beta decay leaves the daughter nucleus in an excited state (energy E_x). The kinetic energy of the disintegration products is then, of course:

$$E_k = Q - E_x. \tag{12–49}$$

Figure 12–22 shows an example, the decay scheme of ^{198}Au. A large fraction (98.6%) of the decay goes to the first excited state of the daughter nucleus ^{198}Hg. This nucleus thereafter de-excites itself by emission of a gamma ray or conversion electron leading to the ground state.

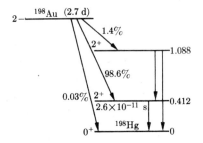

Fig. 12–22 Decay scheme of ^{198}Au showing branching to the ground state and first two excited states of ^{198}Hg.

In beta decay, as in other decay processes, the most important parameters that can be experimentally determined are the half-life or decay constant and the energies of the emitted radiation. In β^- and β^+ decay, the endpoint of the continuous energy spectrum represents the energy released in the process, and this of course is an important parameter. Because beta spectra are continuous rather than displaying sharp lines, they are much harder to interpret than alpha and gamma spectra. For instance, the three beta "lines" shown in Fig. 12–22 produce three overlapping continuous spectra.

The theory of β-decay, giving the half-life of the nucleus and the shape of the beta spectrum, is not very complex, but we cannot take space for it here. In the case of a photon emission, we saw that the interaction bringing about the transition was the electromagnetic force acting on an electron or proton (Section 8–6). Beta decay is caused by a different interaction, called the *weak interaction*. This does not manifest itself in any forces measurable in the macroscopic world and was first postulated by Fermi to explain beta decay. It plays an important role also in elementary particle physics (Section 12–15).

Beta transitions, obeying the following selection rule, are called *allowed* transitions:

$$\Delta J = \pm 1 \quad \text{or} \quad 0, \qquad \text{no parity change}$$

In these transitions, the leptons can be emitted in $l = 0$ states. In any other case, one or the other of the leptons has to be emitted with an orbital angular momentum $l = 1$ or higher. Because linear momenta of the leptons are so small, the probability for emission in a state with $l > 0$ is small. These transitions therefore have much longer half-life and are called *forbidden transitions*.

12–11 PARITY VIOLATION IN BETA DECAY

The theory of macroscopic physics includes a number of conservation laws, notably the laws of conservation of energy, linear momentum, and angular momentum. In atomic and nuclear physics, the same laws apply; and in addition, we also have a law expressing the fact that parity is conserved. That a system possesses a definite parity essentially means that it is equal to its own mirror image. If parity is conserved, the mirror image of a real experiment should also correspond to an experiment that can actually be performed. The law of conservation of parity rests on the assumption that the potentials involved in a nuclear or atomic experiment are mirror-symmetric. In the macroscopic world, systems of course are not mirror-symmetric in general; a human being, for instance, is not equal to his own mirror image. A helix is not equal to its own mirror image, and for this reason systems that are not mirror-symmetric are said to possess helicity. Even systems as small as organic molecules possess helicity; all life on this planet consists of organic material with one kind of helicity. Molecules of the opposite helicity could form living organisms with the same properties, and it is possible that such life exists on other planets.

As an example of a macroscopic experiment that apparently violates the parity law, we study the deflection of a compass needle under the influence of a magnetic field from a current conductor (Fig. 12–23a). The north pole of

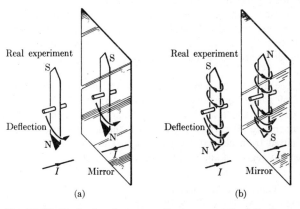

Fig. 12–23 Study of parity conservation in a magnetic-deflection experiment.

the compass needle in the real experiment, which is shown to the left, will deflect in the direction toward the reader. We recognize the north pole on the needle in the real experiment and in the mirror as the tip which is painted black, for instance. In the mirror we also see this tip being deflected toward the reader. If, however, the experiment we see in the mirror were a real experiment, the north pole of the compass needle would deflect in the opposite direction. It appears then as if parity is violated in this experiment. However, if we look at the same experiment on the atomic scale, as in Fig. 12–23(b), the situation is different. Here, in the real experiment, the currents (spinning electrons) producing the magnetic field in the compass needle are indicated, and in the mirror we see the images of these currents. The north pole of the compass needle in this *true mirror image* on the atomic scale is pointing up. Therefore the experiment seen in the mirror can actually be performed; that is, the deflection will be in the direction out of the plane of the paper just as seen in the mirror. The law of conservation of parity is therefore not violated on the atomic scale.

The conclusion to be drawn from this and a vast number of other experiments on the atomic scale is that, on this scale, nature appears to be perfectly symmetric, or, expressed differently, the systems appear to have definite parities. However, it is perfectly possible for us to combine atoms into molecules and more complicated bodies that are not like their own mirror images, that is, they possess helicity (right-handedness or left-handedness), which means that they do not have a definite parity.

Strong indications of parity violation in a process governed by the so-called weak interaction, of which beta decay is an example, came first from elementary-particle physics. Two particles called the τ^+ and θ^+ mesons had been observed to have, within experimental errors, identical masses and identical lifetimes. The only thing that distinguished them from each other was the fact that one decays into three π-mesons, which represent a negative parity state, and the other decays into two π-mesons, which represent a positive parity state. Therefore, if parity were to be conserved, the particles could not be identical. We now believe that they are identical, and we have given the same label, K^+, to these mesons (see Section 12–15).

In 1956 T. D. Lee and C. N. Yang* pointed out that there existed no experimental proof of parity conservation in weak interactions. They also suggested several experiments to test whether or not parity is conserved. The first of these experiments to be carried out concerns the angular distribution of beta particles emitted from aligned ^{60}Co nuclei.† The sample is actually a nitrate in which a high degree of alignment of the *atomic* angular momentum

---

* T. D. Lee and C. N. Yang, *Phys. Rev.* **104** (1956), p. 254.

† C. S. Wu, E. Ambler, R. W. Hayward, D. D. Hoppes, and R. P. Hudson, *Phys. Rev.* **105** (1957), p. 1413.

vectors can be achieved by an external field at very low temperatures. This produces an internal magnetic field which is strong enough to align a large percentage of the nuclear angular momentum vectors.

In Fig. 12–24, the C. S. Wu experiment is sketched to the left of our imaginary mirror. Assume that there is an anisotropy in the intensity of the emitted β^- radiation such that there are more electrons emitted upward, that is, in a direction opposite to the direction of the angular momentum vector, than in any other direction. Look in the mirror. The predominant direction of beta radiation is seen to be up, as in the real experiment, but the angular momentum vector has changed direction. In the mirror we therefore see the electrons being predominantly emitted in the direction of the angular momentum vector. Obviously then, the experiment that we see in the mirror cannot be performed in reality because the predicted results contradict the results we have assumed for the original experiment. Therefore observation of an asymmetry of the kind assumed for the real experiment would constitute a proof of parity violation.

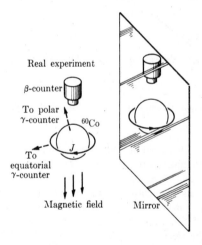

Fig. 12–24 Parity violation experiment. From C. S. Wu *et al., Phys. Rev.* **105** (1957), p. 1413.

If, instead of assuming a single direction of predominance, we had assumed two, namely parallel and antiparallel to the angular momentum vector, the experiment would be identical to its own mirror image. The parity law would then presumably rest in peace. It was known to Wu and coworkers that the latter kind of anisotropy could be detected in the gamma radiation from aligned ^{60}Co nuclei. They therefore used two gamma counters to check the alignment. The sample was cooled to 4.2°K by liquid helium and further cooled to below $0.01°K$ by adiabatic demagnetization.* The ^{60}Co nuclei were then aligned by an external field, as indicated, and the counting rates observed as a function of time as the sample warmed up again. The experiment was then repeated with the magnetic field in the opposite direction.

Figure 12–25 shows the results. To the left is plotted the counting rate in the two gamma counters. The polar counter read lower than the equatorial counter for both field directions, as expected for $E2$ radiation. The beta counter, however, indicated that more electrons were emitted in the direction antiparallel to the angular momentum vector than parallel to it. This is proof of parity violation in the beta process.

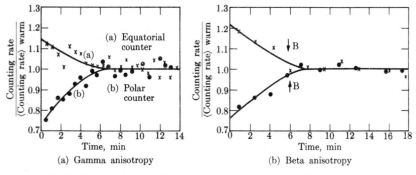

Fig. 12–25 Results of parity violation experiment. From C. S. Wu *et al.*, *Phys. Rev.* **105** (1957), p. 1413.

The results of the experiment described here and of others involving helicity in weak interactions point to the neutrino (antineutrino) as the culprit of parity violation. The antineutrino involved in the β^- decay is presumed to have its angular momentum vector aligned with its momentum vector; it moves as a right-handed screw, whereas the neutrino moves as a left-handed screw. In the ^{60}Co decay, the transition is from a 5^+ state to a 4^+. To conserve angular momentum, the spin vectors of both the electron and the antineutrino must be aligned with the angular momentum vector of the nucleus. The antineutrino, because it behaves as a right-handed screw, will be ejected predominantly in

---

* The sample is an anisotropic crystal. With the aid of an external magnetic field, electron spins are oriented in the direction of maximum susceptibility while the crystal is in thermal contact with the liquid helium. The heat of orientation is absorbed by the helium. The sample is thereafter isolated from the helium, and the magnetic field is removed. The electrons then again become randomly oriented, and in the process absorb energy from the crystal lattice which thereby is cooled. The magnetic field needed for the parity experiment is applied in the direction of minimum susceptibility. This prevents excessive heating of the crystal again.

the direction of the angular momentum vectors. Because in this type of decay there is a correlation (or rather, an anticorrelation) between the direction of motion of the electron and the antineutrino, the experiment yields the results described above. Note that there is no change in parity of the nuclear state in this allowed transition. The neutrino violates the parity law, and the electron compensates for it.

12–12 NUCLEAR REACTIONS

Much information is gained about the structure of nuclei by studying the radioactive disintegrations discussed in the previous sections. Another method of gaining such information is to study the effect on the nuclei of bombardment by a beam of particles or gamma rays. In Fig. 12–26, a particle or gamma ray is entering a target nucleus, and subsequently the same particle or another particle or gamma ray is leaving the nucleus. The initial condition for a nuclear reaction is usually well defined experimentally; that is, the type of target nucleus and the energy and type of bombarding particles are given. In general, however, there are a number of possible end results of the reaction.

There are many ways of classifying nuclear reactions. The following classification is one that is natural for the experimenter.

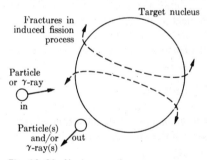

Fractures in induced fission process

Target nucleus

Particle or γ-ray in

Particle(s) and/or γ-ray(s) out

Fig. 12–26 Nuclear reactions.

a) Nuclear-particle reactions and scattering. A nuclear particle in this connection means a nucleon (neutron or proton) or one of the nuclei of light atoms (for example, deuteron, alpha particle, etc.). A beam of charged particles with energy high enough to overcome the electrostatic repulsion of the nucleus can be produced in a positive-ion accelerator (for example, a Van de Graaff generator or a cyclotron). Neutrons are produced in a nuclear reactor or as secondary particles in a nuclear reaction.

In nuclear-particle reactions, a particle in the incident beam may come close enough to one of the nuclei in the target so that it interacts with its nucleons, or it may even penetrate into the target nucleus. The same particle or the same kind of particle may subsequently be expelled from the nucleus. In this case, the process is called *scattering*. If a different kind of particle or more than one particle is emitted from the nucleus, the process is called a *reaction of transmutation*, since the *residual* nucleus has been transmuted into a different nuclear species. Both in a scattering process and in a reaction of transmutation, the residual nucleus may be left in an excited state. Usually, it then decays to the ground state through the emission of one or more gamma rays. Typical examples of nuclear-particle reactions and scattering processes are:

$$\text{Target} + \text{Incident particle} = \text{Residual nucleus} + \text{Emitted particle},$$

$$^{26}\text{Mg} + \quad \text{p} \quad = \quad ^{26}\text{Mg} \quad + \quad \text{p},$$

$$^{26}\text{Mg} + \quad \text{p} \quad = \quad ^{23}\text{Na} \quad + \quad \alpha.$$

The first of these two processes, the $^{26}\text{Mg}(\text{p}, \text{p})^{26}\text{Mg}$ process, for brevity, is an elastic scattering event if ^{26}Mg is left in its ground state, and an inelastic scattering event if it is left in an excited state. The second process, $^{26}\text{Mg}(\text{p}, \alpha)^{23}\text{Na}$ is a reaction of transmutation. Note that in the equations above the total number of protons as well as the total number of neutrons always balances between the two sides.

b) Radiative capture. A low-energy neutron or proton may be captured by a nucleus which thereby is transformed into a residual nucleus in a highly excited state. Instead of expelling the incident particle again (scattering), the residual nucleus may decay to the ground state and rid itself of the binding energy of the particle by the emission of one or more gamma rays. This is called radiative capture. A typical example is

$$^{26}\text{Mg} + \text{p} \rightarrow {}^{27}\text{Al} + \gamma.$$

c) Photodisintegration. In the photodisintegration process, the target nucleus is bombarded by electromagnetic radiation. If the quantum energy is high enough, one or more particles may be liberated. An example is

$$^{27}\text{Al} + \gamma \rightarrow {}^{26}\text{Mg} + \text{p}.$$

Radiative capture and photodisintegration are inverse processes. However, the experimental techniques involved in the study of these two processes are very different.

d) Induced fission. On capturing a particle, a heavy nucleus may undergo a more violent transformation, namely, induced fission, which is virtually a nuclear explosion. The process that is responsible for most of the mass-to-energy transformation in the uranium reactor is

$$^{235}_{92}\text{U} + \text{n (slow)} \rightarrow X + Y + \nu \text{ neutrons.}$$

The target nucleus absorbs a slow neutron and breaks up into two large fragments X and Y (for instance, $^{140}_{54}\text{Xe}$ and $^{93}_{38}\text{Sr}$) and a few neutrons. The free neutrons can be slowed down and, in turn, induce new fission events (chain reaction).

As an example, let us study what possible end products may result from reactions initiated by 6-MeV deuterons on a $_{19}^{39}$K target. In a nuclear reaction of transmutation or scattering process, the number of protons and the number of neutrons are conserved. We therefore make an energy-level diagram containing nuclei and nuclear particles with a total proton number of 20 and a total neutron number of 21. All such systems of interest in this connection are shown in Fig. 12–27. The lowest level in each column represents the sum of the rest energies of the nuclei involved (e.g., ^{39}K and deuteron). A reaction will convert mass to kinetic energy if the resulting level is below that for ^{39}K + d and produce mass from energy if the level is higher. The net gain in kinetic energy (loss in rest energy) is called the *Q-value* of the reaction (compare Section 12–10).

$$Q = \Sigma(Mc^2)_{\text{before}} - \Sigma(Mc^2)_{\text{after}} = \Sigma E_{k\text{after}} - \Sigma E_{k\text{before}} \qquad (12\text{–}50)$$

The total energy in the center-of-mass system equals the sum of the rest energies of ^{39}K and ^{2}H plus the 6-MeV kinetic energy reduced from laboratory to center-of-mass coordinates, as follows (nonrelativistic):

CM velocity, $\quad V = \dfrac{mv}{m + M}$,

KE in CM, $\quad E_{k\text{CM}} = \frac{1}{2}m(v - V)^2 + \frac{1}{2}MV^2 = \dfrac{E_{k\text{lab}}}{1 + m/M}$,

where m is the mass of the incident particle, the deuteron, and M is the mass of the target nucleus, ^{39}K. With $m = 2$, $M = 39$, and $E_{k\text{lab}} = 6.00$ MeV, we get $E_{k\text{CM}} = 5.71$ MeV.

In Fig. 12–27, the top dashed horizontal line at 20.18 MeV above the ground state of ^{41}Ca represents the total energy of the system. The following reactions are all seen to be energetically possible (with one exception):

^{39}K(d, d)^{39}K   elastic scattering or inelastic scattering, leaving ^{39}K in any state below 5.71-MeV excitation

^{39}K(d, γ)^{41}Ca   deuteron capture at an excitation energy of $E_x = 20.18$ MeV in ^{41}Ca with gamma-ray cascades to the ground state

^{39}K(d, p)^{40}K   leaving ^{40}K in any state below 11.28-MeV excitation

^{39}K(d, n)^{40}Ca   leaving ^{40}Ca in any state below 11.82-MeV excitation

^{39}K(d, α)^{37}Ar   leaving ^{37}Ar in any state below 13.57-MeV excitation

^{39}K(d, ^{3}He)^{38}Ar   leaving ^{38}Ar in any state below 4.83-MeV excitation

^{39}K(d, np)^{39}K   leaving ^{39}K in any state below 3.48-MeV excitation

^{39}K(d, t)^{38}K   not energetically possible at 6-MeV bombarding energy

When a residual nucleus is formed in the ground state, the available energy $Q_{\text{gnd}} + E_{k\text{CM}}$ is given off as kinetic energy of the reaction products (in the

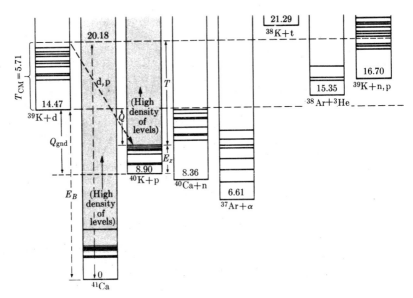

Fig. 12–27 Energy diagram of nucleus plus particle systems with 20 protons and 21 neutrons.

center-of-mass system). When the residual nucleus is formed in an excited state, this energy is shared between the internal excitation E_x and the kinetic energy of the reaction products [see example indicated for the (d, p) transition in Fig. 12–27]. It is clear then that measurements of the type and energy of the emitted particle uniquely determine the energy level of the residual nucleus formed. The emitted particles are usually analyzed by the aid of a magnetic spectrograph or with a semiconductor particle detector.

Nuclear-reaction studies of this kind have produced a wealth of data on energy levels of stable and unstable nuclides. In addition to the excitation energies, these data include in many cases angular momentas and parities, as well as more detailed information about the wave functions of the outermost ("valence") nucleons. We cannot take space for a more detailed discussion of nuclear reactions in this book.

12–13 FISSION

O. Hahn and F. Strassemann discovered in 1939 that alkaline earth metals are produced when uranium is irradiated with neutrons.* Lise Meitner and O. R. Frisch† suggested that by absorption of a neutron, the uranium nucleus

---

*   O. Hahn and F. Strassemann, *Die Naturwissenschaften* **27** (1939), p. 11.

†   Lise Meitner and O. R. Frisch, *Nature* **143** (1939), p. 239.

becomes sufficiently excited to split into two fragments of approximately equal mass. That such a process is energetically possible can easily be seen from a study of atomic masses or binding energies. In Fig. 12–28 the average binding energy per particle in beta-stable nuclei is plotted as a function of the mass number A. In the intermediate mass range ($A \approx 120$), the binding energy per particle is approximately 8.5 MeV; in the uranium region, however, it is only 7.6 MeV. If a heavy nucleus is split into two fragments, the increased binding energy per particle will be released in the form of kinetic energy of the fragments and in the form of various other types of radiation. The total energy released in a fission process should, in accordance with these considerations, be approximately

$$240(8.5 - 7.6) = 220 \text{ MeV.}$$

Since heavier nuclei are richer in neutrons, relatively speaking, than are intermediate-mass nuclei, two to three neutrons are released in each fission process. This costs energy, and after allowing for this, we find that about 200 MeV is released. Table 12–7 shows how this energy is distributed between the various types of radiation.

Shortly after the discovery by Hahn and Strassemann, Bohr and Wheeler[*] worked out a theory of the fission process. They essentially saw the fission

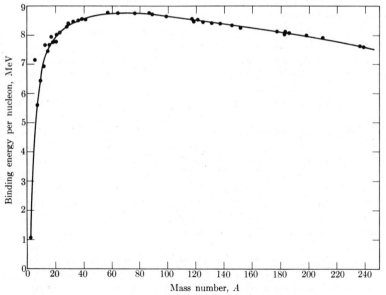

Fig. 12–28 Binding energy per nucleon versus nucleon number A in beta-stable nuclei.

---

[*] N. Bohr and J. A. Wheeler, *Phys. Rev.* **56** (1939), p. 426.

process as a tug-of-war between the Coulomb repulsion among the nucleons (protons) and the surface tension of the nucleus. For a spherical nucleus, the sum of the surface energy and the Coulomb energy is

$$E = 4\pi R^2 s + \tfrac{3}{5}(Ze)^2/4\pi\varepsilon_0 R, \tag{12–51}$$

Table 12–7 Distribution of fission energy

	MeV
Kinetic energy of fission fragments	165 ± 5
Instantaneous gamma-ray energy	7 ± 1
Kinetic energy of fission neutrons	5 ± 0.5
Beta particles from fission products	7 ± 1
Gamma rays from fission products	6 ± 1
Neutrinos from fission products	10
Total energy per fission	200 ± 6

where s is the surface tension, that is, the surface energy per unit area, and R is the nuclear radius. If the nucleus is deformed, as indicated in Fig. 12–29(b), the surface energy will increase, but the Coulomb energy will decrease because the repulsive charges are moved farther apart. Whether the sum of the two terms will increase or decrease depends on the value of Z^2/R^3 or Z^2/A.

The surface tension s can be found from a study of the systematics of nuclear masses. Bohr and Wheeler found that for $Z^2/A > 47.8$, the sum of the surface and Coulomb energy decreases by distorting the nucleus. There are therefore no forces that can stop such a nucleus from becoming more and more distorted, and the final result is that it splits into two or more fragments while releasing approximately 200 MeV, as calculated above. When $Z^2/A <$ 47.8, distortion causes a change in surface energy that is larger than the change in Coulomb energy. The nucleus therefore resists distortion. This resistance, however, must have the character of a barrier only, since the total separation of two fragments leads to a state with lower rest energy. The curve in Fig. 12–29 indicates schematically the total potential energy as a function of the distance between the centers of the two fragments. Except for details, this curve is very similar to the curve showing the potential energy of an alpha particle as a function of its separation from the daughter nucleus in alpha decay. In analogy with alpha decay, the fission process can proceed by barrier penetration when $Z^2/A < 47.8$. However, because of the large masses of the fission fragments, the height of the barrier must be much smaller than for alpha decay in order to produce observable decay rates. The process described is called *spontaneous fission*, and the height of the barrier is called the *activation energy* (E_A in Fig. 12–29).

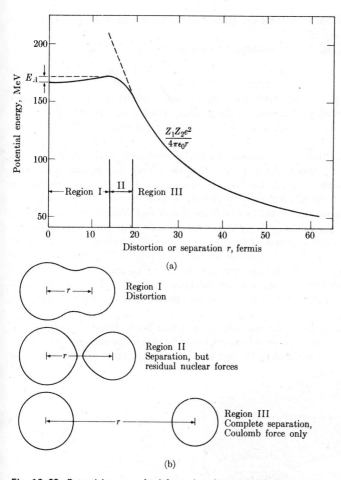

Fig. 12–29 Potential energy of a deformed nucleus and of fission fragments versus separation or distortion.

For ^{236}U the activation energy is only 6.4 MeV. This happens to be approximately the binding energy for the last neutron in ^{236}U, so that when this nucleus is formed by slow neutron capture in ^{235}U, it is formed in an excited state at about 6.4 MeV. From this excited state, it can then decay to the ground state by gamma emission, or it can decay by fission. Experimentally, it has been shown that in about 85% of the cases, it does decay by fission. The fission lifetime is so short that other processes, such as alpha and beta decay from the excited state, that are energetically possible cannot compete to any significant degree.

The fission reaction initiated by slow neutrons on ^{235}U is

$$^{235}\text{U} + \underset{\text{(slow)}}{n} \rightarrow {}^{236}\text{U} \rightarrow X + Y + \underset{\text{(fast)}}{vn} \ , \qquad (12\text{--}52)$$

where X and Y stand for two intermediate-mass nuclei and v is the average number of neutrons released in each process. For the reaction of Eq. (12–52), the number is $v = 2.47$, and for the corresponding reaction on ^{239}Pu, it is $v = 2.91$.

It is clear that, for a chain reaction to be sustained, we must have $v > 1$, such that the neutrons from one event on the average can initiate more than one new event. Indeed, because of competition with gamma emission, as mentioned above, and leakage of neutrons, we must have $v > 1.2$, at least.

In a nuclear reactor the fast neutrons are slowed down by elastic collision in a *moderator* (carbon or heavy water) to thermal energy and then reabsorbed by the fissionable material. Figure 12–30 shows the arrangement in a natural uranium reactor. Natural uranium has only 0.72 percent ^{235}U and the balance is ^{238}U. When slow neutrons are absorbed in ^{238}U, they lead to ^{239}U plus gammas and are therefore lost for the chain reaction. However, the cross section is less than a barn (10^{-24}cm^2), compared to 582 barns for the reaction Eq. (12–52).

The rate at which the reactions go and heat is developed is controlled by introducing neutron-absorbing material into the core of the reactor (Fig. 12–30). This control is simplified by the fact that a small percentage of the neutrons is

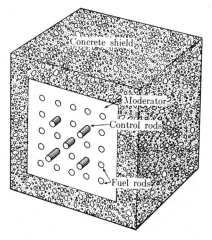

Fig. 12–30 Cross section of a natural uranium reactor showing the fuel rods, control rods, moderator, and concrete shielding.

delayed in emission. Hence the buildup time for heat production is slow enough for mechanical adjustments of the control rods.

As mentioned in Section 12–6, a neutron unstable nuclide decays within about 10^{-20} s, so the delayed neutrons must have another explanation. The process is one in which a fission product is β unstable, and the *daughter* product is neutron unstable. Hence the delay time is caused by the slow β-decay process.

Practically all the energy released in a fission process (Table 12–7) is converted into heat in the core (not the neutrino energy). For the energy to be utilized, it has to be transported to a heat engine via a coolant.

12–14 FUSION; THERMONUCLEAR ENERGY

It is clear from a glance at Fig. 12–28 that energy can also be gained by building up an intermediate-mass nuclide from lighter ones. The nuclei of the iron group are most tightly bound, but even heavier elements can be formed in exoergic reactions by successive absorption of very light particles, e.g., nucleons. In the two main cosmological theories currently being discussed, all elements are assumed to be formed or to have been formed by successive fusion of nucleons to heavier nuclei with release of energy.

According to the original *Big Bang* theory of George Gamow, the universe was at one time an extremely densely packed assembly of neutrons, so densely packed that the neutrons were stable, which, of course, the free neutron is not. In Gamow's view, the universe was formed in a gigantic explosion, in which the elements were formed by consecutive absorptions of neutrons, interspersed with beta decays toward the line of highest beta stability in the Chart of the Nuclides. This explosion could, in Gamow's view, have been preceded by an implosion.

Another main cosmological theory describes the universe as existing in a *steady state*, in which matter is continuously created in interstellar space.* To conserve energy, it is assumed that the rest energy and kinetic energy of the particles created are equal in magnitude to their negative gravitational energy in the universe. According to this theory, the rate at which mass is produced is exactly equal and opposite to the rate at which it is diluted by the observed expansion of the universe. One difficulty with this theory is that according to present views, matter cannot be created without simultaneous creation of antimatter. It is, of course, quite possible that half of the universe consists of matter and the other half of antimatter, but it is difficult to understand the mechanism of separation of the two factions. Also, certain recent observations, demonstrating that the gamma-ray intensity in interstellar space is extremely low, seem to indicate that the requisite mixture of matter and antimatter is not present.

---

* See, for instance, F. Hoyle, *Frontiers of Astronomy,* New York: Harper & Brothers, (1955), p. 320.

Other recent observations concerning the rate of expansion of the universe and the acceleration of this rate point toward modifications of the steady-state theory in the direction of a pulsating universe. Maybe the truth lies somewhere between the two extreme views, the Big Bang and the Steady State.

In the theory of Hoyle *et al.*, the creation of stars and the synthesis of elements start from the extremely thin hydrogen gas that is known to exist in interstellar space. The manner in which this hydrogen gas is originally created is actually irrelevant to the discussion of the theory of synthesis, which is based on careful measurements and calculations.* Because of statistical fluctuations in the density of the gas, it condenses into clusters under the influence of gravitational forces. Once a cluster is formed, it will grow in mass, extracting more and more hydrogen from the surroundings. As the cluster grows heavier and contracts more and more, the temperature inside rises because of conversion of the gravitational potential energy into kinetic energy. Eventually, it becomes hot enough for the nuclear burning process to start. This sets in at a temperature of about 10^7 degrees ($\frac{3}{2}kT \approx 1.3$ keV) at which temperature the penetration of Coulomb barriers is not completely negligible. Two protons combine to a mass 2 nucleus, and since ^{2}He is not stable, the only process that must be considered is

$$^1\text{H} + {}^1\text{H} \rightarrow {}^2\text{H} + e^+ + v + 0.42 \text{ MeV}. \tag{12–53}$$

The positron annihilates with an electron thereby releasing an additional energy of 1.02 MeV.

The burning of light hydrogen (Eq. 12–53) goes by way of the weak interaction and is therefore a very slow process. The cross section is so small that the process has not been observed in the laboratory even at higher bombarding energies, but the reaction rate in a hydrogen gas of given temperature and density can be calculated accurately and it agrees with astronomical observations. Once heavy hydrogen is formed, the synthesis of the heavier nuclides can go by way of the strong interaction with relatively large cross sections. For instance, ^{3}He can be formed through the reaction

$$^2\text{H}(p, \gamma)^3\text{He}, \qquad Q = 5.49 \text{ MeV} \tag{12–54}$$

and two ^{3}He atoms can combine to form ^{4}He and two protons through the following process:

$$^3\text{He}(^3\text{He, pp})^4\text{He}, \qquad Q = 12.86 \text{ MeV}. \tag{12–55}$$

This shows one possible chain of events that can lead to the fusion of hydrogen atoms into helium with the release of a considerable amount of energy.

---

* E. M. Burbidge, G. R. Burbidge, W. A. Fowler, and F. Hoyle, *Revs. Mod. Phys.* **29** (1957), p. 547.

In the continued synthesis of the elements beyond ^{4}He, a difficulty arises in that no stable elements with mass 5 or 8 exist. However, two alpha particles can combine to ^{8}Be, which stays together for approximately 10^{-15} s. In a sufficiently high density of helium, this will result in an adequately high concentration of ^{8}Be so that by combination with a third alpha particle, the nucleus ^{12}C is formed. As shown by Cook et al.,* the reaction has a resonance which strongly enhances the production rate of ^{12}C in a helium gas of 10^8 °K.

The production of free neutrons can take place through the following chain of events

$$^{12}\text{C}(p, \gamma)^{13}\text{N}, \qquad Q = 1.94 \text{ MeV};$$
$$^{13}\text{N}(\beta^+)^{13}\text{C}, \qquad Q = 1.20 \text{ MeV plus } 1.02 \text{ MeV}; \qquad (12\text{–}56)$$
$$^{13}\text{C}(\alpha, n)^{16}\text{O}, \qquad Q = 2.21 \text{ MeV}.$$

The existence of free neutrons is necessary to explain the synthesis of the neutron-rich isotopes of the heavier elements in Hoyle's theory.

Once carbon has been formed, the burning of four protons to form ^{4}He can go through a sequence of reactions in which carbon and nitrogen serve as catalysts. The main branch of this cycle starts with the first two reactions in Eq. (12–56) and continues with the reactions

$$^{13}\text{C}(p, \gamma)^{14}\text{N}, \qquad Q = 7.55 \text{ MeV};$$
$$^{14}\text{N}(p, \gamma)^{15}\text{O}, \qquad Q = 7.29 \text{ MeV};$$
$$^{15}\text{O}(\beta^+)^{15}\text{N}, \qquad Q = 1.74 \text{ MeV plus } 1.02 \text{ MeV};$$
$$^{15}\text{N}(p, \alpha)^{12}\text{C}, \qquad Q = 4.96 \text{ MeV}.$$

The total energy released in the process is about 26.73 MeV, of which about 6% is lost from the star by the neutrinos emitted in the two beta decays.

Although the sequences of events that we have described in this section appear to be the main sources of stellar energy, the complete picture of stellar evolution and synthesis of elements is much more complex than we can describe here. In the stars, the burning of hydrogen and of helium takes place at a noncatastrophic rate which is determined by the density and temperature of the gas and of the cross sections or lifetimes of the reactions involved. The gas is contained because of the action of the gravitational force. In the fusion bomb, the temperature needed for the reaction to start is attained by using a fission bomb as a trigger. The containing forces are inertial forces of the reacting gases themselves, as well as of the mantle containing the gases. Since the total process takes only about a microsecond, inertial containment is possible.

* C. W. Cook, W. A. Fowler, C. C. Lauritsen, and T. Lauritsen, *Phys. Rev.* **107** (1957), 508.

On a very large scale, it is possible to use the catastrophic process in a semicontrolled manner, and this possibility has been seriously looked into. A large canyon could be lined with concrete and fitted with a concrete roof so as to produce a giant steam boiler. Once every hour or so, a hydrogen bomb could be detonated inside the boiler so as to produce enough steam for an hour's consumption. This may be a last-resort scheme for the peaceful use of fusion energy; it obviously would be much more attractive if the gas in which the fusion reaction takes place could be contained in a controlled manner at the high temperatures involved. It appears to be a fair possibility that this can be accomplished by use of the focusing action on ions by magnetic fields.

The most attractive reactions for use in a thermonuclear fusion reactor appear to be the D-D reaction

$$^2\text{H}(d, n)^3\text{He}, \qquad Q = 3.27 \text{ MeV},$$
$$^2\text{H}(d, p)^3\text{H}, \qquad Q = 4.03 \text{ MeV},$$

and the D-T reaction

$$^3\text{H}(d, n)^4\text{He}, \qquad Q = 17.59 \text{ MeV}.$$

At the very high temperatures considered, these gases are completely dissociated into interpenetrating gases of nuclei and electrons, called a *plasma*. The plasma is electrically neutral so that in the absence of electric or magnetic fields, there are no external forces acting on it except gravity, which is negligible on the laboratory scale. Because of the internal pressure, the plasma would expand in a vacuum to fill the container in which it is kept. When it comes in contact with the walls, it cools off and in the process, of course, heats up the walls. The problems to be solved are therefore: First, how to bring a plasma up to sufficient temperature and density; and second, how to contain this plasma for a sufficiently long time to produce a net energy gain. The first problem can be solved in various ways. The second appears to be more difficult. Various schemes for containing the plasmas in magnetic fields are being tried in fusion laboratories around the world. Hot plasmas of high enough concentration can be produced. The principal difficulty to date has been that instabilities have kept the containment time of the plasma below the critical value.

12–15 ELEMENTARY PARTICLES

One of the most exciting areas of research in physics and chemistry has always been the study of how matter can be subdivided into smaller and smaller particles. The existence of atoms and molecules was firmly established in the nineteenth century, and the first particle that still is classified as an elementary particle was discovered by J. J. Thomson in 1897. Early in the twentieth century, the experiments and ideas of Rutherford, Bohr, and others put the nuclear atom on a rather firm basis. The early experiments on radioactivity by the Curies and by Rutherford indicated that the nucleus could be subdivided.

The first nuclear reaction, studied by Rutherford in 1919, supported this view, and the discovery of the neutron by Chadwick in 1932, ended the discussion concerning the kind of particles the nucleus contains.

In the 1930's, the picture of the world appeared quite satisfactory to the physicists. Matter could be built up of a limited number of different species of atoms, and each atom consisted of a nucleus with a cloud of electrons around it. The nucleus consisted of protons and neutrons held together by a strong force that needed further investigation but which did not necessarily need to be very complex in nature. One apparently superfluous particle, the neutrino, had already started to cast its shadow over this idyllic picture—but there was more to come!

Many discoveries of new so-called "elementary" particles have been made through the studies of cosmic rays. This is the penetrating radiation which mostly originates outside our solar system, but which changes character through interactions in the earth's atmosphere. In later years, however, most of the discoveries and all of the detailed studies of these particles have been made by the use of radiations produced in man-made machines.

We shall here present some of the most important information so far obtained about the elementary particles and their excited states and to point out some of the systematics of this information. No basic theoretical interpretation of these data exists to date, although relatively simple mathematical laws have been found, which on occasion have predicted correctly the exact properties of new particles.

In classifying the various particles, several discrete quantum numbers are used. First, we have the intrinsic spin and parity J^π, as well as the isospin T, which is used extensively also in nuclear-structure physics and discussed briefly below. Second, some completely new quantum numbers have made their appearance in elementary-particle research. Best known is the strangeness quantum number S, which was introduced to resolve the puzzle of anomalously long lifetimes of certain excited states of the nucleons. These long-lived or metastable states, called *hyperons*, their production, and decay are discussed briefly below.

The positron and the electron are said to be antiparticles. They have the same mass and the same spin but opposite charge, and they annihilate each other with the emission of photons when they come in contact with each other. The existence of an antiparticle for the electron was actually predicted by Dirac because of a symmetry of the equations of the relativistic quantum theory of the electron. It has been found that this symmetry of matter persists throughout the list of particles; for instance, the proton has an antiparticle the negative proton, which was found in 1955 by Chamberlain *et al.**

---

* O. Chamberlain, E. Segrè, C. Weigand, and T. Ypsilantis, *Phys. Rev.* **100** (1955), p. 947.

Table 12–8, from a paper by Barbaro-Galtieri *et al.*,* gives the most important physical properties of the elementary particles or long-lived particles, as known today. The table has been somewhat abbreviated, and all error limits have been left out to keep it short. In column 1 the particles are classified as photons, leptons, mesons, and baryons. The term *baryon* is used for the nucleons and higher excited states that decay to nucleons by emission of mesons. Only the long-lived or metastable states of the baryons are listed in Table 12–8.

Column 2 gives the symbol of the particle, in accordance with presently accepted, but rapidly changing, convention. Note that two pairs of neutrinos are listed: the electron neutrinos and the muon neutrinos. One class is associated with normal beta decay; the other class (also called neutretto), with decay of the muon. Column 3 gives the isospin T. This is a measure of the symmetry of a nuclear or particle wave function, and its "projection" T_3 is a measure of the charge. In nuclear-structure physics, the definition for T_3 is

$$T_3 \equiv \tfrac{1}{2}(Z - N) = Z - A/2. \tag{12-57}$$

For strange elementary particles, this definition is slightly modified (see below). The isospin is treated formally in the same way as an angular momentum, but we cannot go into details of this theory. For the present, it suffices to say that, when a particle has isospin T, there are altogether $2T + 1$ different substates, with different T_3 and therefore different charge, but otherwise with nearly identical properties. The "nearly" refers to the fact that the energy of the particle or state is slightly dependent upon the charge. The neutron and the proton are two different substates of the nucleon, one with $T_3 = \tfrac{1}{2}$ (Eq. 12–57), the other with $T_3 = -\tfrac{1}{2}$. Since no particles with $T_3 = \tfrac{3}{2}$ or $-\tfrac{3}{2}$ have been observed with nucleon mass, it is concluded that the nucleon isospin is $T = \tfrac{1}{2}$. For leptons, the isospin T cannot be defined, nor can the parity.

Column 4 in Table 12–8 gives the ordinary spin and parity J^π whenever observable and observed. For mesons, a new type of parity, *G-parity*, can be defined, but we are not going into a discussion of that rather intricate concept here. Column 5 gives the strangeness quantum number, which is discussed briefly below. This quantum number again cannot be defined for leptons.

The mass, or the rest energy, of the particles in Table 12–8 is given in MeV, and the mean lives are given in seconds. The particles in this table have been called long-lived particles because their mean lives are extremely long compared with a unit appropriate for decay by the strong (nuclear) interaction

$$\tau_0 = \hbar/m_\pi c^2 = 4.7153 \times 10^{-24} \text{ s}.$$

This is approximately the lifetime of a virtual pion produced in nuclear encounters (see Section 12–4).

---

* A. Barbaro-Galtieri, S. E. Derenzo, L. R. Price, A. Rittenberg, A. H. Rosenfeld, N. Barash-Schmidt, C. Bricman, M. Roos, P. Söding, and C. G. Wohl, *Revs. Modern Phys.* **42** (1970) p. 87.

Most of the baryon resonance states discussed below have lifetimes that are of the order of magnitude unity on this scale. The particles or states listed in Table 12–8 are all stable against decay by the strong interaction because of the operation of selection rules. The last column of the table gives the common decay modes for the unstable particles, the relative rate of occurrence, and the energy released in the various modes.

Figure 12–31 is an energy-level diagram for baryons in which the lowest lying resonance states are shown as well as all metastable states. A similar

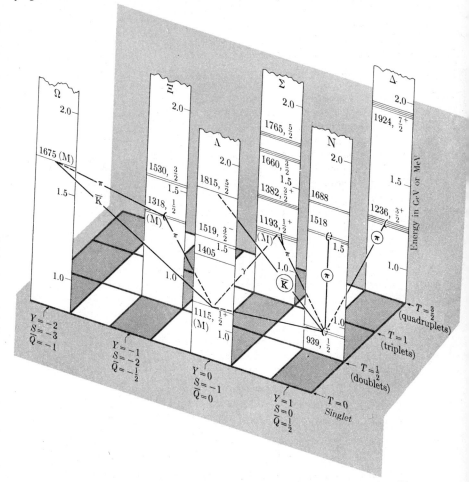

Fig. 12–31 Baryon states ($A = 1$) plotted versus isospin and hypercharge. Only selected decays are indicated, and strong decays are encircled. The symbol (M) stands for metastable. (Data from Barbaro-Galtieri *et al., loc. cit.*)

Table 12–8 Elementary (long-lived) particles*

Class	Symbol and charge	T	J^π	S	Mass MeV	Mean life, s	Principal decays Partial mode	Fraction	Q, MeV
Photon	γ		1		$0(<2\times10^{-21})$	Stable	Stable		
Leptons	ν^e		1/2		$0(<6\times10^{-3})$	Stable	Stable		
	ν_μ				$0(<1.6)$				
	$e^\mp$		1/2		0.511006	Stable	Stable		
	$\mu^\mp$		1/2		105.659	2.1983×10^{-6}	$e\nu\bar\nu$	100%	105.15
	$\pi^\pm$	1	0^-	0	139.578	2.603×10^{-8}	$\mu\nu$	$\approx100\%$	33.92
							$e\nu$	1.24×10^{-4}	139.07
							$\mu\nu\gamma$	1.24×10^{-4}	33.92
							$\pi^0 e\nu$	1.02×10^{-8}	4.09
	π^0			0	134.975	0.89×10^{-16}	$\gamma\gamma$	98.83%	134.97
							γe^+e^-	1.17%	133.95
	$K^\pm$	1/2	0^-	$\pm$	493.82	1.235×10^{-8}	$\mu\nu$	63.77%	388.1
							$\pi^\pm\pi^0$	20.93%	219.2
							$\pi^\pm\pi^-\pi^+$	5.57%	75.0
							and others		
Mesons	K^0			1	497.76	50% K_1, 50% K_2			
	K_1			±1		0.862×10^{-10}	$\pi^+\pi^-$	68.7%	218.6
							$\pi^0\pi^0$	31.3%	227.8
	K_2			±1		5.38×10^{-8}	$\pi^0\pi^0\pi^0$	21.5%	92.8
							$\pi^+\pi^-\pi^0$	12.6%	83.6
							$\pi\mu\nu$	26.8%	252.5
							$\pi e\nu$	38.8%	357.7
							and others		

	I	J^P	S	Mass	Mean life	Decay mode	Fraction	
η	0	0^-	0	548.8	$>10^{-22}$	$\gamma\gamma$	38.2%	548.8
						$3\pi^0$ or $\pi^0\,2\gamma$	33.4%	143.7
						$\pi^+\pi^-\pi^0$	23.0%	134.5
						$\pi^+\pi^-\gamma$	5.4%	269.5

Baryons

	I	J^P	S	Mass	Mean life	Decay mode	Fraction	
p	1/2	$1/2^+$	0	938.256	Stable			
n			0	939.550	0.932×10^3	$pe^-\nu$	100%	0.78
Λ	0	$1/2^+$	-1	1115.60	2.51×10^{-10}	$p\pi^-$	65.3%	37.8
						$n\pi^0$	34.7%	41.1
						and others		
Σ^+	1	$1/2^+$	-1	1189.40	0.802×10^{-10}	$p\pi^0$	51.7%	116.17
						$n\pi^+$	48.3%	110.27
						and others		
Σ^0			-1	1192.46	$<1.0 \times 10^{-14}$	$\Lambda\gamma$	100%	76.9
Σ^-			-1	1197.32	1.49×10^{-10}	$n\pi^-$	$\approx$100%	117.79
						and others		
Ξ^0	1/2	$1/2^+$	-2	1314.7	3.03×10^{-10}	$\Lambda\pi^0$	$\approx$100%	63.9
						and others		
Ξ^-			-2	1321.25	1.66×10^{-10}	$\Lambda\pi^-$	$\approx$100%	64.1
						$\Lambda e^-\nu$	0.67×10^{-3}	205.1
						and others		
Ω^-	0	$3/2^+$	-3	1672.5	1.3×10^{-10}	$\Xi\pi$	?	228
						ΛK	?	63

* Reprinted in abbreviated form from A. Barbaro-Galtieri, S. E. Derenzo, L. R. Price, A. Rittenberg, A. H. Rosenfeld, N. Barash-Schmidt, C. Bricman, M. Roos, P. Söding and C. G. Wohl, *Revs. Modern Phys.*, **42** (1970), p. 87.

diagram can be drawn for the antiparticles. The information for this figure is taken from the paper by Barbaro-Galtieri *et al.** and the system of labeling follows a proposal by Chew *et al.*† The states are ordered in a three-dimensional coordinate system according to strangeness from $S = 0$ to -3, isospin from $T = 0$ to $\frac{3}{2}$, and energy mc^2 from 939 MeV and up. Each set of states with identical S and T is given a symbol which is an upper-case Greek letter, except for the nucleons (N) and the other states with $S = 0$ and $T = \frac{1}{2}$. The energy splitting of the various states into $2T + 1$ substates with different isospin projection (charge) is somewhat exaggerated.

For particles with strangeness different from 0, Eq. (12–57) has to be modified (extended) to agree with observations. We now write, replacing Z with Q,

$$Q = T_3 + A/2 + S/2 = T_3 + Y/2, \tag{12–58}$$

where we have introduced another quantum number, the *hypercharge Y*, which replaces S. Since, for any charge multiplet, the average of T_3 is zero, we see that the average charge of a multiplet is

$$\bar{Q} = Y/2. \tag{12–59}$$

Each state of the baryon system has a corresponding antibaryon state with opposite baryon number A, hypercharge Y, isospin projection T_3, and charge Q. In some cases these antistates have been observed; however, more energy is required to produce them than to produce the baryon states.

All the baryon states can be regarded as excited states of the nucleon. In atomic and nuclear physics, excited states may decay by emission of an electromagnetic field quantum, a photon. In the case of a baryon excited state a pion (π), kaon (K), or in some cases a photon is emitted. Since the pion and the kaon both have nonzero rest energies, a minimum energy difference is required for such decays.

The particles or states not in the two right-hand columns in Fig. 12–31 are produced in nucleon-nucleon collisions, but never alone (associated production). This fact, as well as the long life-times of the hyperons, led to the idea of the new quantum number, the *strangeness*, S. Strangeness and parity are conserved in reactions involving the strong (nuclear) interaction, but not in reactions involving the weak interaction. For instance, one particle with $S = 2$ and another with $S = -2$ can be produced simultaneously in a nucleon-nucleon collision. Strangeness is then conserved. The hyperons or metastable states marked (M) in Fig. 12–31 cannot reach a lower state without violating

---

* A. Barbaro- Galtieri, *et al., loc. cit.*

† G. F. Chew, M. Gell-Mann, and A. H. Rosenfeld, *Scientific American*, February (1964), p. 74.

strangeness. For instance, $\Sigma 1193$ cannot decay to the nucleon by kaon emission ($\Delta S = \pm 1$), because there is not enough energy available. It can decay by pion emission ($\Delta S = \pm 0$), but this violates strangeness, so it proceeds via the relatively slow weak interaction (like beta decay).

We cannot finish this section on elementary particles without mentioning the newest theory, or call it speculations, about the internal structure of these particles. First, it should be pointed out that the force between the baryons (e.g., nucleons) with all its complexities is similar in many respects to the forces that are binding the atoms together to molecules. We have seen that, in the case of molecular forces, the complexity is a result of the complex internal dynamics of the interacting particles, the atoms. Could it be that our "elementary" particles are atom-like, that is, consist of super-elementary particles?

In 1964, Gell-Mann* pointed out that the known properties of the baryon and meson states could be accounted for by compounding them from three particles called *quarks*, and their antiparticles. Figure 12–32(a) shows some important properties of the three hypothetical quarks, labeled p, n, and λ, meaning proton-like, neutron-like, and lambda-like, and their antiparticles. The quarks are supposed to have spin $\frac{1}{2}$, which is not unusual, but charge $+2e/3$, $-e/3$, and $-e/3$, respectively, which is highly unusual if it proves to be correct.

Figure 12–32(b) shows how three quarks can be combined in different ways to form the lowest of the multiplets shown in the six columns of Fig. 12–31. The higher energy states can also be constructed with the quark scheme, and even decay rates can be predicted with fair precision.*

The baryons cannot decay further down in rest mass than to the lowest baryon state, the proton. This experimental fact is recognized by an *ad hoc* law, the *law of conservation of baryon number*. In the quark scheme, we must assume that this law reflects a law of conservation of quark number. Mesons, on the other hand, are "quanta" that are created and absorbed in baryon transitions. They are presumed to be constructed of quark-antiquark pairs which supposedly can be created and annihilated. Figure 12–33 shows how the most important mesons are constructed of such pairs. The ρ mesons, which are excited states of the pions are constructed simply by flipping the spin of one of the quarks in the pion.

As of this moment, no conclusive experimental evidence for the existence of quarks has been unveiled. The next generation of high-energy accelerators about to come into operation could change this state of affairs abruptly.

---

* M. Gell-Mann, Phys. Lett. **8** (1964), p. 274.

* See, for instance, R. Van Royen and V. F. Weisskopf, *Nuovo Cimento*, Ser. X. **50** (1967), p. 617.

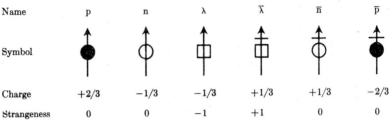

Name	p	n	λ	$\bar{\lambda}$	$\bar{n}$	$\bar{p}$
Symbol						
Charge	+2/3	−1/3	−1/3	+1/3	+1/3	−2/3
Strangeness	0	0	−1	+1	0	0

Fig. 12–32a Three quarks, and their antiparticles (right), have been proposed as the hypothetical building blocks of baryons and mesons. Unlike all particles discovered so far, quarks would carry less than a whole unit of the charge of the electron. The lambda (λ) quark is provided with a negative unit of strangeness. Each quark and antiquark carries half a unit of spin, the direction of which is shown by an arrow. As in the world of known particles, the hypothetical antiquarks mirror the properties of the quarks.

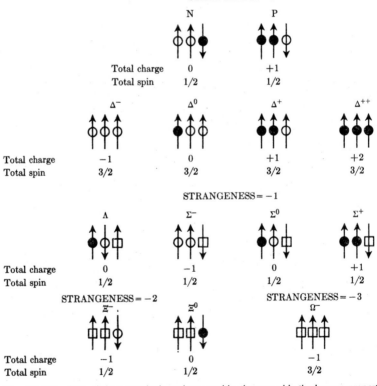

Fig. 12–32b Sets of three quarks in various combinations provide the known properties of baryons. When two spin arrows point in opposite directions, they cancel, thus the net spin of most of the baryons is $\frac{1}{2}$. When all three arrows point the same way, the spin is $\frac{3}{2}$.

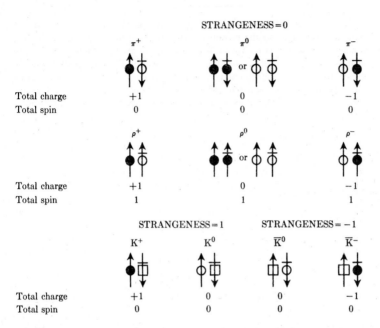

Fig. 12-33 A quark and an antiquark account for the observed properties of the principal mesons. Pi (π) and rho (ρ) mesons have strangeness equal to zero, hence do not include a lambda quark. In the kaon sets, normal lambda quarks produce a strangeness of -1 for the K^0 and K^- pair and antilambda quarks produce a strangeness of $+1$ for K^0 and K^+.

Figures 12-32 and 12-33 are from "The Three Spectroscopies" by V. F. Weisskopf.

PROBLEMS

12-1 Using Eq. (12-1), calculate the approximate density in $kg\,cm^{-3}$ and metric ton $\cdot\, mm^{-3}$ of nuclear matter (1 metric ton = 1000 kg).

12-2 Find the energy difference in joules between the two possible states of a proton in a magnetic field of $B = 1\, Wb \cdot m^{-2}$. What is the frequency of a photon that has the energy required to cause a transition between these two states (spin flip)?

12-3 Calculate the electric quadrupole moment (Eq. 12-4) of a charge of magnitude Ze distributed over a ring of radius R and with axis along a) the z-axis, b) the x-axis.

12-4 If, in the treatment of the deuteron problem we omit the repulsive core ($c = 0$), the boundary condition at the origin becomes $u = 0$ at $r = 0$. Why?

12-5 Assume that a central potential with an r-dependence, as given in Fig. 12–34, binds the neutron and the proton together to form the deuteron. Solve the radial $l = 0$ wave equation for the three regions. (Use a hyperbolic sine function in region I, a sine function with phase shift in region II, and an exponential in region III.) Apply the boundary conditions at $r = 0$ and $r = \infty$ and match the wave functions at the two other boundaries to obtain two equations between c and b, relevant wave numbers, and the phase angle for the wave function in region II.

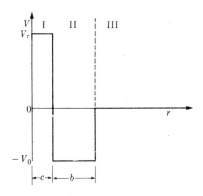

Figure 12–34

12-6 A spinless particle of mass m is bound to an infinitely heavy "sticky" sphere. The potential is as shown in Fig. 12–35. The well is very deep and narrow ($b \to 0$). Find an expression for the well depth V_0 needed to bind the particle in a state with orbital angular momentum l. Take $E_B \approx 0$.

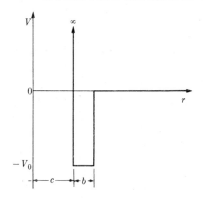

Figure 12–35

12-7 In a nucleon-nucleon scattering event, as viewed in the *CM* system, the two particles travel initially along a parallel line separated by a distance d (the impact parameter). The total kinetic energy in the *CM* system is 10 MeV. Calculate the value of d in fermis needed to give the system, classically, an angular momentum of $[l(l + 1)]^{1/2}\hbar$, with $l = 1, 2$, and 3. Compare these values of d with the range of nuclear forces.

12-8 Show that Eq. (12-25) is a solution of Eq. (12-23). For spherically symmetric solutions ∇^2 is given in Problem 7-7.

12-9 A neutron is bound in the lowest possible state ($l = 0$) to a heavy nucleus. The binding energy is $E_B = 16$ MeV ($E = -16$ MeV). The potential acting on the neutron is a square well with depth $V_0 = 32$ MeV and radius r_0 unknown. a) Solve the radial wave equation for $l = 0$ inside and outside the well, and sketch the wave function u. b) Apply boundary conditions at $r = 0$ and $r = r_0$ to obtain an equation between pertinent wave numbers and r_0. c) Find the numerical values of the wave numbers and solve the equation mentioned under b) for r_0. For the reduced mass, use $m = 1$ atomic mass unit.

12-10 a) Write the radial wave functions for $l = 0$ and $l = 1$ as given in Eq. (12-34). b) Find the values of kr which give the first zeros of the two functions. c) Use the results of a) and b) to calculate the distance in MeV between the lowest s-state and the lowest p-state in an infinitely deep well of radius 5 F.

12-11 What angular momenta and parities are predicted by the shell model for the ground states of ^{12}C, ^{11}B, ^{17}O, ^{20}Ne, ^{27}Al, ^{41}Ca, and ^{69}Ga?

12-12 Show that if the parent of a radioactive series is very long-lived, that is, $\lambda_1 \ll \lambda_n$, where λ_n is the decay constant for any other nuclide in the series, an equilibrium in production and decay of all daughter products will be reached such that

$$\lambda_1 N_1 = \lambda_2 N_2 = \lambda_3 N_3 = \cdots.$$

12-13 A fictitious nuclide has a $J = 1/2^+$ ground state and approximately evenly spaced excited states with $J = 9/2^+, 3/2^-, 1/2^+, 5/2^+, 7/2^-$ in order of ascending energy. Draw an energy-level diagram for this nuclide and indicate on this diagram the most likely gamma transition (down) from each level (five lines in all). Write beside the lines their multipolarity ($E1$, $M2$, etc.).

12-14 The ground state of ^{211}Po may decay by alpha emission to the ground state of ^{207}Pb. A metastable (isomeric) state of ^{211}Po may also decay by alpha emission to the ground state of ^{207}Pb ("long-range" alpha particles). a) Draw an energy-level diagram showing these processes. b) The two alpha-particle groups are observed simultaneously in a homogeneous-field 180° magnetic spectrograph. The radii of curvatures of their trajectories are r_1 and r_2 (longest). What is the ratio between their energies? c) Given the excitation energy of the metastable state E in addition to the information above, find an expression for the magnetic induction B in the spectrograph. Use nonrelativistic mechanics.

12-15 a) In the following table of isobars, *atomic* mass differences between element $Z + i$ and Z are given in MeV (i is an integer from -3 to $+2$, as shown). Find the possible beta-decay modes and the total energies of the emitted particles in each case, assuming only ground-state transitions.

Element number	$(m_{Z+i} - m_Z)c^2$	Ground-state J^π
$Z - 3$	3.57	$\frac{1}{2}^+$
$Z - 2$	1.12	$\frac{3}{2}^+$
$Z - 1$	1.97	$\frac{5}{2}^+$
Z	0	$\frac{5}{2}^+$
$Z + 1$	2.27	$\frac{1}{2}^+$
$Z + 2$	5.15	$\frac{7}{2}^+$

b) Assume that element $Z + 1$ has a low-lying excited state with $J^\pi = \frac{9}{2}^+$. Will this change any of the decay modes determined in part a)?

12-16 The atomic masses of the isobars of mass number 10 are

$$^{10}_{4}\text{Be}: \ 10.016711 \qquad ^{10}_{5}\text{B}: \ 10.016114 \qquad ^{10}_{6}\text{C}: \ 10.020605$$

Determine what is the maximum energy of any electrons and/or positrons that result from radioactive transformations among these isobars. (Electron rest energy = 0.511 MeV; 1 amu = 931 MeV.)

12-17 Neutrons of mass m and kinetic energy E_K are incident on a monoisotopic target of nuclear mass M. The neutrons are inelastically scattered from the target nuclei in such a way that they have zero energy (in the laboratory system) after the collision. Find the corresponding excitation energy E for the state to which the target nuclei are being excited. Use *nonrelativistic* formulas.

12-18 The nuclear reaction $^7\text{Li}(p, n)^7\text{Be}$ has a reaction energy of $Q = -1.646$ MeV. a) Apply the principles of conservation of energy and conservation of momentum to find the kinetic energy the protons must have in order to give neutrons that have "zero" energy in the laboratory system. Use classical dynamics in the formulas for momentum and kinetic energy, and integral mass values. b) Calculate the $^7\text{Be} - {}^7\text{Li}$ atomic mass difference (rest energy difference) in MeV. Determine which member of the pair is unstable and what kind of disintegration will take place. The neutron-hydrogen mass difference is $n - {}^1_1\text{H} = 0.782$ MeV.

12-19 About 6-eV energy is released when an atom of carbon combines with two oxygen atoms. Calculate the energy in joules released by a) the burning of 1 gm carbon; b) the fission of 1 gm ^{235}U; c) the fusion of 1 gm deuterium; d) the annihilation of 1 gm antimatter with 1 gm matter.

12-20 The carbon-nitrogen cycle is

$$^{12}\text{C}(p, \gamma)^{13}\text{N}, \qquad Q = 1.945 \text{ MeV},$$
$$^{13}\text{N}(\beta^+)^{13}\text{C}, \qquad \beta^+ \text{ max energy} = 1.202,$$
$$^{13}\text{C}(p, \gamma)^{14}\text{N}, \qquad Q = 7.542 \text{ MeV},$$
$$^{14}\text{N}(p, \gamma)^{15}\text{O}, \qquad Q = 7.347 \text{ MeV},$$
$$^{15}\text{O}(\beta^+)^{15}\text{N}, \qquad \beta^+ \text{ max energy} = 1.683,$$
$$^{15}\text{N}(p, \alpha)^{12}\text{C}, \qquad Q = 4.961 \text{ MeV}.$$

Calculate the total energy release in this cycle and compare with that calculated for the direct conversion of four protons into helium (proton mass = 1.008142; alpha-particle mass = 4.003873.

12–21 Using the properties of the pions and the kaons given in Table 12–8 and using Fig. 12–31 as a reference, list several channels open for strong (fast) decay of the state $\Sigma 1660$, 3/2.

APPENDIX 1

The MKSA System of Units

In the rationalized system of mksa units, the primary units are meter (m) for length, kilogram (kg) for mass, second (s) for time, and ampere (A) for electric current or, equivalently, coulomb (coul = A·s) for electric charge. All other units are derived from these primary units. For example, the unit of force is the newton. This is defined through Newton's Second Law as 1 kg·m·s^{-2}. The unit of energy then becomes $1 \text{ kg·m}^2\text{·s}^{-2}$; this is called 1 joule. The unit of power, the watt, becomes $1 \text{ kg·m}^2\text{·s}^{-3}$. The unit for electrical potential is $1 \text{ volt} = 1 \text{ kg·m}^2\text{·s}^{-2}\text{·coul}^{-1}$. The electrical units, the amp, the volt, and the watt, are thus the ones used in practice. The only exception is the unit for magnetic induction. In the mksa system this is the weber/m², which is equal to 10,000 gauss. Some of the important mksa units are listed in Table A1–1.

The great advantage of the mksa system over the cgs system is that the electrical units used are the same as those used in practice. However, this advantage is purchased at the expense of introducing two new constants. One is the *permeability of free space* μ_0. This appears in Ampère's law applied to free space

$$\oint \mathbf{B} \cdot d\mathbf{l} = \mu_0 i. \qquad \text{(A1–1)}$$

The permeability of free space is

$$\mu_0 = 4\pi \times 10^{-7} \text{ kg·m·coul}^{-2} \quad (\textit{or henry/m}).$$

The other new constant is the *permittivity constant* that appears in Coulomb's force law

$$F = \frac{1}{4\pi\varepsilon_0} \frac{q_1 q_2}{r^2}. \qquad \text{(A1–2)}$$

The permittivity of free space is

$$\varepsilon_0 = 1/c^2\mu_0 = 8.85415 \times 10^{-12}\ \text{coul}^2 \cdot \text{s}^2 \cdot \text{m}^{-3} \cdot \text{kg}^{-1} \quad \text{(or farad/m)},$$

where c is the velocity of light.

Table A1–1 MKSA units

Quantity	Unit	Abbreviation	Usual symbol	Dimension	Derivation
Length	Meter	m	l	L	Basic unit
Mass	Kilogram	kg	m	M	Basic unit
Time	Second	s	t	T	Basic unit
Charge	Coulomb	coul	q	Q	Basic unit
Velocity		$\text{m} \cdot \text{s}^{-1}$	v	LT^{-1}	$v = ds/dt$
Momentum		$\text{kgm} \cdot \text{s}^{-1}$	p	MLT^{-1}	$p = mv$
Force	Newton	N	F	MLT^{-2}	$F = dp/dt$
Energy, work	Joule	J	E, V, T, W	ML^2T^{-2}	$\Delta F = W \int \mathbf{F} \cdot d\mathbf{s}$
Angular velocity		$\text{rad} \cdot \text{s}^{-1}$	ω	T^{-1}	$\omega = d\theta/dt$
Angular momentum		$\text{kgm}^2 \cdot \text{s}^{-1}$	L	ML^2T^{-1}	$L = \mathbf{r} \times \mathbf{p}$
Current	Ampere	A	I	QT^{-1}	$I = dq/dt$
Voltage, emf	Volt	V	U or V	$ML^2T^{-2}Q^{-1}$	$U = \Delta E/q$
Resistance	Ohm	Ω	R	$ML^2T^{-1}Q^{-2}$	$R = U/I$
Capacitance	Farad	F	C	$M^{-1}L^{-2}T^2Q^2$	$Q = CU$
Inductance	Henry	H	L	ML^2Q^{-2}	$U = -LdI/dt$
Magnetic flux	Weber	Wb	ϕ	$ML^2T^{-1}Q^{-1}$	$U = -\partial\phi/\partial t$
Magnetic induction	(Tesla)	$\text{Wb} \cdot \text{m}^{-2}$	B	$MT^{-1}Q^{-1}$	$\phi = \int \mathbf{B} \cdot d\mathbf{S}$

In nuclear physics, it has become standard practice to use as a secondary unit of length, the fermi (1 fermi = 10^{-15} m). Somewhat inconsistently, the barn (1 barn = 10^{-28} m^2) is used as a secondary unit for cross section. As an alternative unit for mass, the mass unit, u, is used; as an alternative unit for energy, the electron volt is used.

The Periodic Table
of Elements

The values in parentheses in the column of atomic masses are the mass numbers of the longest lived isotopes of those elements which are radioactive.

The densities given are the values when the element is a solid, usually at 20°C, except where indicated as a gas (g), or a liquid (l). For gases, the values are at a pressure of one atmosphere and a temperature of 0°C when they are in their usual molecular states, such as H_2, He, O_2, Ne, etc.

Table A2–1

Z	Element	Atomic mass $u(^{12}C)$	Density, ρ, $g \cdot cm^{-3}$	Ionization potential, V	Atom in the ground state		
					Electron configuration	Outermost shell occupied	Spectral term
1	H	1.00797	8.988×10^{-5}(g)	13.595	$1s$	K	$^2S_{1/2}$
2	He	4.0026	1.7847×10^{-4}(g)	24.581	$1s^2$	K	$^1S_0$
3	Li	6.939	0.534	5.390	2s	L	$^2S_{1/2}$
4	Be	9.0122	1.848	9.320	$2s^2$	L	$^1S_0$
5	B	10.811	2.34 (crys.) 2.37 (am.)	8.296	$2s^2$ 2p	L	$^2P_{1/2}$
6	C	12.01115	3.52 (dia.) 2.25 (graph)	11.258	$2s^2$ $2p^2$	L	$^3P_0$
7	N	14.0067	1.2568×10^{-3}(g)	14.53	$2s^2$ $2p^3$	L	$^4S_{3/2}$
8	O	15.9994	1.4277×10^{-3}(g)	13.614	$2s^2$ $2p^4$	L	$^3P_2$
9	F	18.9984	1.6954×10^{-3}(g)	17.418	$2s^2$ $2p^5$	L	$^2P_{3/2}$
10	Ne	20.183	8.9990×10^{-4}(g)	21.559	$2s^2$ $2p^6$	L	$^1S_0$

Helium core—2 electrons

Z		Atomic weight	Density	Ionization	Configuration		Term
11	Na	22.9898	0.9712	5.138	$3s$	M	$^2S_{1/2}$
12	Mg	24.312	1.741	7.644	$3s^2$	M	$^1S_0$
13	Al	26.9815	2.699	5.984	$3s^2\,3p$	M	$^2P_{1/2}$
14	Si	28.086	2.42 (crys.) 2.35 (am.)	8.150	$3s^2\,3p^2$	M	$^3P_0$
15	P	30.9738	yell. 1.83, red 2.20 met. 2.34, blk. 2.70	10.49	$3s^2\,3p^3$	M	$^4S_{3/2}$
16	S	32.064	rhomb 2.07	10.357	$3s^2\,3p^4$	M	$^3P_2$
17	Cl	35.453	3.164×10^{-3}(g)	13.01	$3s^2\,3p^5$	M	$^2P_{3/2}$
18	A	39.948	1.784×10^{-3}(g)	15.755	$3s^2\,3p^6$	M	$^1S_0$
19	K	39.102	0.87	4.340	$4s$	N	$^2S_{1/2}$
20	Ca	40.08	1.54	6.111	$4s^2$	N	$^1S_0$
21	Sc	44.956	2.992	6.55	$3d\,4s^2$	N	$^2D_{3/2}$
22	Ti	47.90	4.528	6.82	$3d^2\,4s^2$	N	$^3F_2$
23	V	50.942	6.10	6.74	$3d^3\,4s^2$	N	$^4F_{3/2}$
24	Cr	51.996	6.99	6.763	$3d^5\,4s$*	N	$^7S_3$
25	Mn	54.9380	7.42	7.432	$3d^5\,4s^2$	N	$^6S_{5/2}$
26	Fe	55.847	7.874	7.88	$3d^6\,4s^2$	N	$^5D_4$
27	Co	58.9332	8.82	7.86	$3d^7\,4s^2$	N	$^4F_{9/2}$
28	Ni	58.71	8.88	7.633	$3d^8\,4s^2$	N	$^3F_4$
29	Cu	63.54	8.92	7.724	$3d^{10}\,4s$*	N	$^2S_{1/2}$
30	Zn	65.37	7.133	9.390	$3d^{10}\,4s^2$	N	$^1S_0$
31	Ga	69.72	5.905	6.0	$3d^{10}\,4s^2\,4p$	N	$^2P_{1/2}$
32	Ge	72.59	5.40	7.88	$3d^{10}\,4s^2\,4p^2$	N	$^3P_0$
33	As	74.9216	5.72	9.81	$3d^{10}\,4s^2\,4p^3$	N	$^4S_{3/2}$
34	Se	78.96	4.80	9.75	$3d^{10}\,4s^2\,4p^4$	N	$^3P_2$
35	Br	79.909	3.12 (l)	11.84	$3d^{10}\,4s^2\,4p^5$	N	$^2P_{3/2}$
36	Kr	83.80	3.728×10^{-3}(g)	13.997	$3d^{10}\,4s^2\,4p^6$	N	$^1S_0$

Neon core—10 electrons

Argon core—18 electrons

* Irregularity

TableA2-1—(cont.)

Z	Element	Atomic mass $u(^{12}C)$	Density, ρ, $g \cdot cm^{-3}$	Ionization potential, V	Electron configuration	Outermost shell occupied	Spectral term
37	Rb	85.47	1.531	4.176	$5s$	O	$^2S_{1/2}$
38	Sr	87.62	2.54	5.692	$5s^2$	O	$^1S_0$
39	Y	88.905	4.45	6.38	$4d\ 5s^2$	O	$^2D_{3/2}$
40	Zr	91.22	6.49	6.84	$4d^2\ 5s^2$	O	$^3F_2$
41	Nb	92.906	8.54	6.88	$4d^4\ 5s*$	O	$^6D_{1/2}$
42	Mo	95.94	10.21	7.11	$4d^5\ 5s$	O	$^7S_3$
43	Tc	98(?)	11.5	7.27	$4d^6\ 5s^2$	O	$^6S_{5/2}$
44	Ru	101.07	12.4	7.364	$4d^7\ 5s$	O	$^5F_5$
45	Rh	102.905	12.42	7.46	$4d^8\ 5s$	O	$^4F_{9/2}$
46	Pd	106.4	12.07	8.33	$4d^{10}*$	O	$^1S_0$
47	Ag	107.870	10.50	7.574	$4d^{10}\ 5s$	O	$^2S_{1/2}$
48	Cd	112.40	8.66	8.991	$4d^{10}\ 5s^2$	O	$^1S_0$
49	In	114.82	7.30	5.785	$4d^{10}\ 5s^2\ 5p$	O	$^2P_{1/2}$
50	Sn	118.69	7.30	7.342	$4d^{10}\ 5s^2\ 5p^2$	O	$^3P_0$
51	Sb	121.75	6.69	8.64	$4d^{10}\ 5s^2\ 5p^3$	O	$^4S_{3/2}$
52	Te	127.60	6.24	9.01	$4d^{10}\ 5s^2\ 5p^4$	O	$^3P_2$
53	I	126.9044	4.93	10.454	$4d^{10}\ 5s^2\ 5p^5$	O	$^2P_{3/2}$
54	Xe	131.30	$5.88 \times 10^{-3}(g)$	12.127	$4d^{10}\ 5s^2\ 5p^6$	O	$^1S_0$

Krypton core—36 electrons

* Irregularity
† Implies uncertainty

Z	Symbol	Atomic weight	Density	Ionization energy	Electron configuration (Xenon core—54 electrons)		Term
55	Cs	132.905	1.873	3.89	$6s$	P	$^2S_{1/2}$
56	Ba	137.34	3.75	5.21	$6s^2$	P	$^1S_0$
57	La	138.91	6.10	5.61	$5d6s^2$	P	$^2D_{3/2}$
58	Ce	140.12	7.0	5.6	$4f5d6s^2*$ $(4f^26s^2)$	P	$^1G_4$
59	Pr	140.907	6.71	5.45	$4f^3\,6s^2$	P	$^4I_{9/2}$
60	Nd	144.24	6.97	5.51	$4f^4\,6s^2$	P	$^5I_4$
61	Pm	(145)	...	...	$4f^5\,6s^2$	P	$^6H_{5/2}$
62	Sm	150.35	7.5	5.6	$4f^6\,6s^2$	P	$^7F_0$
63	Eu	151.96	5.26	5.67	$4f^7\,6s^2$	P	$^8S_{7/2}$
64	Gd	157.25	7.85	6.16	$4f^7\,5d\,6s^2*$	P	$^9D_2$
65	Tb	158.924	8.27	5.98	$4f^9\,6s^2$	P	$^6H_{15/2}$
66	Dy	162.50	8.54	6.8	$4f^{10}\,6s^2$	P	$^5I_8$
67	Ho	164.930	8.79	...	$4f^{11}\,6s^2$	P	$^4I_{15/2}$
68	Er	167.26	9.0	6.08	$4f^{12}\,6s^2$	P	$^3H_6$
69	Tm	168.934	9.33	5.81	$4f^{13}\,6s^2$	P	$^2F_{7/2}$
70	Yb	173.04	6.96	6.2	$4f^{14}\,6s^2$	P	$^1S_0$
71	Lu	174.97	9.87	...	$4f^{14}\,5d\,6s^2$	P	$^2D_{3/2}$
72	Hf	178.49	13.27	7	$4f^{14}\,5d^2\,6s^2$	P	$^3F_2$
73	Ta	180.948	16.6	7.88	$4f^{14}\,5d^3\,6s^2$	P	$^4F_{3/2}$
74	W	183.85	19.3	7.98	$4f^{14}\,5d^4\,6s^2$	P	$^5D_0$
75	Re	186.2	21.0	7.87	$4f^{14}\,5d^5\,6s^2$	P	$^6S_{5/2}$
76	Os	190.2	22.56	8.5	$4f^{14}\,5d^6\,6s^2$	P	$^5D_4$
77	Ir	192.2	22.42	9	$4f^{14}\,5d^9*$	P	$^4F_{9/2}$
78	Pt	195.09	21.44	9.0	$4f^{14}\,5d^9\,6s$	P	$^3D_3$
79	Au	196.967	19.32	9.22	$4f^{14}\,5d^{10}\,6s$	P	$^2S_{1/2}$
80	Hg	200.59	13.596(l)	10.43	$4f^{14}\,5d^{10}\,6s^2$	P	$^1S_0$
81	Tl	204.37	11.85	6.11	$4f^{14}\,5d^{10}\,6s^2\,6p$	P	$^2P_{1/2}$
82	Pb	207.19	11.34	7.414	$4f^{14}\,5d^{10}\,6s^2\,6p^2$	P	$^3P_0$
83	Bi	208.980	9.75	7.287	$4f^{14}\,5d^{10}\,6s^2\,6p^3$	P	$^4S_{3/2}$
84	Po	(209)	9.32	8.43	$4f^{14}\,5d^{10}\,6s^2\,6p^4$	P	$^3P_2$
85	At	(210)	...	9.5	$4f^{14}\,5d^{10}\,6s^2\,6p^5$	P	...
86	Rn	(222)	9.80×10^{-3}(g)	10.75	$4f^{14}\,5d^{10}\,6s^2\,6p^6$	P	$^1S_0$

* Irregularity

Table A2–1—(cont.)

Z	Element	Atomic mass u(^{12}C)	Density, ρ, g · cm^{-3}	Ionization potential, V	Atom in the ground state		
					Electron configuration	Outermost shell occupied	Spectral term
87	Fr	(223)	...	4	$7s$	◯	$^2S_{1/2}$ (?)
88	Ra	(226)	5(?)	5.28	$7s^2$	◯	$^1S_0$
89	Ac	(227)	...	6.9	$6d\,7s^2$	◯	$^2D_{3/2}$
90	Th	232.038	11.6(?)	6.95	$6d^2 7s^2$	◯	$^3F_2$
91	Pa	(231)	15.4(?)	...	$5f^2\,6d\,7s^2$*	◯	$^4K_{11/2}$
92	U	238.03	18.9	6.08	$5f^3\,6d\,7s^2$	◯	$^5L_6$
93	Np	(237)	19.5	...	$5f^4\,6d\,7s^2$	◯	$^6L_{11/2}$
94	Pu	(244)	19.8	5.1	$5f^6\,7s^2$	◯	$^7F_0$
95	Am	(243)	11.7	...	$5f^7\,7s^2$	◯	$^8S_{7/2}$
96	Cm	(247)	7(?)	...	$5f^7\,6d\,7s^2$	◯	$^9D_2$
97	Bk	(247)	...	...	$5f^8\,6d\,7s^2$	◯	:
98	Cf	(251)	...	...	$5f^{10}\,7s^2$	◯	:
99	Es	(254)	...	...	$5f^{11}\,7s^2$	◯	:
100	Fm	(257)	...	...	$5f^{12}\,7s^2$	◯	:
101	Md	(256)	...	...	$5f^{13}\,7s^2$	◯	:
102	No	(255)	...	...	:	◯	:
103	Lw	(257)	...	...	:	◯	:
104	Ku?	(260)?	...	...	:		:

Emanation (radon) core—86 electrons

* Irregularity

Relativity

A3–1 THE SEARCH FOR A FRAME OF REFERENCE—THE ETHER

About a hundred years ago, James Clerk Maxwell demonstrated that electricity and light are related phenomena. Starting with known properties of electricity and magnetism, as expressed by his celebrated equations, Maxwell derived a wave equation for the electric and magnetic field. He could demonstrate, furthermore, that the velocity of the waves he discovered was the same as the velocity of light. He could derive many other properties of light, and it was soon accepted that he had put the wave theory of light on a firm foundation. In this theory, light is an electromagnetic wave motion.

Every wave motion has something that "waves." Sound waves have air and water waves have water. Surely, it was argued, light waves must involve the waving of something even in free space. No one knew what it was, but it was given the name "luminiferous ether."

Light passes through many kinds of materials. It passes through relatively heavy materials like glass and it passes through the nearly perfect vacuum that must lie between the stars and the earth. Thus ether must permeate all of space. Light is a transverse wave motion. This comes out of Maxwell's theory and from many experimental observations, particularly those on polarized light. This implies that the ether is a solid. Transverse waves involve shear forces and can occur only in solids which can support shear. Sound waves in air must be longitudinal because of this fact. Furthermore, the ether must be a rigid solid. The propagation velocity of mechanical waves in various materials depends on the elastic constants of the material. These are much greater for steel than for air. The very great velocity of light thus implies that the ether must have a very large shear modulus. It is rather hard on the imagination to suppose that all space is filled with this rigid solid and that all material objects move through this solid without resistance, yet it was supposed to exist. However fanciful it may seem to us, physicists felt that this ether might be just the thing to which to attach a Newtonian coordinate system. It was conceived that Newton's laws would hold exactly for an observer moving without acceleration *relative to the ether.*

If the ether is assumed to be at rest, then the interesting question is: How fast are we moving through the ether? Since all speculations about the ether stem from its properties as a medium for carrying light, an optical experiment is indicated. It is not hard to compute how sensitive the apparatus must be in order to measure the ether drift. Assuming, for the sake of argument, that the sun has no ether drift, the velocity of the earth through the ether must be its orbital velocity. If the sun has an ether drift, then the drift of the earth will be even greater than its orbital velocity at some seasons. Knowing that the radius of the earth's orbit is about 93 million miles, we can find the orbital velocity to be about 18.5 mi/s. By performing the experiment at the best season of the year, we know that we should be able to find an ether drift of at least $18.5 \text{ mi} \cdot \text{s}^{-1}$. The velocity of light is $186{,}000 \text{ mi} \cdot \text{s}^{-1}$. Great as our orbital velocity is, it is only about 10^{-4} times the velocity of light and, as it turns out (see the next section), the measurable effects of ether drift, if any, would be proportional to the square of this number, i.e., 10^{-8}. It is therefore evident that a very sensitive instrument is required.

A3–2 THE MICHELSON INTERFEROMETER

A device of sufficient sensitivity was made and used in the United States by Michelson and Morley in 1887. The principle of their apparatus is brought out by the following analogy. Suppose two equally fast swimmers undertake a race in a river between floats anchored to the river bed. Two equal courses, each having a total length $2L$, are laid out from the starting point, float A, as shown in Fig. A3–1. One course is AD, parallel to the flow of the river relative to

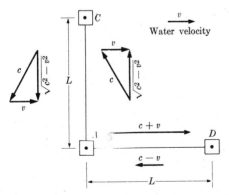

Fig. A3–1 Swimming analogy to the Michelson-Morley experiment.

the earth, and the other is AC, perpendicular to it. How will the times compare if each of the swimmers goes out and back on his course? Let the speed of each swimmer relative to the water be c, and let the water drift or velocity with respect to the earth be v. When the swimmer on the parallel course goes downstream, his velocity will add to that of the water, giving him a resultant velocity of $(c + v)$ with respect to the earth. The time required for him to swim the distance L from A to D is $L/(c + v)$. On his return, he must overcome the water drift. His net velocity then is $(c - v)$, and his return time is $L/(c - v)$. His total time is the sum of these two times. This is seen to depend upon the velocity of the water, and is given by

$$t_{\parallel} = \frac{L}{c + v} + \frac{L}{c - v} = \frac{2Lc}{c^2 - v^2}. \tag{A3–1}$$

The other swimmer, going perpendicular to the water drift, spends the same time on each half of his trip, but he must head upstream if he is not to be carried away by the current. The component of his velocity that carries him toward his goal is $\sqrt{c^2 - v^2}$ with respect to the earth. The total time for his trip also depends on the water drift, and is

$$t_{\perp} = \frac{2L}{\sqrt{c^2 - v^2}}. \tag{A3–2}$$

To see how these two times compare, we divide the parallel course time, Eq. (A3–1), by the perpendicular course time, Eq. (A3–2), and obtain

$$\frac{t_{\parallel}}{t_{\perp}} = \frac{2Lc}{c^2 - v^2} \cdot \frac{\sqrt{c^2 - v^2}}{2L} = \frac{1}{\sqrt{1 - (v^2/c^2)}}. \tag{A3–3}$$

In still water $v = 0$, the ratio of the times is unity, and the race is a tie, as we would expect. In slowly moving water, the ratio is greater than unity and the swimmer on the perpendicular course wins; or, put differently, if the swimmers are stroking in phase when they leave float A, they will be out of phase when they return to it. If the velocity of the river increases to nearly that of the swimmers, then the ratio tends toward infinity. If the river velocity exceeds the swimmer velocity, the entire analysis breaks down. The ratio becomes imaginary and both swimmers are swept off the course by the current. The point is that, by observing the race, the water velocity relative to the anchored floats can be measured.

The optical equivalent of the above situation is to have a race between two light rays over identical courses, one parallel and one perpendicular to the ether drift. The instrument used, called a Michelson interferometer, is shown schematically in Fig. A3–2.

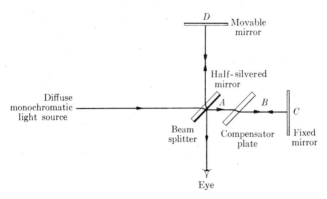

Fig. A3–2 The Michelson interferometer.

Let us follow a ray of light which enters the apparatus from an extended source at the left. At A, it is incident on a glass plate that is half silvered on its right side. This surface reflects half of the light up toward D, while the other half goes on to C. Both C and D are full silvered, front-surface mirrors that reflect their beams back toward A. The beam from D is partly reflected at A, and the remainder goes on through to the eye of the observer. A portion of the beam from C is reflected at A to the observer, and the rest goes through the glass plate and is lost. The plate of glass at B has the same thickness and inclination as that at A, so that the two light paths from source to observer pass through the same number of thicknesses of glass. If the light from the source did not diverge and remained very narrow in going through the apparatus, the observer would see a line of light. The brightness of this line would depend on the difference in the optical length* of the two light paths. If these differed by any whole number of wavelengths of the light (including zero), the line would be bright. If the paths differed by an odd number of half-wavelengths, then the line would be dark. Between these extremes every brightness gradation would be observed. In practice, the light does diverge in the apparatus, and there are a great many slightly different paths being traversed simultaneously. Consequently, the observer does not see one line but a multiplicity of lines. The loci of points where the paths differ by whole wavelengths are bright, and where the paths differ by an odd number of half-wavelengths there is darkness.

---

* Two paths have the same optical length if light traverses both in the same time. The optical lengths of the interferometer paths can be changed by changing their physical length, by changing the index of refraction of the region through which the light passes, or, if the swimming analogy applies, by moving the apparatus relative to the light-carrying medium.

Thus, as one path length is varied, the observer sees fringes, like the teeth of a comb, move across the field, rather than a single line becoming lighter and darker. It is fortunate that the optical system works as it does, since it is easier for the eye to detect differences in position than differences in intensity.

The precision of this device is remarkable. If yellow light from sodium is used, the wavelength is 5.893×10^{-7} m. Moving the mirror D away from A one-half this distance will increase one path length by a whole wavelength and cause the pattern to move an amount equal to the separation of two adjacent dark lines. If we can estimate to hundredths of fringes, then the smallest detectable motion is only 2.9×10^{-9} m. Upon moving a mirror one-thousandth of an inch, 86 fringes would go by.

The similarity between the Michelson interferometer and the swimming race should be evident. Light corresponds to the swimmers and has the free-space velocity, c, with respect to its ether medium. The ether drift corresponds to the water current drift and has the velocity v with respect to the earth. Just as we could learn about the river flow by seeing the outcome of the swimmers' race, so we wish to measure the ether drift by conducting a "light race" over equal paths parallel and perpendicular to the ether drift.

Suppose that instead of taking the ratio of the times for the two paths of the river race we now take their difference; then

$$\Delta t = \frac{2Lc}{c^2 - v^2} - \frac{2L}{\sqrt{c^2 - v^2}} = \frac{2L}{c} \left[\left(1 - \frac{v^2}{c^2} \right)^{-1} - \left(1 - \frac{v^2}{c^2} \right)^{-1/2} \right] . \quad \text{(A3–4)}$$

Using the first two terms of the binomial expansion, we have, to a good approximation if $v \ll c$, that

$$\Delta t = \frac{2L}{c} \left[\left(1 + \frac{v^2}{c^2} \right) - \left(1 + \frac{v^2}{2c^2} \right) \right] = \frac{Lv^2}{c^3} . \quad \text{(A3–5)}$$

In the interferometer, the time difference should appear as a fringe shift from the position the fringes would have if there were *no* ether drift. The distance light moves in a time Δt is $d = c \, \Delta t$ and if this distance represents n waves of wavelength λ, then $d = n\lambda$. Therefore the fringe shift would be

$$n = \frac{Lv^2}{\lambda c^2} . \quad \text{(A3–6)}$$

Thus if the light race is carried out with light of speed c and wavelength λ in an interferometer whose arms are of length L, one of which is parallel to the ether drift of velocity v, then Eq. (A3–6) gives the number of fringes that should be displaced because of the motion of the earth through the ether compared with their positions if the earth were *at rest* in the ether.

A3–3 THE MICHELSON–MORLEY EXPERIMENT

The apparatus used was large and had its effective arm length increased to about 10 m by using additional mirrors to fold up the path. The entire apparatus was floated on mercury so that it could be rotated at constant speed without introducing strains that would deform the apparatus. *Rotation was necessary* in order to make the fringes shift, and by rotating through 90°, first one arm and then the other could be made parallel to the drift, thereby *doubling* the fringe displacement of Eq. (A3–6). We can now estimate whether this instrument should be sensitive enough to detect the ether drift. Recall that at some time of the year the ether drift v was expected to be at least the orbital velocity of the earth, which is about $10^{-4} c$. Thus we expect v/c to be at least 10^{-4}. Using light of wavelength 5×10^{-7} m, the computed shift is $\Delta n = 0.4$ fringe. Michelson and Morley estimated that they could detect a shift of one-hundredth of a fringe. Sensitivity to spare!

Measurements were made over an extended period of time at all seasons of the year, but no significant fringe shift was observed. Thinking that the earth might drag a little ether along with it just as a boat carries a thin layer of water when it glides, Michelson and Morley took the entire apparatus to a mountain laboratory in search of a site which would project into the drifting ether. Again a diligent search failed to measure an ether drift. The experiment "failed."

Few experimental "failures" have been more stimulating than this. The negative result of the Michelson-Morley experiment presented a challenge to explain its failure. Fitzgerald and Lorentz proposed an *ad hoc* explanation. They pointed out that there might be an interaction between the ether and objects moving relative to it, such that the object became shorter in all its dimensions parallel to the relative velocity. Recall that in the flowing-river analogy the ratio of the times of the swimmers in Eq. (A3–3) was

$$\frac{1}{\sqrt{1 - v^2/c^2}} .$$

If the route parallel to the flow had been shorter by this factor, then the ratio of the times would have been one and the race would have been a tie. A similar shortening of the parallel interferometer arm would account for the tie race Michelson and Morley always observed. The shortening could never be measured because any rule used to measure it would also be moving relative to the ether and would shorten also. Whether you accept the Fitzgerald-Lorentz contraction hypothesis or not, the Michelson-Morley experiment indicates that all observers who measure the velocity of light will get the same result regardless of their own velocity through space.

A3-4 THE CONSTANT SPEED OF LIGHT

Speed trials of cars, boats, and airplanes are never official unless they are made in the following way. The record contender must drive his craft in opposite directions over a measured course and the speed attained is calculated to be the double distance divided by the total time spent between markers. This technique is used to make any wind, water, or other conditions which may be helpful in one direction be cancelled out by their hindrance on the reverse trip. Measurements of the speed of light are similarly made by timing a flash of light as it goes to a distant mountain and returns. This technique is rather good and, *to a first approximation*, the influence of a moving medium does cancel out. But the cancellation is not perfect and *to a second approximation*, the effect of a moving medium does *not* cancel. This becomes obvious if the medium moves faster than the speed under test. In this case, the test cannot be made, since the thing tested is carried away. The fact that Fizeau, in France, and others obtained consistent results for the velocity of light at a variety of times, places, and in different directions was in itself evidence that the speed of the earth through the ether (if any) was small compared with the velocity of light. It is highly significant that the Michelson-Morley interferometer was sensitive enough to detect the second-order term. Referring to Eq. (A3–5), you will note that the first terms (the ones) cancel out and the significant result remains only because the second terms do not cancel. The Michelson-Morley experiment was sensitive to the second-order terms because, instead of trying to measure the times of transit of light through their apparatus, they measured the *difference* of times. Michelson and Morley found that the speed of the earth through space made *no difference* in the speed of light relative to them. The inference is clear either that the earth moves in some way through the ether space more slowly than it moves about the sun, or that *all observers must find that their motion through space makes no difference in the speed of light relative to them.*

The consideration of electromagnetic phenomena led Einstein to conclude, apparently without knowledge of the Michelson-Morley experiment, that the speed of light does not depend upon the motion of the observer and that there is no preferred reference frame for the laws of physics. We quote the beginning of his first paper on relativity which is titled "On the Electrodynamics of Moving Bodies."*

"It is known that Maxwell's electrodynamics—as usually understood at the present time—when applied to moving bodies leads to asymmetries which

---

* Excerpt from A. Einstein, "Zur Electrodynamik bewegter Körper," *Annalen der Physik* **17** (1905), p. 891, translated by W. Perrett and G. B. Jeffery, in *The Principle of Relativity* by Einstein, Lorentz, Minkowski, and Weyl. New York: Dover Publications; reprinted through permission of the publisher.

do not appear to be inherent in the phenomena. Take, for example, the reciprocal electrodynamic action of a magnet and a conductor. The observable phenomenon here depends only on the relative motion of the conductor and the magnet, whereas the customary view draws a sharp distinction between the two cases in which either the one or the other of these bodies is in motion. For if the magnet is in motion and the conductor at rest, there arises in the neighborhood of the magnet an electric field with a certain definite energy, producing a current at the places where parts of the conductor are situated. But if the magnet is stationary and the conductor in motion, no electric field arises in the neighborhood of the magnet. In the conductor, however, we find an electromotive force, to which in itself there is no corresponding energy, but which gives rise—assuming equality of relative motion in the two cases discussed—to electric currents of the same path and intensity as those produced by the electric forces in the former case.

"Examples of this sort, together with the unsuccessful attempts to discover any motion of the earth relatively to the 'light medium,' suggest that the phenomena of electrodynamics as well as of mechanics possess no properties corresponding to the idea of absolute rest. They suggest rather that, as has already been shown to the first order of small quantities, the same laws of electrodynamics and optics will be valid for all frames of reference for which the equations of mechanics hold good. We will raise this conjecture (the purport of which will hereafter be called the 'Principle of Relativity') to the status of a postulate, and also introduce another postulate, which is only apparently irreconcilable with the former, namely, that light is always propagated in empty space with a definite velocity c which is independent of the state of motion of the emitting body. These two postulates suffice for the attainment of a simple and consistent theory of the electrodynamics of moving bodies based on Maxwell's theory for stationary bodies. The introduction of a 'luminiferous ether' will prove to be superfluous inasmuch as the view here to be developed will not require an 'absolutely stationary space' provided with special properties, nor assign a velocity-vector to a point of the empty space in which electromagnetic processes take place.

"The theory to be developed is based—like all electrodynamics—on the kinematics of the rigid body, since the assertations of any such theory have to do with the relationships between rigid bodies (systems of coordinates), clocks, and electromagnetic processes. Insufficient consideration of this circumstance lies at the root of the difficulties which the electrodynamics of moving bodies at present encounters."

A3–5 CLASSICAL RELATIVITY

Let us first consider the pre-Einstein relativity of physical quantities in classical or Galilean-Newtonian physics, and ask how events in one system, S, moving with constant linear velocity, appear from another system S', also moving with constant linear velocity.

No generality will be lost if one of the systems, say S, is regarded as being at rest, and the other, S', as moving with a uniform velocity v. Our problem, then, is like that of comparing the observations of a man on the ground with those of a man on a uniformly moving train.

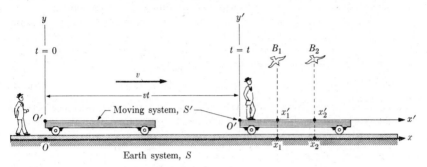

Fig. A3–3 Coordinate systems S and S'.

In Fig. A3–3 the earth observer considers himself to be at the origin O of his system S and he chooses an x-axis parallel to the track. The train observer in S' likewise measures distances from himself at O' and chooses his x'-axis parallel to the track. Let us measure time from the moment when the two observers are exactly opposite each other. Suppose that at some later time t each observer decides to measure the separation of two birds, B_1 and B_2, which happen to be hovering over the track. The observer at O' observes that the positions of B_1 and B_2 are the small distances x'_1 and x'_2. The observer at O finds the positions of B_1 and B_2 are the larger distances x_1 and x_2. The observer at O can compute the O' observations by noting that the observer at O' has moved a distance vt, with the result

$$x'_1 = x_1 - vt \quad \text{and} \quad x'_2 = x_2 - vt. \quad (A3\text{-}7)$$

The observer on the train (who may think the train is at rest with the earth moving under it) can account for the difference in their observations by observing that O has drifted away from him a distance vt. He obtains

$$x_1 = x'_1 + vt \quad \text{and} \quad x_2 = x'_2 + vt. \quad (A3\text{-}8)$$

These are transformation equations in that they transform observations from one system to the other. By solving either set of equations for the separation of the birds, we get

$$x_2 - x_1 = x'_2 - x'_1 \quad \text{or} \quad \Delta x = \Delta x'. \quad (A3\text{-}9)$$

This shows that the two observers agree on how far apart the two birds are. Note that the relative velocity v of the observers need not be known. Similarly, the time t since the two observers were opposite each other need not be known, but all observations must be *simultaneous*—even if the birds cooperate by staying the same distance apart.

What we have just shown is that *distance* or length is an *invariant* quantity when transformed from one Newtonian coordinate system to another.

We now compare results by the same two observers for a velocity measurement. Suppose that one bird flies from position B_1 at time t_1 to position B_2 at time t_2. The transformation equations of the positions of the bird are of the same form except for the difference of time, thus

$$x_1' = x_1 - vt_1, \qquad x_2' = x_2 - vt_2. \qquad \text{(A3–10)}$$

To solve for the average observed velocity u', we take the difference between the two transformation equations and divide by the time interval, obtaining

$$x_2' - x_1' = (x_2 - vt_2) - (x_1 - vt_1)$$
$$= (x_2 - x_1) - v(t_2 - t_1), \qquad \text{(A3–11)}$$

or

$$\Delta x' = \Delta x - v\,\Delta t. \qquad \text{(A3–12)}$$

Therefore the velocity relation is

$$u' = \frac{\Delta x'}{\Delta t} = \frac{\Delta x}{\Delta t} - v = u - v. \qquad \text{(A3–13)}$$

Thus the *velocities* measured by the two observers are *not* the same. They are *not* *invariant* under a transformation between Galilean-Newtonian coordinate systems.

Suppose the bird again cooperates and swoops over the train with different velocities at positions 1 and 2. Each observer could measure the velocity at each position. Using the result just derived, we find that the velocity transformation equations are

$$u_1' = u_1 - v \qquad \text{and} \qquad u_2' = u_2 - v. \qquad \text{(A3–14)}$$

If the observers also measured the time Δt it took the bird to get from one position to the other, they could solve for the average acceleration. Taking the difference between the velocity transformations gives

$$u_2' - u_1' = u_2 - u_1. \qquad \text{(A3–15)}$$

Dividing by Δt, we have $a' = a$, which shows that velocity difference and *acceleration* are *invariant* under transformation between Newtonian inertial frames of reference.

We have assumed that the two coordinate systems coincide at time $t = 0$ and that the relative velocity is in the x-direction. In this case, we always have $y = y'$ and $z = z'$. In classical relativity, we also *assume* $t = t'$. As we shall see later, this last assumption is one that we will be forced to drop in Einsteinian relativity. To summarize we write the Galilean-Newtonian or classical transformations.

$$
\begin{aligned}
x' &= x - vt, & x &= x' + vt', \\
y' &= y, & y &= y', \\
z' &= z, & z &= z', \\
t' &= t, & t &= t'.
\end{aligned}
\tag{A3-16}
$$

The first set of equations can be used to find the space-time coordinates (x', y', z', t') of one *event* as seen by the observer in $0'$ terms of the coordinates recorded for the same event by the observer in 0. The second set transforms from $0'$ to 0. An *event* here means any occurrence that can be specified by three space coordinates and time, e.g., the firing of a flashbulb. The flight of a bird, as discussed above, can be regarded as a series of events.

The transformation equations we have just derived formally are fairly obvious. The most complicated result, the *variant* velocity transformation, is used without formal proof in the study of impact and Doppler effect, and was used in our recent discussion of the Michelson-Morley experiment. In fact, the problem presented by the negative result of that experiment was that, contrary to the Newtonian transformation, observers *must* find the velocity of light the *same* whether the observers are moving or not.

The classical transformation equations just derived apply only for reference frames moving with *constant linear velocity* with respect to one another. It is their failure in cases involving uniform motion that leads us into Einstein's special theory of relativity. We have not treated the classical transformation equations which deal with accelerated or rotating frames of reference, since these are more complicated.

In the derivations above we have tacitly made the *classical assumption* that time intervals are the same for all observers. Actually, there is no *a priori* reason* for assuming that time or any other physical quantity is invariant under a transformation of coordinates. Whether or not an assumption is correct is determined solely by the experimental verification of the results predicted with its aid. We will find later that the invariance of time interval will have to be abandoned, when the invariance of the free-space velocity of light is assumed.

---

* An *a priori* reason is one deduced from previous assumptions or known causes.

A3–6 THE EINSTEIN-LORENTZ TRANSFORMATION EQUATIONS

The Michelson-Morley experiment was carried out to measure the velocity of the earth through the ether in the hope that the ether would provide a fixed frame of reference relative to which Newton's laws would hold exactly. Einstein assumed that all experiments designed to locate a fixed frame of reference would fail. Since he assumed that a fixed frame of reference could never be found, he went to the other extreme and postulated that the laws of physics should be so stated that they apply relative to any frame of reference.

We are here going to derive new equations for transforming the space-time coordinates of one event from one frame to another. We shall assume that the frames are *inertial* frames; i.e., they are not accelerated. However, we can, of course, study accelerated motion of some object relative to the inertial frames. The relativity of intertial frames is called *Special Relativity*. The much more complicated General Relativity dealing with accelerated frames was proposed by Einstein in 1915. Limiting ourselves to special relativity, we may state its two postulates as follows:

1. *The laws of physics apply equally well for any two observers moving with constant linear velocity relative to each other or, in other words, the observations on one reference frame are not preferred above those on any other.*

2. *All observers must find the same value of the free-space velocity of light regardless of any motion they may have.*

The equations we are about to derive were first obtained by Lorentz as he successively refined electromagnetic theory to conform with the results of experiments. As stated earlier, both Fitzgerald and Lorentz obtained an ad hoc explanation of the negative result of the Michelson-Morley experiment by supposing that the interferometer shortened along its velocity vector through the ether. But we shall derive the relativistic transformation equations as consequences of Einstein's two postulates.

We return to our two observers at O and O' in systems S and S'. We ask the observer at O' to go back and pass the observer at O again. This time—just as O is opposite O'—we fire a photographic flashbulb. Thus at time $t = 0$, each observer is at the source of a spherical light wave. If we endow each observer with a supernatural power so that each can "see" the light spread out into space, then *each* observer must feel that *he* is at the center of the growing sphere of light. This must be the case, since we are now imposing the condition that the velocity of light is the same for all observers even if the velocity of an object is not.

The equation of the expanding sphere seen by the observer at O is

$$x^2 + y^2 + z^2 = c^2t^2, \tag{A3-17}$$

where c is the velocity of light. Similarly, the observer at O' writes for his equation of the sphere

$$x'^2 + y'^2 + z'^2 = c^2 t'^2. \qquad (A3–18)$$

Now the reader can readily verify that, if we substitute x', y', etc. from the first set of the transformation equations (A3–16) into Eq. (A3–18), we do not obtain Eq. (A3–17). We must therefore look for a new or modified set of transformations in order that Eqs. (A3–17) and (A3–18) can be satisfied simultaneously. In particular, we will be forced to drop the assumption of a universal time scale $t = t'$. Clearly, the relativistic transformation equations must be different from the classical ones if both observers are *each* to seem to be at the center of the same sphere.

As we consider what the new transformation equations are to be, we find that we are somewhat limited. These new equations must be linear. Any quadratic equation has two solutions and higher-order equations have more solutions. Surely any observations from the system S must have a unique interpretation in the system S'. There must be a "one-to-one" correspondence between what each observer "sees." The transformation equations must be linear in the space coordinates and in the times. Since the classical transformation equations for the x-coordinates were found to be $x' = x - vt$ and $x = x' + vt'$, let us here assume the next simplest linear equations,

$$x' = \gamma(x - vt) \qquad \text{and} \qquad x = \gamma'(x' + vt'), \qquad (A3–19)$$

where the γ's are transformation quantities to be determined. From the first equation, we find $x = vt$ for $x' = 0$. This describes correctly the motion of the origin of S' as seen by the observer in S. Conversely, we get from the second equation $x' = -vt'$ for $x = 0$. This describes correctly the motion of the origin of S as seen by the observer in S'. Note that these two equations give the same relative speed with which the two origins move away from each other and as measured by the two different observers. This is a necessary requirement that follows from the isotropy of space (implied by the first postulate).

The factor γ scales an observation of length, $x - vt$, made by one observer to match it with a corresponding observation x' made by the other. The other factor γ' performs the identical scaling for transformation in the other direction. It follows from Einstein's first postulate that the two γ's are equal. The reader may wonder how γ can possibly be anything but unity. Consider the following experiment.

Two observers, each holding a meter stick, pass by each other with their relative velocity being in the direction of the meter sticks. They compare the length of the sticks as they pass by. If they find that one appears to be shorter than the other because of this motion, this has clearly violated Einstein's first postulate. So, we must have $\gamma = 1$. What is wrong with this argument?

First of all, we have to be a bit careful about how to deal with the time t when we use Eqs. (A3–19) to calculate how the length of a material object changes in the transformation from one system to the other. We shall treat this in the next section and indeed shall find that there is a factor γ involved. The important question right now is how the two observers compare the lengths of their meter sticks. How does the observer in S know that one end of his meter stick matches up with the end of the other stick *simultaneously* with a match at the other end. This is clearly his basis for judgment as to whether they have the same length or not.

The key to the problem is that the two observers have different concepts of time. *Two events judged to be simultaneous by one observer are not simultaneous for the other.* Because of this, two rods judged to be of the same length by one observer are judged to be of different lengths by the other. The transformation equation for time, replacing $t' = t$, can be found by solving the two equations (A3–19) for t', eliminating x'. We find

$$t' = \gamma \left[\frac{x}{v} \left(\frac{1}{\gamma^2} - 1 \right) + t \right].$$

$$\text{(A3–20)}$$

If the experiment discussed above is repeated with two rods pointing in the y-direction, the result will be that, if one observer judges them to be of the same length, the other observer will agree. Place one observer in the middle of one rod and the other in the middle of the second rod. Two helpers at the ends of one rod sets off light flashes when and if two corresponding ends match up. If one observer sees two light flashes simultaneously, the other observer will too. Both will then judge that the rods are equal in length. By symmetry, then, they must be equal.* This means that the transformation equations for y and z remain

$$y' = y,$$
$$z' = z.$$

$$\text{(A3–21)}$$

Substituting Eqs. (A3–20), (A3–21), and the first of Eqs. (A3–19) into Eq. (A3–18), we obtain

$$\gamma^2(x - vt)^2 + y^2 + z^2 = c^2\gamma^2 \left[\frac{x}{v} \left(\frac{1}{\gamma^2} - 1 \right) + t \right]^2.$$

---

* In the x-direction, the setup is not symmetric in the same sense. The *front* end of one rod matches up with the *back* end of the other, front and back being defined by the direction of relative motion.

Upon expanding and collecting terms we have

$$\left[\gamma^2 - \frac{c^2\gamma^2}{v^2}\left(\frac{1}{\gamma^2} - 1\right)^2\right]x^2 - \left[2v\gamma^2 + \frac{2c^2\gamma^2}{v}\left(\frac{1}{\gamma^2} - 1\right)\right]xt + y^2 + z^2$$
$$= [c^2\gamma^2 - v^2\gamma^2]t^2.$$

(A3-22)

Equation (A3-22) must be identical to Eq. (A3-17). For this to be the case, the quantities in brackets in Eq. (A3-22) must be equal to 1, 0, and c^2, respectively. It is easily seen that all three requirements are fulfilled if we make

$$\frac{1}{\gamma^2} - 1 = \frac{v^2}{c^2},$$

which gives

$$\gamma = \frac{1}{\sqrt{1 - v^2/c^2}}.$$

(A3-23)

The consistency of these results means that mathematically it is possible to devise linear transformation equations which permit the transformation of one velocity to be invariant. We have chosen that one velocity to be the free-space velocity of light by assuming our two observers to be "watching" an expanding light wave. We need only modify the classical transformation equations by the inclusion of $\gamma = (1 - v^2/c^2)^{-1/2}$ and note that time, which was the same for all Newtonian observers, must now be transformed along with the space coordinates. Knowing γ, we can simplify Eq. (A3-20) to

$$t' = \gamma\left[t - \frac{vx}{c^2}\right].$$

(A3-24)

We can now summarize both classical and relativistic transformation equations for two observers having a relative velocity v parallel to the x-axis as follows:

Galileo-Newton (classical)	Lorentz-Einstein (relativistic)	
$x' = x - vt$	$x' = \gamma(x - vt)$	
$y' = y$	$y' = y$	
$z' = z$	$z' = z$	
$t' = t$	$t' = \gamma\left(t - \dfrac{vx}{c^2}\right),$	(A3-25)

where

$$\gamma = \frac{1}{\sqrt{1 - v^2/c^2}}.$$

Note that if $v \ll c$, then γ is nearly 1 and the relativistic transformation equations reduce to the Newtonian forms. Thus Newtonian physics can be regarded as a special case of relativistic physics. Recall that the tremendous velocity of the earth about the sun is $18 \text{ mi} \cdot \text{s}^{-1}$, but that this is still only one ten-thousandth of the velocity of light. Thus the relativity correction for the observation of positions from the earth compared with observations from the sun is only about 5×10^{-7} percent. Relativity makes no significant difference for "ordinary" engineering applications.

The relativistic transformation equations, however, point the way to important philosophical advances. The portion of special relativity we have developed applies only to observers not accelerated relative to each other. Note, however, that neither of these observers has a *preferred* viewpoint. If the transformation equations for primed quantities in terms of unprimed quantities are solved for the unprimed in terms of the primed ones, we obtain the *inverse transformations*. The resulting forms are the same except that the sign of their relative velocity, v, changes. [Thus $x = \gamma(x' + vt')$.] This one difference is expected, since if O' moves north relative to O, then O must move south relative to O'. A step has been taken toward the goal of general relativity, namely, that the laws of physics shall take on the same form for *all* observers.

A3–7 LENGTH CONTRACTION

Let us now consider a rod placed in the O' or primed reference frame, (Fig. A3–3) with its length parallel to the x-axis. Let the coordinate of the left end be x_1' and that of the right end be x_2'. The length of the rod as measured by an observer at rest with respect to the rod is called its *proper length*. Its value is $(x_2' - x_1')$ in this case. What is the length of the rod measured by an observer in the O, or unprimed, frame when the primed frame is moving in the positive x-direction with speed v? From Eq. (A3–25) we find that

$$x_1' = \gamma(x_1 - vt_1) \quad \text{and} \quad x_2' = \gamma(x_2 - vt_2).$$

Subtracting the first of these expressions from the second, we obtain

$$(x_2' - x_1') = \gamma[(x_2 - x_1) - v(t_2 - t_1)]. \tag{A3–26}$$

This equation shows that the measured distance between the ends of the rod in the O-frame can have many different values which depend upon the choice of t_1 and t_2, the times when the ends of the rod are observed. Because of this, we define the length of a moving rod as the measured distance between its ends obtained when the two ends are observed *simultaneously*. Then $t_1 = t_2$ and Eq. (A3–26) reduces to

$$(x_2' - x_1') = \gamma(x_2 - x_1) \tag{A3–27}$$

or

$$L' = \gamma L = (1 - v^2/c^2)^{-1/2}L.$$

Since γ is always greater than unity, L will always be less than the proper length, L', and therefore it is said that the rod has contracted. We now see that the Fitzgerald-Lorentz contraction discussed in Section A3–3 is mathematically the same as the relativistic length contraction given by Eq. (A3–27). However, the two equations are based on significantly different concepts. In the Fitzgerald-Lorentz contraction, v is the speed of the rod relative to the ether, whereas in the relativistic equation, it is the speed of the rod relative to an observer.

Assuming sufficient visual acuity, could one see that a moving body is contracted in the direction of its motion? It turns out that one could not if the moving body subtends a small angle at the observer. The situation here is not the same as that when we obtained Eq. (A3–27), the length contraction equation. When we see an object we have a retinal image produced by light quanta which arrive simultaneously at the retina from different points of the object. Therefore these light quanta could not have been emitted by every point on the object at the same time. The points farther away from the observer must have emitted their part of the image earlier than the closer points. In this case we cannot let $t_1 = t_2$ in Eq. (A3–26) and obtain Eq. (A3–27). When the differences in the times of emission are taken into account, it is found that a moving body which subtends a small angle at the observer will appear to have undergone a rotation but not a contraction. It is not at all difficult to derive this result, but it is too long for inclusion here. The method of arriving at this interesting conclusion is given in a paper by Terrell* and summarized and discussed in one by Weisskopf.† For the case when the moving object subtends a large angle at the observer, then, under suitable conditions which are stated in a paper by Scott and Viner,‡ the length contraction will be visible. The reader is urged to study these three articles.

A3–8 TIME DILATION AND CAUSAL SEQUENCE

The classical concept of time is contained in Newton's statement that "Absolute, true, and mathematical time, of itself and from its own nature, flows equably without relation to anything external." There is implicit in this that information can be transmitted at velocities so enormous compared with the relative velocity of observers on different reference frames that no question about defining simultaneity arises. When, however, we assume that light signals are the fastest possible way of communicating, we can expect to encounter difficulties in describing the motion of objects having velocities approaching that of light.

How is the time interval between two events in one reference frame related to the interval between events as observed from another frame moving with respect to the first? Again, as in Fig. A3–3, let the x-axes of the frames be

---

*   J. Terrell, *Phys. Rev.* **116** (1959) p. 1041.

†   V. F. Weisskopf, *Phys. Today* **13** (1960), p. 24.

‡   G. D. Scott and M. R. Viner, *Am. J. Phys.* **33** (1965), p. 354.

parallel and the relative velocity of the origins O and O' be v. Consider an event which occurs at time t_1 at place x_1 in the unprimed frame and a later event in the same frame at t_2, x_2. The transformations to t', obtained from Eq. (A3–25), are

$$t'_1 = \gamma \left(t_1 - \frac{vx_1}{c^2} \right) \quad \text{and} \quad t'_2 = \gamma \left(t_2 - \frac{vx_2}{c^2} \right).$$

By taking the difference between these expressions, we find the time interval in the primed frame to be

$$(t'_2 - t'_1) = \gamma \left[(t_2 - t_1) - \frac{v}{c^2}(x_2 - x_1) \right]. \tag{A3–28}$$

To discuss this equation, let us start by considering the case when both events in the O-frame occur at the same place, that is, $x_1 = x_2$. The time interval between two such events measured in the coordinate frame in which the two events occur at the same place is called the *proper time* or local time. In the case under discussion, $(t_2 - t_1)$ is the proper time and Eq. (A3–28) becomes

$$(t'_2 - t'_1) = \gamma(t_2 - t_1). \tag{A3–29}$$

Since γ is greater than unity, the time interval between two events measured by the observer in the O'-frame will be longer than the proper time, which is the value of the time interval between the same two events obtained by the observer in the O-frame. This is *time dilation* and we say that the "clock" in the O-frame, the moving clock, runs more slowly than the one in the O'-frame. It is to be noted that although $x_1 = x_2$, the coordinates x'_1 and x'_2 are not the same because of the relative displacement of the reference frames during the time $t_2 - t_1$. If two events had occurred at the same place in the primed system at times t'_1 and t'_2, then the inverse transformation shows that the unprimed system would also have reported time dilation given by

$$t_2 - t_1 = \gamma(t'_2 - t'_1).$$

Returning to Eq. (A3–29), we see that if the events in the unprimed frame are simultaneous, that is, $t_2 - t_1 = 0$, then we also have $t'_2 - t'_1 = 0$. Therefore two observers will agree on the simultaneity of two events if they occur simultaneously at the *same* place in either system of coordinates. Finally, note that if the speed of light were infinite, then $\gamma = 1$ and the time intervals in each frame would be equal or absolute, as Newton assumed.

Direct confirmation of time dilation is found in an experiment with mu-mesons. These are subatomic particles which can be created in the laboratory by high-energy particle accelerators. These particles are unstable and it is found that they disintegrate at an exponential rate such that one-half of them remain unchanged after 3.1×10^{-6} s, measured in the reference frame in which the mesons are at rest. These particles are also formed high in the earth's atmosphere by cosmic ray bombardment and are projected towards the earth's surface with a very high velocity. Consider a beam of these particles traveling down toward the earth at a speed of 0.9c. (For this speed, $\gamma = [1 - (0.9c/c)^2]^{-1/2} = [0.19]^{-1/2} = 2.3$.) This beam would traverse a distance of 840 m in 3.1×10^{-6} s. Therefore one would expect that if a meson counter were placed 840 m above another one in the atmosphere, then the count observed at the lower level would be half of that at the upper one. But it is found to be significantly greater than one half of the count at the upper level. The error in the prediction arose because the earth-bound observer used the proper half-life instead of the dilated one in his computations. The dilated half-life of the mesons, calculated from Eq. (A3–29), is $2.3 \times 3.1 \times 10^{-6}$ s = 7.2×10^{-6} s. Therefore the earth observer will obtain a higher count at a lower level than he first expected because this dilated half-life is much longer than 3.1×10^{-6} s, the time of flight between the counters. Let the earth observer increase the distance between counters to 1920 m, the product of the dilated half-life and the relative velocity of the reference frames. This observer will now find the lower level count to be half of that at the higher level. What does the observer riding along with the mesons report as the ratio of the counts? From his point of view, the separation of the counters is not 1920 m but, because of length contraction, is 840 m. This contracted length divided by 0.9c gives his time of flight between counters to be 3.1×10^{-6} s, which is equal to the proper half-life. Therefore, the observer in the meson frame will also find the lower-level count to be half of the upper-level one. Thus, both observers do agree upon the relative number of mesons that survived the trip between the counters, although the basic data each used in his calculations were quite different.

Let us now discuss the transformed time interval when the two events in the unprimed system do *not* occur at the same place. In this case the value of $t'_2 - t'_1$ is given by Eq. (A3–28). If the quantity within the brackets in this equation is equal to zero, then the two events are simultaneous in the primed frame. If the quantity is positive with $t_2 > t_1$, then events are observed in the same order in the primed frame as in the unprimed one. If it is negative, then the two events in O should appear in the reverse order from O'. To find the mathematical condition for a reversal, we will rewrite Eq. (A3–28) as follows:

$$t'_2 - t'_1 = \gamma(t_2 - t_1)\left[1 - \frac{v}{c}\frac{x_2 - x_1}{c(t_2 - t_1)}\right].$$

This shows that the quantity within brackets will be negative only if

$$\frac{x_2 - x_1}{c(t_2 - t_1)} > \frac{c}{v}.$$

This inequality can be realized only if the distance between x_2 and x_1 is greater than the distance traveled by light in the time $t_2 - t_1$. But if the separation of the two places were that large, then a light signal leaving event 1 could not reach event 2 soon enough to cause event 2. Thus, if two events appear in different time order to two observers, one event cannot be the cause of the other. Therefore, we must conclude that cause and effect will never appear in the reverse order to different observers.

Is time *really* dilated and is the length of a moving rod *really* contracted in the direction of its motion? The answers depend upon what is meant by *really*. In the physical sciences what is real is what is measured. Only through measurement can one obtain the information needed for assigning properties to a clock, to a rod, to an atom and so forth. Time dilation and length contraction are real in this sense. Proper time and proper length have nothing of an absolute nature about them. Time, length, area, volume and other quantities are all relations between an observed body and the observer.

A3–9 THE RELATIVISTIC VELOCITY TRANSFORMATION

To illustrate further how the transformation equations of space and time are used, let us repeat a calculation we made classically. We found the classical velocity transformation for observers with relative velocity v to be $u' = u - v$. To get the corresponding relativistic expression, we use the defining equations

$$u'_x = \frac{dx'}{dt'} \quad \text{and} \quad u_x = \frac{dx}{dt}.$$

We now express u' in terms of the differentials of unprimed quantities obtained from the relativistic transformation equations. The result is

$$u'_x = \frac{dx'}{dt'} = \frac{\gamma(dx - v\,dt)}{\gamma(dt - v\,dx/c^2)}$$

$$= \frac{dx/dt - v}{1 - (v/c^2)(dx/dt)},$$

or

$$u'_x = \frac{u_x - v}{1 - u_x v/c^2}. \tag{A3–30}$$

In a similar way we find the velocity components parallel to the other two axes to be

$$u'_y = \frac{u_y}{\gamma(1 - u_x v/c^2)} \quad \text{and} \quad u'_z = \frac{u_z}{\gamma(1 - u_x v/c^2)}. \tag{A3–31}$$

Note that the velocity components which are transverse to the relative motion of the reference frames depend upon the relative motion but that transverse distances do not.

Equation (A3–30) is the relativistic rule for transforming velocities when the observed velocity is *parallel* to the relative velocity of the observers. We see that as in the classical case, the velocity transformation is not invariant. Consider, however, what happens when the velocity under observation is the velocity of light, c. If one observer measures the velocity of light and gets $u_x = c$, what will another observer moving relative to the first obtain? The equation yields

$$u'_x = \frac{u_x - v}{1 - (u_x v/c^2)} = \frac{c - v}{1 - (cv/c^2)} = \frac{c - v}{(c - v)/c} = c.$$

Thus, regardless of their own relative velocity v, any two observers will agree that the velocity of light is c. In relativity, the velocity of light is *invariant*. This result should not surprise us, since it was used as a basic assumption for the derivation of the transformation equations. It is one example of the "uncommon" sense we promised to discuss at the very beginning of this book.

Although the result just derived follows logically from the assumptions of relativity and therefore should not surprise us, a further comment may be helpful. Suppose observer O measures the distance light travels during an interval of time and computes the velocity of light, obtaining c. Let another observer O' moving relative to O perform the same experiment. Intuitively we feel he cannot get the same result, c. But if O and O' both have "rubber" rulers and "defective" clocks, we see that their results may have any values— including c. The transformation equations of the special theory of relativity are a description of how "rubber" rulers and "defective" clocks vary so that the velocity of light can be unique, so that velocities small compared with c behave classically, and so that intermediate cases lead to no contradictions.

Einstein presented his theory of special relativity in 1905. The theory immediately resolved the apparent controversy over ether motion presented by three different experiments. One was the Michelson-Morley experiment that could earlier be explained if one assumed that the ether was dragged by the earth in its orbit. The second was the stellar aberration experiments which dealt with the apparent change in the position of a star when the earth changes direction of motion in its orbit, as measured over a year. The stellar aberration observations were consistent with an ether fixed in the system of the sun. The third experiment was Fizeau's experiment on the velocity of light through a moving liquid. This required an ether that was partly dragged with the liquid. Einstein's theory did away with the ether and correctly predicted the results of all three types of experiments. The study of the atomic nucleus and the elementary particles has produced more dramatic tests of the theory. To discuss these matters, we need to investigate the effect of the transformation equation on other physical laws dealing not only with position, time, and velocity, but also with mass, force, and energy.

A3–10   RELATIVISTIC MASS TRANSFORMATION

Consider two basketballs which are spherical, perfectly elastic and have identical masses when compared by an observer at rest relative to them. We give one ball to an observer O' on a railroad train, moving relative to the ground with a constant translational velocity v. We give the other ball to an observer O on the ground at a distance d from the railroad track. The observers have not yet passed each other and we tell each that he is to throw his ball with a certain velocity in a direction perpendicular to the track in such a way that the basketballs bounce perfectly off each other just at the moment when the two observers pass each other. (Deflections caused by gravity are irrelevant to this discussion.)

Assuming sufficient skill, this experiment could be carried out and fully understood on the basis of classical mechanics. Each observer sees his ball hit and return to him just as though it had bounced from a perfectly elastic wall with kinetic energy conserved. Each observer must anticipate the moment of passing, and the movements of the balls are as shown in Fig. A3–4.

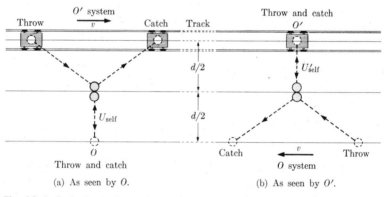

Fig. A3–4 Perfectly elastic collision of two identical basketballs as viewed from systems in relative motion.

In the analysis that follows we will consider four velocities. U'_{self} is the velocity O' observes he has given to his ball, and U_{self} is the velocity O observes he has given to his ball. By a condition of the experiment, $U'_{self} = U_{self}$. The velocity that observer O assigns to the ball thrown by O' will be called U'_{other}, and the velocity O' assigns to the ball thrown by O will be U_{other}.

If we now treat the situation just described from the standpoint of Einsteinian relativity, a new idea emerges. Distances perpendicular to the relative velocity of the balls are unaffected by relativity considerations, since we found that $y = y'$ and $z = z'$. Thus both observers agree that their basketballs move to and from the impact point a total distance d. But the two observers have different kinds of time. Observer O' was told how fast he should throw his ball. He throws at time t'_1 and catches at time t'_2, so that in his opinion

$$U'_{\text{self}} = \frac{d}{t'_2 - t'_1}. \tag{A3–32}$$

Observer O disagrees with observer O' as to when and where he threw and caught his ball. Observer O says O' threw the ball from x_1 at the time $t_1 = \gamma[t'_1 + (vx'_1/c^2)]$ and caught it as x_2 at the time $t_2 = \gamma[t'_2 + (vx'_2/c^2)]$. Observer O computes the velocity with which O' threw his ball to be U'_{other}, where

$$U'_{\text{other}} = \frac{d}{t_1 - t_2} = \frac{d}{\gamma[(t'_2 - t'_1) + (v/c^2)(x'_2 - x'_1)]}. \tag{A3–32a}$$

In this expression, the quantity $(x'_2 - x'_1)$ is the amount observer O' must displace himself in order to catch the ball. Since we stated that the ball comes directly back to each observer, this quantity is zero, and Eq. (A3–32a) becomes

$$U'_{\text{other}} = \frac{d}{\gamma(t'_2 - t'_1)} = \frac{U'_{\text{self}}}{\gamma}. \tag{A3–33}$$

Since γ is always greater than unity, it appears to observer O that observer O' has thrown his ball slower than he was told to. A similar calculation would show that observer O' would think observer O had thrown *his* ball slower than he was told to, or

$$U_{\text{other}} = \frac{U_{\text{self}}}{\gamma}. \tag{A3–33a}$$

We are now faced with a dilemma. If we assume that the masses remain the same as when they were compared without relative velocity, then conservation of momentum is violated. If we keep conservation of momentum, then the relative motion which made a difference in the observed velocities of the basketballs also resulted in an observed difference in their masses. *Let us choose to retain the law of conservation of momentum.* Observer O, who sees his ball change in momentum an amount $2m_{\text{self}}U_{\text{self}}$, equates this change to the change he observes for the other ball. He writes

$$2m_{\text{self}}U_{\text{self}} = 2m_{\text{other}}U'_{\text{other}}. \tag{A3–34}$$

When the value of U'_{other} from Eq. (A3–33) is substituted in Eq. (A3–34), it becomes

$$2m_{\text{self}}U_{\text{self}} = 2m_{\text{other}}\frac{U_{\text{self}}}{\gamma}, \tag{A3–35}$$

which, since the throws were equal such that $U'_{\text{self}} = U'_{\text{self}}$, reduces to

$$m_{\text{other}} = \gamma m_{\text{self}}. \tag{A3–36}$$

Thus observer O concludes that the masses of the balls are not equal and that there must be a transformation equation for mass in addition to those for the other quantities we have discussed.

Equation (A3–36) gives the relationship between a mass moving relative to the observer with a velocity U_{self} and one moving with a velocity $(v^2 + U'^2_{other})^{1/2}$. We should like to have a relationship between the mass of a body at rest in the observer's frame and one moving with a velocity v, for instance. This is most easily obtained from Eq. (A3–36) by the simple trick of letting the transverse velocities U approach zero. In the limit, then, we have

$$ m = \gamma m_0 = \frac{m_0}{\sqrt{1 - (v^2/c^2)}}, \qquad (A3\text{–}37) $$

where m_0 (called the rest mass) is the mass of a body at rest relative to the measurer, and m (called the moving, or relativistic, mass) is the observed mass of the body when it has a velocity v relative to the measurer. The system in which the observer is located is usually called the laboratory system.

This result, which has been deduced from the space transformation equations, with the additional requirement that momentum be conserved, can be tested experimentally. What is required is the measurement of the mass of a body moving at great speed relative to an observer. J. J. Thomson was startled when he computed the speed of electrons in his cathode-ray tubes. These speeds were greater than any previously measured by man and, by modern methods, can be made significant compared with the free-space velocity of light, c. Furthermore, an e/m_e experiment is a measure of m_e if we assume that the charge e of the particle is constant. In principle, then, J. J. Thomson provided a technique for the testing of the mass-transformation equation. The first adequate test and verification was made in 1908 by Bucherer, using electrons from a radioactive source, and since then the mass-transformation equation has been confirmed innumerable times. It is now a cornerstone of atomic, nuclear, and particle physics.

A3–11 RELATIVISTIC MASS-ENERGY EQUIVALENCE

The derived and experimentally verified mass-transformation equation has important consequences, one of which is a new expression for the kinetic energy to replace $E_k = \frac{1}{2} mv^2$. Suppose we increase the kinetic energy of a body an amount dE_k by exerting a force through a distance. The change of kinetic energy equals the work done, or

$$ dE_k = \mathbf{F} \cdot d\mathbf{s}. $$

This is the classical expression relating a change in kinetic energy to the work, defined as $\mathbf{F} \cdot d\mathbf{s}$. We choose to retain this expression in our development of a relativistic mechanics. Similarly, we choose to retain Newton's second law, which can be considered the definition of force:

$$F = \frac{dp}{dt} = \frac{d(mv)}{dt},$$

where we have as before written $p = mv$, but with m now being the relativistic (increased) mass.

The change of kinetic energy then is

$$dE_k = \frac{d(mv)}{dt} \cdot ds. \qquad (A3\text{--}38)$$

But since $ds/dt = v$, we can write the preceding equation as

$$dE_k = v \cdot d(mv) = v^2\,dm + mv \cdot dv. \qquad (A3\text{--}39)$$

This expression can be simplified by using the mass-transformation equation, Eq. (A3–37), which after squaring and rearranging becomes

$$m^2c^2 = m^2v^2 + m_0^2c^2. \qquad (A3\text{--}40)$$

We now differentiate, noting that $v^2 = v \cdot v$ and that both m_0 and c are constant. We obtain

$$2mc^2\,dm = 2mv^2\,dm + 2m^2v\,dv. \qquad (A3\text{--}41)$$

When $2m$ is divided out of this equation, the right side becomes identical with our expression for dE_k in Eq. (A3–39), so we have, finally,

$$\boxed{dE_k = c^2\,dm.} \qquad (A3\text{--}42)$$

This famous equation shows that in relativity a change in kinetic energy can be expressed in terms of mass as the variable. This equation is valid for a change of energy in any form whatever, although it was derived here for a change of kinetic energy.

Since the kinetic energy is zero when $v = 0$, then it is also zero when $m = m_0$. Therefore we integrate, and obtain

$$E_k = \int_0^{E_k} dE_k = c^2 \int_{m_0}^{m} dm = c^2(m - m_0)$$

or

$$\boxed{E_k = mc^2 - m_0c^2.} \qquad (A3\text{--}43)$$

This is the relativistic expression for kinetic energy. The classical relation $E_k = \frac{1}{2}mv^2$ does *not* give the correct value of the kinetic energy even when the relativistic values of the mass and the velocity are used.

Like the other transformation equations, this expression for E_k should reduce to the classical expression for $v \ll c$. If we transform m in Eq. (A3–43), we obtain

$$E_k = \frac{m_0 c^2}{\sqrt{1 - (v^2/c^2)}} - m_0 c^2.$$ (A3–44)

Now, since $v \ll c$, we can say

$$\frac{1}{\sqrt{1 - (v^2/c^2)}} = \left(1 - \frac{v^2}{c^2}\right)^{-1/2} = \left(1 + \frac{v^2}{2c^2} + \frac{3}{8}\frac{v^4}{c^4} + \cdots\right),$$ (A3–45)

where we have carried three terms of the binomial expansion. We then have, from Eq. (A3–44),

$$E_k = m_0 c^2 \left(1 + \frac{v^2}{2c^2} + \frac{3}{8}\frac{v^4}{c^4} + \cdots - 1\right)$$

$$= \frac{1}{2} m_0 v^2 + \frac{3}{8} m_0 \frac{v^4}{c^2} + \cdots$$ (A3–46)

The first term of this is the classical expression for the kinetic energy. Obviously, it is the only significant term for low velocities.

In our derivation of a relativistic mechanics, we have used:

1. The relativistic transformation equation for distance, time, and velocity;
2. The law of conservation of momentum which, together with point 1, led to the concept of a mass increasing with the velocity of a body relative to the observer;
3. The definition of force by Newton's second law;
4. The classical definition of work and the relationship between work and change in kinetic energy.

By retaining the classical conservation laws and concepts, we have constructed a relativistic mechanics that is as simple as possible and also as close to classical mechanics as possible. The important changes that we need to remember when solving problems in relativistic mechanics (i.e., when v/c is not small) are the variable mass and the new formula for kinetic energy.

Equation (A3–42) or (A3–43) shows that there is a very intimate relationship between mass and energy. Einstein suggested that there also is energy associated with the rest mass of a body. According to this view, Eq. (A3–43) can be written as

$$E = mc^2 = m_0 c^2 + E_k$$ (A3–47)

where E or mc^2 is the total energy, $m_0 c^2$ is the rest energy and E_k is the kinetic energy of a body. All relevant experimental data show that Einstein was right.

Potential energy could also be included in Eq. (A3–47), but not without including other interacting bodies. Potential energy is a result of conservative forces acting *between* two or more bodies. For such a system of bodies, the total energy mc^2 is the sum of all rest energies, kinetic energies, and potential energies. An interesting consequence of this statement is that the rest mass of the hydrogen atom is less than the sum of the rest mass of the two constituents, the proton and the electron. The difference is the mass equivalent of 13.6 eV or, stated as a fraction: $\Delta m/m = 1.45 \times 10^{-8}$.

We can now obtain an important relation between the total mass-energy E of a body and its momentum p from Eq. (A3–40). If we multiply through this equation by c^2 and make the appropriate substitutions from $E = mc^2$ and $p = mv$, we get

$$E^2 = p^2c^2 + m_0^2c^4. \tag{A3–48}$$

This equation gives the relationship between the total energy, the rest energy, and the momentum. By substituting E from Eq. (A3–47) and solving for the momentum, we obtain

$$p = \sqrt{2m_0E_k + E_k^2/c^2}. \tag{A3–49}$$

Except for the second term under the square root, this equation is identical with the classical formula for momentum. The last term is therefore called the *relativistic-correction term*.

As an aid for the memory, Eq. (A3–48) is represented graphically in Fig. A3–5. The figure has no real meaning, but is merely given as a mnemonic device.

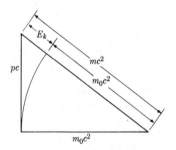

Fig. A3–5 Mnemonic triangle for the relationship $(mc^2)^2 = (m_0c^2)^2 + (pc)^2$.

The equivalence of mass and energy brings a satisfying consequence. The broad principle of conservation of energy now takes unto itself another broad conservation principle, the conservation of mass. The identity of mass and energy resulting in a unified concept of mass-energy is certainly the most "practical" consequence of relativity. In Chapter 12, it is shown how nuclear reactions and nuclear disintegration processes demonstrate the fact that neither mass nor energy as conceived classically is conserved separately. In relativity we see that it is mass-energy that is conserved. In any interaction the *total mass*, m (which includes any kinetic energy in mass units), is *the same before and after* the interaction. Similarly, in any interaction, the *total energy E* (which includes any rest mass in energy units), is *the same before and after* the interaction. We are now witnessing the growth of the whole new field of nuclear engineering which is based on E equals mc^2.

Most of the mass-energy we use comes from the sun, where rest mass-energy is converted into thermal energy. Today mankind is converting rest mass-energy into thermal energy here on the earth. Nuclear fission and fusion are the techniques for this conversion.

A3–12 THE UPPER LIMIT OF VELOCITY

An examination of Eq. (A3–37), the mass-transformation equation, shows that for $v = c$, $m = \infty$. Thus, as the velocity of a body increases toward the free-space velocity of light, the mass of the body increases toward infinity. Since it is absurd for any body with finite rest mass m_0 to have infinite energy, we must conclude that it is impossible for such a body to move with the free-space velocity of light. Thus in relativistic mechanics the free-space velocity of light is the greatest velocity that can be given to any material particle. If a tiny particle is given equal increments of energy, the first increments increase the velocity significantly and the mass insignificantly. But as the particle gains more and more energy, the velocity changes become less as the velocity approaches the velocity of light. As the velocity changes become insignificant, the mass changes become significant.

Putting the same argument another way, we have two equations for the kinetic energy of a body, both of which are correct relativistic expressions. Equation (A3–44) expresses E_k in terms of m_0 and v. For v small compared with c, this is the convenient formula, especially since it reduces to the first term of Eq. (A3–46), the classical expression. The other equation is $E_k = c^2(m - m_0)$, Eq. (A3–43). This equation expresses E_k in terms of m_0 and the variable moving mass, m. When the velocity is near c, the mass is the more convenient variable. We can express E_k in terms of either m or v, since we have the mass-variation equation, Eq. (A3–37), relating m and v.

Since we argued that the free-space velocity of light is an upper limit for material particles, it is fair to ask whether any velocities equal or exceed this velocity. We have been careful in this discussion to emphasize that the limit is the *free-space* velocity of light. Light itself often travels more slowly than its free-space velocity. The index of refraction of a medium is the ratio of the free-space velocity of light to the actual velocity in the medium. In water, for example, a particle may travel faster than light *in that medium*.

Photons in free space obviously travel with the free-space velocity of light. We have found that photons have energy $h\nu$, and since we have shown that mass and energy are equivalent we can conclude that each photon has a mass hv/c^2. Here, then, is a mass particle actually traveling with the free-space velocity of light. But there is no contradiction here. A photon has no rest mass m_0. If we stop a photon to measure its mass, all its mass-energy is transferred to something else and the photon no longer exists. Perhaps the main difference between a "material" particle and a photon particle is that one has rest mass while the other does not.

There are times when one may encounter velocities greater than the free-space velocity of light, but on these occasions the thing moving is a mathematical function rather than a physical reality. The transmission of a "dot" in radio telegraphy may be regarded as the resultant of the transmission of several frequencies having different velocities. These velocities, called phase velocities, may exceed the free-space velocity of light. The motion of the resultant "dot" is called a group velocity, and it can never exceed the free-space velocity of light. We may state with complete generality that no observer can find the *velocity of mass-energy in any form to exceed the free-space velocity of light.*

A3–13 MOTION OF CHARGED PARTICLES IN MAGNETIC FIELDS

In Section 2–2, we discussed the motion of a charged particle in a magnetic field in terms of classical mechanics. We stated that the formula relating the momentum mv of the particle and the orbit radius R,

$$qBR = mv, \tag{A3–50}$$

is relativistically correct. This is so because the magnetic force is always perpendicular to v; there is therefore no change of speed and no change of m. In the following, we are assuming that the particles move in a plane perpendicular to B. We have therefore dropped the subscript $\perp$ on v used in Eq. (2–5).

The product BR is called the *magnetic rigidity* of the particle. Equation (A3–50) shows that the magnetic rigidity is equal to the momentum divided by the charge

$$BR = \frac{p}{q}. \tag{A3–51}$$

The utility of this concept is that it enables us to determine quickly the orbit radius of the particle in a given magnetic field B.

If the kinetic energy and rest mass of a particle are given, rather than the momentum, we can find the magnetic rigidity by combining Eqs. (A3–51) and (A3–49). We obtain

$$BR = \frac{1}{cz} \sqrt{\frac{2m_0c^2}{e}\frac{E_k}{e} + \left(\frac{E_k}{e}\right)^2}. \tag{A3–52}$$

Here z is the number of elementary charges carried by the particle and e is the elementary charge in Coulombs (mks), numerically equal to the conversion factor e_c between Coulombs and electron volts. With the energies including m_0c^2 inserted in electron volts, Eq. (A3–52) becomes

$$BR = \frac{1}{cz} \sqrt{2(m_0c^2)E_k + E_k^2}. \tag{A3–52a}$$

The magnetic rigidity here comes out in mksa units, i.e., Webers/meter. In practice, BR is measured in kilogauss-centimeters, and the energies for relativistic particles are measured in MeV (million electron volts). By inserting the value of c and using MeV as units for m_0c^2 and E_k, we find

$$BR = \frac{3.334}{z} \sqrt{2(m_0c^2)E_k + E_k^2} \text{ kilogauss-cm.} \tag{A3–52b}$$

The rest energy for the electron is $m_ec^2 = 0.511004$ MeV and for the proton $m_pc^2 = 938.259$ MeV. Equation (A3–52) shows that the relativistic correction term is not important if $E_k \ll m_0c^2$.

The magnetic rigidity is plotted versus kinetic energy in Fig. A3–6 for the electron, the proton, the alpha particle, and for the two heavier hydrogen isotopes, the deuteron (mass number 2) and the triton (mass number 3).

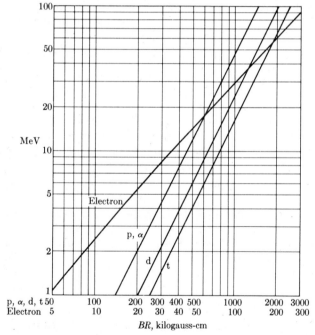

Fig. A3–6 Magnetic rigidity for electrons, alpha particles, protons, deuterons, and tritons.

Matrix Algebra

A matrix is simply a collection of numbers, real or complex, ordered in a rectangular array, thus

$$\mathbf{R} \equiv \begin{bmatrix} R_{11} & R_{12} & R_{13} & \cdots \\ R_{21} & R_{22} & R_{23} & \cdots \\ \vdots & \vdots & \vdots & \end{bmatrix}. \tag{A4-1}$$

The number R_{ij} is called a *matrix element*. Its place in the matrix is the ith row and jth column.

If two matrices $\mathbf{R}$ and $\mathbf{S}$ have the same number of rows and columns, they can be added

$$\mathbf{R} + \mathbf{S} = \mathbf{T}, \tag{A4-2}$$

and this operation means, by definition, that we add each individual element, thus:

$$\mathbf{R}_{ij} + \mathbf{S}_{ij} = \mathbf{T}_{ij}. \tag{A4-3}$$

A matrix with only one column, such as

$$\mathbf{a} = \begin{bmatrix} a_1 \\ a_2 \\ a_3 \\ \vdots \end{bmatrix}, \tag{A4-4}$$

is called a *column vector* or *column matrix*. The multiplicative operation

$$\mathbf{b} = \mathbf{Ra} \tag{A4-5}$$

can be performed when $\mathbf{a}$ has as many elements (rows) as $\mathbf{R}$ has columns. By definition, the operation means that the elements of the new column matrix $\mathbf{b}$ are given by

$$b_i = \sum_j R_{ij} a_j. \tag{A4-6}$$

Example:

$$\begin{bmatrix} 6 \\ -2 \\ 5 \end{bmatrix} = \begin{bmatrix} 2 & 1 & 2 \\ 0 & 1 & -1 \\ 3 & 0 & 1 \end{bmatrix} \begin{bmatrix} 1 \\ 0 \\ 2 \end{bmatrix}.$$

The first element in the product matrix is, according to Eq. (A4–6), formed by multiplying the first line in R with the elements of a, one by one, and adding the products. The second and third elements are formed similarly.

In general, two matrices can be multiplied together, such as

$$\mathbf{T = RS,} \qquad (A4\text{–}7)$$

when the number of columns of R equals the number of rows of S. The law of multiplication is then (by definition)

$$T_{ij} = \sum_k R_{ik} S_{kj}. \qquad (A4\text{–}8)$$

The resultant matrix has the number of rows of S and the number of columns of R.

Example:

$$\begin{bmatrix} -2 & 1 \\ 6 & -3 \end{bmatrix} = \begin{bmatrix} 2 & 1 & -2 \\ 0 & -1 & 3 \end{bmatrix} \begin{bmatrix} 1 & -1 \\ 0 & 3 \\ 2 & 0 \end{bmatrix}.$$

The element in the first row and first column of T is the sum of products of the first row in R and the first column in S, etc.

In general, multiplication is noncommutative; i.e.,

$$\mathbf{RS \neq SR.} \qquad (A4\text{–}9)$$

This can easily be shown by simple examples. In the special cases where $RS = SR$, we say that the two matrices *commute*.

The distributive law of multiplication holds for matrices, thus

$$\mathbf{R(S + T) = RS + RT.} \qquad (A4\text{–}10)$$

The associative law of multiplication also holds

$$\mathbf{R(ST) = (RS)T.} \qquad (A4\text{–}11)$$

A square matrix *may* have an inverse, such that

$$\mathbf{RR^{-1} = I = R^{-1}R,} \qquad (A4\text{–}12)$$

where I is the identity matrix defined by

$$I_{ij} = \delta_{ij}, \qquad (A4\text{–}13)$$

where δ_{ij} is the Kronecker symbol. In other words, I has nonzero elements only along the $i = j$ diagonal, and all these elements are equal to unity.

Addition of Angular Momenta

Two angular momenta, J_1 and J_2, with quantum numbers J_1 and J_2 can be combined to a resultant J with quantum number

$$|J_1 - J_2| \lesssim J \lesssim J_1 + J_2. \tag{A5-1}$$

The angular-momentum eigenstate having a fixed value of M, as well as of J, does not, in general, have fixed values of M_1 and M_2. This point is illustrated in the semiclassical diagram, Fig. A5–1, which is identical to Fig. 7–10.

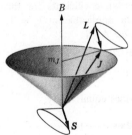

Fig. A5–1 Coupling of L and S to a total angular momentum J in a weak magnetic field. The L- and S-vectors precess in synchronization about the J-vector.

In this case, $J_1 = L = 3$, $J_2 = S = \frac{1}{2}$, $J = \frac{5}{2}$, and $M = \frac{3}{2}$. The two vectors J_1 and J_2, according to the explanation accompanying Fig. 7–10, precess about their resultant J because of a mutual torque. Therefore, their z-components, M_1 and M_2, are continuously changing.

In the rigorous quantum-mechanical description, the eigenstate with quantum numbers J and M resulting from adding J_1 and J_2 is a linear combination of all possible states satisfying the relationship

$$M_1 + M_2 = M. \tag{A5-2}$$

In the example just quoted, there are only two such combinations

$$M_1 = 2, \qquad M_2 = -\tfrac{1}{2},$$
$$M_1 = 1, \qquad M_2 = \tfrac{1}{2}.$$

In general, we can write

$$|J_1 J_2 J M\rangle = \sum_{M_1 + M_2 = M} |J_1 J_2 M_1 M_2\rangle \langle J_1 J_2 M_1 M_2 \mid J_1 J_2 J M\rangle. \qquad \text{(A5–3)}$$

In this equation, $|J_1 J_2 J M\rangle$ means the final angular-momentum eigenstate with quantum numbers J and M formed by combining two angular momenta with quantum numbers J_1 and J_2. Further, $|J_1 J_2 M_1 M_2\rangle$ signifies a state (not a final eigenstate) described by specifying J_1, J_2, M_1, and M_2. The symbol $\langle J_1 J_2 M_1 M_2 \mid J_1 J_2 J M\rangle$ stands for a coefficient numerically smaller than unity, giving the amplitude of the partial wave function $|J_1 J_2 M_1 M_2\rangle$ in $|J_1 J_2 J M\rangle$. The sum in Eq. (A5–3) is taken over all possible combinations satisfying Eq. (A5–2).

The coefficients $\langle J_1 J_2 M_1 M_2 \mid J_1 J_2 J M\rangle$ are calculated by requiring that $|J_1 J_2 J M\rangle$ be an eigenfunction of the angular-momentum operator L_{op}^2 and the operator $L_{z\,\text{op}}$ for the z-component. The coefficients are called *Clebsch-Gordan vector-addition coefficients*. There are about as many different notations for these coefficients as there are textbooks using them. We are here following the notation of the fundamental spectroscopy text by Condon and Shortley.*

Table A5–1 gives formulas for the Clebsch-Gordan coefficients for the special case $J_2 = \tfrac{1}{2}$, and Table A5–2 shows the formulas applicable for $J_2 = 1$.

For the example quoted above, we find from Table A5–1:

$$\langle 3\ \tfrac{1}{2}\ 2\ -\tfrac{1}{2} \mid 3\ \tfrac{1}{2}\ \tfrac{5}{2}\ \tfrac{3}{2}\rangle = -(\tfrac{2}{7})^{1/2}$$
$$\langle 3\ \tfrac{1}{2}\ 1\quad \tfrac{1}{2} \mid 3\ \tfrac{1}{2}\ \tfrac{5}{2}\ \tfrac{3}{2}\rangle = (\tfrac{5}{7})^{1/2}.$$

Note that the sum of the squares of the two amplitudes equals unity.

Table A5–1   Clebsch-Gordan Coefficients for the Case $J_2 = 1/2$

J	$M_2 = 1/2$	$M_2 = -1/2$
$J_1 + 1/2$	$\sqrt{\dfrac{J_1 + M + 1/2}{2J_1 + 1}}$	$\sqrt{\dfrac{J_1 - M + 1/2}{2J_1 + 1}}$
$J_1 - 1/2$	$-\sqrt{\dfrac{J_1 - M + 1/2}{2J_1 + 1}}$	$\sqrt{\dfrac{J_1 + M + 1/2}{2J_1 + 1}}$

* E. U. Condon and G. H. Shortley, *The Theory of Atomic Spectra*. Cambridge: The University Press (1964).

Table A5–2 Clebsch-Gordan Coefficients for the Case $J_2 = 1$.

J	$M_2 = 1$	$M_2 = 0$
$J_1 + 1$	$\sqrt{\dfrac{(J_1 + M)(J_1 + M + 1)}{(2J_1 + 1)(2J_1 + 2)}}$	$\sqrt{\dfrac{(J_1 - M + 1)(J_1 + M + 1)}{(2J_1 + 1)(J_1 + 1)}}$
J_1	$\sqrt{\dfrac{(J_1 + M)(J_1 - M + 1)}{2J_1(J_1 + 1)}}$	$\dfrac{M}{\sqrt{J_1(J_1 + 1)}}$
$J_1 - 1$	$\sqrt{\dfrac{(J_1 - M)(J_1 - M + 1)}{2J_1(2J_1 + 1)}}$	$-\sqrt{\dfrac{(J_1 - M)(J_1 + M)}{J_1(2J_1 + 1)}}$

J	$M_2 = -1$
$J_1 + 1$	$\sqrt{\dfrac{(J_1 - M)(J_1 - M + 1)}{(2J_1 + 1)(2J_1 + 2)}}$
J_1	$\sqrt{\dfrac{(J_1 - M)(J_1 + M + 1)}{2J_1(J_1 + 1)}}$
$J_1 - 1$	$\sqrt{\dfrac{(J_1 + M + 1)(J_1 + M)}{2J_1(2J_1 + 1)}}$

Relativistic Spin-Orbit Effect

This subject can be dealt with satisfactorily only with relativistic quantum mechanics, which would be beyond the scope of this book. However, with a crude dynamic model it is possible to get a qualitative understanding of the effect, and with a Lorentz transformation between the electron and laboratory frames it is possible to justify the quantitative result.

Figure A6–1 shows a ring spinning about its own axis and at the same time moving in a circle about a fixed point O. At any point on the ring, the orbital velocity v is superimposed upon the velocity ωa due to the spinning motion. At point A, the two velocities add arithmetically to a maximum, and at point B, the resultant velocity is a minimum. Therefore, *the relativistic mass per unit length of the ring is larger at A than at B.* The result is that the center of mass of the ring is not at C, but is displaced towards A to some point C'. This displacement represents for the case shown an increase in the orbital radius to the center of mass and, therefore, an increase in the orbital angular momentum. If the ring were spinning in the opposite direction, the highest velocity would be at B, and the oribital radius to the center of mass would be decreased.

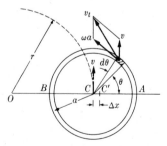

Fig. A6–1   Ring with spin and orbital angular momentum.

In relativistic quantum mechanics, the same quantization rules for the total angular momentum J hold as in the nonrelativistic theory. Therefore r has to be adjusted by an amount $-\Delta r$ and $+\Delta r$, respectively, in the two cases discussed above, so that the radius to the center of mass is the same in both.

We will now go a step further with our model and assume that the ring is uniformly charged and moving in a hydrogenlike orbit, i.e., under the influence of an attractive potential of the form $V(r) = -Ze^2/4\pi\varepsilon_0 r$. After adjusting the position of the ring as described above, the energy has changed by an amount

$$\Delta E = -\frac{dV}{dr}\,\Delta r. \tag{A6-1}$$

We are assuming that the only significant effect of the combined motion not earlier accounted for is a shift of the center of mass. In general, we are performing these calculations to the lowest significant order neglecting such refinements as the relativistic contraction of the ring in the direction of the velocity vector v and relativistic compounding of velocities.

We shall now proceed to estimate Δr. The mass of a section of the ring between θ and $\theta + d\theta$ can be expressed as

$$dm = \frac{m_0}{2\pi}\,\gamma\,d\theta, \tag{A6-2}$$

where

$$\gamma = (1 - v_t^2/c^2)^{-1/2}, \tag{A6-3}$$

and m_0 is the mass of the ring *completely at rest*.

The velocity v_t is given by

$$\begin{aligned} v_t^2 &= (v + \omega a \cos\theta)^2 + (\omega a \sin\theta)^2 \\ &= v^2 + \omega^2 a^2 + 2\omega a v \cos\theta. \end{aligned} \tag{A6-4}$$

We now find the displacement Δr of the center of mass as

$$\Delta r = \frac{\int a \cos\theta\,dm}{\int dm} = \frac{a\int \gamma \cos\theta\,d\theta}{\int \gamma\,d\theta}. \tag{A6-5}$$

Expanding Eq. (A6-3) and retaining only two terms of the expansion, we get

$$\int_0^{2\pi} \gamma \cos\theta\,d\theta \approx \int_0^{2\pi} \left[1 + \frac{1}{2c^2}(v^2 + \omega^2 a^2 + 2\omega a v \cos\theta)\right]\cos\theta\,d\theta. \tag{A6-6}$$

The three first terms in the integrand multiplied with $\cos\theta$ average zero. The last term varies as $\cos^2\theta$, which averages $\frac{1}{2}$ over the period. Therefore

$$\int_0^{2\pi} \gamma \cos\theta\,d\theta \approx \frac{\pi\omega v a}{c^2}. \tag{A6-7}$$

We write the integral in the denominator of Eq. (A6–5) as

$$\int_0^{2\pi} \gamma \, d\theta = 2\pi\gamma_{av}, \tag{A6–8}$$

with γ_{av} meaning the average γ for the ring. The expansion (Eq. A6–6) is only valid for $v_t^2/c^2 \ll 1$, so to be consistent, we must put $\gamma_{av} \simeq 1$. By inserting Eqs. (A6–7) and (A6–8) into Eq. (A6–5), we then get

$$\Delta r = \frac{\omega a^2 v}{2c^2} . \tag{A6–9}$$

We now introduce the spin of the ring $S = ma^2\omega$ and the orbital angular momentum $L = mrv$. This yields, with Eq. (A6–1),

$$\Delta E = -\frac{1}{2} \frac{dV}{dr} \frac{LS}{m^2c^2r} . \tag{A6–10}$$

By inserting the coulomb potential $V = -Ze^2/4\pi\varepsilon_0 r$, we get for the relativistic part of the spin-orbit energy

$$\Delta E = -\frac{1}{2} \frac{Ze^2LS}{4\pi\varepsilon_0 m^2 c^2 r^3} . \tag{A6–11}$$

It is interesting to note that the parameters a and ω enter only into the final expression by being implicit in the factor S. If the spinning object were not a ring but could be subdivided into rings of constant a's and ω's, the result of the calculation would be identical to Eq. (A6–11).

Equation (A6–11) happens to be the correct expression for the relativistic part of the spin-orbit energy if we interpret LS as a scalar product, m as the electron rest mass, and replace r^{-3} with $\langle r^{-3} \rangle$. At first glance this is surprising because we have used a simple mechanical model of the electron which, for other applications, has been shown to fail miserably. In particular, we are not justified at all in assuming that $v_t^2/c^2 \ll 1$. Qualitatively, however, we have shown that there must be a relativistic spin-orbit energy, assuming a quantized total angular momentum. We have also demonstrated what the sign of the energy is relative to the sign of the scalar product $L \cdot S$.

Our discussion has led to the conclusion that flipping the spin of an electron relative to its orbital angular momentum involves a change in relativistic energy. This means that, viewed from the laboratory frame, an apparent torque is acting on the electron other than that produced by the magnetic coupling, as discussed in Section 7–9, but similar to it. This torque would, if acting alone, produce a precession of the spin vector in exact analogy with the Larmor precession discussed in Section 7–5. Indeed, it is not difficult to prove, using the model of Fig. A6–1, but with the spin axis horizontal, that the mass increase on one side of the ring will make the spin axis precess. This relativistic effect is called *Thomas precession* after Thomas,* who first derived the formula for the precession frequency and from that concluded what the energy shift should be.

Thomas did not use our dubious mechanical model of the electron, but a relatively simple kinematic argument. He pointed out that a Lorentz transformation between the laboratory frame and a frame moving in a circle of radius r, with a velocity v and therefore having an acceleration $a = v^2/r$, leads to a predicted slow *rotation* of the second frame. In other words, a spinning electron moving in a circle about a nucleus will precess slowly, as viewed from the laboratory frame, even if there is no external torque acting on it. The angular frequency of precession is†

$$\Omega_T = -(v \times a)/2c^2. \tag{A6-12}$$

Inserting $a = F/m_e = -Ze^2r/4\pi\varepsilon_0 m_e r^3$, we get

$$\Omega_T = \frac{Ze^2(v \times r)}{8\pi\varepsilon_0 m_e c^2 r^3} = -\frac{Ze^2 L}{8\pi\varepsilon_0 m_e c^2 r^3}. \tag{A6-13}$$

This is just half of the Larmor frequency (Eq. 7–60 with Eq. 7–75 inserted) and of opposite sign. Therefore the apparent relativistic torque cancels exactly one-half of the magnetic spin-orbit torque. Consequently, the spin-orbit energy is only half of what is calculated from the magnetic interaction.

Returning now to our crude mechanical model, we see that it had to yield the correct result, in spite of the dubious assumption $v_t^2/c^2 \ll 1$. Thomas's argument shows that the result is independent of v_t^2/c^2, or better, independent of the model of the electron.

---

* L. H. Thomas, Nature, **117** (1926), p. 514.

† For proof, see, for instance, R. M. Eisberg, *Fundamentals of Modern Physics*. New York: Wiley (1961), p. 340.

Answers to Selected Odd-Numbered Problems

Chapter 1

1–5 b) $2N/V^2$ c) $2V/3, V/\sqrt{2}, V$ d) 56%, 50%

1–9 0.67

1–11 a) $11.2 \times 10^3 \text{ m} \cdot \text{s}^{-1}$

1–13 a) $3.24 \times 10^{24} \text{ °K}$

1–15 c) 3

1–17 a) $4.00 \times 10^{-21} \text{ J}$ b) $2.19 \times 10^3 \text{ m} \cdot \text{s}^{-1}$

1–19 a) $8.47 \times 10^6 \text{ m} \cdot \text{s}^{-1}$ b) $5.8 \times 10^9 \text{ °K}$

1–21 a) Decrease   b) Increase

1–23 a) 327 °C   b) 0.76 torr

1–25 a) 0.368, 0.632   b) 0.693 L

Chapter 2

2–1 (a) 3.58×10^{13} b) 1.94×10^{10} c) Yes

2–3 3.67×10^6 V/m downward

2–5 a) 0.56 mm, $\varphi = 4.03°$ b) 1.11 cm

2–7 a) 7.5×10^5 V   b) 0.354 T

2–9 $4.8 \times 10^7 \text{ C} \cdot \text{kg}^{-1}$

2–11 1.34×10^{-3} T

2–13 b) No

2–25 $f = Bq/2\pi m$

2–17 a) 2.50×10^{-4} m · s^{-1}

b) 1.11×10^{-4} m · s^{-1}, 3.48×10^{-4} m · s^{-1}, 2.30×10^{-4} m · s^{-1}, 5.30×10^{-4} m · s^{-1}, 1.67×10^{-4} m · s^{-1}

c) 3.61×10^{-4} m · s^{-1}, 5.98×10^{-4} m · s^{-1}, 4.80×10^{-4} m · s^{-1}, 7.80×10^{-4} m · s^{-1}, 4.17×10^{-4} m · s^{-1}

d) 6, 10, 8, 13, 7   e) 1.63×10^{-19} C

2–19 a) E and B down   b) E up, B down   c) E and B up

2–21 Higher velocity, collision of gas molecules

2–23 70%, 30%

Chapter 3

3–3 a) 4.02×10^{17} m^{-3} b) 6.65×10^{-8} J, 5.66×10^{-15} J

3–5 $(8\pi^5 k^4/15\ c^3 h^3)T^4$ J · m^{-3}

3–7 5660 °K

3–9 a) 1500%   b) 46%
c) 4%   d) 0.4%

3–11 1.41×10^{19} s^{-1}

3–13 13.6 eV

3–15 a) 5.26×10^{-33} J   b) 2.05×10^{-17} m   c) 2.38×10^{31}

3–17 a) 0.0253 eV   b) 0.00025 eV

3–19 a) 1.70 s   b) 21 min

3–21 a) 4.58×10^{14} Hz   b) 6450 Å
c) 1.90 eV   d) 6.62×10^{-34} J · s

3–23 0.016 V greater

3–25 0.78 eV

Chapter 4

4–1 a) 2.23×10^{21} V · m^{-1} b) 2.32×10^{21} V · m^{-1}

4–3 Al, $n = 6.02 \times 10^{22}$ cm^{-3}; Au, $n = 6.13 \times 10^{22}$ cm^{-3}
b) 299 s^{-1} c) 8.00×10^4 s^{-1} d) 802 s^{-1}

4–5 86 min^{-1}

4–13 a) -74.5 keV   b) 55.9 keV, 0.222 Å   c) x-ray

4–15 Lyman: 912 Å, 13.6 eV   Balmer: 3640 Å, 3.40 eV
Paschen: 8200 Å, 1.51 eV   Brackett: 14,550 Å, 0.85 eV
Pfund: 22,800 Å, 0.54 eV

4–17 a) 12.75 eV   b) 6

4–19 a) 4630 Å, 3910 Å, 3700 Å   b) 3470 Å
c) -3.57 eV, -0.89 eV, -0.38 eV, -0.23 eV
d) 0.38 eV   e) (1) excite $n = 2$, (2) none

4-21 a) None   b) 6563 Å, 1216 Å, 1026 Å
       c) 6563 Å, 1216 Å, 1026 Å   d) None
       e) None

4-25 a) 8560 °K   b) Photon absorption

Chapter 5

5-3 a) 2.28   b) 3.41×10^{-2} c) 4.85×10^{-6}
       d) No significant change for (a) and (b). Impossible for (c), but if the whole atom is recoiling, 2.19×10^{-10}

5-5 a) 570 eV   b) 2.6×10^{-2} c) $44°, 45°$

5-7 a) 5.44×10^{-27} kg $\cdot$ m $\cdot$ s^{-1} b) $5.53 \times 10^{-7}\%$

5-13 a) 3.32×10^{-22} kg $\cdot$ m $\cdot$ s^{-1} b) 1.87×10^{-22} kg $\cdot$ m $\cdot$ s^{-1}
       c) 0.0354 Å

5-23 60 cm

Chapter 6

6-1 $A = a^{1/2}$
      $P = ae^{-2}\, dx$
      $P = (e^{-2} - e^{-4})/2$

6-3 $k^2 = 3/2a^3$
      $\langle x^2 \rangle = a^2/10$
      $\langle P_x^2 \rangle = 3\hbar^2/a^2$ (integrate by parts)

6-7 $\langle H \rangle = a_1^2 E_1 + a_2^2 E_2 + a_3^2 E_3 + \cdots$

6-9 $k_x a = n_x \pi$, etc.
$$E = \frac{\pi^2 \hbar^2}{2ma^2}(n_x^2 + n_y^2 + n_z^2)$$

6-11 $A^2 = 4a/9$
       $E = -\hbar^2 a^2/2m$
       $V = -\hbar^2 a^2/m(1 \pm ax)$

6-15 $v = \hbar(a^2 + b^2)^{1/2}/m$

6-17 $B = 0.0062$

6-19 $B = 4 \exp(-1.9 \times 10^{24})$

6-21 $A = \hbar^{1/2}/(km)^{1/4} = 1.83 \times 10^{-15}\ m$

Chapter 7

7-9 $E_0 = 4.94\hbar^2/ma_0^2,\ E_1 = 10.07\hbar^2/ma_0^2$

7-11 $l = 2,\ m = 1,\ E = -\mu e^4/288\pi^2 \varepsilon_0^2 \hbar^2 = e^2/72\pi\varepsilon_0 a_0,\ A^{-1} = 81\pi^{1/2}a_0^{7/2}$

7-15 $\alpha = 55.5\ L/A$ radians with L = length of magnet in meters and A = atomic mass in u.

Chapter 8

8–5 $\Delta E = v_0/2$ (for all states)

8–7 $\psi_1 = a_{11}\psi_{10} + a_{21}\psi_{20}$ with energy
$E_1 \simeq E_{10} + v_0/2 - 16v_0^2/9\pi^2(E_{20} - E_{10})$
$a_{21}/a_{11} \simeq -4v_0/3\pi(E_{20} - E_{10})$
$\psi_2 = a_{21}\psi_{10} + a_{22}\psi_{20}$ with energy
$E_2 \simeq E_{20} + v_0/2 + 16v_0^2/9\pi^2(E_{20} - E_{10})$
$a_{12}/a_{22} \simeq 4v_0/3\pi(E_{20} - E_{10})$

8–9 $H'_{13} = H'_{15} = \cdots = 2C/a$
$|\dot{a}_3|^2 = 4C^2/\hbar^2a^2$, etc. (at $t = 0$)

Chapter 9

9–1 a) 24.6 eV $= 4.10 \times 10^{-18}$ J
b) 1.48×10^5 °K

9–3 $\psi = \dfrac{2\sqrt{6}}{\pi a_0^3}\left[\left(1 - \dfrac{r_2}{a_0}\right)\exp\left(-\dfrac{2r_1 + r_2}{a_0}\right)\cos\theta_2\right.$

$\left. - \left(1 - \dfrac{r_1}{a_0}\right)\exp\left(-\dfrac{2r_2 + r_1}{a_0}\right)\cos\theta_1\right]\alpha\alpha$

9–5 $\langle V_{12}\rangle = e^2/2\pi\varepsilon_0 a_0 = 54.4$ eV

9–7 280

9–9 a) 20

9–11 a) $(1s)^2(2s)^2$ b) $^1S_0$ c) $(1s)^2(2s)^1(2p)^1$
d) $^1P_1, {}^3P_0, {}^3P_1, {}^3P_2$ e) 1 (with $\Delta S = 0$)   f) 3

9–13 a) $^2S_{1/2}, {}^4S_{3/2}, {}^2P_{1/2,3/2}, {}^4P_{1/2,3/2,5/2}, {}^2D_{3/2,5/2}, {}^4D_{1/2,3/2,5/2,7/2}, {}^2F_{5/2,7/2},$
${}^4F_{3/2,5/2,7/2,9/2}$
b) $^4S_{3/2}, {}^2P_{1/2,3/2}, {}^2D_{3/2,5/2}$
c) $^4F_{3/2}, {}^4S_{3/2}$

Chapter 10

10–1 a) 3.53 Å   b) 7.06 Å

10–3 a) 1.24 Å   b) 0.413 Å

10–5 a) $(1s)^1(2s)^2(2p)^6 \ldots$, etc., and $(1s)^2(2s)^2(2p)^5 \ldots$, etc.
b) $^2S_{1/2}$ and $^2P_{1/2}$ c) 11.4 keV

10–7 b) 10.6 keV   c) 1.46 Å
d) 0.124 Å   e) 0.178 Å

10–9 a) 0.950 cm, 0.050 cm, and 0.0124 cm
b) 4.75 cm, 0.25 cm, and 0.0620 cm
c) 5.30 cm, 0.280 cm, and 0.0697 cm

10–13 1.56×10^{-22} kg·m·s^{-1}

10–15 a) 2.9×10^{18} ohms

10–17 $14.2°, 37.2°$

Chapter 11

11–1 c) $\alpha \simeq 2/e = 0.735$ (overestimated)

11–3 $\mu r_0^2 \simeq 1.33 \times 10^{-45}$ kg · m^2; $\hbar^2/2\mu r_0^2 \simeq 2.6 \times 10^{-5}$ eV

11–9 $E_f \simeq 34$ MeV

11–11 a) Fraction $\simeq (3kT/2E_f) \exp(-E_k/2kT) = 5.5 \times 10^{-17}$ with $E_f \simeq 7.5$ eV)
 b) 6×10^{-31}

11–13 $\Delta V = 0.0267$ V

Chapter 12

12–1 3.25×10^{17} kg · m^{-3} = 3.25×10^5 tons · mm^{-3}

12–3 a) $-ZR^2$ b) $ZR^2/2$

12–5 $\kappa_1 \cot \kappa_1 c = \cot(Kc - \delta)$
 $K \cot [K(b + c) - \delta] = -\kappa_2$

12–7 $d = 2.9$ F, 5.0 F, and 7.1 F

12–9 b) $\cot Kr_0 = -1$ c) $r_0 = 2.7$ F

12–11 $0^+, \frac{3}{2}^-, \frac{5}{2}^+, 0^+, \frac{5}{2}^+, \frac{7}{2}^-, \frac{3}{2}^-$

12–17 $E = (1 - m/M)E_K$

12–19 a) 4.8×10^4 J
 b) 8.2×10^8 J
 c) 2.0×10^{10} J
 d) 1.8×10^{14} J

Name Index

Subject Index

Adjusted Values of Physical Constants (MKSA)

Selected from B. N. Taylor, W. H. Parker, and D. N. Langenberg, *Revs. Modern. Phys.* **41**, (1969), p. 375.

CONSTANT	SYMBOL	VALUE
Speed of light in vacuum	c	2.997925×10^8 m $\cdot$ sec^{-1}
Elementary charge	e	1.602192×10^{-19} coul
Avogadro constant	N_A	6.02217×10^{23} mole^{-1}
Electron rest mass	m_e	9.10956×10^{-31} kg
		$= 5.48593 \times 10^{-4}$ u
Proton rest mass	m_p	1.67261×10^{-27} kg
		$= 1.00727661$ u
Neutron rest mass	m_n	1.67492×10^{-27} kg
		$= 1.0086652$ u
Faraday constant	F	9.64867×10^4 coul $\cdot$ mole^{-1}
Planck constant	h	6.62620×10^{-34} joule $\cdot$ sec
	$\hbar$	1.054592×10^{-34} joule $\cdot$ sec
Compton wavelength of electron	$h/m_e c$	2.42630×10^{-12} m
Compton wavelength of proton	$h/m_p c$	1.321441×10^{-15} m
Gyromagnetic ratio of proton	γ_p	2.67597×10^8 rad $\cdot$ m^2 $\cdot$ sec^{-1} $\cdot$ Wb$^-$
	$\gamma_p/2\pi$	4.25771×10^7 Hz $\cdot$ m^2 $\cdot$ Wb^{-1}
(uncorrected for diamagnetism, H$_2$O)	γ_p'	2.675127×10^8 rad $\cdot$ m^2 $\cdot$ sec^{-1} $\cdot$ Wb
	$\gamma_p'/2\pi$	4.257597×10^7 Hz $\cdot$ m^2 $\cdot$ Wb^{-1}
Bohr magneton	μ_B	9.27410×10^{-24} joule $\cdot$ m^2 $\cdot$ Wb^{-1}
Nuclear magneton	μ_N	5.05095×10^{-27} joule $\cdot$ m^2 $\cdot$ Wb^{-1}
Proton moment	μ_p	1.410620×10^{-26} joule $\cdot$ m^2 $\cdot$ Wb^{-1}
	μ_p/μ_N	2.79278
Gas constant	R_0	8.3143 J $\cdot$ mole^{-1} $\cdot$ °K^{-1}
		$= 1.9872$ cal $\cdot$ mole^{-1} $\cdot$ °K^{-1}
Boltzmann constant	k	1.38062×10^{-23} joule $\cdot$ °K^{-1}
Stefan-Boltzmann constant	σ	5.6696×10^{-8} W $\cdot$ m^{-2} $\cdot$ °K^{-4}
Gravitational constant	G	6.673×10^{-11} N $\cdot$ m^2 $\cdot$ kg^{-2}

Energy Conversion Factors

Selected from *Physics Today*, February 1964; recommended by National Academy of Sciences—National Research Council.

	FORMULA	FACTOR
Thermochemical calorie	cal_{th}	4.1840 joules
Electron volt	eV	1.602192×10^{-19} joule $(eV)^{-1}$
Energy Associated With		
unified atomic mass unit	$c^2/N_A e$	9.31481×10^8 $eV \cdot u^{-1}$
proton mass	$m_p c^2/e$	9.38259×10^8 $eV \cdot m_p^{-1}$
neutron mass	$m_n c^2/e$	9.39553×10^8 $eV \cdot m_n^{-1}$
electron mass	$m_e c^2/e$	5.11004×10^5 $eV \cdot m_e^{-1}$
cycle	e/h	2.41804×10^{14} $Hz(eV)^{-1}$
wavelength	ch/e	1.239854×10^{-6} $eV \cdot m$
°K	e/k	1.16049×10^4 $°K(eV)^{-1}$